Handbook of Lipoprotein Testing

Edited by:

Nader Rifai
G. Russell Warnick
Marek H. Dominiczak

AACC Press
2101 L Street, N.W., Suite 202
Washington, DC 20037-1526

Library of Congress Cataloging-in-Publication Data

Handbook of lipoprotein testing /
edited by Nader Rifai, G. Russell Warnick, Marek H. Dominiczak
   p.   cm.
   Includes bibliographical references.
ISBN 0-915274-92-2
1. Blood lipoproteins—Analysis.
I. Rifai, Nader. II. Warnick, G. Russell. III. Dominiczak, Marek H.
RB46.H36 1997
616.07'561—dc21   97-13361
                                           CIP

Cover design by Gaye Roth, Paper Graphiti Print Services

Editorial /production supervision by Evalyn Schoppet, Sterling Publishing Services

ISBN 0-915274-92-2

Printed in the United States of America.

*This book is dedicated to all those behind the scenes
who contributed to its publication: to the lipid researchers;
to our technical and administrative staff members;
and not the least to our wives, Dorothy, Nancy, and Anna;
our children, Sarah, Sami, Karl, Kristan, Maren, Kathryn, David,
and Peter; their spouses, Shauna, Matt, and Larry; and their
children, Merrill, Rachel, Adam, and Moriah, for their support
and the many sacrifices they have made over the years.*

Contributors

Joseph D. Artiss, PhD
Associate Professor, Department of Pathology
Wayne State University School of Medicine, and
Technical Director of Chemistry
DMC University Laboratories
Detroit, MI

Melissa A. Austin, PhD
Professor, Department of Epidemiology
School of Public Health and Community Medicine
University of Washington
Seattle, WA

Paul S. Bachorik, PhD
Professor, Department of Pediatrics
The Johns Hopkins University
School of Medicine
Baltimore, MD

Deepak Bhatnagar, MBBS, PhD, FRCP, MRCPath
Consultant in Metabolic Medicine and Clinical Biochemistry
The Royal Oldham Hospital, and
Lecturer and Honorary Consultant in Metabolic Medicine
University of Manchester Department of Medicine
Manchester Royal Infirmary
Manchester, United Kingdom

Diane H. Bick, PhD
Assistant Professor, Department of Pathology
The University of Texas Health Science Center
Houston, TX

Dr. Alfred Böttcher
Assistant Lecturer
Institute for Clinical Chemistry and Laboratory Medicine
University of Regensburg
Regensburg, Germany

John D. Brunzell, MD
Professor, Department of Medicine
Division of Metabolism, Endocrinology, and Nutrition
University of Washington
Seattle, WA

Muriel J. Caslake, PhD
Research Lab Manager
Department of Pathological Biochemistry
University of Glasgow
Glasgow Royal Infirmary University NHS Trust
Glasgow, Scotland

Thomas G. Cole, PhD
Research Associate Professor of Biochemistry in Medicine
Department of Medicine
Director, Core Laboratory for Clinical Studies
Lipid Research Center
Washington University School of Medicine
St. Louis, MO

Gerald R. Cooper, MD, PhD
Research Medical Officer
Division of Environmental Health Laboratory Sciences
National Center for Environmental Health
Centers for Disease Control and Prevention
Atlanta, GA

Sridevi Devaraj, PhD
Fellow, Division of Clinical Chemistry
Department of Pathology
University of Texas Southwestern Medical Center
Dallas, TX

Ian N.M. Day, MA, MB, BChir, PhD, MRCPath
Lister Institute Fellow
University College London Medical School
London, United Kingdom

Marek H. Dominiczak, Dr Med, PhD, FRCPath, MRCPath
Head of Biochemistry Service
West Glasgow Hospitals University NHS Trust, and
Physician, The Lipid Clinic and Cardiovascular Risk Factor Clinic
West Glasgow Hospitals University NHS Trust, and
Senior Lecturer, University of Glasgow
Glasgow, Scotland

Robert Dufour, MD
Professor, Department of Pathology
The George Washington University Medical Center, and
Chief of Pathology and Laboratory Services
Veterans Affairs Medical Center
Washington, DC

Patrick Duriez, PhD
Professor, Department of Physiology
Faculty of Pharmacy, University of Lille II, and
Assistant, Department of Research on Atherosclerosis
Pasteur Institute
Lille, France

Paul N. Durrington, BSc, MD, FRCP, FRCPath
Professor, Department of Medicine
University of Manchester, and
Honorary Consultant Physician
Manchester Royal Infirmary
Manchester, United Kingdom

Christopher J. Fielding, PhD
Professor, Department of Physiology
Cardiovascular Research Institute
University of California San Francisco Medical Center
San Francisco, CA

Jean-Charles Fruchart, PhD
Professor, Department of Clinical Biochemistry
Faculty of Pharmacy, University of Lille II, and
Head, Department of Research on Atherosclerosis
Pasteur Institute
Lille, France

David J. Hassemer, MS
Assistant Director, Outreach Programs
State Laboratory of Hygiene
University of Wisconsin
Madison, WI

Richard J. Havel, MD
Professor, Department of Medicine
Cardiovascular Research Institute
University of California, San Francisco
San Francisco, CA

L. Omar Henderson, PhD
Assistant Chief, Clinical Biochemistry Branch
Division of Laboratory Sciences
National Center for Environmental Health
Centers for Disease Control and Prevention
Atlanta, GA

John E. Hokanson, MPH, PhD
Research Scientist, Division of Metabolism, Endocrinology, and Nutrition
Department of Medicine
University of Washington
Seattle, WA

Paul N. Hopkins, MD, MSPH
Associate Professor, Cardiovascular Genetics
Department of Internal Medicine, Cardiology Division
University of Utah School of Medicine
Salt Lake City, UT

Seijin Hosaki, MD, PhD
Professor, School of Allied Health Science
Tokyo Medical and Dental University
Bunkyo-ku, Tokyo, Japan

Steve E. Humphries, PhD, FRCPath
British Heart Foundation Professor of Cardiovascular Genetics
University College London Medical School
London, United Kingdom

Ishwarlal Jialal, MD, PhD, DABCC, FRCPath
Professor, Departments of Internal Medicine and Pathology, and
Director of Clinical Chemistry
University of Texas Southwestern Medical Center
Dallas, TX

Mary M. Kimberly, PhD
Coordinator, Cholesterol Reference Method Laboratory Network
Division of Laboratory Sciences
National Center for Environmental Health
Centers for Disease Control and Prevention
Atlanta, GA

Sigrid G. Klotzsch, MS
Senior Chemist
Biomedical Data Company
Irvington, NY

Marlys L. Koschinsky, PhD
Associate Professor, Department of Biochemistry
Queen's University
Kingston, Ontario, Canada

Christine Labeur, PhD
Universiteit Gent
Labo Lipoproteine Chemie
Gent, Belgium

Santica M. Marcovina, PhD, DSc
Research Professor, Department of Medicine
Division of Metabolism, Endocrinology and Nutrition
Director, Core Laboratory, Northwest Lipid Research Laboratories
University of Washington School of Medicine
Seattle, WA

John B. Massey, PhD
Associate Professor, Department of Medicine
Division of Atherosclerosis and Lipoprotein Research
Baylor College of Medicine
Houston, TX

Judith R. McNamara, MT (ASCP)
Senior Research Assistant, Lipid Metabolism Laboratory
Jean Mayer USDA Human Nutrition Research Center on Aging
Tufts University, and
Research Associate, Lipid Research Laboratory
New England Medical Center
Boston, MA

W. Greg Miller, PhD
Professor, Department of Pathology
Director, Pathology Information Systems
Co-Director, Clinical Chemistry Laboratory
Medical College of Virginia
Virginia Commonwealth University
Richmond, VA

Dr. Christoph Möllers
Assistant Lecturer
Institute for Clinical Chemistry and Laboratory Medicine
University of Regensburg
Regensburg, Germany

Toshio Muramatsu, PhD
Professor, Laboratory of Chemistry
College of Liberal Arts and Sciences
Tokyo Medical and Dental University
Ichikawa-shi, Chiba, Japan

Gary L. Myers, PhD
Chief, Special Activities Branch
Division of Laboratory Sciences
National Center for Environmental Health
Centers for Disease Control and Prevention
Atlanta, GA

Herbert K. Naito, PhD, MBA
Chief, Clinical Chemistry
Pathology and Laboratory Medicine Service, and
Associate Director, VA National Center for Laboratory
    Accuracy and Standardization
Cleveland VA Medical Center
Cleveland OH, and
Clinical Associate Professor
The Ohio State University College of Medicine
Columbus, OH

Mitsuyo Okazaki, PhD
Professor, Laboratory of Chemistry
College of Liberal Arts and Sciences
Tokyo Medical and Dental University
Ichikawa-shi, Chiba, Japan

Gunilla Olivecrona, PhD
Department of Medical Biochemistry
Umeå University
Umeå, Sweden

Thomas Olivecrona, MD, PhD
Professor, Department of Medical Biochemistry
Umeå University
Umeå, Sweden

James D. Otvos, PhD
Professor, Department of Biochemistry
North Carolina State University
Raleigh, NC

Christopher J. Packard, DSc, FRCPath
Top Grade Biochemist and
Professor, Department of Pathological Biochemistry
University of Glasgow
Glasgow Royal Infirmary University NHS Trust
Glasgow, Scotland

Judith Ploch, Dipl. Chem.
Scientific Co-worker
Institute for Clinical Chemistry and Laboratory Medicine
University of Regensburg
Regensburg, Germany

Henry J. Pownall, PhD
Professor, Department of Medicine, and
Chief, Division of Atherosclerosis and Lipoprotein Research
Baylor College of Medicine
Houston, TX

P. Haydn Pritchard, PhD
Professor, Department of Pathology, and
Director, Atherosclerosis Specialty Lab
Healthy Heart Program
St. Paul's Hospital
The University of British Columbia
Vancouver, British Columbia, Canada

Nader Rifai, PhD
Associate Professor, Department of Pathology
Harvard Medical School, and
Director, Clinical Chemistry Laboratory
Children's Hospital
Boston, MA

Maryvonne Rosseneu, DSc
Universiteit Gent
Labo Lipoproteine Chemie
Gent, Belgium

Keiko Sasamoto, BS
Laboratory of Chemistry
College of Liberal Arts and Sciences
Tokyo Medical and Dental University
Ichikawa-shi, Chiba, Japan

Ernst J. Schaefer, MD
Professor, Departments of Medicine and Nutrition, and
Director, Lipid Research Laboratory and Lipid and Heart Disease
    Prevention Clinic
New England Medical Center School of Medicine, and
Director, Lipid Metabolism Laboratory
Jean Mayer USDA Human Nutrition Research Center on Aging
Tufts University
Boston, MA

Gerd Schmitz, Prof. Dr. Med.
Director
Institute for Clinical Chemistry and Laboratory Medicine
University of Regensburg
Regensburg, Germany

Anne K. Soutar, PhD
MRC Lipoprotein Team
Clinical Sciences Centre
Royal Postgraduate Medical School
Hammersmith Hospital
London, United Kingdom

Papasani V. Subbaiah, PhD
Professor, Departments of Medicine and Biochemistry
Rush Medical College
Chicago, IL

Kory M. Ward, PhD, MT (ASCP)
Director of Medical Technology, and
Associate Professor, School of Allied Medical Professions
    and Pathology Department
The Ohio State University
Columbus, OH

G. Russell Warnick, MS, MBA
Founder and Chief Scientific Officer
Pacific Biometrics, Inc.
Seattle, WA

Donald A. Wiebe, PhD
Associate Professor, Department of Pathology and Laboratory Medicine
University of Wisconsin Hospital & Clinics
Madison, WI

James T. Wu, PhD
Professor, Department of Pathology
Director, Special Chemistry Laboratory and Reagent Development Laboratory
Associated Regional University Pathologists (ARUP)
University of Utah School of Medicine
Salt Lake City, UT

Lily L. H. Wu, PhD
Associate Professor, Departments of Pathology and Internal Medicine, and
Director, Reagent Production Laboratory
Associated Regional University Pathologists (ARUP), and
Director, Biochemistry Laboratory, Cardiovascular Genetics
University of Utah School of Medicine
Salt Lake City, UT

Bennie Zak, PhD
Emeritus Professor, Department of Pathology
Wayne State University School of Medicine, and
Consultant in Chemistry
DMC University Laboratories
Detroit, MI

Contents

Preface

The transport of cholesterol and triglycerides in blood plasma lipoproteins is now of daily interest to the primary care physician and to most of his or her patients. Armed with national guidelines for diagnosis and goal setting in the management of lipoprotein disorders, and with truly effective therapies for achieving these goals, it is possible to make important contributions to reducing the risk of death and disability from cardiovascular disease. The crucial role of the laboratory in supporting this effort has become clear as clinical trials have documented the value of identifying elevated low-density lipoprotein cholesterol and lowering it 10 to 40 percent. The application of this information would be a futile exercise without the marked improvement in precision and accuracy achieved by clinical laboratories in the assessment of blood plasma lipoprotein concentrations.

This Handbook represents a highly focused and distilled compilation of the knowledge of many experts who have helped bring about this successful application of technique to clinical medicine. Valid assessment of total plasma cholesterol, triglycerides, and of the cholesterol content of low-density and high-density lipoproteins remains a concern of the first order for any clinical laboratory, and this book offers information to laboratory personnel, at any level of training that should prove useful in setting up or improving assessment methods. The material is enriched by clearly written chapters on the fundamentals of lipoprotein metabolism and of the clinical disorders which cause the lipoproteins to be of interest to the clinician.

This book goes far beyond the now routine lipoprotein measurements and represents a valuable resource for the research laboratory as well. Lipoprotein metabolism is complicated, involving at least nine apolipoproteins and a series of other plasma and cell surface proteins with enzymatic and lipid transfer functions. We are in the process of learning to assess these components and to use this new knowledge to better assess risk of related clinical disorders. This Handbook contains a series of chapters which provide a state-of-the-art description of our current understanding of these various biochemical and physiologic systems as well as clear and complete descriptions of the latest in relevant measurement techniques. Even the assessment of specific genes as potentially important measures is presented, in the final chapter.

Every laboratory with a serious interest in assessing lipoprotein composition, structure, or function should have a copy of this Handbook available for use by all of its staff: from the beginning students, to senior technicians, to the laboratory director.

W. Virgil Brown, MD
Charles Howard Chandler Professor of Medicine
Director of the Division of Arteriosclerosis
and Lipid Metabolism
Emory University School of Medicine

Introduction

The national and international efforts to combat coronary heart disease (CHD) have generated considerable enthusiasm over the past three decades. By some estimates, these efforts may result in one of the greatest contributions to public health that clinical chemistry has made to date.

Recent clinical studies clearly demonstrate a decrease in morbidity and mortality from CHD following lipid-lowering therapy. The laboratory measurements of lipids and lipoproteins underpin all the clinical studies and are essential to the assessment of cardiovascular risk and to monitoring individuals on treatment. The American Association for Clinical Chemistry (AACC), primarily through its Lipids and Lipoproteins Division, has made a major contribution to the development and clinical utilization of these tests. Just thirteen years ago, the Lipid Research Clinics Program reported the findings of its Coronary Primary Prevention Trial, demonstrating that decreasing serum cholesterol concentration reduces the incidence of CHD. Subsequently, a consensus conference sponsored by the National, Heart, Lung and Blood Institute recommended launching a national intervention program. The result was the inception of the National Cholesterol Education Program (NCEP), which with time became a template for many other similar intervention programs worldwide. The AACC's Lipids and Lipoproteins Division itself grew out of the activities of the Lipid Research Clinics Program, which fostered a highly successful laboratory collaboration among academic scientists, those in industry, and especially the Centers for Disease Control and Prevention, which has long promoted standardization and method improvement. Division members were involved in the various expert panels of the NCEP. Division-sponsored educational workshops and symposia for practicing laboratorians and industry scientists also contributed to the evolution.

The first predecessor of this book, *Methods for Clinical Laboratory Measurement of Lipid and Lipoprotein Risk Factors,* published in 1991, had its genesis in the Lipids and Lipoproteins Division and in the atmosphere of method improvement stimulated by the NCEP. The key chapters on the basic lipid and lipoprotein measurements were authored by ad hoc committees previously convened by the Division to recommend improvements in the laboratory methods. The book was published in soft-cover format to keep it affordable and to signal the intent to update it as measurement technologies evolved.

The second book, *Laboratory Measurement of Lipids, Lipoproteins, and Apolipoproteins*, published three years later, built on the first but was considerably expanded to cover topics of increasing clinical interest and research tests that demonstrated clinical utility. This book continues to be sought after and has recently been translated to Russian by Professor Alexander Sigalov and published by Pharmarus Print.

In producing the current book, *Handbook of Lipoprotein Testing*, we have further updated the chapters to describe both methodological and clinical interface aspects. In particular, we have added a considerable segment to address research methodologies. Several internationally recognized lipidologists joined the team of contributors. We trust that the book will continue to be of value to laboratorians involved both in the service and research aspects of lipidology and cardiovascular prevention. We hope it will be particularly useful to those who are involved in, or responsible for, the standardization of laboratory methods. We again wish to thank all who have contributed their time, knowledge, and experience to this exciting project.

Nader Rifai
G. Russell Warnick
Marek H. Dominiczak

Apolipoproteins and Lipoproteins in Human Plasma

1

Marek H. Dominiczak

INTRODUCTION

❖　This chapter provides an overview of lipoprotein metabolism. The reader will find a fascinating account of early work in an article by Fredrickson.[1] Lipoprotein metabolic pathways are a part of the overall body fuel metabolism. Lipids are an important source of energy and are essential components of cell structure. Fatty acids are a high-energy metabolic fuels, whereas cholesterol and phospholipids are essential components of cell membranes. Cholesterol is a precursor of bile acids, vitamin D, and other steroids.

The storage form of fatty acids are their glycerol esters, triacylglycerols (triglycerides [TG]). The main sites of fatty acid metabolism are liver and muscle, while the main storage depot is the adipose tissue. Hydrophobic lipids cannot be transported directly in the aqueous environment. They move between tissues as components of lipoprotein particles.

Lipoproteins are classified on the basis of their hydrated density. It is important to remember that such classification is somewhat arbitrary, and implies the existence of clearly separate structures in what are populations of constantly interchanging particles.

Each lipoprotein includes lipid components and contains proteins known as apolipoproteins. Apolipoproteins determine particle metabolism by binding to specific receptors. They also act as cofactors for enzymes. Their functions are summarized in Table 1–1. Lipoproteins in plasma constantly change their size, density and composition. They are successively hydrolyzed by lipoprotein lipase (LPL) and hepatic triglyceride lipase (HTGL).[2] In the high-density cholesterol particles, another enzyme, lecithin:cholesterol acyltransferase (LCAT),[3] esterifies cholesterol. This changes the size of affected particles. There is a constant traffic of apolipoproteins and other components between different lipoprotein particles. Changes in particle size affect the conformation of apoproteins residing on the lipoprotein surface, and thus the exposure of receptor-binding domains. This may change the rate at which a particle is metabolized, or may channel it to a different receptor.

Lipoprotein separation may be accomplished by several different methods. Lipoprotein particles are characterized by their size, density, flotation constant, and electrophoretic mobility (see Table 1–2). The hydrophobic core of a lipoprotein particle

Table 1–1 ✧ The Apolipoproteins

Apolipoprotein	Main Functions	Association with CHD Risk
Apo A-I	Structural for HDL. Ligand for HDL binding. LCAT cofactor.	Yes
Apo A-II	Structural for HDL. Ligand for HDL binding. LCAT cofactor. Modulator of LPL and HTGL activity (?)	No
Apo A-IV	Ligand for HDL binding. LCAT activator.	No
Apo (a)	Structural for Lp(a). Structural analogy with plasminogen	Yes
Apo B-48	Structural for chylomicrons.	No
Apo B-100	Structural for VLDL, IDL and LDL. LDL receptor ligand.	Yes
Apo C-I	LCAT and LPL activator.	No
Apo C-II	LCAT and LPL activator.	No
Apo C-III	LPL inhibitor. Modulator of uptake of triglyceride-rich lipoproteins by LRP.	No
Apo D	Unknown.	No
Apo E	Ligand for B/E receptors, LRP and apo E2 receptor.	Phenotype, yes
Apo F	Unknown.	No
Apo H	Unknown.	No
Apo J	Membrane protection (?)	No

HDL = High-density lipoprotein, LCAT = Lecithin:cholesterol acyltransferase, LPL = Lipoprotein lipase, HTGL = Hepatic triglyceride lipase, VLDL = Very-low-density lipoprotein, LDL = Low-density lipoprotein, IDL = Intermediate-density lipoprotein, LRP = LDL receptor-related protein

Table 1–2 ✧ The Lipoproteins

Lipoprotein	Density (kg/L)	Particle Diameter (nm)	Flotation Rate (Sf)	Electrophoretic Mobility
Chylomicrons	< 0.95	80–1200	> 400	Origin
VLDL	0.95–1.006	30–80	60–400	Pre-beta
IDL	1.006–1.019	23–35	20–60	Broad beta
LDL	1.019–1.063	18–25	0–20	Beta
HDL	1.063–1.21	5–12	0–9	Alpha

VLDL = Very-low density lipoprotein, IDL = Intermediate-density lipoprotein, LDL = Low-density lipoprotein, HDL = High-density lipoprotein consists of cholesteryl esters and TG. The surface contains an amphipathic phospholipid bilayer, non-esterified cholesterol, and apolipoproteins. When separated by ultracentrifugation, the main lipoprotein classes present in plasma are chylomicrons, very-low-density lipoproteins (VLDL), intermediate-density lipoproteins (IDL), low-density lipoproteins (LDL), and high-density lipoproteins (HDL).[4] Further subspecies are present within main classes. Particle density increases from chylomicrons to HDL, and particle size decreases from chylomicrons to HDL.

Agar electrophoresis separates plasma lipoproteins on the basis of electrical charge into pre-beta (VLDL), beta (LDL), and alpha (HDL) fractions.[1] An ultracentrifugal separation procedure performed according to the Lipid Research Clinics protocol, known as beta-quantification,[5, 6] separates VLDL and combined LDL and HDL fractions on the basis of their density. HDL-cholesterol (HDL-C) is then separated by polyanion/divalent cation precipitation and measured, and LDL-cholesterol (LDL-C) is calculated. More complex procedures separate VLDL, IDL, and LDL (and their subfractions) by flotation ultracentrifugation (discussed in Chapter 29).[4] Discrete subpopulations of LDL[7] and HDL[8] particles can be identified by non-denaturing gradient polyacrylamide gel electrophoresis. Subspecies of HDL particles with different apoprotein composition may be separated by affinity chromatography.[9] These methods are described in Chapters 13 and 24 of this book.

MAIN PATHWAYS OF LIPOPROTEIN METABOLISM

The Traditional View

An overview of lipoprotein metabolism is given in Figure 1–1. Lipoprotein metabolism is traditionally described as an exogenous pathway, endogenous pathway, and the pathway of reverse cholesterol transport. The exogenous pathway is the pathway of dietary lipid transport from the intestine to the liver. The endogenous pathway is the transport of lipoproteins synthesized in the hepatocytes from the liver to peripheral tissues. The two pathways overlap at the stage of hydrolysis by LPL in the periphery and by HTGL in the liver. Reverse cholesterol transport is the pathway of cholesterol transport from peripheral tissues to the liver by HDL.

The Secondary Remnant Concept of Lipoprotein Metabolism

Transport of lipids is a phenomenon integral to body fuel metabolism. Fatty acid metabolism indirectly determines the state of the lipid transport system. In the fed state, fatty acids are provided in the diet. In the postabsorptive and fasting states, free fatty acids are provided by lipolysis of stored fat. Free fatty acids do not require lipoprotein particles for transport. They travel in plasma bound to albumin, and are taken up by muscle and liver cells at a rapid rate. In the cells, their fate depends on cell energy status; they either become oxidized to yield energy or re-esterified to form TG. Most of the TG produced in the liver are transported to the adipose tissue for long-term storage.

Figure 1–1 ✧ An Overview of Cholesterol Metabolism

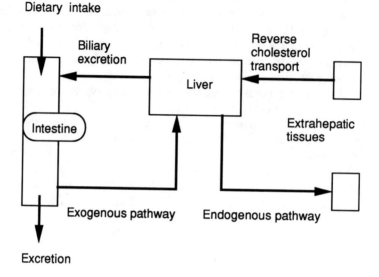

One could imagine lipoprotein metabolism as occurring in two pathways: a short "fuel transport pathway," which deals with TG transport, and a longer, more complex "overflow pathway" which handles cholesterol-rich particles. The overflow pathway draws its substrates from the fuel transport pathway. This concept is illustrated in Figure 1–2.

The fuel transport pathway involves lipoprotein generation in the intestine and liver. Enterocytes and hepatocytes are the primary sources of TG in the body. Both enterocytes and hepatocytes "send" excess high-energy substrates to adipose tissue for long-term storage.

Intestinal cells acquire free fatty acids and monoacylglycerols from the gastrointestinal tract. Dietary cholesterol is absorbed in the intestine, mostly as cholesteryl esters. Esters are hydrolyzed by cholesterol esterase to release free cholesterol and fatty acids. TG are hydrolyzed by pancreatic and intestinal lipases and absorbed mainly as free fatty acids and monoglycerides. Long-chain fatty acids and cholesterol are then re-synthesized in the intestinal epithelial cells. These are re-assembled within cells into TG and then, on the backbone of apo B-48, a variant of apolipoprotein B,[10] into TG-rich particles, chylomicrons. Enterocytes secrete chylomicrons into the thoracic duct. From there, chylomicrons enter plasma.

Hepatocytes assemble TG into VLDL—lipoprotein particles smaller than chylomicrons—on the backbone of apo B-100.[11] VLDL are also TG-rich, and are secreted into plasma.

The chylomicron and VLDL pathways converge at the periphery where particles containing both apo B-48 and apo B-100 particles undergo partial hydrolysis by LPL present on vascular endothelium. LPL digests TG, allowing fatty acids to be taken up by the cells (see Chapter 19). The particles that remain are known as remnants.[12]

Figure 1–2 ◆ The Secondary Remnant Concept of Lipid Metabolism

LPL = Lipoprotein lipase   CR = Chylomicron remnants
VLDLR = VLDL remnants   HTGL= Hepatic triglyceride lipase

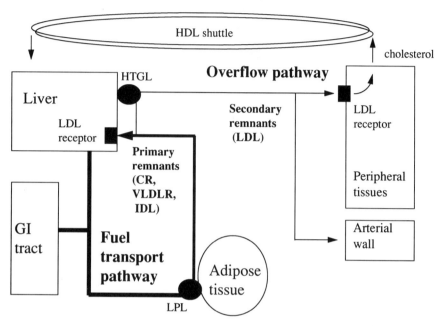

Chylomicron remnants still contain apo B-48, and VLDL remnants have apo B-100. Apo B-100 receptor-binding properties are different from apo B-48, so final metabolism of VLDL is in part different from that of chylomicrons. VLDL remnants are metabolized primarily by a hepatic apo B/E receptor. Only approximately 35% of chylomicron remnants are so metabolized;[13] the rest of the chylomicron remnants are metabolized using LDL receptor-related protein (LRP) as a binding site.[14] The definition of a remnant particle is functional: the remnant is a stage in the metabolism of the TG-rich lipoproteins that diverts the particles from LPL to catabolic sites.[12] The metabolism of chylomicrons is summarized in Figure 1–3, and the metabolism of VLDL in Figure 1–4.

Cholesterol is endogenously synthesized from acetyl-CoA by most of the cells. Liver requires cholesterol for the synthesis of primary bile acids, cholic and chenodeoxycholic, with an enzyme, 7-alpha hydroxylase, being rate-limiting. The bile acids are secreted into bile, and with bile into the intestine. There they are converted into secondary bile acids, deoxycholic and lithocholic. Bile acids emulsify fats in the gastrointestinal tract and are then re-absorbed and taken up again by the liver.[15, 16] Approximately 0.5 g of bile acids derived from hepatic cholesterol are lost with feces every day.

Only a small proportion (10–20%) of VLDL remnants participating in the fuel transport pathway are further transformed into LDL.[17] Also, approximately 80% of cholesterol secreted by the liver with lipoproteins returns back to the hepatocytes. One

Figure 1–3 ✧ The Metabolism of Chylomicrons

CHYLO = Chylomicrons   LPL = Lipoprotein lipase   FFA = Free fatty acids
HTGL = Hepatic triglyceride lipase   LRP = LDL receptor-related protein

The relative size of the lipoprotein particles shown is not to scale.

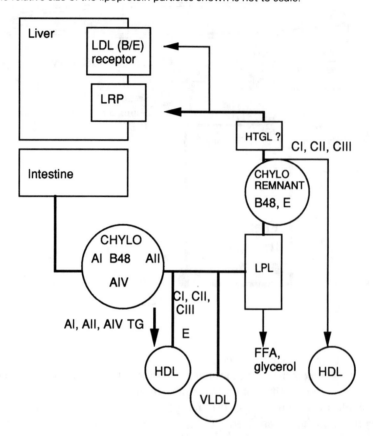

could argue that cholesterol is primarily a structural component of fuel-carrying lipo-proteins and view the LDL particle as a secondary remnant which is simply less efficiently removed from circulation than the primary VLDL remnant.

Developing this concept further, the "overflow" pathway of lipoprotein metabolism involves metabolism of cholesterol-rich particles (LDL) generated from the fuel transport pathway described above. This pathway includes both plasma transport and intracellular traffic of cholesterol. LDL travel to the periphery and are taken up by cells, where cholesterol is incorporated into cell membranes or used for synthetic purposes. LDL is internalized after binding to the apo B/E receptor.[18, 19] Cholesterol taken up by the cell through the receptor pathway regulates both the rate of intracellular cholesterol synthesis (3-hydroxy-3-methylglutaryl-CoA [HMG-CoA] reductase activity) and the avail-

Figure 1-4 ✧ The Metabolism of VLDL

LPL = Lipoprotein lipase   FFA = Free fatty acids
HTGL = Hepatic triglyceride lipase

The relative size of the lipoprotein particles shown is not to scale.

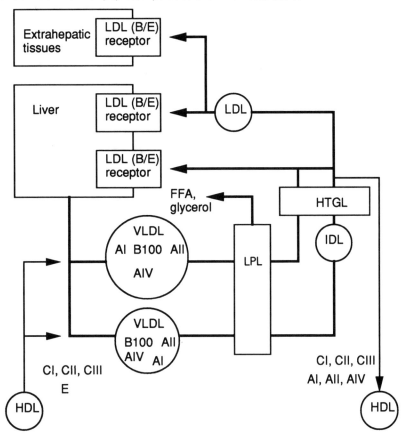

ability of LDL receptors.[20, 21] The receptor uptake constitutes a gate which controls the amount of cholesterol incorporated into cells. No lipoprotein particle needs to be assembled in the peripheral cells to remove excess cholesterol. This is accomplished by circulating HDL, derived from the liver or intestine, which shuttles between the periphery, where it removes cholesterol from membranes, and the liver, where it off-loads cholesterol without internalization of the whole particle.[22, 23] The metabolism of HDL is illustrated in Figure 1-5.

Thus, from the metabolic point of view, LDL is not at the center of the lipid transport system. It is a particle generated at the post-hydrolysis stage from the primary remnants containing apo B-100. This concept may help to explain why is it so difficult to determine a lower cutoff point for cholesterol concentration associated with increased cardiovascular risk.[24] One could speculate that the low risk threshold would be reached

Figure 1–5 ✧ The Metabolism of HDL: Reverse Cholesterol Transport

LCAT = Lecithin:cholesterol acyltransferase   TG = Triglycerides
HTGL = Hepatic triglyceride lipase   CETP = Cholesteryl ester transfer protein

The relative size of the lipoprotein particles shown is not to scale.

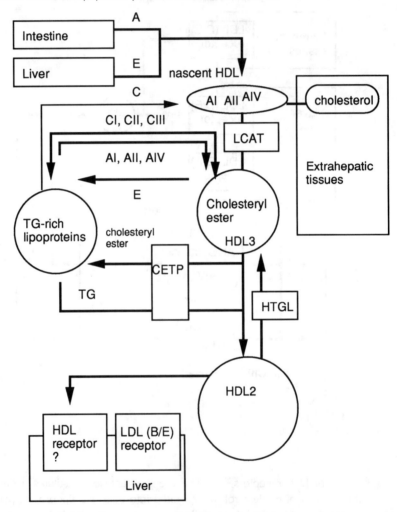

when there is zero, or near-zero, activity in the overflow pathway, and only a trace of LDL present. Such a situation would theoretically occur at a total cholesterol concentration of approximately 80 mg/dL (2.1 mmol/L) (approx. 23 mg/dL [0.6 mmol/L] VLDL, 10 mg/dL [0.3 mmol/L] IDL, and 46 mg/dL [1.2 mmol/L] HDL).

Thus, the summary of the secondary remnant concept of lipid transport is as follows:

1.   Lipoprotein transport is determined by body fuel metabolism and depends on the availability of fatty acids and, consequently, TG.

2. The main pathway of lipid transport is the fuel transport pathway, which carries dietary or endogenous TG from either intestine or liver to the peripheral tissues. After the TG transport is accomplished, the remaining primary remnant particles, comprising chylomicron remnants, VLDL remnants, and IDL, are taken up by the liver.

3. A small proportion of remnants undergo further hydrolysis and are channeled into the overflow pathway as secondary remnants, LDL. They are metabolized by the apo B/E (LDL) receptor, but have a relatively long residence time in plasma and can deposit in the arterial walls.

4. The LDL uptake by cells (and intracellular cholesterol synthesis) is controlled by the amount of intracellular cholesteryl ester.

5. Finally, to further fine-tune the cell cholesterol content, HDL removes cholesterol from cell membranes. The removed cholesterol affects the exchange of components between HDL and other lipoproteins.

The Consequences of Overload of Lipid Transport Pathways

The key event determining atherogenic potential of plasma is the channeling of particles from the fuel transport pathway to the overflow pathway. Lipoproteins participating in the fuel transport pathway have relatively short half-life. Generation of excess of LDL particles results in its increased deposition in the arterial wall.[25, 26] HDL is the only small lipoprotein which does not deposit in the vascular wall. Its observed anti-atherogenic effect is probably associated with the quality of the cell membrane.

KEY COMPONENTS OF THE LIPID TRANSPORT SYSTEM

Assembly of Apo B Containing Particles

The backbone of the assembly process of VLDL in the hepatocyte is apo B-100. This large protein consists of 4536 amino acids (see also Chapter 10). Apo B-48, the main protein of chylomicrons, contains 2152 amino acids and structurally is an N-terminal 48% fragment of apo B-100.[27] Newly synthesized apo B polypeptide translocates from the cytosolic to the luminal side of the endoplasmic reticulum.[11] This is facilitated by a microsomal TG transfer protein (MTP) which mediates the transfer of TG, cholesterol esters, and phospholipids between membranes and lipoproteins.[28] Translocation is also facilitated by the presence of TG or fatty acid, and probably cholesterol esters and phosphatidyl choline.[11, 29] Hydrophobic sequences in the apo B-100 molecule play a role in lipid recruitment.[30] Apo B-100 appears to be synthesized in excess of what is required for lipid transport with the excess degraded in the hepatocyte.[27]

In examining the studies on lipoprotein assembly, it is important to take into account species differences in hepatic lipoprotein secretion. Human and rabbit hepatocytes secrete apo B-100 containing VLDL only.[31] Rat hepatocytes secrete both apo B-48 and apo B-100.[32] Human hepatoma cells (HepG2) secrete particles in the density range of LDL and HDL, rather than VLDL.[33]

Triglyceride-Rich Particles

Particles participating in the fuel transport pathway—chylomicrons, VLDL, VLDL remnants, and IDL—are all multi-apolipoprotein particles. Chylomicrons are composed of more than 90% TG. They are normally present in plasma in the postprandial state only. The presence of chylomicrons is reflected by an increased plasma TG concentration; if a large amount of chylomicrons is present, there will also be a considerable increase in plasma cholesterol.

Chylomicrons contain apo B-48.[10] Apo B-48 cannot bind to the LDL receptor because the receptor-binding domain is present in the C-terminal of the apo B-100 molecule. Nascent chylomicrons also contain apo AI, apo AII, and apo AIV.[34] When they reach plasma, chylomicrons receive apo C (CI, CII, and CIII-1 and CIII-2) and apo E from HDL and VLDL.[35-37] Apo E and apo C control further chylomicron metabolism. The C apolipoproteins also control the activity of LPL; apo CII activates and apo CIII inhibits LPL.[2, 38] (See also Chapter 19.)

LPL hydrolyses chylomicron TG to glycerol and free fatty acids, which are then taken up by cells. Interestingly, the recently discovered VLDL receptor appears to bind LPL, and thus may play a role in the metabolism of this enzyme in the endothelium.[39] The off-loading of TG results in an approximate twenty-fold decrease in chylomicron mass. The size of a particle determines the conformation of particle apoproteins and thus the exposure of receptor binding domains of apo B and apo E. Some of the surface components such as phospholipids and apo A are lost from the particle at this stage.[40] They may serve as a substrate for intravascular HDL formation.[41] At this point the chylomicron transforms into a chylomicron remnant.

VLDL are assembled in the hepatocytes as a range of different size TG-rich particles, each containing one apo B-100 molecule. In common with chylomicrons, VLDL exchange components with HDL. Cholesteryl esters, apo C (CI, CII, and CIII), and apo E are transferred from HDL to VLDL in exchange for TG.[37] VLDL enriched in apo C and apo E undergo hydrolysis by LPL.[2, 12] This generates smaller particles, VLDL remnants. At this stage apo A-I and A-IV are transferred back to HDL. As lipolysis progresses, remnants lose TG, phospholipids, apo C, and apo E. This results in the formation of LDL.[12] VLDL remnants have higher affinity towards the LDL receptor than LDL itself. They may either be directly taken up by the liver or further hydrolyzed in plasma, probably by HTGL, to yield IDL.[42] HTGL deficiency[43] results in the accumulation of VLDL remnants in plasma. The metabolic fate of VLDL depends on its size. Remnants of large VLDL are directly metabolized, whereas remnants of small VLDL enter the IDL-LDL route.[44, 45] In LDL receptor defects, less VLDL is removed directly and more is available for transformation into LDL.[44]

The cholesterol content of cell membranes may affect remnant metabolism. In human HepG2 cells, an increase in the cholesterol content of hepatocyte membrane reduced the binding of beta-VLDL, probably by affecting the membrane receptor pattern.[46] VLDL remnants and IDL are closely related. Essentially, IDL are partially hydrolyzed VLDL remnants. IDL possess apo E and apo B-100.[12] They either bind to the LDL receptor or are transformed into LDL. There are multiple subclasses of IDL.[47] IDL transform into LDL by losing TG, apo C, and apo E, probably through interaction with HDL. For more information on remnant particles refer to Chapter 25.

The Role of Apolipoprotein E

Apo E targets remnants towards the liver.[48] Remnants bind to the B/E (LDL) receptor, and also to the chylomicron remnant receptor, which is the LRP.[48, 49] LRP is a dual-function receptor capable of binding chylomicron remnants and the protein α-2-macroglobulin. Again, apo C plays a modulatory role at this stage: apo CI alters the binding of apo E to liver receptors and may inhibit clearance of TG-rich lipoprotein particles.

Apo E is continuously produced in the liver. However, VLDL cannot receive apo E directly from hepatocytes. As much as 58% of apo E in plasma is in the HDL fraction. Apo E mediates the hepatic uptake of chylomicron remnants, VLDL remnants, and IDL. It has a greater affinity for the apo B/E receptor than does apo B. The binding of apo-E-containing remnants to the receptor involves heparin sulphate proteoglycans.[12] Apo E is also synthesized in extrahepatic tissues—the brain, kidney, adrenals, and spleen[50]—and is present in the amyloid plaque.[51, 52] It is synthesized and secreted by brain astrocytes.[53] Apo E may be involved in nerve regeneration. Human brain expresses an apo E receptor 2, which is related to the VLDL receptor.[19] Apo E is secreted by macrophages.[54] A ε4 allele has been found to occur more frequently in familial and late-onset Alzheimer disease.[55, 56] There are several genetically determined apo E isoforms. They differ in their affinity for the LDL receptor.[48, 57] Apo E4 and E2 are products of different alleles at one locus and differ from apo E3 in patterns of amino-acid residues. Less common apo E variants also exist. The most common E3/3 phenotype is present in 60% of the population and the E2/3 phenotype is present in approximately 25%. Apo E seems to play a major role in determining the plasma cholesterol level. In one study, 47% of variance in cholesterol levels was explained by apo E polymorphism.[58] For additional information on this subject refer to Chapters 17 and 25.

Apo B metabolism seems to be slower in persons with the E4 allele.[58, 59] Individuals with the E4 allele also have increased cholesterol absorption efficiency and enhanced apo B production.[57] Individuals with apo E4/4 and E4/3 have higher cholesterol levels than those with E3/3 and E2/2.[60, 61] Individuals with apo E2/3 and E2/4 have lower levels than those with E3/3.

The E2/2 phenotype results in apo E with lowest affinity for LDL receptors and is characteristic of individuals with familial dysbetalipoproteinemia. It is associated with a Type III hyperlipidemic pattern in plasma, which is characterized by an increased IDL concentration, broad beta band on electrophoresis, and an increase in TG and total cholesterol. Interestingly, although up to 1% of the population possess the E2/2 phenotype, overt type III hyperlipidemia occurs only in 1 in 10,000 individuals. Diabetes, hypothyroidism, or genetic dyslipidemia need to be present for type III hyperlipidemia to develop in these individuals.[62] The association of apo E polymorphism with response to dietary cholesterol has been intensively investigated, but with conflicting results.[57]

LDL

LDL is the main cholesterol-containing particle in plasma. The major component of LDL is cholesteryl ester. LDL contain very little TG and free cholesterol. Each particle contains one molecule of apo B and no other apolipoproteins. In normolipidemic individuals, about half of LDL is metabolized through the apo B/E receptor path-way.[18, 20, 21, 63] The LDL receptor controls the rate of LDL metabolism and, through this, its plasma concentration. The rates of receptor synthesis and LDL clearance are inversely related to the amount of intracellular free cholesterol.[64] Mutations of the LDL receptor affect both LDL binding and receptor processing. Plasma LDL are heteroge-neous.[65] The degree of cholesterol enrichment of LDL particles is determined at the stage of their precursors' formation.[17, 66] This is influenced by cholesteryl ester transfer protein (CETP) activity and a transfer of cholesteryl esters from HDL to VLDL. When CETP[67, 68] or LCAT[69] activity is high, the cholesterol content of LDL increases.

Several LDL subclasses have been identified by gradient gel electrophoresis. One scheme defines four LDL subclasses[70] within the LDL density band. LDL1 is the largest in size and most buoyant, whereas LDL3 and LDL4 are small and dense. For additional information on this subject refer to Chapters 14 and 29.

Lipolysis of core TG in LDL1 and LDL2 may lead to the formation of LDL3.[71] The predominance of LDL1 and LDL2 in plasma, which occurs in 75% of subjects, is known as pattern A. The predominance of LDL3 is called pattern B.[72] LDL subclass phenotype is influenced by an allele with an autosomal-dominant inheritance. Individ-uals with pattern B have higher plasma TG, higher VLDL-C concentration and VLDL mass, increased IDL-C, and low HDL-C concentrations. Apo B concentration is higher and apo AI lower. Changes associated with pattern B are known as atherogenic lipo-protein phenotype (ALP).[73, 74] ALP could be particularly important in diabetes. Kaiser Permanente data demonstrated that 15% of non-diabetic women, but 67% of women with non-insulin dependent diabetes (NIDDM), have pattern B. Pattern B is also com-mon in women with glucose intolerance (33%). Also, pattern B is associated with insulin resistance syndrome.[75]

HDL

HDL is the smallest and most dense lipoprotein particle with alpha or sometimes pre-beta electrophoretic mobility. It is also the most underestimated in terms of its importance in lipoprotein metabolism. HDL changes in size, density, and composition while carrying cholesterol from the peripheral tissues to the liver. Since, together with LCAT and CETP, HDL is involved in bi-directional exchange of components with lipoproteins of both pathways, it plays a controlling role in lipoprotein metabolism. HDL is a chaperon, an overseer of lipoprotein metabolism. In contrast to other particles, it is packed with apoproteins which account for 50% of its mass. It exchanges them with chylomicrons and particles in the VLDL and LDL range. This affects a complex pattern of metabolic channeling, particle hydrolysis, and component exchange.

There are two main HDL subclasses, HDL2 and HDL3, but at least seven further subfractions have been identified by gradient polyacrylamide gel electrophoresis (for more details see Chapters 13 and 24).[76] HDL2 is larger and richer in lipids than HDL3. HDL3 is smaller and denser.[22] The most important other subfractions, in order of decreasing size, are 2b, 2a, 3a, 3b, 3c.[76]

Apo A (A-I, A-II, and A-IV) are the main apolipoproteins of HDL.[23] HDL also contains apo C, and in particular apo E. Approximately 60% of HDL particles contain both apo A-I and A-II; the rest contain only apo A-I.[77] Particles containing apo A-I are present in HDL2 and HDL3, whereas particles containing Apo A-I and A-II are present only in HDL3. Most plasma apo E is present in HDL; HDL serves as a reservoir of this molecule.

HDL transports cholesterol from peripheral cells to the liver in a process known as reverse cholesterol transport. The liver and intestine secrete nascent, discoid HDL containing apo A and apo E. Some apo-C-containing discoid forms are generated from VLDL and chylomicrons during TG hydrolysis. Free cholesterol released from cells is taken up by nascent HDL and converted into cholesteryl ester by LCAT.[69] This increases the size of the particles and changes their shape to spherical. Apo A-I and apo A-II are cofactors of LCAT which is inhibited by its product, cholesteryl esters. LCAT deficiency leads to a decrease in HDL through increased metabolism of A-I and A-II.[78, 79]

Cholesteryl esters carried by HDL are either transported to the liver or transferred to TG-rich lipoproteins, VLDL and chylomicrons. This is facilitated by CETP[80] in exchange for TG, phospholipids, apo A-I, apo E, and apo C.[81]. CETP activity tends to be high in conditions associated with low HDL.[82-85] Transfer of TG to HDL further increases its size.[84] CETP deficiency leads to an increase in HDL concentration through slower catabolism. It seems that high cholesteryl ester content of HDL stabilizes the particle and protects it from degradation.[23] Smaller HDL particles are catabolized faster. Most cholesterol transport occurs without the need to internalize HDL, but there probably is a specific receptor(s) capable of binding apo A.[86] Due to their apo E content, some particles in the HDL range may be taken up by either the LDL receptor or the remnant receptor.

Apo A-I and A-II modulate HDL metabolism. In the absence of A-II, A-I catabolism is more rapid. Conversely, apo A-I is required for normal apo A-II catabolism. Apo A-II levels in plasma are determined by the production rate but apo A-I levels are regulated by its degradation.[23]

HDL also has functions unrelated to lipid transport. It decreases LDL oxidation. In addition, paraoxonase, an enzyme present on HDL, prevents the accumulation of lipoperoxides in LDL.[87, 88] HDL may have an antioxidant function[89, 90] Also, it appears to decrease the expression of adhesion molecules[91] such as VCAM-1, ICAM-1 and E-selectin induced by TNF-alpha.[22]

Lipoprotein (a)

Lipoprotein (a) [Lp(a)] links lipid metabolism with the blood coagulation system.[92] On electrophoresis, Lp(a) migrates as pre-beta lipoprotein. Lp(a) is synthesized in the liver and comprises an apo B-100 molecule linked by a disulfide bridge to apo(a). Apo(a) is highly glycosylated and because of the presence of multiple isoforms, its mass varies between 200–800 kDa.[92, 93] Apo E is present in 20% of Lp(a) particles. Lp(a) concentration is controlled by a series of autosomal alleles at a single locus designated Lp(a)F, Lp(a)B, Lp(a)S1, Lp(a)S2, Lp(a)S3, Lp(a)S4, and Lp(a)0. Phenotypes S3 and S4 are associated with low Lp(a) concentrations in plasma, and phenotypes B, S1, and S2 with high concentrations.[94]

There is a structural homology between apo(a) and plasminogen. The Lp(a) sequence includes a copy of plasminogen kringle 5 and multiple copies of kringle.[4, 95] However, the protease activity of Lp(a), unlike that of plasminogen, is minimal. There is an antigenic similarity between plasminogen and apo(a).[96] Lp(a) binds to the LDL receptor, although with lesser affinity than apo B.[97, 98] For additional information on Lp(a) refer to Chapter 15.

LIPOPROTEIN PARTICLES AND ATHEROGENESIS

The Fuel Transport Pathway: Chylomicrons, VLDL, and Remnant Particles

Postprandial increases in chylomicron and TG-rich remnant concentrations may exceed the critical level above which there is deposition of these particles in the arterial wall.[9, 10] Postprandial lipemia may also induce changes in LDL and HDL. It was previously reported that there was no excess cardiovascular risk in LPL deficiency, in which chylomicron concentrations are extremely high. This has been contradicted by recent case reports.[99] It has been suggested that postprandial lipemia can contribute to atherogenesis, through the deposition of chylomicron remnants in the arterial wall.[100] It seems that although chylomicrons cannot enter the arterial wall, the post-hydrolysis remnant particles can. The arterial clearance of VLDL and apo B-100 is less than that of IDL and LDL. The degree of penetration of these particles into the vessel wall is inversely related to their size.[101] Also, postprandial lipemia may affect the HDL level. CETP facilitates transfer of TG to HDL2. High TG content converts HDL2 to HDL3 and results in low HDL2 levels.[102] Concomitant transfer of cholesteryl esters to chylomicrons may increase potential atherogenicity of remnants. It was suggested that a general impairment of TG transport, affecting either chylomicrons or both chylomicrons and VLDL, may increase the risk of atherogenesis. This was described as the "triglyceride intolerance hypothesis."[103]

VLDL can be taken up by macrophages and form foam cells.[104, 105] This was demonstrated using human cholesteryl-ester-rich VLDL from hypertriglyceridemic, but not from normotriglyceridemic, patients. IDL particles are directly atherogenic. Patients with type III hyperlipidemia are prone to coronary heart disease (CHD). Diabetic individuals, whose CHD risk is 2–3 times that of non-diabetic individuals, also have an increased IDL concentration.[106, 107]

The Overflow Pathway: LDL

The atherogenic potential of LDL stems from its ability to accumulate in the extracellular matrix and in cells in the arterial intima. While the LDL receptor-mediated cellular uptake is carefully controlled, the uptake mediated by the macrophage scavenger receptor is uncontrolled and results in cellular cholesterol overload and generation of foam cells.[108] Native LDL is not readily taken up by the macrophages. Modification of LDL is required before this can take place. The most important modification is LDL oxidation.[109, 110] Nonenzymatic glycation of LDL may also play a role.[111] Plasma autoantibodies to oxidized LDL have been identified which suggests that LDL modification may occur in plasma.[112] However, LDL oxidation predominantly occurs after the particle has penetrated the endothelial barrier. Oxidized LDL is present in the arteriosclerotic plaque.[113] Also, CHD is more prevalent in patients with smaller, denser LDL.[114] These species can more easily penetrate the endothelial barrier. They are more susceptible to oxidation than larger, more buoyant LDL1.[115] For additional information on LDL oxidation, refer to Chapter 18.

Thus, a high concentration of LDL-C, whatever the cause, leads to an increased cardiovascular risk.[116, 117] High levels of LDL-C may result from defects in the LDL receptor, as in familial hypercholesterolemia (FH);[118] from defects in apo B, as in familial defective apo B-100 (FDB), where glutamine has been substituted by arginine at position 3500 of apo B-100;[119, 120] or from increased apo B synthesis or secretion, as in familial combined hyperlipidemia (FCH).[121, 122] Importantly, hyperapobetalipoproteinemia due to overproduction of apo B-100 may occur at relatively low plasma cholesterol concentrations[123-125] and is also associated with increased cardiovascular risk. Permeability of the endothelial layer to LDL may be an important factor in atherogenesis.[26]

As is discussed elsewhere in this book, the assessment of cardiovascular risk is often based on the measurements of total serum or plasma cholesterol, which is used as a surrogate marker of LDL-C. Data on the significance of apo B in CHD risk prediction conflict, but most studies suggest that apo B is a good discriminant of patients with CHD (see also Chapter 10). Apo B measurement was the best discriminator for men with early-onset CHD.[126] Apo B has also predicted the risk of myocardial infarction[127] and of angiographically defined CHD.[128] The recent Quebec Heart Study also suggests that apo B was the best predictor of the risk of vascular disease. In this study, the risk was increased in both hyperlipidemic and normolipidemic individuals with an increased apo B concentration, but not in hyperlipidemic patients with normal apo B.[129] In the same study, the presence of small, dense LDL was associated with increased CHD risk.[130]

HDL

It is well established that a high concentration of HDL-C is cardioprotective, and that a low HDL-C is associated with an increased cardiovascular risk.[131-133] The protective effect of HDL is primarily associated with the HDL2 subfraction.[134, 135] There is also an inverse correlation between HDL-C and plasma TG concentration. Obesity, smoking, and type II diabetes lower HDL-C, while exercise and ethanol consumption raise HDL-C.[132, 133] Apo A-II deficiency does not cause premature atherosclerosis. In apo A-I deficiency, the association with CHD was observed to be greater if LCAT activity was also impaired.[134]

The mechanisms underlying the role of HDL in the formation of atherosclerotic plaques have not yet been elucidated, but it is known that HDL particles can remove cholesterol from lipid-rich macrophages through either scavenging the released lipids or through receptor-mediated cholesterol efflux.[135] Importantly, HDL may impede LDL oxidation.[136] Recently it becomes clear that the role of HDL in the reverse cholesterol transport may not be the only function related to its cardioprotective effect.[20] Controversy exists as to whether measurements of apo AI add much discriminatory value to HDL-C measurement in the assessment of cardiovascular risk (see also Chapters 10 and 24).[137, 138]

Lipoprotein (a)

The ability of Lp(a) to deposit in the extracellular matrix, together with its possible interference with the fibrinolytic mechanism, suggest a direct role in atherogenesis. There is also evidence that Lp(a) is deposited in the arterial intima and in the atherosclerotic plaques.[139] An increased fatty streak formation was observed in a transgenic mouse line expressing human apo(a).[140] Lp(a) binds to fibronectin in aortic plaques.[141] It stimulates proliferation of human smooth muscle cells in culture.[142]

Lp(a) inhibits clot lysis in plasma. By competing with plasminogen for its binding sites on the cell surface, it decreases the plasminogen activation by tissue plasminogen activator.[143-145] In *in vitro* experiments, Lp(a) competed with plasminogen for binding to fibrin.[146] There is a considerable clinical and epidemiological evidence linking Lp(a) concentrations to CHD. Apo(a) isoforms predict the risk of CHD.[147] There is also a relationship between Lp(a) concentration and the risk of peripheral vascular disease and stroke.[148] The Lp(a) concentration was also higher in asymptomatic men with carotid plaques.[149] There is a link between Lp(a) concentration and parental history of premature CHD.[150, 151] Lp(a) is an independent risk factor for CHD in women below age 65.[152] In the Framingham Heart study, the presence of sinking pre-beta lipoprotein, a surrogate marker of Lp(a), predicted fatal and nonfatal CHD.[153] Lp(a)-associated risk increases in the presence of elevated LDL-C.[154] There is an additive effect of LDL and Lp(a) in producing angiographically detectable CHD.[155] Lp(a) concentration appears to lose its predictive power after intensive cholesterol lowering.[156]

Thus Lp(a) particle, a derivative of apo B, has both atherogenic and thrombogenic potential. Its predictive power appears greater in the presence of high LDL-C.[154-156] Heterogeneity of apo(a) causes different reactivities of antibodies used in immunochemical methods of measurement problems.[157, 158] Refer to Chapter 15 for additional information on this subject.

MINOR APOLIPOPROTEINS

There are several other apolipoproteins the function of which in lipid transport and metabolism remains unknown.[159, 160] Apo J is associated with the HDL fraction and may be involved in inhibition of complement-mediated cell lysis and in sperm maturation. Due to its capacity to interact with hydrophobic molecules, apo J has a membrane-protective role. Apo J has been detected in plasma and urine and also in cerebrospinal fluid, breast milk, and seminal fluid. Apo D, similarly to apo J and apo E, is expressed in a variety of extrahepatic tissues such as spleen, adrenal, lungs, brain, and testes.[161] Finally, apo H, a 43–54 kDa protein present in all major lipoprotein fractions, has been reported to affect platelet response to ADP. The functions of apo F and apo G remain unknown.

CONCLUSIONS

The lipid transport system exists primarily to transport energy-rich lipids from intestine and liver to the adipose tissue. TG must be transported in the aqueous environment of plasma as a component of lipoprotein particles. Cholesterol-rich lipoproteins are generated from the TG-transporting particles. Among these, the particle with the longest residence time in plasma is LDL. LDL enters the arterial wall and plays a central role in the formation of atherosclerotic plaque.

At present, clinical laboratory methods do not measure lipoprotein concentration. Instead, we rely either on total concentrations of cholesterol and TG in plasma, or use selected components of lipoproteins, such as cholesterol or apoproteins, as markers of lipoprotein concentration. Considering the complexity of the lipid transport system, it is surprising how much has been achieved in understanding the role of the lipoproteins in contributing to CHD using these relatively crude, surrogate measurements.

The challenge for laboratory medicine is to further develop measurements of components of lipoprotein metabolism, so as to more accurately characterize individual patients at risk of cardiovascular disease. ✧

Acknowledgments: *This work was partially supported by grants from the Chest Heart and Stroke Association (Scotland), the Kidney Research Fund, and the Scottish Hospitals Endowment Research Trust (SHERT). The author is grateful to Ms. S. Cathcart, Dr. E. Kilpatrick, and Dr. S. Kilpatrick for their helpful comments, and to Ms. J. Gardiner and Mrs. Anne Cooney for excellent secretarial assistance.*

REFERENCES

1. Fredrickson DS. Phenotyping: on reaching base camp (1950–1975). Circulation 1993; 87(Suppl III):III-1–15.
2. Olivecrona T, Bengtsson-Olivecrona G. Lipoprotein lipase and hepatic lipase. Curr Opin Lipidol 1990;1:222–30.
3. Applebaum-Bowden D. Lipases and lecithin:cholesterol acyltransferase in the control of lipoprotein metabolism. Curr Opin Lipidol 1995;6:130–5.
4. Havel RJ, Eder HA, Bragdon J. Distribution and chemical composition of ultracentrifugally separated lipoproteins in human serum. J Clin Invest 1955;34:1345–53.
5. Lipid Research Clinic Program manual of laboratory operations, revised. Washington DC: U.S. Government Printing Office, 1982:63–77.
6. Cathcart S, Dominiczak MH. The measurement of lipoprotein subfractions in plasma using a tabletop ultracentrifuge. Ann Clin Biochem 1990;27:459–64.
7. Austin MA, Hokanson JE, Brunzell JD. Characterization of low-density lipoprotein subclasses: methodological approaches and clinical relevance. Curr Opin Lipidol 1994;5: 395–403.
8. von Eckardstein A, Huang Y, Assman G. Physiological role and clinical relevance of high-density lipoprotein subclasses. Curr Opin Lipidol 1994;5:404–16.
9. Fruchart JC, Ailhaud G. Apolipoprotein A-containing particles: physiological role, quantification and clinical significance. Clin Chem 1992;38:793–7.
10. Powell LM, Wallis SC, Pease RJ, Edwards YH, Knott TJ, Scott J. A novel form of tissue specific RNA processing produces apolipoprotein B48 in intestine. Cell 1987;50:831–40.
11. Pease RJ, Leiper JM. Regulation of hepatic apolipoprotein-B-containing lipoprotein secretion. Curr Opin Lipidol 1996;7:132–8.
12. Eisenberg S, Sehayek E. Remnant particles and their metabolism. In: Baillieres Clin Endocrinol Metab 1995;9:739–53.
13. Thuren T, Wilcox RW, Sisson P, Waite M. Hepatic lipase hydrolysis of lipid monolayers. Regulation by apolipoproteins. J Biol Chem 1991;266:4853–61.
14. Herz J. The LDL-receptor related protein: portrait of a multifunctional receptor. Curr Opin Lipidol 1993;4:107–13.

15. Wikvall K. Conversion of cholesterol into bile acids. Curr Opin Lipidol 1990;1:248-54.

16. Stravitz RT, Hylemon PB, Vlahcevic ZR. The catabolism of cholesterol. Curr Opin Lipidol 1993;4:223-9.

17. Packard CJ. Plasma lipid and lipoprotein metabolism in the 1990s: what we know and what we need to know. In Betteridge DJ, ed. Lipids: current perspectives, Vol. 1. London: Martin Dunitz 1996:1-14.

18. Schneider WJ, Nimpf J. Lipoprotein receptors: old relatives and new arrivals. Curr Opin Lipidol 1993;4:205-9.

19. Yamamoto T, Bujo H. Close encounters with apoprotein E receptors. Curr Opin Lipidol 1996;7:298-302.

20. Brown MS, Goldstein JL. A receptor-mediated pathway for cholesterol homeostasis. Science 1986;232:34-47.

21. Brown MS, Goldstein JL. Lipoprotein receptors in the liver. Control signals for plasma cholesterol traffic. J Clin Invest 1983;72:743-7.

22. Barter PJ, Rye K-A. High density lipoproteins and coronary heart disease. Atherosclerosis 1996;121:1-12.

23. Rader DJ, Ikewaki K. Unravelling high-density lipoprotein-apolipoprotein metabolism in human mutants and animal models. Curr Opin Lipidol 1996;7:117-23.

24. Law MR, Wald NJ, Thompson SG. Serum cholesterol reduction and health: by how much and how quickly is the risk of ischaemic heart disease lowered? Brit Med J 1994;308:367-72.

25. Ross R. The pathogenesis of atherosclerosis: a perspective for the 1990s. Nature 1993;362:801-9.

26. Nielsen LB. Transfer of low density lipoprotein into the arterial wall and risk of atherosclerosis. Atherosclerosis 1996;123:1-15.

27. Cartwright IJ, Higgins JA. Intracellular events in the assembly of very-low-density-lipoprotein lipids with apolipoprotein B in isolated rabbit hepatocytes. Biochem J 1995; 310:897-907.

28. Fielding CJ. Lipid transfer proteins: catalysts, transmembrane carriers and signalling intermediates for intracellular and extracellular lipid reactions. Curr Opin Lipidol 1993;4: 218-22.

29. Watts G, Naumova R, Cummings MH, Umpleby AM, Slavin BM, Sonksen PH, Thompson GR. Direct correlation between cholesterol synthesis and secretion of apolipoprotein B100 in normolipidemic subjects. Metabolism 1995;44:1052-57.

30. McLeod RS, Wang Y, Wang S, Rusiñol A, Links P, Yao Z. Apolipoprotein B sequence requirements for hepatic very low density lipoprotein assembly. Evidence that hydrophobic sequences within apolipoprotein B48 mediate lipid recruitment. J Biol Chem 1996;271:18445-55.

31. Arbeeny CM, Meyers DS, Berquist KE, Gregg RE. Inhibition of fatty acid synthesis decreases very low density lipoprotein secretion in the hamster. J Lipid Res 1992;33: 843-51.

32. Cartwright IJ Hebbachi AM, Higgins JA. Transit and sorting of apolipoprotein B within the endoplasmic reticulum and Golgi compartments of isolated hepatocytes from normal and orotic acid fed rats. J Biol Chem 1993;268:20937-52.

33. Gibbons GF. A comparison of in vitro models to study hepatic lipid and lipoprotein metabolism. Curr Opin Lipidol 1994;5:191-99.

34. Beisiegel U, Utermann G. An apolipoprotein homolog of rat apolipoprotein AIV in human plasma: isolation and partial characterisation. Eur J Biochem 1979;93: 601-8.

35. Eisenberg S. Metabolism of apolipoproteins and lipoproteins. Curr Opin Lipidol 1990;1: 205-15.

36. Blum CB. Dynamics of apolipoprotein E metabolism in humans. J Lipid Res 1982;23: 1308-16.

37. Huff MW, Breckenridge WC, Strong WLP, Wolfe BM. Metabolism of apolipoproteins C-II, C-III and B in hypertriglyceridemic men: changes after heparin-induced lipolysis. Arteriosclerosis 1988;8:471-9.

38. Ginsberg HN, Le N-A, Goldberg IJ, Gibson JC, Rubinstein A, Wang-Iverson P, et al. Apolipoprotein B metabolism in subjects with deficiency of apolipoproteins CIII and AI. J Clin Invest 1986;78:1287-95.
39. Argaves KM, Battey FD, MacCalman CD, McCrae KR, Gafvels M, Kozarsky KM, et al. The very low density lipoprotein receptor mediates the cellular catabolism of lipoprotein lipase and urokinase-plasminogen activator inhibitor type I complexes. J Biol Chem 1995;270:26550-7.
40. Schaefer EJ, Jenkins LL, Brewer HB. Human chylomicron apoprotein catabolism. Biochem Biophys Res Commun 1978;80:405-12.
41. Tall AR, Small DM. Plasma high-density lipoproteins. N Engl J Med 1978; 299:1232-6.
42. Havel RJ. The formation of LDL: mechanisms and regulation. J Lipid Res 1984;25:1570-6.
43. Clay HA, Hopkins GJ, Ehnholm C, Barter PJ. The rabbit as an animal model of hepatic lipase deficiency. Biochim Biophys Acta 1989;1002:173-81.
44. Grundy SM. Multifactorial etiology of hypercholesterolemia. Arterioscler Thromb 1991; 11:1619-35.
45. Packard CJ, Boag DE, Clegg RJ, Bedford DK, Shepherd J. Effects of 1,2-cyclohexanedione modification on the metabolism of VLDL apoprotein B: potential role of receptors in IDL catabolism. J Lipid Res 1985;26:1058-67.
46. Mas-Oliva J, Velasco-Loyden G, Haines TH. Receptor pattern formation as a signal for the capture of lipoproteins. Biochem and Biophys Res Comm 1996;224:212-8.
47. Musliner TA, Giotas C, Krauss RM. Presence of multiple subpopulations of lipoproteins of intermediate density in normal subjects. Arteriosclerosis 1986;6:79-87.
48. Mahley RW, Innerarity TL, Rall JSC, Weisgraber KH, Taylor JM. Apolipoprotein E: genetic variants provide insights into its structure and function. Curr Opin Lipidol 1990;1:87-95.
49. Beisiegel U, Weber W, Ihrke G, Herz J, Stanley KK. The LDL-receptor-related protein, LRP, is an apolipoprotein E-binding protein. Nature 1989;341:162-4.
50. Blue ML, Williams DL, Zucker S, Khan SA, Blum CB. Apolipoprotein E synthesis in human kidney, adrenal gland and liver. Proc Natl Acad Sci USA 1983;80:283-7.
51. Strittmatter WJ, Saunders AM, Schmechel D, Pericakvance M, Enghild J, Salvesen GS, et al. Apolipoprotein E: high-avidity binding to β-amyloid and increased frequency of type 4 allele in late onset familial Alzheimer disease. Proc Natl Acad Sci USA 1993;90:1977-81.
52. Strittmatter WJ, Weisgraber KH, Huang DY, Dong LM, Salvesen GS, Pericakvance M, et al. Binding of human apolipoprotein E to synthetic amyloid β peptide: isoform-specific effects and implications for late onset Alzheimer disease. Proc Natl Acad Sci USA 1993;90:8098-102
53. Boyles JK, Pitas RE, Wilson E, Mahley RW, Taylor JM. Apolipoprotein E associated with astrocytic glia of the central nervous system and with nonmyelinating glia of the peripheral nervous system. J Clin Invest 1985;76:1501-13.
54. Mazzone T. Apolipoprotein E secretion by macrophages:its potential physiological functions. Curr Opin Lipidol 1996;7:303-7.
55. Saunders AM, Schmader K, Breitner JCS, Benson MD, Brown WT, Goldfarb L, et al. Apolipoprotein ε4 allele distributions in late-onset Alzheimer's disease and in other amyloid-forming diseases. Lancet 1993;342:710-11.
56. Weisgraber KH, Roses AD, Strittmatter WJ. The role of apoprotein E in the nervous system. Curr Opin Lipidol 1994;5:110-6.
57. Kesäniemi YA. Genetics and cholesterol metabolism. Curr Opin Lipidol 1996;7:124-31.
58. Gylling H, Kontula K, Miettinen TA. Cholesterol absorption and metabolism and LDL kinetics in healthy men with different apoprotein E phenotypes and apoprotein B Xba I and LDL receptor Pvu II genotypes. Arterioscler Thromb Vasc Biol 1995;15:208-13.
59. Kesaniemi YA, Miettinen TA. Metabolic epidemiology of plasma cholesterol. Ann Clin Res 1988;20:26-31.

60. Utermann G. Apolipoprotein E polymorphisms in health and disease. Am Heart J 1987;113:433-40.

61. Enholm C, Lukka M, Kaussi T, Nikkila E, Utermann G. Apoprotein E polymorphism in the Finnish population: gene frequencies and relation to lipoprotein concentrations. J Lipid Res 1986;27:227-35.

62. Brewer HB, Zech LA, Gregg RE, Schwartz D, Schaeffer EJ. Type III hyperlipoproteinemia: diagnosis, molecular defects, pathology and treatment. Ann Int Med 1983; 98:623-40.

63. Shepherd J, Packard CJ. Lipid transport through the plasma: the metabolic basis of hyperlipidaemia. [Review]. In: Shepherd J, ed. Lipoprotein metabolism. Baillieres Clin Endocrinol Metab 1987;1:495-514.

64. Havel RJ, Hamilton RL. Hepatocytic lipoprotein receptors and intracellular lipoprotein catabolism. Hepatology 1988;8:1689-704.

65. Griffin BA. Low-density lipoprotein heterogeneity. [Review]. In: Betteridge DJ, ed. Dys-lipidaemia. Baillieres Clin Endocrinol Metab 1995;9:687-703.

66. Roheim PS, Asztalos BF. Clinical significance of lipoprotein size and risk for coronary atherosclerosis. Clin Chem 1995;41:147-52.

67. Hesler CB, Swenson TL, Tall AR. Purification and characterization of a human plasma cholesterol ester transfer protein. J Biol Chem 1987;262:2275-82.

68. Inazu A, Brown ML, Hesler CB, Agellon LB, Koizumi J, Takata K, et al. Increased high-density lipoprotein levels caused by a common cholesteryl-ester transfer protein gene mutation. N Engl J Med 1990;323:1234-8.

69. Glomset JA. The plasma lecithin: cholesterol acyltransferase reaction. J Lipid Res 1968; 9:155-67.

70. Krauss RM, Burke DJ. Identification of multiple subclasses of plasma low density lipo-proteins in normal humans. J Lipid Res 1982;23:97-104.

71. Austin MA, Edwards KL. Small, dense low density lipoproteins, the insulin resistance syndrome and noninsulin-dependent diabetes. Curr Opin Lipidol 1996;7:167-71.

72. Kraus RM. Low-density lipoprotein subclasses and risk of coronary artery disease. [Re-view]. Curr Opin Lipidol 1991;2:248-52.

73. Austin MA, King M-C, Vranizan KM, Krauss RM. Atherogenic lipoprotein phenotype: a proposed genetic marker for coronary heart disease risk. Circulation 1990;82:495-506.

74. Nishina PM, Johnson JP, Naggert KJ, Krauss RM. Linkage of atherogenic lipoprotein phenotype to the low density lipoprotein receptor locus on the short arm chromosome 19. Proc Natl Acad Sci USA 1992;89:708-12.

75. Selby JV, Austin MA, Newman B, Zhang D, Quesenberry CP Jr, Mayer EJ, Krauss RM. LDL subclass phenotypes and the insulin resistance syndrome in women. Circulation 1993;88:382-7.

76. Blanche PJ, Gong EL, Forte TM, Nichols AV. Characterisation of human high-density lipoproteins by gradient gel electrophoresis. Biochim Biophys Acta 1981;665:408-19.

77. Cheung M, Albers JJ. Distribution of high density lipoprotein particles with different apoprotein composition: particles with AI and AII and particles with AI but no AII. J Lipid Res 1982;23:747-53.

78. Barter PJ, Hopkins GJ, Gorjatschko L. Lipoprotein substrates for plasma cholesterol esterification: influence of particle size and composition of the high-density lipoprotein subfraction-3. Atherosclerosis 1985;58:97-107.

79. Ikeda Y, Ohta T, Matsuda I. Interaction between apo-A-I-containing lipoproteins and lecithin:cholesterol acyl-transferase. Biochim Biophys Acta 1994;1215:307-13.

80. Cholesteryl ester transfer protein. [Editorial]. Lancet 1991;338:666-7.

81. Tall AR. Plasma cholesteryl transfer protein and high density lipoproteins: new insights from molecular genetic studies. J Internal Med 1995;237:5-12.

82. Ruhling K, Zane-Langhenning R, Till U, Thielmann K. Enhanced net mass transfer of HDL cholesteryl ester to apo B-containing lipoproteins in patients with peripheral vas-cular disease. Clin Chim Acta 1989;184:289-96.

83. Yamashita S, Hui DY, Wetterau JR, Sprecher DL, Harmony JAK, Sakai N, et al. Characterisation of plasma lipoproteins in patients heterozygous for human plasma CETP deficiency: plasma CETP regulates high-density lipoprotein concentrations and composition. Metabolism 1991;40:756-63.

84. Bagdade JD, Ritter MC, Subbaiah PV. Accelerated cholesteryl ester transfer in plasma of patients with hypercholesterolemia. J Clin Invest 1991;87:1259-65.

85. Bagdade JD, Ritter MC, Subbaiah PV. Accelerated cholesteryl ester transfer in patients with insulin-dependent diabetes mellitus. Eur J Clin Invest 1991;21:161-7.

86. Tozuka M, Fidge N. Purification and characterization of two high-density lipoprotein-binding proteins from rat and human liver. Biochem J 1989;261:239-44.

87. Mackness MI, Arrol S, Abbott CA Durrington PN. Protection of low-density lipoprotein against oxidative modification by high-density lipoprotein associated paraoxonase. Atherosclerosis 1993;104:129-35.

88. Mackness MI, Arrol S, Durrington PN. Paraoxonase prevents accumulation of lipoperoxides in low density lipoproteins. FEBS Lett 1991;286:152-4.

89. Decossin C, Tailleux A, Fruchart J-C, Fievet C. Prevention of in vitro low-density lipoprotein oxidation by an albumin-containing LpA-I subfraction. Biochim Biophys Acta 1995;1255:31-8.

90. Kilimov AN, Gurevich VS, Nikiforova AA, Shatilina LV, Kuzman AA, Plawinsky SL, Teryukova NP. Antioxidative activity of high density lipoproteins in vivo. Atherosclerosis 1993;100:13-8.

91. Cockerill GW, Rye KA, Gamble JR, Vadas MA, Barter PJ. High-density lipoproteins inhibit cytokine-induced expression of endothelial cell adhesion molecules. Arterioscler Thromb Vasc Biol 1995;15:1987-94.

92. Loscalzo J. Lipoprotein(a): a unique risk factor for atherothrombotic disease. Arteriosclerosis 1990;10:672-9.

93. Seed M. Lipoprotein(a): its role in cardiovascular disease. In: Betteridge DJ, ed. Lipids: current perspectives. Lipids and lipoproteins, Vol. 1. London: Martin Dunitz 1996;69-88.

94. Utermann G, Menzel HJ, Kraft HG, Duba HC, Kemmler HG, Seitz C. Lp(a) glycoprotein phenotypes. J Clin Invest 1987;80:458-65.

95. McLean JW, Tomlinson JE, Kuang W-J, Eaton DL, Chen EY, Fless GM, et al. cDNA sequence of human apolipoprotein(a) is homologous to plasminogen. Nature 1987;330:132-7.

96. Karadi I, Kostner GM, Gries A, Nimpf J, Romics L, Malle E. Lipoprotein(a) and plasminogen are immunochemically related. Biochim Biophys Acta 1988;960:91-7.

97. Floren C-H, Albers JJ, Bierman EL. Uptake of Lp(a) by cultured fibroblasts. Biochem Biophys Res Commun 1981;102:636-9.

98. Krempler F, Kostner GM, Rascher A, Haslauer F, Bolzano K, Sandhofer F. Studies on the role of specific cell surface receptors in the removal of lipoprotein(a) in man. J Clin Invest 1983;71:1431-41.

99. Benlian P, de Gennes JL, Foubert L, Zhang HF, Gagne SE, Hayden M. Premature atherosclerosis in patients with familial chylomicronemia caused by mutations in the lipoprotein lipase gene. New Engl J Med 1996;335:848-54.

100. Zilversmit DB. Atherogenesis: a postprandial phenomenon. Circulation 1979;60:473-85.

101. Zilversmit DB. Atherogenic nature of triglycerides, postprandial lipidemia, and triglyceride-rich remnant lipoproteins. Clin Chem 1995;41:153-8.

102. Kirchmair R, Ebenbichler CF, Patsch JR. Post-prandial lipaemia. In: Betteridge DJ, ed. Dyslipidaemia. Bailliere's Clin Endocrinol Metab 1995;9:705-37.

103. Miesenbock G, Patsch JR. Postprandial hyperlipidemia: the search for atherogenic protein. Curr Opin Lipidology 1992;3:196-201.

104. Koo C, Wernette-Hammond ME, Innerarity TL. Uptake of canine β-very low density lipoproteins by mouse peritoneal macrophages is mediated by a low density lipoprotein receptor. J Biol Chem 1986;261:11194-201.

105. Huff MW, Evans AJ, Sawyez CG, Wolfe BM, Huff MW. Cholesterol accumulation in J774 macrophages induced by triglyceride-rich lipoproteins: comparison of very low density lipoproteins from subjects with type II, IV and V hyperlipoproteinaemia. Arterioscler Thromb 1991;11:221-32.
106. Winocour PH, Durrington PN, Ishola M, Anderson DC. Lipoprotein abnormalities in insulin-dependent diabetes mellitus. Lancet 1986;1:1176-8.
107. American Diabetes Association. Consensus statement. Role of cardiovascular risk factors in prevention and treatment of macrovascular disease in diabetes. Diabetes Care 1989;12:573-9.
108. Badimon JJ, Fuster V, Chesebro JH, Badimon L. Coronary atherosclerosis: a multifactorial disease. Circulation 1993;87 (suppl II): II-3-16.
109. Steinberg D, Parthasarathy S, Carew TE, Khoo JC, Witztum JL. Beyond cholesterol: modifications of low-density lipoprotein that increase its atherogenicity. [Review]. N Engl J Med 1989;320:915-22.
110. Navab M, Berliner JA, Watson AD, Hama SY, Territo MC, Lusis AJ, et al. The yin and yang of oxidation in the development of the fatty streak. Arterioscler Thromb Vasc Biol 1996;16:831-42.
111. Witztum JL, Mahoney EM, Branks MJ, Fisher M, Elam R, Steinberg D. Nonenzymatic glucosylation of low-density lipoprotein alters its biologic activity. Diabetes 1982;31:283-91.
112. Salonen JT, Yla-Herttuala S, Yamamoto R, Butler S, Korpela H, Salonen R, et al. Autoantibodies against oxidised LDL and progression of carotid atherosclerosis. Lancet 1992;339:883-7.
113. Yla-Herttuala S, Palinski W, Rosenfeld ME, Parthasarathy S, Carew TE, Butler S, et al. Evidence for the presence of oxidatively modified low density lipoprotein in atherosclerotic lesions of rabbit and man. J Clin Invest 1989;84:1086-95.
114. Austin MA, Breslow JL, Hennekens CH, Buring JE, Willett WC, Krauss RM. Low-density lipoprotein subclass patterns and risk of myocardial infarction. JAMA 1988;260:1917-21.
115. De Graaf J, Hak-Lemmers HLM, Hectors MPC, Demacker PNM, Hendriks JCM, Stalenhoef AFH. Enhanced susceptibility to in vitro oxidation of the dense low density lipoprotein subfraction in healthy subjects. Arteriosclerosis 1991;11:298-306.
116. The Expert Panel. Summary of the second report of the National Cholesterol Education Panel (NCEP) Expert Panel on Detection, Evaluation and Treatment of High Blood Cholesterol in Adults (Adult Treatment Panel II). JAMA 1993;269:3015-23.
117. European Atherosclerosis Society, International Task Force for Prevention of Coronary Heart Disease. Prevention of coronary heart disease: scientific background and new clinical guidelines. Nutr Metab Cardiovasc Dis 1992;2:113-56.
118. Bild DE, Williams RR, Brewer HB, Herd JA, Pearson TA, Stein E. Identification and management of heterozygous familial hypercholesterolemia: summary and recommendations from an NHLBI workshop. Am J Cardiol 1993;72:1D-5D.
119. Innerarity TL, Mahley TL, Weisgraber KH, Bersot TP, Krauss RM, Vega GL, et al. Familial defective apolipoprotein B-100: a mutation of apolipoprotein B that causes hypercholesterolemia. J Lipid Res 1990;31:1337-49.
120. Tybjaerg-Hansen A, Gallager A, Vincent J, Houlston R, Talmud P, Seed AM, et al. Familial defective apolipoprotein B-100: detection in the United Kingdom and Scandinavia, and clinical characteristics of ten cases. Atherosclerosis 1990;80:235-42.
121. Goldstein JL, Schrott HG, Hazzard WR, Bierman EL, Motulsky AG. Hyperlipidaemia in coronary heart disease. II. Genetic analysis of lipid levels in 176 families and delineation of a new inherited disorder, combined hyperlipidaemia. J Clin Invest 1973;52:1544-68.
122. Kissebah AH, Alfarsi S, Evans DC. Low density lipoprotein metabolism in familial combined hyperlipidemia: mechanism of the multiple lipoprotein phenotypic expression. Arteriosclerosis 1984;4:614-24.
123. Teng B, Sniderman AD, Soutar AK, Thompson GR. Metabolic basis of hyperapobetalipoproteinemia: turnover of apolipoprotein B in low density lipoproteins and its pre-

cursors and subfractions compared with normal and familial hypercholesterolemia. J Clin Invest 1986;77:663-72.

124. Sniderman A, Shapiro S, Marpole D, Skinner B, Teng B, Kwiterovich PO. Association of coronary atherosclerosis with hyperapobetalipoproteinemia (increased protein but normal cholesterol levels in human plasma low density (beta) lipoprotein). Proc Natl Acad Sci USA 1980;77:604-8.

125. Teng B, Thompson GR, Sniderman A, Forte TM, Krauss RM, Kwiterovich PO Jr. Composition and distribution of low density lipoprotein fractions in hyperapobetalipoproteinemia, normolipidemia and familial hypercholesterolemia. Proc Natl Acad Sci USA 1983;80;6662-6.

126. Kwiterowich PO, Coresh HH, Bachorik PS, Derby CA, Pearson TA. Comparison of plasma levels of apolipoproteins B and A-I and other risk factors in men and women with premature coronary artery disease. Am J Cardiol 1992;69:1015-21.

127. Stampfer MJ, Sacks FM, Salvini S, Willett WC, Hennekens CH. A prospective study of cholesterol, apolipoproteins and the risk of myocardial infarction. N Engl J Med 1991;325:373-81.

128. Schmidt SB, Wasserman AG, Muesing RA, Schlesselman SE, La Rosa JC, Roos AM. Lipoprotein and apolipoprotein levels in angiographically defined coronary atherosclerosis. Am J Cardiol 1985;55:1459-62.

129. Lamarche B, Moorjani S, Lupien PJ, Cantin B, Bernard P-M, Dagenais GR, Després J-P. Apolipoprotein A-I and B levels and the risk of ischemic heart disease during a five-year follow-up of men in the Québec cardiovascular study. Circulation 1996;94: 273-78.

130. Lamarche B, Tchernof A, Moorjani S, Cantin B, Dagenais GR, Lupien PJ, Després J-P. Small, dense low-density lipoprotein particles as a predictor of the risk of ischemic heart disease in men. Prospective results from the Québec cardiovascular study. Circulation 1997;95:69-75.

131. Gordon JG, Rifkind BM. High-density lipoprotein: the clinical implications of recent studies. N Eng J Med 1989;321:1311-6.

132. Heiss G, Johnson NJ, Reiland S, Davis CE, Tyroler HA. The epidemiology of plasma high-density lipoprotein cholesterol levels: The Lipid Research Clinics Program Prevalence Study, summary. Circulation 1980;62(Suppl IV):IV-116-36.

133. Davis CE, Gordon D, LaRosa J, Wood PDS, Halperin M. Correlations of plasma high-density lipoprotein cholesterol levels with other plasma lipid and lipoprotein concentrations: The Lipids Research Clinics Program Prevalence Study. Circulation 1980; 62(Suppl IV):IV-24-30.

134. Schaefer EJ, Genest Jr JJ, Ordovas JM, Salem DN, Wilson WF. Familial lipoprotein disorders and premature coronary artery disease. Curr Opin Lipidol 1993;4: 288-98.

135. Schmitz G, Williamson E. High-density lipoprotein metabolism, reverse cholesterol transport and membrane protection. Curr Opin Lipidol 1991;2:177-89.

136. Parthasarathy S, Barnett J, Fong LG. High density lipoprotein inhibits the oxidative modification of low density lipoprotein. Biochim Biophys Acta 1990;1044:275-83.

137. Bhatnagar D, Durrington PN. Clinical value of apolipoprotein measurement. Ann Clin Biochem 1991;28:427-37.

138. Laker MF, Evans K. Analysis of apolipoproteins. Ann Clin Biochem 1996;33:5-22.

139. Rath M, Niendorf A, Reblin T, Dietel M, Krebber H-J, Beisiegel U. Detection and quantification of lipoprotein(a) in the arterial wall of 107 coronary bypass patients. Arteriosclerosis 1989;9:579-92.

140. Wade DP. Lipoprotein (a). Curr Opin Lipidol 1993;4:244-9.

141. Salonen E-M, Jauhiainen M, Zardi L, Vaheri A, Ehnholm C. Lipoprotein(a) binds to fibronectin and has serum proteinase activity capable of cleaving it. EMBO J 1989;8: 4035-40.

142. Myiata M, Biro S, Kaieda H, Tanaka H. Lipoprotein (a) stimulates the proliferation of cultured human arterial smooth muscle cells through two pathways. FEBS Lett 1995; 377:493-6.

143. Miles LA, Fless GM, Levin EG, Scanu AM, Plow EF. A potential basis for the thrombotic risks associated with lipoprotein(a). Nature 1989;339:301-3.
144. Hajjar KA, Gavish D, Breslow JL, Nachmann RL. Lipoprotein(a) modulation of endothelial surface fibrinolysis and its potential role in atherosclerosis. Nature 1989;339:303-5.
145. Ranby M. Studies on the kinetics of plasminogen activation by tissue plasminogen activator. Biochim Biophys Acta 1982;704:461-9.
146. Loscalzo J, Weinfeld M, Fless G, Scanu AM. Lipoprotein(a), fibrin binding and plasminogen activation. Arteriosclerosis 1990;10:240-5.
147. Sandholzer C, Saha N, Kark JD, Rees A, Jaross W, Dieplinger H, et al. Apo(a) isoforms predict risk for coronary heart disease: a study in six populations. Arterioscler Thromb 1992;12:1214-26.
148. Zenker G, Koltringer P, Bone G, Niederkorn K, Pfeiffer K, Jurgens G. Lipoprotein (a) as a strong indicator for cerebrovascular disease. Stroke 1986;17:942-5.
149. Cambillau M, Simon A, Amar J, Giral Ph, Atger V, Segond P, et al. Serum Lp(a) as a discriminant marker of early atherosclerotic plaque at three extracoronary sites in hypercholesterolemic men. Arterioscler Thromb 1992;12:1346-52.
150. Berg K, Dahlen G, Borrenson A-L. Lp(a) phenotypes, other lipoprotein parameters and family history of heart disease in middle-aged males. Clin Genet 1977;16:347-52.
151. Durrington PN, Hunt L, Ishola M, Arrol S, Bhatnagar D. Apolipoproteins (a), AI and B and parental history in men with early onset ischaemic heart disease. Lancet 1988;1:1070-3.
152. Orth-Gomér K, Mittleman MA, Schenck-Gustafsson K, Wamala SP, Eriksson M, Belkic K, et al. Lipoprotein(a) as a determinant of coronary heart disease in young women. Circulation 1997;95:329-34.
153. Bostom AG, Gagnon DR, Cupples LA, Wilson PWF, Jenner JL, Ozdovas JM, et al. A prospective investigation of elevated lipoprotein (a) detected by electrophoresis and cardiovascular disease in women. Circulation 1994;90:1688-95.
154. Maher VM, Brown G. Lipoprotein (a) and coronary heart disease. Curr Opin Lipidol 1995;6:229-35.
155. Armstrong VW, Cremer P, Eberle E, Manke A, Schulze F, Wieland H, et al. The association between serum lp(a) concentration and angiographically assessed coronary atherosclerosis: dependence on serum LDL levels. Atherosclerosis 1986;62:249-57.
156. Maher VMG, Brown BG, Marcovina SM, Hillger LA, Zhao Z-Q, Albers JJ. Effects of lowering elevated LDL cholesterol on the cardiovascular risk of lipoprotein (a). JAMA 1995;274;1771-4.
157. Fortmann SP, Marcovina SM. Lipoprotein (a), a clinically elusive lipoprotein particle. Circulation 1997;95:295-6.
158. Superko HR. Beyond LDL cholesterol reduction. [Editorial]. Circulation 1996;94:2351-54.
159. Bhatnagar D, Durrington PN. Does measurement of apolipoproteins add to the clinical diagnosis and management of dyslipidemias? Curr Opin Lipidol 1993;4:299-304.
160. Jordan-Starck TC, Witte DP, Aronow BJ, Harmony JAK. Apolipoprotein J: a membrane policeman? Curr Opin Lipidol 1992;3:75-85.
161. Provost PR, Villeneuve L, Weech PK, Milne RW, Marcel YL, Rassart E. Localization of the major sites of apolipoprotein D gene transcription by in situ hybridization. J Lipid Res 1991;32:1959-70.

Overview of the Diagnosis and Treatment of Lipid Disorders

2

Ernst J. Schaefer and Judith R. McNamara

INTRODUCTION

✧　Current guidelines published by the National Cholesterol Education Program (NCEP) Adult Treatment Panel focus on dietary treatment of all adults over age 20 if their serum low-density lipoprotein cholesterol (LDL-C) values are ≥ 160 mg/dL (4.1 mmol/L), or ≥ 130 mg/dL (3.4 mmol/L) in the presence of two or more coronary heart disease (CHD) risk factors, or ≥ 100 mg/dL (2.6 mmol/L) in the presence of CHD.

CHD risk factors include: male ≥ 45 y, female ≥ 55 y or with premature menopause and not on hormonal replacement therapy, family history of premature CHD (< 55 y in male first degree relative, or < 65 y in female first degree relative), cigarette smoking, hypertension, high-density lipoprotein cholesterol (HDL-C) < 35 mg/dL (0.91 mmol/L), or diabetes. A risk factor is subtracted if the HDL-C value is ≥ 60 mg/dL (1.6 mmol/L).[1, 2] After an adequate trial of a diet restricted in total fat (≤ 30% of calories), saturated fat (< 7%) and cholesterol (< 200 mg/day), and after ruling out secondary causes of hypercholesterolemia, especially thyroid, renal and liver disease, persons with LDL-C values ≥ 190 mg/dL (4.9 mmol/L), or ≥ 160 mg/dL (4.1 mmol/L) in the presence of two or more CHD risk factors, or ≥ 130 mg/dL (3.4 mmol/L) in the presence of CHD, are candidates for pharmacologic therapy with agents such as hydroxymethlyglutaryl-CoA (HMG CoA) reductase inhibitors, anion exchange resins, niacin, or a combination of these agents.

Guidelines for the entire United States adult population, and for children and adolescents, have also been formulated which focus on dietary modification in the general population, to include ≤ 30% fat, < 10% saturated fat, < 300 mg cholesterol/day, and use of diet therapy, and in some cases resins in high-risk children.[3, 4] The rationale for all of these guidelines is that increased LDL-C concentrations have clearly been shown to be associated with premature CHD in prospective studies, and that lowering LDL-C with diet therapy or a combination of diet and drug treatment has been shown to reduce CHD risk prospectively.

LIPOPROTEIN METABOLISM

Plasma cholesterol and triglycerides (TG), along with phospholipids and proteins, are carried on lipoprotein particles. As shown in the overview of lipoprotein metabolism presented in Figure 2–1,[5] dietary fats are packaged by the intestine into large, TG-rich chylomicrons (Step 1), which rapidly lose much of their TG after entry into plasma due to lipolysis (Step 4). Apolipoprotein (apo) B-48 is the important structural protein of chylomicrons and contains the initial 48% of the apo B-100 sequence. During lipolysis, chylomicron remnants are formed which contain apo E and cholesterol obtained from other lipoproteins. These remnants are rapidly taken up by the liver via an apo E receptor-mediated process (Step 5). If such remnants, of either intestinal or hepatic origin, accumulate in the blood stream, they are potentially atherogenic.[6, 7] An assay has recently been developed to isolate and measure remnant concentration, providing the potential for information on increased CHD risk.[8, 9] See Chapter 25 for more details.

The liver synthesizes very-low-density lipoproteins (VLDL) (Step 2), which are the major TG-carrying lipoproteins in serum or plasma obtained from fasting subjects. Much of VLDL TG and phospholipids are rapidly removed via lipolysis, and in the process VLDL can be converted to LDL (Step 6) or catabolized directly (Step 7). LDL generally are the major cholesterol-carrying lipoproteins in the serum or plasma and are mainly catabolized in the liver and other tissues by an LDL receptor-mediated process (Steps 8 and 9). Apo B-100 is the major structural protein of both VLDL and LDL. When present in excessive amounts, LDL, as well as chylomicron and VLDL remnants, can be deposited in the arterial wall, modified, and taken up by macrophages, causing atherosclerosis.[10] For additional information on this process, refer to Chapters 1 and 18.

HDL are synthesized in both the liver and the intestine (Step 3). They can pick up lipids (phospholipids, TG) and proteins (apo AI, apo E, C apolipoproteins) from TG-rich lipoproteins (chylomicrons and VLDL) (Steps 4 and 6). The major protein of HDL is apo AI. HDL accept cholesterol from tissues (Step 10) and deliver it to the liver directly (Step 12) or transfer it to other lipoproteins, such as chylomicron or VLDL remnants, which are then taken up by the liver. In the liver, cholesterol can either be excreted directly into bile, converted to bile acids, or re-utilized in lipoprotein production. A decreased HDL-C level is a significant independent CHD risk factor, while an elevated level is protective for CHD. A more extensive review of lipoprotein metabolism is provided in Chapter 1.

Another lipoprotein not shown in Figure 2–1 is lipoprotein(a) or Lp(a). This lipoprotein consists of an LDL particle with apo(a) attached to it by a disulfide bond. Apo(a) is a unique glycoprotein with protein domains, known as kringles, which have homology with similar protein domains in plasminogen. Apo(a) contains multiple and variable numbers of kringle 4-like domains and one kringle 5-like domain. Variability in Lp(a) concentration relates to apo(a) molecular weight, number of kringle 4-like domains, and differences in hepatic apo(a) secretion rates.[11-15] Increased concentrations may interfere with fibrinolysis or clot lysis.[16-18] Like LDL, Lp(a) can be deposited directly in the arterial wall, promoting atherosclerosis.[12] Increased Lp(a) concentrations have been associated with premature CHD in most studies.[19-38] Lp(a)-C can now be measured, thereby circumventing some of the problems associated with Lp(a) protein standardization.[39] For additional information, refer to Chapter 15.

Figure 2–1 ✧ A Simplified Overview of Lipoprotein Metabolism

Open arrows signify synthetic pathways, thin closed arrows signify transfer pathways, thick closed arrows signify catabolic pathways, dotted arrows signify minor pathways, and solid boxes or symbols signify receptors. Fats absorbed in the intestine are packaged into large TG-rich particles known as chylomicrons (Step 1). These lipoproteins undergo lipolysis (removal of TG) to form chylomicron remnants (Step 4), which are taken up by the liver via an apo E receptor (Step 5). The liver can also secrete TG-rich lipoproteins known as VLDL (Step 2). Following lipolysis, these particles can be converted to LDL (Step 6) or taken up by the liver via an apo E receptor (Step 7). LDL are catabolized mainly by the liver (Step 8) or other tissues (Step 9) via LDL receptors that recognize both apo B-100 and apo E but not apo B-48. If LDL are modified, they can also be taken up by scavenger receptors on macrophages (Step 11). HDL are synthesized by both the liver and the intestine (Step 3). HDL pick up lipid and protein constituents from chylomicrons and VLDL as these particles undergo lipolysis (Steps 4 and 6). HDL pick up free cholesterol from peripheral tissues (Step 10) and macrophages (Step 11) and are catabolized mainly in the liver (Step 12).

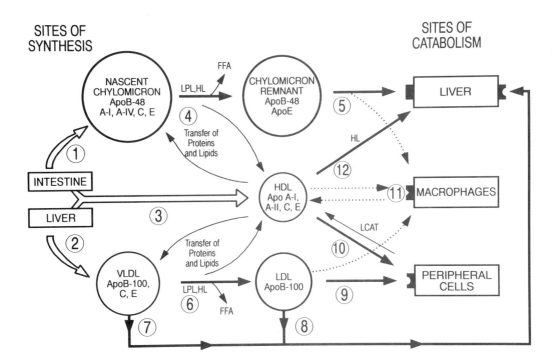

RATIONALE FOR TREATMENT OF LIPID DISORDERS

Plasma LDL-C values are increased by diets high in saturated fat and cholesterol mainly because of decreased LDL receptor-mediated catabolism. Animals that consume such diets develop high LDL-C levels and atherosclerosis. Such diets can also increase HDL-C concentrations; this change may be compensatory. Human populations on diets high in saturated fat and cholesterol have increased LDL-C concentrations and have significantly greater incidence of CHD due to atherosclerosis than populations on diets low in saturated fat and cholesterol.[1-3] In U.S. society, increased LDL-C concentrations as well as decreased HDL-C values are independent risk factors for premature CHD.[1-3, 40-44] Women have higher HDL-C values than men and have a lower risk of CHD.

Prospective studies indicate that dietary treatment or combined dietary and drug therapy which decreases LDL-C can reduce subsequent CHD morbidity and mortality.[41, 42, 45-61] Moreover, studies indicate that aggressive lipid modification in CHD patients to get LDL-C concentrations to < 100 mg/dL (2.6 mmol/L) can result in stabilization of existing coronary atherosclerosis, as well as some regression of this process.[48, 62-72] Small changes in angiographic results appear to translate into large benefits in clinical CHD event reduction, consistent with the concept of plaque stabilization.[66, 67, 69]

The NCEP guidelines focus on LDL-C values because LDL-C has clearly been shown to be an independent risk factor for CHD and because lowering of CHD risk has been documented to occur with LDL-C lowering by diet with or without drugs in patients with increased LDL-C concentrations and/or CHD. Because of these studies, consensus has been reached on use of drugs for lowering LDL-C,[73] but not for lowering TG or raising HDL-C.[74] Decreased HDL-C has been shown to be an independent CHD risk factor, and HDL-C increases have been associated with reduced CHD risk within both the Lipid Research Clinics Trial and the Helsinki Heart Study.[41, 42, 55, 75, 76]

In a meta-analysis, but not always in individual studies, increased TG concentration has been shown to be an independent CHD risk factor, especially in women.[43, 77] Increased TG concentrations are correlated with decreased HDL-C values. While it was shown that raising HDL-C concentration with medication was beneficial for CHD risk reduction in both the Lipid Research Clinics Trial and the Helsinki Heart Study, along with LDL-C lowering, no such data are available for triglyceride lowering.[41, 42, 54, 55, 75] Surprisingly, despite a 34% reduction in triglycerides in the Helsinki Heart Study, no benefit in CHD risk reduction could be ascribed to this effect.[55] Moreover, no prospective study has as yet been completed in patients selected for decreased HDL-C or increased TG concentrations. For these reasons, the NCEP guidelines focus on LDL-C concentrations. Two prospective secondary prevention studies are currently ongoing to assess whether raising HDL-C in men with CHD and low HDL-C levels is of benefit in risk reduction.[78]

EVALUATION OF THE PATIENT

Serum or plasma total cholesterol (TC) and HDL-C concentrations can be measured in the fasting or non-fasting state for screening purposes.[2] Plasma values for TC are approximately 3% lower than serum values and should be adjusted upward if EDTA

Table 2–1 ❖ Lipid Abnormalities in Adults*				
	Desirable	*Borderline High Risk for CHD*	*High Risk for CHD*	*High Risk for Pancreatitis*
Cholesterol	< 200 (5.2)	200–239 (5.2–6.2)	≥ 240 (6.2)	–
LDL Cholesterol	< 130 (3.4)	130–159 (3.4–4.1)	≥ 160 (4.1)	–
HDL Cholesterol	> 60 (1.6)	–	< 35 (0.9)	–
Triglyceride	< 200 (2.3)	200–400 (2.3–4.5)	> 400 (4.5)	> 1000 (11.3)
TC/HDL	< 5.0	5.0–6.0	> 6.0	

*All values in mg/dL; values in parentheses are in mmol/L. Elevated triglycerides have been shown to be a risk factor for pancreatitis (> 1000 mg/dL or 11.3 mmol/L), but have not been clearly shown to be an independent risk factor for CHD.

is the anticoagulant used. For screening programs, compact analyzers using finger-stick specimens are now available for TC, TG, and HDL-C.[79]

Lipid values have been classified as listed in Table 2-1 for adults over age 20. According to guidelines issued by the U.S. NCEP Adult Treatment Panel II, patients without CHD who have a desirable TC value of < 200 mg/dL (5.2 mmol/L) and an HDL-C value of ≥ 35 mg/dL (0.9 mmol/L) should have their values checked again within 5 y.[2] In addition, education on the recommended general population diet guidelines (≤ 30% fat, < 10% saturated fat, and < 300 mg of cholesterol/day), exercise, and risk factor reduction should be provided to all patients. If the patient has TC values in the borderline range of 200–239 mg/dL (5.2-6.2 mmol/L), information about other CHD risk factors should be obtained.[2] These risk factors are listed in Table 2-2.

In the absence of CHD (prior myocardial infarction, angina), if a patient has a TC value in the borderline range, a normal HDL-C value, and less than two CHD risk factors, information on diet and CHD risk reduction should be provided and the patient's values checked within the next 1-2 y. If the patient has CHD, a TC value ≥ 240 mg/dL (6.2 mmol/L), a borderline TC value in the presence of two or more CHD risk factors, or an HDL-C value < 35 mg/dL (0.9 mmol/L), it is recommended that a fasting (at least 9 h) lipid profile (TC, TG, HDL-C) be measured. Laboratories should maintain a coefficient of variation (CV) of ≤ 3% and a bias of ≤ 3% for their TC assay as compared to the National Reference System for Cholesterol (NRS/CHOL).[80] The formula commonly used to calculate LDL-C is:[81]

$$LDL\text{-}C = TC - HDL\text{-}C - TG/5$$

when values are in mg/dL, or TG/2.22 when values are in mmol/L.

It has been documented that this formula cannot be used for values obtained on serum or plasma from non-fasting individuals or those whose TG values are > 400 mg/dL (4.5 mmol/L). Moreover, there is considerable variability in calculated LDL-C concentrations when TG values are 200–400 mg/dL (2.3-4.5 mmol/L) as compared to values obtained by ultracentrifugation.[82] Our data indicate that about 5% of the population have fasting TG values > 400 mg/dL (4.5 mmol/L), and that an additional

Table 2–2 ❖ NCEP ATP II Major Risk Factors for CHD in Addition to Elevated LDL Cholesterol*

❖	Male ≥ 45 years, Female ≥ 55 years or with premature menopause without estrogen replacement therapy
❖	Family history of premature CHD (definite myocardial infarction or sudden death before age 55 in a male first-degree relative or before age 65 in a female first-degree relative)
❖	Current cigarette smoking
❖	Hypertension (≥ 140/90 mmHg or taking antihypertensive medication)
❖	HDL cholesterol < 35 mg/dL (0.9 mmol/L)
❖	Diabetes mellitus

*A risk factor should be subtracted if the HDL-C concentration is ≥ 60 mg/dL (1.6 mmol/L).

14% have calculated LDL-C values that are not placed in the appropriate NCEP categories as compared to values obtained by ultracentrifugation.[82]

The Lipoprotein Working Group of the NCEP has recommended development of more direct methods of measuring LDL-C.[83] One direct LDL-C assay has been developed and is available from Sigma Diagnostics (St. Louis, MO), Roche Diagnostics (Somerville, NJ), and the Genzyme Corporation (Cambridge, MA). The principle of the assay is to immunoprecipitate chylomicrons, VLDL, and HDL from serum or plasma, leaving LDL behind, and then measure the cholesterol content of the LDL by automated enzymatic techniques. This assay has been evaluated in multiple studies and found to correlate very highly with LDL-C measured following ultracentrifugation (r = 0.88 to 0.98) based on analyses of serum samples obtained from subjects with TG concentrations up to 4000 mg/dL (45 mmol/L).[84-86] Within-run precision was reflected by CVs ranging from 1.2 to 3.8% and between-run precision by CVs ranging from 1.2 to 5.1%. Moreover, it was documented that this assay gave accurate and reliable results on non-fasting as well as fasting serum. For additional information, refer to Chapter 8.

An LDL-C concentration of 160 mg/dL (4.1 mmol/L) represents approximately the 75th percentile for middle-aged Americans. LDL-C values have been classified by NCEP as shown in Table 2–1.[1, 2] Since values are subject to considerable biologic variation, it is important to confirm the presence of abnormalities by repeat determinations. Hospitalization or acute illness can also affect lipid values, and therefore lipid determinations should generally be carried out when subjects are in the free-living state. Getting LDL-C and HDL-C at the time of screening may be more cost-effective. For additional information on biological variation, refer to Chapter 4.

Although an increased TG concentration has not consistently been shown to be an independent risk factor for CHD, TG concentration is inversely associated with a low concentration of HDL-C, which has been shown to be a significant risk factor for CHD. Moreover, markedly increased TG concentrations are associated with pancreatitis.

Common secondary causes of lipid abnormalities are shown in Table 2–3.[1,2] These secondary causes should be screened by measuring TSH, glucose, liver enzymes,

Table 2–3 ✦ Secondary Causes of Lipid Abnormalities*	
✦	Obesity
✦	Diet
✦	Lack of Exercise
✦	Cigarette Smoking
✦	Alcohol Intake
✦	Diabetes Mellitus
✦	Hypothyroidism
✦	Obstructive Liver Disease
✦	Renal Insufficiency
✦	Nephrotic Syndrome
✦	Medications (hormones, beta blockers, diuretics)

*Screen by measuring glucose, TSH, creatinine, urinary protein, transaminases, and alkaline phosphatase.

and kidney function tests. They should be treated if possible, prior to initiating drug therapy for lipid disorders. Some forms of dyslipidemia are genetic and therefore can be identified by family studies.

In some studies, low apo AI values and decreased LDL particle size as well as increased apo B concentrations have been reported to be superior to LDL-C and HDL-C concentrations as markers for CHD.[87-92] However, these have all been case-control studies. In our view, apo AI and apo B concentrations are less affected by dietary modification and the use of beta blockers than are TG, LDL-C, and HDL-C concentrations, and LDL particle size.[25, 93] Most CHD patients have modified their diet and are often on beta-adrenergic blocking agents, and these are confounders in such case-control studies.[26] Supporting this view is our finding that LDL size is not an independent CHD risk factor after controlling for the effects of beta blockers and LDL-C and HDL-C concentrations.[93] Recent data from the Physicians' Health Study also indicate that LDL size does not provide additional information about CHD risk above and beyond that provided by a standard lipid profile.[94] Moreover, of several prospective studies assessing the utility of apo AI and apo B versus LDL-C and HDL-C concentrations as CHD markers, none has documented that apolipoprotein values added significant additional information about CHD risk.[30, 95-100] Adequate standardization for apo AI and apo B is now available;[101-104] also, gels for running LDL sizing are now commercially available. It is our view that apo AI, apo B, and LDL size measurements are not likely to have significant additional clinical utility and for cost considerations cannot be recommended for CHD risk assessment at this time. However, more data from large-scale prospective studies are required before definitive conclusions can be reached in this regard.

In contrast, an increased Lp(a) concentration is likely to be a significant independent CHD risk factor. This concept is supported by many case-control studies and nine of thirteen prospective studies.[19-38, 98, 99, 105, 106] Problems associated with Lp(a) measurement include lack of assay standardization and considerable heterogeneity within the protein. When calibrated to total mass of the particle, an Lp(a) value of

> 40 mg/dL is clearly above the 90th percentile, but many authorities feel that a value > 30 mg/dL is a high-risk value. Our data indicate that familial Lp(a) excess (values above the 90th percentile) is a highly heritable disorder found in 15–20% of kindreds with premature CHD.[27] Niacin administration has been shown to lower Lp(a) concentrations, as well as to reduce CHD morbidity and mortality in unselected men with CHD.[52, 54, 107] For these reasons, it is our view that Lp(a) concentrations should be measured in patients who are candidates for drug therapy for LDL lowering, especially those with CHD, as well as individuals with a strong family history of CHD. Patients whose values are increased—with Lp(a) > 30 mg/dL or lipoprotein (a) cholesterol [Lp(a)-C] > 10 mg/dL—should be treated with niacin if they can tolerate it, or in postmenopausal women, with hormonal replacement. Both niacin and hormonal replacement have been shown to reduce CHD risk as well as lower both LDL-C and Lp(a). Therefore, their use in this situation can be justified before use of a statin. The cholesterol content of Lp(a) can be assessed, and this method may aid in the standardization process.[39] Moreover, this method is now commercially available.

FAMILIAL LIPOPROTEIN DISORDERS

An overview of familial hypercholesterolemic states is provided in Table 2–4. By far the most common of these disorders is familial combined hyperlipidemia, in which affected kindred members may have increased LDL-C alone (above the 90th

Table 2–4 ✧ Familial Hypercholesterolemic States			
	Familial Combined Hyperlipidemia	*Familial Hypercholesterolemia*	*Familial Dysbetalipoproteinemia*
Physical findings:	Arcus senilis	Arcus senilis, tendinous xanthomas	Arcus senilis, tubo-eruptive and planar xanthomas
Associated findings:	Obesity, glucose intolerance, hyperuricemia, HDL deficiency	—	Obesity, glucose intolerance, hyperuricemia
Mode of inheritance:	Autosomal dominant	Autosomal co-dominant	Autosomal recessive
Defect:	Overproduction of hepatic VLDL apo B-100	Defective LDL receptor or defective apo B-100	Defective apo E
Estimated population frequency:	1:50	1:500	1:5000
Estimated frequency in CHD patients:	15%	1–3%	0.5%
CHD risk:	Moderate	High	Low
Treatment:	Diet, niacin, resin, statins, gemfibrozil	Diet, niacin and resin, statins and resin, or triple therapy	Diet, niacin, gemfibrozil, statins

percentile of age- and gender-adjusted norms), increased TG alone, or increases of both parameters. Family studies (which are often difficult), with sampling of available first degree relatives (parents, siblings, and offspring), are required to make the diagnosis.[27, 108, 109] These patients also often have decreased HDL-C values due to enhanced degradation of HDL protein (Step 12 in Figure 2–1).[27] They have also been shown to have overproduction of VLDL apo B-100, but not TG (Step 2).[110, 111] Approximately 15% of patients with premature CHD have this disorder.[27] Sporadic or polygenic hypercholesterolemia is also quite common and is observed in approximately 2% of kindreds with premature CHD.[27, 108] Treatment consists of diet and, if necessary, HMG CoA reductase inhibitors, niacin, gemfibrozil, or combinations of these medications with anion exchange resins.[112]

A much more rare form of combined increases of TC and TG is known as familial dysbetalipoproteinemia (Type III hyperlipoproteinemia), in which affected subjects have accumulations of chylomicron remnants and VLDL in the fasting state. These patients usually are homozygous for a mutation in the apo E protein (apo E 2/2 phenotype), or in rare cases have apo E deficiency, resulting in defective hepatic clearance of chylomicron remnants and VLDL particles as well as increased VLDL production (Steps 2, 5, and 6).[113–117] They may also have tubo-eruptive and palmar xanthomas. Diagnosis requires documentation of a VLDL-C/TG ratio > 0.3 after measurement of VLDL-C following ultracentrifugation, and documentation of the apo E 2/2 phenotype by isoelectric focusing, or of the genotype by DNA analysis. Treatment consists of diet, niacin, gemfibrozil, or HMG CoA reductase inhibitors. Patients with both familial combined hyperlipidemia and familial dysbetalipoproteinemia often have obesity, glucose intolerance, and hyperuricemia.[115]

Isolated increases of LDL-C are also found in patients with a disorder known as familial hypercholesterolemia, often associated with tendinous xanthomas. These patients generally have marked hypercholesterolemia (> 350 mg/dL [9.0 mmol/L]) with normal TG values, and have defects at the LDL receptor locus or abnormalities of the apo B protein (apo B-3500 mutation).[108, 109, 117–119] The major metabolic abnormality in these individuals is an impaired ability to catabolize LDL (Steps 8 and 9).[120] Approximately 0.1% of the population and 1% of patients with premature CHD have this disorder due to mutations at the LDL receptor locus.[27, 108] Apo B mutations, specifically at residue 3500, are even less common. Phenotypically, these patients are similar to familial hypercholesterolemic (FH) patients. Treatment generally consists of diet and a combination of medications (generally HMG CoA reductase inhibitors and resin).[121–123]

Isolated deficiency of HDL-C (below the 10th percentile of normal) can be genetic in nature, and is then known as familial hypoalphalipoproteinemia. This disorder is found in approximately 4% of patients with premature CHD.[27, 124–126] In our own recent studies, patients in families with HDL deficiency and premature CHD had decreases in all lipoproteins containing apo AI (Lp AI, Lp AI/AII) and increases in lipoproteins containing apo B, including those containing both apo B and apo E (LpB:E).[124] Treatment of HDL deficiency consists of diet, weight reduction if indicated, and an exercise program.[74] Efforts should be made in these patients to optimize their LDL-C values according to NCEP guidelines, and the agent of choice would be an HMG CoA reductase inhibitor.

An overview of familial hypertriglyceridemic states is provided in Table 2–5. By far the most common of these disorders is familial hypertriglyceridemia, an autosomal-dominant disorder in which obesity, glucose intolerance, hyperuricemia, and HDL deficiency are often present.[27, 108] The disorder is associated with overproduction of hepatic VLDL TG but not VLDL apo B-100 (Step 2).[110, 112] Some patients may have defects in VLDL clearance as well (Steps 6 and 7). CHD risk appears to be increased in those kindreds in whom HDL deficiency is also present. Approximately 15% of patients with premature CHD appear to have this disorder.[27] HDL concentrations are low in these subjects because of enhanced degradation (Step 12). Treatment with diet, exercise, and abstinence from the use of alcohol and exogenous estrogens is recommended. In patients with CHD, lipid values can be optimized by use of HMG CoA reductase inhibitors, niacin, or gemfibrozil.

Severe hypertriglyceridemia, wherein TG values are above 1000 mg/dL (11.3 mmol/L), is often observed in middle-aged or elderly individuals who are obese and have glucose intolerance and hyperuricemia. These subjects usually have familial hypertriglyceridemia or familial combined hyperlipidemia which is exacerbated by other factors, such as obesity, alcohol consumption, and/or diabetes mellitus. These patients generally also have HDL deficiency and may develop lipemia retinalis and eruptive xanthomas. They are at increased risk for developing pancreatitis due to TG deposition

Table 2–5 ✧ Familial Hypertriglyceridemic States			
		Severe Hypertriglyceridemia	
	Familial Hypertriglyceridemia	*Early Onset*	*Adult Onset*
Physical findings:	None	Lipemia retinalis, eruptive xanthomas	Lipemia retinalis, eruptive xanthomas
Associated findings:	Obesity, glucose intolerance, hyperuricemia, HDL deficiency	HDL deficiency, pancreatitis	Obesity, glucose intolerance, hyperuricemia, HDL deficiency, pancreatitis, paresthesias, emotional lability
Mode of inheritance:	Autosomal dominant	Autosomal recessive	Autosomal recessive
Defect:	Overproduction of hepatic VLDL triglyceride	Lipoprotein lipase deficiency, apo C-II deficiency	Overproduction of VLDL triglyceride, delayed catabolism of chylomicrons and VLDL
Estimated population frequency:	1:50	< 1:10,000	1:1000
Estimated frequency in CHD patients:	15%	—	1:500
CHD risk:	Low	—	Low
Treatment:	Diet, niacin, gemfibrozil	Diet	Diet, gemfibrozil, fish oil

in the pancreas and may have paresthesias and emotional lability. These patients often have delayed chylomicron and VLDL clearance and excess VLDL production (Steps 2, 4, 6, and 7). Treatment consists of a calorie-restricted Step 2 diet. In patients with diabetes mellitus, it is crucial to control blood glucose concentrations as much as possible. Medications that are effective in lowering TG to < 1000 mg/dL (11.3 mmol/L in these patients, thereby reducing their risk of pancreatitis, include gemfibrozil, or other fibric acid derivatives, and/or fish-oil capsules (6–10 capsules/day).

Patients who present with severe hypertriglyceridemia in childhood or early adulthood and who are not obese often have a deficiency of the enzyme lipoprotein lipase or its activator protein, apo CII, resulting in markedly impaired removal of TG, which affects chylomicron and VLDL catabolism (Steps 4, 6, and 7). These patients are at increased risk for recurrent pancreatitis, and it is important to restrict their dietary fat to less than 20% of calories. Niacin and/or gemfibrozil are generally ineffective in these patients; however, fish-oil capsules may be helpful in certain patients to keep their TG concentrations below 1000 mg/dL (11.3 mmol/L) and minimize their risk of pancreatitis.

TREATMENT GUIDELINES FOR INCREASED LDL-C

The NCEP Adult Treatment Panel has developed guidelines for the diagnosis and treatment of individuals over age 20 years who have increased TC concentrations associated with increased LDL-C concentrations.[1,2] The NCEP's decision values for LDL-C are given in Table 2–6. Concentrations of LDL-C requiring the initiation of diet and drug therapy as well as the goals of therapy are dependent upon the presence or absence of CHD or CHD risk factors (see Table 2–6) and the presence of secondary causes of lipid abnormalities (see Table 2–3).

Diet Therapy

Diet therapy is the cornerstone of the treatment of lipid disorders.[2] According to our estimates, 50% of the saturated fat and 70% of the cholesterol in the U.S. diet come from hamburgers, cheeseburgers, meat loaf, butter, whole milk products, cheeses, beef dishes, hot dogs, ham, luncheon meats, pork, doughnuts, cookies, and cakes. Hence, such foods should be restricted. Instead, foods such as poultry (white meat without

Table 2–6 ❖ NCEP ATP II LDL Cholesterol Decision Values			
	Initiate Diet Therapy	*Initiate Drug Therapy After Diet Therapy*	*Goal of Therapy*
< 2 CHD risk factors	≥ 160 mg/dL (4.1 mmol/L)	≥ 190 mg/dL (4.9 mmol/L)	< 160 mg/dL) (4.1 mmol/L)
2 or more CHD risk factors	≥ 130 mg/dL (3.4 mmol/L)	≥ 160 mg/dL (4.1 mmol/L)	< 130 mg/dL (3.4 mmol/L)
CHD	≥ 100 mg/dL (2.6 mmol/L)	≥ 130 mg/dL (3.4 mmol/L)	< 100 mg/dL (2.6 mmol/L)

Table 2–7 ◆ NCEP ATP II Dietary Therapy*			
Nutrient	*Average U.S. Diet*	*Step 1 Diet*	*Step 2 Diet*
Total Fat	36%	≤ 30%	≤ 30%
Saturated Fat	15%	< 10%	< 7%
Polyunsaturated Fat	6%	< 10%	< 10%
Mono-unsaturated Fat	15%	< 15%	< 15%
Cholesterol (mg/d)	400–500	< 300	< 200
Total Calories	To achieve and maintain desired weight		
*% indicates percentage of total calories.			

skin), fish, skimmed milk, non-fat or low-fat yogurt, and low-fat cheeses are recommended. The use of fruits, vegetables, and grains is encouraged.

Oils rich in saturated fat, such as coconut oil, palm oil, and palm kernel oil, should be restricted.[127–131] Oils that can be used are unsaturated vegetable oils containing polyunsaturated and mono-unsaturated fatty acids, such as canola, soybean, olive, and corn oil. However, such oils should only be used in moderation because they are pure fat and very calorie rich.

Excellent patient dietary pamphlets are available from the American Heart Association and the National Cholesterol Education Program. NCEP guidelines on dietary therapy are given in Table 2–7. The benefits of the NCEP's Step 1 and Step 2 diets in terms of lowering LDL-C may not be striking unless patients restrict total fat and calories, increase exercise, and lose excess weight.[35] Patients who are unable to get an adequate response from diet modification after being given pamphlets and counseling can be referred to a registered dietitian for instructions on the Step 2 diet. In most cases, diet therapy should be tried for at least 6 months prior to initiating drug therapy.

Drug Therapy

An overview of available lipid-lowering medications is provided in Table 2–8. These medications can be divided into two general classes: those that are effective in decreasing LDL-C by more than 15% and those that are effective in decreasing TG concentrations by more than 15%. Currently, three classes of agents meet the LDL-lowering criteria: HMG CoA reductase inhibitors (lovastatin, pravastatin, simvastatin, fluvastatin, and atorvastatin), anion exchange resins (cholestyramine and colestipol), and niacin. Of these three types of drugs, patient acceptance and compliance with resins and niacin is often poor, while with HMG CoA reductase inhibitors it is generally excellent. Moreover, long-term safety in adults has now been documented with all three types of agents, and CHD risk reduction has also been reported. Because of efficacy and compliance, HMG CoA reductase inhibitors are now the drugs of choice for LDL-C lowering in all patients. Recent data clearly indicate that these drugs are safe and reduce CHD risk in primary and secondary prevention studies, and are equally effective in men and women, and in young and elderly patients.[58–61] These agents reduce LDL-C and CHD risk by approximately one third.

Table 2-8 ✧ Lipid Medications

	Resins	Niacin	HMG CoA Reductase Inhibitors*	Gemfibrozil
Patient acceptance and compliance:	Often poor	Often poor	Generally excellent	Generally excellent
Side effects:	Constipation, bloating, decreased absorption of certain medicines	Flushing, itching, gastritis, hepatotoxicity, hyperuricemia, hyperglycemia	Hepatotoxicty, myositis, GI side effects	Myositis, hpeatotoxicity, GI side effects, coumadin interaction
Usual dose:	8-10 g po BID	1 g po BID or TID with food	10, 20, or 40 mg po QD	600 mg po BID
LDL reduction:	10-20%	10-20%	25-35%	10%
Triglyceride reduction:	**	40%	20%	35%
HDL increase:	5%	15-20%	5-15%	5-20%
CHD risk reduction documented:	Yes 19% 7 y	Yes 20% 5 y	Yes 50% 2 y	Yes 34% 5 y
Long-term safety documented:	Yes	Yes	Yes	Yes

*Current HMG CoA reductase inhibitors include lovastatin, pravastatin, simvastatin, and fluvastatin.
**May increase triglycerides.

There are currently three classes of agents that decrease TG concentrations by more than 15%: niacin, fibric acid derivatives (gemfibozil, bezafibrate, ciprofibrate, fenofibrate), and HMG CoA reductase inhibitors. All of these agents generally also lower LDL-C concentrations and increase HDL-C concentrations. Both niacin and gemfibrozil have been shown to lower CHD risk prospectively.[52, 54, 55, 132] The combination of a reductase inhibitor and an anion exchange resin is very effective, as is the combination of resins and niacin. However, the introduction of atorvastatin, which is extremely effective in lowering LDL-C and TG, may obviate the need for combination drug therapy.

It should be noted that in postmenopausal women, estrogen replacement is quite effective in lowering LDL-C and raising HDL-C, but can also raise TG. If hormonal replacement is undertaken in postmenopausal women who are hypertriglyceridemic, the estrogen patch should be used, since there is little or no lipid effect with this form of therapy. Progesterone must be given along with estrogen in women with an intact uterus. Use of estrogens has been associated with a significant reduction in CHD mortality in postmenopausal women.[133, 134] However, these were observational studies and not randomized placebo-controlled studies.

For patients with increases in both LDL-C and TG, the agent of choice is an HMG CoA reductase inhibitor.

For patients with hypertriglyceridemia only and normal LDL-C concentrations, there are as yet no clear guidelines in the United States for the use of medication. If the patient's fasting TG concentration is in excess of 1000 mg/dL (11.3 mmol/L) while on a restricted diet, use of a medication to reduce the risk of pancreatitis is recommended. However, prior to taking this step, the physician should make sure that these patients are not taking estrogens, thiazides, or beta blockers, are not consuming alcohol, and do not have uncontrolled diabetes mellitus. Use of these agents or of alcohol should be discontinued, and every effort should be made to control their diabetes. Calorie and fat restriction and exercise are important in these patients. The drug of choice for these patients is generally gemfibrozil (600 mg po bid) or another fibric acid derivative, such as bezafibrate or fenofibrate. In the absence of glucose intolerance, niacin can be tried. In patients for whom these agents are not effective, or if additional TG reduction is needed, fish-oil capsules (1 g) at a dose of 3–5 capsules twice daily are effective in lowering TG.

In patients with moderate hypertriglyceridemia, especially in the presence of HDL-C deficiency, lifestyle changes including weight reduction and an exercise program are very helpful, as are cessation of the use of alcohol and beta blockers, and control of diabetes if present. If patients have established CHD, the use of HMG CoA reductase inhibitors to optimize their LDL-C concentrations should be considered. The goal of therapy in CHD patients is to get their LDL-C concentrations to < 100 mg/dL (2.59 mmol/L). In patients with moderate hypertriglyceridemia and/or HDL deficiency in the absence of CHD, only lifestyle modification (diet and exercise) and following the guidelines for LDL-C lowering can currently be recommended.

Properties of Lipid Medications

HMG CoA reductase inhibitors inhibit the activity of HMG CoA reductase, the rate-limiting enzyme in cholesterol biosynthesis, causing up-regulation of LDL receptors, enhancing LDL catabolism (Steps 8 and 9), and decreasing plasma LDL-C by 30–45%. They may also decrease VLDL and LDL production (Steps 2 and 6). These agents decrease plasma levels of TC and TG and moderately increase HDL-C.[69] The drugs are usually started at 10–20 mg/day and can be increased to a maximal dose of 40–80 mg/day po. At 40 mg/day for lovastatin, pravastatin, simvastatin, fluvastatin, and atorvastatin, LDL-C reductions of 27%, 34%, 38%, 25%, and approximately 50%, respectively, have been reported. CHD risk reduction and benefit in atherosclerosis have been reported for lovastatin, pravastatin, and simvastatin. Safety and efficacy in CHD risk reduction have also recently been established. These drugs are generally well tolerated, but may occasionally cause liver enzyme increases, CPK increases with myalgias and myositis, and gastrointestinal upset. Large-scale studies with these agents have now been completed. These studies show reductions not only in CHD risk and mortality, but also in risk of stroke in patients with established CHD, and in total mortality as well.[58-61]

Cholestyramine and colestipol are anion exchange resins which bind bile acids, increase conversion of liver cholesterol to bile acids, and up-regulate LDL receptors in liver, increasing LDL catabolism (Step 8 and 9 of Figure 2–1) and decreasing plasma LDL-C by about 20%. Side effects include bloating and constipation, increased TG, and interference with the absorption of digoxin, tetracycline, d-thyroxine, phenylbutazone, and coumadin (these drugs should be given 1 h before or 4 h after resin). Cholestyramine (4 g scoops) or colestipol (5 g scoops) can be started at 1 scoop twice per day and gradually increased to 2 scoops twice per day (the scoops are half the price of the packets) or two scoops three times daily. Constipation may require treatment. Cholestyramine use has been shown to lower LDL-C by 12% and to reduce CHD risk prospectively by 19% over a 7-y period in middle-aged, asymptomatic, hypercholesterolemic men.[41]

Niacin decreases VLDL (Step 2) and LDL production (Step 6) and raises HDL-C values (by 20%). Niacin should be started at 100 mg po bid with meals and gradually increased to 1 g po bid or tid with meals. Side effects include flushing, gastric irritation, and elevations of uric acid, glucose, and liver enzymes in some patients. Niacin should not be used in patients with liver disease, a history of ulcers, or in diabetic patients not on insulin. Long-acting niacin causes less flushing but more gastrointestinal side effects than regular niacin. One aspirin daily will minimize flushing and can be used initially. Niacin should be discontinued if liver enzymes increase to over twice the upper normal limit. Niacin has been shown to decrease TC concentrations by 10% and reduce the recurrence of myocardial infarction by 20% over a 5-y period of administration in men with CHD. The use of niacin was also associated with an 11% reduction in all-cause mortality 10 y after cessation of niacin. Niacin in combination with clofibrate has been shown to reduce mortality in CHD patients as compared to usual care.[53]

Gemfibrozil is the only fibrate currently used in the United States. However, other fibric acid derivatives, specifically fenofibrate and bezafibrate, are available in many countries. Current data indicate that these other fibrates are as effective as gemfibrozil for TG reduction, and more effective for LDL-C reduction. However, no prospective data from large-scale clinical trials have been reported for the latter two agents. Gemfibrozil is given at a dose of 600 mg po bid and is generally well tolerated. The drug is very effective in lowering TG and VLDL (by 35%) by decreasing production and enhancing breakdown of VLDL (Steps 2 and 6). The drug usually lowers LDL-C by 10% and increases HDL-C by 5–15%. Rarely, patients may experience gastrointestinal symptoms, muscle cramps (increased CPK, 1%), or intermittent indigestion. The drug should not be used in patients with renal insufficiency, and it is also known to potentiate the action of coumadin. The drug may raise LDL-C concentrations in some hypertriglyceridemic patients. Gemfibrozil lowered LDL-C by 9%, increased HDL-C by 10% and reduced CHD prospectively by 34% over a 5-y period in middle-aged asymptomatic hypercholesterolemic men in the Helsinki Heart Study.[54]

Drug Combinations

HMG CoA reductase inhibitors and resins, as well as niacin and resin in combination, are very effective in lowering LDL-C concentrations. The combination of a fibrate and an HMG CoA reductase inhibitor can be used, but myositis incidence may be increased; therefore, this combination should be used with caution.

GOALS OF THERAPY

The NCEP's goals of therapy are to get the LDL-C values to < 100 mg/dL (2.6 mmol/L) in CHD patients, to < 130 mg/dL (3.4 mmol/L) in patients with two or more CHD risk factors, and to < 160 mg/dL (4.1 mmol/L) in all patients. In our view, in CHD patients it may also be prudent to lower TG to < 200 mg/dL (2.25 mmol/L), to lower Lp(a)-C concentrations to < 10 mg/dL, to increase HDL-C concentrations to > 35 mg/dL (0.9 mmol/L), and to try to lower the TC/HDL-C ratio to < 5.0. In patients with severe hypertriglyceridemia and pancreatitis, the goal of therapy is to reduce TG concentrations to < 500 mg/dL (3.65 mmol/L).

CONCLUSION

This chapter is designed to provide laboratory personnel with an overview of the diagnosis and treatment of lipoprotein disorders and NCEP guidelines for therapy. Current diagnostic tests that are recommended include screening for serum TC and HDL-C in the fasting or non-fasting state, and serum TC, TG, HDL-C, and calculated LDL-C in the fasting state. If fasting TG values are > 250 mg/dL (2.8 mmol/L), a direct LDL-C assay should be used for measurement of LDL-C, for greater accuracy. Routine measurement of apo AI, apo B, or LDL size cannot be recommended because of a lack of prospective data documenting that these assays provide significant additional information about CHD risk prediction. Lp(a) or Lp(a)-C is an important addition to lipoprotein assessment, since it provides significant additional information about CHD risk, and can readily be measured. In our view, in the future direct measurement of LDL-C, HDL-C, Lp(a)-C, and, perhaps, lipoprotein remnant-C, along with serum TG, will become standard practice in lipoprotein assessment. Moreover, researchers are actively developing methodologies that will eliminate preanalytical steps, for increased precision, accuracy, and throughput. ✧

REFERENCES

1. The Expert Panel. Report of the National Cholesterol Education Program Expert Panel on Detection, Evaluation, and Treatment of High Blood Cholesterol in Adults. Arch Intern Med 1988;148:36-69.
2. The Expert Panel. Summary of the second report of the National Cholesterol Education Program (NCEP) Expert Panel on Detection, Evaluation, and Treatment of High Blood Cholesterol in Adults (Adult Treatment Panel II). JAMA 1993;269:3015-23.
3. Expert Panel. Blood cholesterol levels in children and adolescents. National Institutes of Health Publication No. 91-2732, 1-119. Washington DC: U.S. Government Printing Office, 1990.
4. Expert Panel. Population strategies for blood cholesterol reduction. National Institutes of Health Publication No. 90-3046, 1-39. Washington, DC: U.S. Government Printing Office, 1991.
5. Schaefer EJ, Levy RI. The pathogenesis and management of lipoprotein disorders. N Engl J Med 1985;312:1300-10.
6. Eisenberg S. Lipoprotein abnormalities in hypertriglyceridemia: significance in athero-sclerosis. [Review] Am Heart J 1987;113:555-61.
7. Phillips NR, Waters D, Havel RJ. Plasma lipoproteins and progression of coronary artery disease evaluated by angiography and clinical events. Circulation 1993;88:2762-70.

8. Nakajima K, Saito T, Tamura A, Suzuki M, Nakano T, Adachi M. Cholesterol in remnant-like lipoproteins in human serum using monoclonal anti apo B-100 and anti apo A-I immunoaffinity mixed gels. Clin Chim Acta 1993;223:53–71.

9. McNamara JR, Shah PK, Nelson SM, Nakajima K, Wilson PWF, Schaefer EJ. Lipoprotein remnant cholesterol and triglyceride values in coronary cases and Framingham controls. [abstract] Circulation 1996;94:I-93.

10. Steinberg D, Parthasarathy S, Carew TE, Khoo JC, Witztum, JL. Beyond cholesterol: modifications of low-density lipoprotein that increase its atherogenicity. New Engl J Med 1989;320:915–24.

11. Berg K. A new serum type system in man: the Lp system. Acta Pathol Microbiol Scand. 1963;59:369–82.

12. McLean JW, Tomlinson JE, Kuang WJ, et al. cDNA sequence of human apolipoprotein (a) is homologous to plasminogen. Nature 1987;330:132–7.

13. Utermann G. The mysteries of lipoprotein(a). Science 1989;246:904–10.

14. Lackner C, Boerwinkle E, Leffert CC, Rahmig T, Hobbs HH. Molecular basis of apolipoprotein(a) isoform heterogeneity as revealed by pulsed-field gel electrophoresis. J Clin Invest 1991;87:2153–61.

15. Boerwinkle E, Leffert CC, Lin J, Lackner C, Chiesa G, Hobbs HH. Apolipoprotein(a) gene accounts for greater than 90% of the variation in plasma lipoprotein(a) concentrations. J Clin Invest 1992;90:52–60.

16. Loscalzo J, Weinfeld M, Fless GM, Scanu AM. Lipoprotein (a), fibrin binding, and plasminogen activation. Arteriosclerosis 1990;10:240–5.

17. Miles LA, Fless GM, Levin EG, Scanu AM, Plow EF. A potential basis of the thrombotic risks associated with lipoprotein (a). Nature 1989;339:301–3.

18. Hajjar KA, Gavish D, Breslow JL, Nachman RL. Lipoprotein (a) modulation of endothelial cell surface fibrinolysis and its potential role in atherosclerosis. Nature 1989;339:303–5.

19. Dahlen GH, Guyton JR, Altar M, Farmer JA, Kautz JA, Gotto AM. Association of levels of lipoprotein (a), plasma lipids, and other lipoproteins with coronary artery disease documented by angiography. Circulation 1986;74:758–65.

20. Armstrong VW, Cremer P, Eberle E, et al. The association between serum Lp(a) concentrations and angiographically assessed coronary atherosclerosis. Atherosclerosis 1986; 62:249–57.

21. Zenker G, Költringer P, Bone G, Niederkorn K, Pfeiffer K, Jurgens G. Lipoprotein(a) as a strong indicator for cerebrovascular disease. Stroke 1986;17:942–5.

22. Murai A, Miyahara T, Fujimoto N, Matsudo M, Kameyama M. Lp(a) lipoprotein as a risk factor for coronary heart disease and cerebral infarction. Atherosclerosis 1986; 59:199–204.

23. Hoefler G, Harnoncourt F, Paschke E, Mitrl W, Pfeiffer KH, Kostner GM. Lipoprotein Lp(a): a risk factor for myocardial infarction. Arteriosclerosis 1988;8:398–401.

24. Sandkamp M, Funke H. Schulte H, Koher E, Assmann G. Lipopoprotein (a) is an independent risk factor for myocardial infarction at a young age. Clin Chem 1990; 36:20–3.

25. Genest J Jr, Jenner JL, McNamara JR, et al. Prevalence of lipoprotein (a) [Lp(a)] excess in coronary artery disease. Am J Cardiol 1991;67:1039–45.

26. Genest JJ Jr, McNamara JR, Ordovas JM, et al. Lipoprotein cholesterol, apolipoprotein A-I and B and lipoprotein(a) abnormalities in men with premature coronary artery disease. J Am Coll Cardiol 1992;19:792–802.

27. Genest JJ Jr, Martin-Munley SS, McNamara JR, et al. Familial lipoprotein disorders in patients with premature coronary artery disease. Circulation 1992;85:2025–33.

28. Jenner JL, Ordovas JM, Lamon-Fava S, et al. Effects of age, sex, and menopausal status on plasma lipoprotein (a) levels. The Framingham Offspring Study. Circulation 1993;87:1135–41.

29. Rosengren A, Wihelmsen L, Eriksson E, Risberg B, Wedel H. Lipoprotein (a) and coronary heart disease: a prospective case-control study in the general population sample of middle aged men. Br Med J 1990;301:1248–51.

30. Sigurdsson G, Baldursdottir A, Sigvalderson H, Agnarsson G, Thorgeirsson G, Sigfusson N. Predictive value of apolipoproteins in a prospective survey of coronary artery disease in men. Am J Cardiol 1992;69:1251-4.

31. Jauhiainen M, Koskinen P, Ehnholm C, et al. Lipoprotein (a) and coronary heart disease risk: a nested case-control study of the Helsinki Heart Study participants. Atherosclerosis 1991;89:59-67.

32. Ridker PM, Hennekens CH, Stampfer MJ. A prospective study of lipoprotein (a) and the risk of myocardial infarction. JAMA 1993;270:2195-9.

33. Schaefer EJ, Lamon-Fava S, Jenner JL, et al. Lipoprotein (a) levels and risk of coronary heart disease in men. The Lipid Research Clinics Coronary Primary Prevention Trial. JAMA 1994;271:999-1003.

34. Cremer P, Nagel D, Labrot B, Mann H, Muche R, Elster H, Seidel D. Lipoprotein Lp(a) as predictor of myocardial infarction in comparison to fibrinogen, LDL cholesterol and other risk factors: results from the prospective Gottingen Risk Incidence and Prevalence Study (GRIPS). Eur J Clin Invest 1994;24:444-53.

35. Cantin B, Moorjani S, Despres J-P, Dagenais GR, Lupien P-J. Lp(a) in ischemic heart disease: the Quebec Cardiovascular Study. [Abstract]. JACC 1994;23:482A.

36. Bostom AG, Gagnon DR, Cupples LA, Wilson PWF, Jenner JL, Ordovas JM, Schaefer EJ, Castelli WP. A prospective investigation of elevated lipoprotein(a) detected by electrophoresis and cardiovascular disease in women. The Framingham Heart Study. Circulation 1994;90:1688-95.

37. Assman G, Schulte H, von Eckardstein A. Hypertriglyceridemia and elevated lipoprotein(a) are risk factors for major coronary events in middle aged men. Am J Cardiol 1996;77:1179-84.

38. Bostom AG, Cupples LA, Jenner JL, Ordovas JM, Seman LJ, Wilson PWF, Schaefer EJ, Castelli WP. Elevated lipoprotein(a) and coronary heart disease in men aged 55 years and younger. JAMA 1996;276:544-48

39. Seman LJ, Jenner JL, McNamara JR, Schaefer EJ. Quantitation of plasma lipoprotein(a) by cholesterol assay of lectin bound lipoprotein(a). Clin Chem 1994;40:400-3.

40. Kannel WB, Castelli WP, Gordon T. Cholesterol in the prediction of atherosclerotic disease: new perspectives based on the Framingham Study. Ann Int Med 1979;90:85-91.

41. The Lipid Research Clinics Program. The Lipid Research Clinics Coronary Primary Prevention Trial. I. Reduction in incidence of coronary heart disease. JAMA 1984;251: 351-64.

42. The Lipid Research Clinics Program. The Lipid Research Clinics Coronary Primary Prevention Trial. II. The relationship of reduction in incidence of coronary heart disease to cholesterol lowering. JAMA 1984;251:365-74.

43. Anderson KM, Wilson PWF, Odell PM, Kannel WB. An updated coronary risk profile. A statement for health professionals. AHA medical/scientific statement science advisory. Circulation 1991;83:356-62.

44. Stamler J, Wentworth D, Neaton JD. Is the relationship between serum cholesterol and risk of premature death from coronary heart disease continuous and graded? Findings in 356,222 primary screenees of the Multiple Risk Factor Intervention Trial (MRFIT). JAMA 1986;256:2823-8.

45. Dayton S, Pearce ML, Hashimoto S, Dixon WJ, Tomiyasu U. A controlled clinical trial of a diet high in unsaturated fat in preventing complications of atherosclerosis. Circulation 1969;40 (Suppl II):11-63.

46. Hjermann I, Holme I, Byre KV, Leren P. Effect of diet and smoking intervention on the incidence of coronary heart disease. Lancet 1981;2:1303-10.

47. Holme I, Hjermann I, Helgelend A, Leren P. The Oslo Study: diet and anti-smoking advice: additional results from a 5 year primary prevention trial in middle aged men. Prev Med 1985;14:279-92.

48. Miettinen M, Karvonen MJ, Turpeiner O, Elosuo R, Paavilainen F. Effect of cholesterol lowering diet on mortality from coronary heart disease and other causes: a twelve year clinical trial in men and women. Lancet 1972;2(782):835-8.

49. Ornish D, Brown SK, Scherwitz LW, et al. Can life-style changes reverse coronary heart disease? Lancet 1990;326:129–33.
50. Leren P. The effect of plasma cholesterol lowering diet in male survivors of myocardial infarction. Acta Med Scand 1966;466(Suppl):92–116.
51. de Lorgeril M, Renaud S, Mamelle N, Salen P, Martin JL, Monjaud I, et al. Mediterranean alpha-linolenic acid-rich diet in secondary prevention of coronary heart disease. Lancet 1994;343:1454–9.
52. Canner PL, Berge KG, Wenger NK, et al. Fifteen-year mortality in Coronary Drug Project patients: long-term benefit with niacin. J Am Coll Cardiol 1986;8:1245–55.
53. Carlson LA, Rosenhamer G. Reduction of mortality in the Stockholm Ischemic Heart Disease Study by combined treatment with clofibrate and nicotinic acid. Acta Med Scand 1988;223:405–18.
54. Frick MH, Elo O, Haapa K, et al. Helsinki Heart Study: primary prevention trial with gemfibrozil in middle-aged men with dyslipidemia. N Engl J Med 1987;317:1237–45.
55. Manninen V, Elo O, Frick MH, et al. Lipid alterations and decline in the incidence of coronary heart disease in the Helsinki Heart Study. JAMA 1988;260:641–51.
56. Manninen V, Tenkanen L, Koskinen P, et al. Joint effects of serum triglyceride and LDL cholesterol and HDL cholesterol concentrations on coronary heart disease risk in the Helsinki Heart Study: implication for treatment. Circulation 1992;85:37–45.
57. Scandinavian Simvastatin Survival Study Group. Randomized trial of cholesterol lowering in 4444 patients with coronary heart disease: the Scandinavian Simvastatin Survival Study (4S). Lancet 1994;344:383–9.
58. Pedersen TR, Kjekshus J, Berg K, Olsson AG, Wilhelmsen L, Wiedel H, et al. Cholesterol lowering and the use of healthcare resources: results of the Scandinavian Simvastatin Survival Study. Circulation 1996;93:1796–802.
59. Byington RP, Jukema JA, Salonen JT, Pitt B, Bruschke AV, et al. Reduction in cardiovascular events during pravastatin therapy. Pooled analysis of clinical events of the Pravastatin Atherosclerosis Intervention Program. Circulation 1995;92:2419–25.
60. Shepherd J, Cobbe SM, Ford I, Isles CG, Lorimer AR, MacFarlane PW, McKillop JH, Packard CJ. Prevention of coronary heart disease with pravastatin in men with hypercholesterolemia: West of Scotland Coronary Prevention Study Group. N Eng J Med 1995;333:1301–7.
61. Sacks FM, Pfeffer MA, Moye LA, Rouleau JL, Rutherford JD, Cole TG, et al. The effect of pravastatin on coronary events after myocardial infarction in patients with average cholesterol levels: Cholesterol and Recurrent Events Trial investigators. N Eng J Med 1996;335:1001–9.
62. Haskell WL, Alderman EL, Fair JM, Maron DJ, Mackey SF, Superko HR, et al. Effects of intensive multiple risk factor reduction on coronary atherosclerosis and clinical cardiac events in men and women with coronary artery disease: the Stanford Coronary Risk Intervention Project (SCRIP). Circulation 1994;89:975–90.
63. Blankenhorn DH, Nessim SA, Johnson RL, Sanmarco ME, Azen SP, Cashin-Hemphill L. Beneficial effects of combined colestipol-niacin therapy on coronary atherosclerosis and coronary venous bypass grafts. JAMA 1987;257:3233–40.
64. Blankenhorn DH, Azen SP, Kramsch DM, et al. Coronary angiographic changes with lovastatin therapy: the monitored atherosclerosis regression study (MARS). Ann Intern Med 1993;1119:969–76.
65. Brensike JF, Levy RI, Kelsey SF, et al. Effects of therapy with cholestyramine on progression of coronary atherosclerosis: results of the NHLBI Type II Coronary Intervention Study. Circulation 1984;69:313–24.
66. Brown BG, Zhao XQ, Sacco DE, Albers JJ. Lipid lowering and plaque regression: new insights into prevention of plaque disruption and clinical events in coronary disease. Circulation 1993;87:1781–91.
67. Brown BG, Albers JJ, Fisher LD, et al. Regression of coronary artery disease as a result of intensive lipid-lowering therapy in men with high levels of apolipoprotein B. N Engl J Med 1990;323:1289–98.

68. Buchwald H, Varco RL, Matts JP, Long JM, Fitch LL, Campbell GS. Effect of partial ileal bypass surgery on mortality and morbidity from coronary heart disease in patients with hypercholesterolemia: report of the Program on Surgical Control of the Hyperlipidemias (POSCH). N Engl J Med 1990;323:946-55.

69. Fuster V, Badimon L, Badimon JJ, Chesbro JH. The pathogenesis of coronary artery disease and the acute coronary syndrome. N Engl J Med 1992;326:242-56, 310-18.

70. Kane JP, Malloy MJ, Ports TA, Phillips NR, Diehl JC, Havel RJ. Regression of coronary atherosclerosis during treatment of familial hypercholesterolemia with combined drug regimens. JAMA 1990;264:3007-12.

71. Watts GF, Lewis B, Brunt JNH, et al. Effects on coronary artery disease of lipid lowering diet: a diet plus cholestyramine in the St. Thomas Atherosclerosis Regression Study (STARS). Lancet 1992;339:563-9.

72. Schuler G, Hambrecht R, Schlierf G, et al. Regular exercise and low fat diet: effects on progression of coronary artery disease. Circulation 1992;86:1-11.

73. NIH Consensus Conference. Lowering blood cholesterol to prevent heart disease. JAMA 1985;253:2080-6.

74. NIH Consensus Conference. Triglyceride, HDL cholesterol and coronary heart disease. JAMA 1993;269:505-10.

75. Gordon DJ, Knoke J, Probstfeld JL, Superko R, Tyroler HA. High density lipoprotein cholesterol and coronary heart disease in hypercholesterolemic men: the Lipid Research Clinics Coronary Primary Prevention Trial. Circulation 1986;74:1217-25.

76. Gordon DJ, Rifkind BM. High-density lipoprotein: the clinical implications of recent studies. N Eng J Med 1989;321:1311-16.

77. Hokanson JE, Austin MA. Plasma triglyceride level as a risk factor for cardiovascular disease independent of high-density lipoprotein cholesterol level: a meta-analysis of population-based prospective studies. J Cardiovasc Risk 1996;3:213-19.

78. Rubins HB, Robins SJ, Iwane MK, Boden WE, Elam MB, Fye CL, Gordon DJ, Schaefer EJ, Schectman G, Wittes JT for the Department of Veterans Affairs HIT study group. Rationale and design of the Department of Veterans Affairs High-Density Lipoprotein Cholesterol Intervention Trial (HIT) for secondary prevention of coronary artery disease in men with low high-density lipoprotein cholesterol and desirable low-density lipoprotein cholesterol. Am J Cardiol 1993;71:45-52.

79. Kaufman HW, McNamara JR, Anderson KM, Wilson PWF, Schaefer EJ. How reliably can compact chemistry analyzers measure lipids? JAMA 1990;263:1245-9.

80. Laboratory Standardization Panel. Recommendations for improving cholesterol measurements. National Institutes of Health Publication No. 90-2964, 1-64. Washington DC: U.S. Government Printing Office, 1990.

81. Friedewald WT, Levy RI, Fredrickson DS. Estimation of the concentration of low density lipoproteins cholesterol without use of the preparative ultracentrifuge. Clin Chem 1972;18:499-502.

82. McNamara JR, Cohn JS, Wilson PWF, Schaefer EJ. Calculated values for low density lipoprotein cholesterol in the assessment of lipid abnormalities and coronary disease risk. Clin Chem 1990;36:36-42.

83. Bachorik PS, Ross JW, for the National Cholesterol Education Program Working Group on Lipoprotein Measurement. National Cholesterol Education Program recommendations for measurement of low-density lipoprotein cholesterol: executive summary. Clin Chem 1995;41:1414-20.

84. McNamara JR, Cole TG, Contois JH, Ferguson CA, Ordovas JM, Schaefer EJ. Immunoseparation method for measuring low-density lipoprotein cholesterol directly from serum evaluated. Clin Chem 1995;41:232-40.

85. Jialal I, Hirany SV, Devaraj S, Sherwood TA. Comparison of an immunoseparation method for direct measurement of LDL-cholesterol with beta quantification (ultracentrifugation). Am J Clin Path 1995;104:76-81.

86. Pisani T, Gepsky CP, Leary ET, Warnick GR, Ollington JF. Accurate direct determination of low-density lipoprotein cholesterol using an immunoseparation reagent and enzymatic cholesterol assay. Arch Pathol Lab Med 1995;119:1127-35.

87. Avogaro P, Bittolo Bon G, Cazzolato G, Quinci GB. Are apolipoproteins better discriminators than lipids for atherosclerosis? Lancet 1979;1:901–3.
88. Sniderman A, Shapiro S, Marpole D, Skinner B, Teng B, Kwiterovich PO Jr. Association of coronary atherosclerosis with hyperapobetalipoproteinemia (increased protein but normal cholesterol levels in human plasma low density lipoproteins). Proc Natl Acad Sci USA. 1980;77:604–8.
89. Whayne TF, Alaupovic P, Curry MD, Lee ET, Anderson PS, Snecter E. Plasma apolipoprotein B and VLDL-, LDL-, and HDL-cholesterol as risk factors in the development of coronary artery disease in male patients examined by angiography. Atherosclerosis 1981;39:411–24.
90. Kwiterovich PO, Jr., Bachorik PS, Smith HH, et al. Hyperapobetalipoproteinaemia in two families with xanthomas and phytosterolaemia. Lancet 1981;1:466–9.
91. Maciejko JJ, Holmes DR, Kottke BA, Zinsmeister AR, Dinh DM, Mao SJT. Apolipoprotein A-I as a marker of angiographically assessed coronary artery disease. N Engl J Med 1983;309:385–9.
92. Austin MA, Breslow JL, Hennekens CH, Buring JE, Willett WC, Krauss RM. Low density lipoprotein subclass patterns and risk of myocardial infarction. JAMA 1988;260:1917–21.
93. Campos H, Genest JJ, Blijlevens E, et al. Low density lipoprotein particle size and coronary artery disease. Arterioscler Thromb 1992;12:187–95.
94. Stampfer MJ, Krauss RM, Ma J, Blanche PJ, Holl LG, Sacks FM, Hennekens CH. A prospective study of triglyceride level, low density lipoprotein particle diameter, and risk of myocardial infarction. JAMA 1996;276:882–8.
95. Ishikawa T, Fidge N, Thelle DS, Forde DH, Miller NE. The Tromso Heart Study: serum apolipoprotein A-I concentration in relation to future coronary heart disease. Eur J Clin Invest 1978;8:179–82.
96. Salonen JT, Salonen R, Penttila I, et al. Serum fatty acids, apolipoproteins, selenium and vitamin antioxidants and the risk of death from coronary artery disease. Am J Cardiol 1985;56:226–31.
97. Stampfer MJ, Sacks FM, Salvini S, Willett WC, Hennekens CH. A prospective study of cholesterol, apolipoproteins, and the risk of myocardial infarction. N Engl J Med 1991;325:373–81.
98. Coleman MP, Key TJ, Wang DY, et al. A prospective study of obesity, lipids, apolipoproteins, and ischemic heart disease in women. Atherosclerosis 1992;92:177–85.
99. Wald NJ, Law M, Watt HC, Wu T, Bailey A, Johnson AM, Craig WY, Ledue TB, Haddow JE. Apolipoproteins and ischaemic heart disease: implications for screening. Lancet 1994;343:75–79.
100. Lamarche B, Despres JP, Moorjani S, Cantin B, Dagenais GR, Lupien P-J. Prevalence of dyslipidemic phenotypes in ischemic heart disease (prospective results from the Quebec Cardiovascular Study). Am J Cardiol 1995;75:1189–95.
101. Marcovina SM, Albers JJ, Henderson LO, Hannon WH. International Federation of Clinical Chemistry standardization project for measurements of apolipoproteins A-I and B. III. Comparability of apolipoprotein A-I values by use of international reference material. Clin Chem 1993;39:773–81.
102. Marcovina SM, Albers JJ, Kennedy H, Mei JV, Henderson LO, Hannon WH. International Federation of Clinical Chemistry standardization project for measurements of apolipoproteins A-I and B. IV. Comparability of apolipoprotein B values by use of international reference material. Clin Chem 1994;40:586–92.
103. Contois JH, McNamara JR, Lammi-Keefe CJ, Wilson PWF, Schaefer EJ. Reference intervals for plasma apolipoprotein A-I as determined with a commercially available immunoturbidimetric assay: results from the Framingham Offspring Study. Clin Chem 1996;42:507–14.
104. Contois JH, McNamara JR, Lammi-Keefe CJ, Wilson PWF, Schaefer EJ. Reference intervals for plasma apolipoprotein B as determined with a commercially available immunoturbidimetric assay: results from the Framingham Offspring Study. Clin Chem 1996;42:515–23.

105. Alfthan G, Pekkanen J, Juuhiainen M, Pitkaniemi J, Karvonen M, Tuomilehto J, Salonen JT, Ehnholm C. Relation of serum homocysteine and lipoprotein(a) concentrations to atherosclerotic disease in a prospective Finnish population based study. Atherosclerosis 1994;106:9-19.

106. Schaefer EJ, Lamon-Fava S, Jenner JL, McNamara JR, Ordovas JM, Davis E, Abolafia JM, Lippel K, Levy RI. Lipoprotein(a) levels and risk of coronary heart disease in men. The Lipid Research Clinics Coronary Primary Prevention Trial. JAMA 1994;271:999-1003.

107. Carlson LA, Hamsten A, Asplund A. Pronounced lowering of serum lipoprotein Lp(a) in hyperlipidemic subjects treated with nicotinic acid. J Intern Med 1989;226:271-6.

108. Goldstein JL, Schrott HG, Hazzard WR, Bierman EL, Motulsky AG. Hyperlipidemia in coronary heart disease. II. Genetic analysis of lipid levels in 176 families and delineation of a new inherited disorder, combined hyperlipidemia. J Clin Invest 1973;52:1544-68.

109. Goldstein JL, Brown MS. Familial hypercholesterolemia. In: Stanbury JB, Wyngaarden JB, et al. (eds.). The metabolic basis of inherited disease, 5th ed. New York: McGraw Hill, 1983:672-712.

110. Janus ED, Nicoll AM, Turner PR, Magill P, Lewis B. Kinetic bases of the primary hyperlipidemias: studies of apolipoprotein B turnover in genetically defined subjects. Eur J Clin Invest 1980;10:161-72.

111. Chait A, Albers JJ, Brunzell JD. Very low density lipoprotein overproduction in genetic forms of hypertriglyceridemia. Eur J Clin Invest 1980;10:17-22.

112. Schaefer EJ. Hyperlipoproteinemia. In: Rakel RE (ed). Conn's current therapy. Philadelphia: W. B. Saunders, 1991:515-24.

113. Rall SC Jr, Weisgraber KH, Innerarity TL, Mahley RW. Structural basis for receptor binding heterogeneity of apolipoprotein E from type III hyperlipoproteinemic subjects. Proc Natl Acad Sci USA 1982;79:4696-700.

114. Schaefer EJ, Gregg RE, Ghiselli G, et al. Familial apolipoprotein E deficiency. J Clin Invest 1986;78:1206-19.

115. Schaefer EJ. Dietary and drug treatment. In: Brewer HB Jr., moderator. Type III hyperlipoproteinemia: diagnosis, molecular defects, pathology and treatment. Ann Int Med 1983;98:623-40.

116. Ordovas JM, Litwack-Klein LE, Schaefer MM, Wilson PWF, Schaefer EJ. Apolipoprotein E isoform phenotyping methodology and population frequency with identification and apo E1 and apo E5 isoforms. J Lipid Res 1987;28:371-80.

117. Fredrickson DS, Levy RI, Lees RS. Fat transport in lipoproteins: an integrated approach to mechanisms and disorders. N Engl J Med 1967;276:34-44, 94-103, 148-56, 215-25, 273-81.

118. Brown MS, Goldstein JL. The LDL receptor concept: clinical and therapeutic implications. In: Stokes J III, Mancini M, eds. Hypercholesterolemia: clinical and therapeutic implications. Atherosclerosis Reviews 1987, Vol 18. New York: Raven Press. 1988:85-94.

119. Innerarity TL, Weisgraber KH, Arnold KS, et al. Familial defective apolipoprotein B-100: low density lipoproteins with abnormal receptor binding. Proc Natl Acad Sci 1987;84:6919-25.

120. Langer T, Strober W, Levy RI. The metabolism of low density lipoprotein in familial type II hyperlipoproteinemia. J Clin Invest 1972;51:1528-36.

121. Kane JP, Malloy MJ, Tun P, et al. Normalization of low density lipoprotein levels in heterozygous familial hypercholesterolemia with a combined drug regimen. New Engl J Med 1981;304:251-8.

122. Mabuchi H, Sakai T, Sakai Y. Reduction of serum cholesterol in heterozygous patients with familial hypercholesterolemia: additive effects of compactin and cholestyramine. New Eng J Med 1983;308:609-19.

123. Hunninghake DB, Stein FA, Dujorne CA, et al. The efficacy of intensive dietary therapy alone or combined with lovastatin in outpatients with hypercholesterolemia. New Engl J Med 1993;328:1213-19.

124. Genest JJ Jr, Bard JM, Fruchart JC, Ordovas JM, Schaefer EJ. Familial hypoalphalipo-proteinemia in premature coronary artery disease. Arterioscler Thromb 1993;13:1728-37.
125. Vergani C, Bettale A. Familial hypoalphalipoproteinemia. Clin Chim Acta 1981;114:45-52.
126. Third JLHC, Montag J, Flynn M, Freidel J, Laskarzewski P, Glueck CJ. Primary and familial hypoalphalipoproteinemia. Metabolism 1984;33:136-46.
127. Lichtenstein AH, Ausman LM, Carr Schaefer EJ. Effects of canola, corn, and olive oils on fasting and postprandial plasma lipoproteins in humans as part of a National Cholesterol Education Program Step 2 diet. Arterioscler Thromb 1993;13:1533-42.
128. Schaefer EJ, Lichtenstein AH, Lamon-Fava S, Contois JH, Li Z, Rasmussen H, McNamara JR, Ordovas JM. Efficacy of a National Cholesterol Education Program Step 2 diet in normolipidemic and hyperlipidemic middle aged and elderly men and women. Arterioscler Thromb Vasc Biol 1995;15:1079-85.
129. Schaefer EJ, Lichtenstein AH, Lamon-Fava S, McNamara JR, Schaefer MM, Rasmussen H, Ordovas JM. Body weight and low density lipoprotein cholesterol changes after consumption of a low fat ad libitum diet. JAMA 1995;274:1450-55.
130. Schaefer EJ, Lichtenstein AH, Lamon-Fava S, Contois JH, Li Z, Goldin BR, Rasmussen H, McNamara JR, Ordovas JM. Effects of National Cholesterol Education Program Step 2 diets relatively high or relatively low in fish-derived fatty acids on plasma lipoproteins in middle-aged and elderly subjects. Am J Clin Nutr 1996;63:234-241.
131. Krauss RM, Deckelbaum RJ, Ernst N, Fisher E, Howard BV, Knopp RH, et al. Dietary guideline for healthy American adults: a statement for health professionals from the Nutrition Committee, American Heart Association. Circulation 1996;94:1795-1800.
132. Schlant RC, Forman S, Stamler J, Canner PL. The natural history of coronary heart disease: prognostic factors after recovery from myocardial infarction in 2,787 men. The 5-year findings of the Coronary Drug Project. Circulation 1982;66:401-14.
133. Stampfer MJ, Colditz GA, Willett WC, Manson JE, Posner B, Speizer FE, Hennekens CH. Postmenopausal estrogen therapy and cardiovascular disease. N Eng J Med 1991;325:756-62.
134. Kim CJ, Jang HC, Min YK. Effect of hormone replacement therapy on lipoprotein(a) and lipids in post-menopausal women. Arterioscler Thromb 1994;14:275-81.

The System of Cardiovascular Prevention

3

Marek H. Dominiczak and Judith R. McNamara

INTRODUCTION

❖   Other chapters in this book address lipid and lipoprotein testing and review metabolic and clinical aspects of dyslipidemias. Here we describe how the laboratory aspects of management of lipid disorders fit into a broader perspective of cardiovascular prevention.

LIPID HYPOTHESIS AND CLINICAL PRACTICE

The association between lipids and atherosclerosis became clear at the beginning of this century.[1] The lipid hypothesis of atherosclerosis, stating that the deposition of LDL in arteries is proportional to its concentration in plasma, was developed in the 1950s.[1] This hypothesis complements the "response to injury" hypothesis developed by Ross, which theorizes that the center of the atherosclerotic process involves the cellular mitogenic and growth factor responses to endothelial injury. Both hypotheses can be combined into one comprehensive theory.[2-4]

Involvement of lipids in atherogenesis is now supported by strong clinical evidence that lowering cholesterol concentration in plasma leads to a decrease in mortality and morbidity caused by coronary heart disease (CHD). Indeed, recent data suggest that cholesterol lowering may also be important in the management of non-coronary atherosclerotic cardiovascular disease, such as stroke.[4, 5]

Recent Clinical Trials of Cholesterol Lowering

The majority of recent clinical trials have been conducted using statins, drugs which inhibit the rate-limiting enzyme in cholesterol synthesis, 3-hydroxy-3-methylglutaryl-COA (HMG-CoA) reductase. Evidence of the clinical benefit is particularly strong in secondary prevention, i.e. studies conducted in patients with already present CHD, such as the Scandinavian Simvastatin Survival Study (4S)[6] and the Cholesterol and Recurrent Events (CARE) trial.[5] These trials have demonstrated a decrease in cardiovascular mortality and, for the first time since the 15-year follow-up results of the Coronary Drug Trial in 1986,[7] the 4S study also demonstrated a decrease in total mortality in the treatment group. The decrease in mortality observed in the niacin-treated group of the Coronary

Drug Trial was only 11%,[7] whereas total mortality in the 4S study decreased by 30%. This decrease was associated with a 25% average lowering of cholesterol in the simvastatin-treated group. Importantly, several secondary endpoints, such as coronary death (42% decrease) and the incidence of coronary events (34% decrease), reinforced the potential clinical benefit. The initial cholesterol levels in the 4S study were 212–309 mg/dL (5.5–8.0 mmol/L).[6]

A large proportion of myocardial infarctions, however, occur in patients with average cholesterol levels. The CARE trial[5] addressed this issue, and can be regarded as an extension of the 4S to individuals with cholesterol levels below 240 mg/dL (6.2 mmol/L) and with mean LDL cholesterol (LDL-C) levels of 139 mg/dL (3.6 mmol/L). The study population (86% men and 14% women) were treated with pravastatin for 5 years. There was a 20% reduction in serum cholesterol and a 24% decrease in combined CHD deaths and non-fatal myocardial infarctions. Interestingly, CARE results suggest that in patients with baseline LDL-C concentrations below 125 mg/dL (3.2 mmol/L), lowering of cholesterol is not associated with a decrease in risk.

Another recent study, the Post Coronary Artery Bypass Graft (CABG) Trial, was conducted in patients with initial LDL-C levels of 130–175 mg/dL (3.4–4.5 mmol/L) who were undergoing coronary bypass surgery. During the average 4.3 years of aggressive cholesterol lowering with statin, and cholestyramine where appropriate, average LDL-C concentrations were lowered to 93–99 mg/dL (2.4–2.6 mmol/L) in the two intensive treatment groups.[8] This drop was associated with a significant decrease in progression of atherosclerosis (in 27% of grafts), compared to a group receiving a moderate cholesterol-lowering regimen (progression in 39% of grafts), and achieved LDL-C levels of 132–136 mg/dL (3.4–3.5 mmol/L). There was also a 29% lower rate of revascularization procedures in the intensively treated group. Low-dose warfarin did not reduce the progression of atherosclerosis.

The status of triglycerides as an independent risk factor remains controversial, but a recent meta-analysis suggests that they do affect risk.[9] In the above described trials, average initial triglyceride levels were below 221 mg/dL (2.5 mmol/L) (4S), 156 mg/dL (1.76 mmol/L) (CARE), and 156–160 mg/dL (1.76-1.80 mmol/L) (CABG).

The West of Scotland Coronary Prevention Study (WOSCOPS), was a primary prevention trial conducted in a population of men aged 45 to 64 with an average cholesterol level of 272±22 mg/dL (7.0±0.6 mmol/L), and an average LDL-C level of 192 mg/dL (5.0 mmol/L), who were treated with pravastatin for an average period of 4.9 years.[10] The mean triglyceride level was 164 mg/dL (1.85 mmol/L). Note that 5% of patients had angina and 3% had peripheral vascular disease, and therefore technically belonged to the secondary prevention group, although not by criteria applied to 4S and CARE. In WOSCOPS the 20% lowering of cholesterol that was achieved with pravastatin treatment resulted in a 31% decrease in the risk of myocardial infarction or coronary death. Although this was not the primary endpoint, there was also a 22% decrease (p = 0.051) in total mortality.[10]

The recently completed secondary prevention study, Bezafibrate Coronary Atherosclerosis Intervention Trial (BECAIT), was conducted in young (30–45 yrs) men who had survived a myocardial infarction.[11] The majority had mild-to-moderate mixed hyperlipidemia, with mean triglycerides of 216 mg/dL (2.44 mmol/L) and mean LDL-C levels of 180 mg/dL (4.66 mmol/L). They were treated with a fibric acid derivative, bezafibrate, for 5 years. Serum cholesterol was decreased by 14%, triglycerides by 26%, and HDL cholesterol (HDL-C) was increased by 9%; LDL-C did not change significantly. In addition to the lipoprotein changes, there also was a 12% decrease in plasma fibrinogen level. The primary endpoints for the trial were angiographic, and differences among angiograms were found after 5 years. The minimum coronary diameter decreased less in the bezafibrate group, but there were no differences in the rate of progression or regression of angiographic changes. The combined number of coronary events and revascularization procedures was lower in the bezafibrate-treated group.

Previous angiographic studies provide strong evidence of plaque regression following cholesterol-lowering treatment. The landmark Cholesterol Lowering of Atherosclerosis Study (CLAS), which involved approximately 200 patients with a history of coronary artery bypass grafting, demonstrated a reduced progression rate for coronary artery stenosis after 2 years of treatment with nicotinic acid and colestipol.[12]

The Pravastatin Limitation of Atherosclerosis in Coronary Arteries (PLAC-1) study in patients with coronary disease demonstrated a 30–40% decrease in the progression of lesions over 36 months, and a reduction in events after 12 months of treatment.[13] The Multicenter Anti-atheroma Study (MAAS), employed quantitative coronary angiography and demonstrated less angiographic progression and more frequent regression in the simvastatin-treated group.[14] The Regression Growth Evaluation Statin Study (REGRESS) employed quantitative coronary angiography and demonstrated a mean 0.04mm smaller decrease in mean segment diameter in the pravastatin-treated group than in controls.[15] There was also a decrease in combined cardiovascular endpoints and revascularization procedures in the pravastatin-treated group.

Two studies have demonstrated particularly large decreases in clinical events: in the Familial Atherosclerosis Treatment Study (FATS), where intensive cholesterol lowering included a combination of lovastatin and colestipol, there was as much as a 73% reduction in events,[16] and in the St. Thomas Atherosclerosis Regression Study (STARS), there was an 89% reduction in events in the group treated with diet and cholestyramine.[17] In the Program on the Surgical Control of the Hyperlipidemias (POSCH), cholesterol lowering was induced not by drugs, but by partial ileal bypass surgery. The incidence of fatal and non-fatal myocardial infarction decreased by 35% after 12 years of follow up.[18]

Thus, there is clinical and anatomical evidence that cholesterol lowering affects the progression of coronary artery disease. Let us examine how these results fit into our knowledge of atherosclerotic lesion development.

Atherosclerotic Plaque

The arterial wall consists of three layers: the intima, the media, and the adventitia. Vascular endothelium controls the function of vascular smooth muscle. This includes the vasodilator effect of nitric oxide.[19-21] Normally, the artery remains in a state of dynamic relaxation, mediated also by prostacyclin and acetylcholine;[22, 23] these mechanisms have recently been reviewed.[19] In addition to the arterial function, arterial wall permeability to LDL may play a role in atherosclerosis.[24]

The main components of the atherosclerotic process include cells, such as macrophages, smooth muscle cells, T-lymphocytes, fibroblasts, and endothelial cells; lipids, particularly LDL; and components of the extracellular matrix, particularly collagens.[2-4, 25] Atherosclerotic plaque, far from being a passive collection of intracellular matrix and debris, is an active structure. Monocytes and macrophages in the plaque continue to secrete growth factors and display metalloproteinase activity.[26]

A recent classification of atherosclerotic lesions proposed by the American Heart Association Committee of Vascular Lesions essentially follows the classification system introduced by Stary[27] and recognizes six stages in the development of atherosclerotic plaques.[28-30] The earliest lesions, designated as type I, can be found in children,[27, 29] and include increased numbers of macrophages in the arterial intima and the appearance of the first foam cells. Type II lesions are fatty streaks, a conglomerate of foam cells, that do not normally protrude into the lumen. These lesions begin to appear around the age of 15 and increase after puberty. Type IIa lesions are prone to develop into more advanced forms. Type IIb lesions have less matrix, less extracellular lipid, and fewer smooth muscle cells, and are progression-resistant. Type III lesions are intermediate between fatty streaks and atheromas. Type IV lesions are "typical" atheromas which now contain a lipid core and may progress rapidly.

Importantly, type IV lesions may be prone to rupture. Type V lesions are advanced plaques which protrude into the arterial lumen and contain a fibrous cap consisting of connective tissue, mainly collagen. If calcification occurs within these lesions, they are described as type Vb. Type Vc lesions contain mainly fibrous tissue, but may also contain organized thrombi. Finally, type VI are the complicated lesions, either with a disrupted surface (VIa) or evidence of hemorrhage or hematoma (VIb), or thrombus (VIc). Complicated lesions may also have a mixed appearance. Stages I to III are slow progression stages. Lesions in stages IV to VI may progress rapidly.[31, 32]

The Concept of Atherosclerotic Plaque Instability

It is important to note that the majority of clinical coronary events are not due to slowly progressing plaque which occludes the vessel. The lesions which are responsible for most clinical incidents cause only 35–65% stenosis. Acute events appear to be precipitated by plaque rupture, which stimulates thrombus formation. It is the occluding thrombi which then cause the majority of myocardial infarctions. Plaque fissuring and rupture are major causes of clinical events.[33, 34] The plaques which rupture most frequently are those containing the highest lipid content, the most reduced collagen and proteoglycan content in the cap, the fewest smooth muscle cells, and the greatest number of macrophages.[35, 36] In advanced lesions, the periphery of the lesion, which is macrophage-rich, is particularly vulnerable to rupture. Thus, there are two distinct processes within what we call atherosclerosis: the slowly progressing formation of occlusive atherosclerotic plaque and, superimposed on this, a much faster process of plaque destabilization and disruption. Processes involved in atherogenesis have recently been reviewed.[37] Figure 3–1 presents a schematic view of the atherosclerotic plaque.

Figure 3–1 ✧ The Atherosclerotic Plaque

Arterial lumen

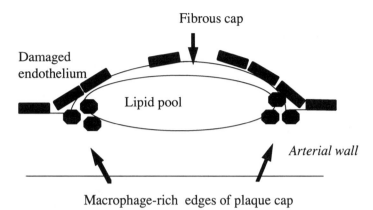

Macrophage-rich edges of plaque cap

Occlusion of the Arterial Lumen and Clinical Event Rate

Results of the trials described above consistently show early divergence of survival curves between treatment and placebo groups, occurring within 6–12 months after initiation of treatment. On the other hand, in studies with angiographic endpoints, the changes in lumen diameter, although significant, are in absolute terms too small to account for the improved clinical event rate. Thus, cholesterol lowering appears to have a shorter-term effect which is different from inducing regression of the plaque. This supposition is strengthened by data showing that, in patients treated with diet and lovastatin for 4–6 months, cholesterol lowering by an average 25% improves ischemic ECG changes, such as ST-segment depression.[38] In addition, a single episode of LDL apheresis improves short-term vascular function.[39] Recent studies indicate that such an effect may be due to improvements in endothelial function resulting from cholesterol lowering, as arterial vasodilation improves.[40, 41] In experimental animals, decreased cholesterol levels reduce the number of inflammatory cells in plaque.[25] The current working hypothesis predicts that cholesterol lowering can stabilize the existing plaque structure.

THE CONCEPT OF TOTAL CARDIOVASCULAR RISK

Risk factors represent characteristics within apparently healthy individuals which have been associated with subsequent occurrence of CHD in observational epidemiological studies.[42] Importantly, several risk factors continue to contribute to disease progression and to prognosis, after CHD has been diagnosed. Also, there are many individuals who have more than one cardiovascular risk factor. For instance, in a survey of hypertension, hypercholesterolemia, and smoking conducted in nine Canadian provinces, based on health insurance registries, 66% of men and 63% of women had more than one cardiovascular risk factor.[43] This rate increased to 80% and 89%, respectively, in the age bracket of 65 to 74 yrs.

Several large epidemiological studies, notably the Framingham Study (discussed below), MRFIT,[44, 45] and the Prospective Cardiovascular Munster (PROCAM) study,[46, 47] have demonstrated the multiplicative effect of risk factors on the risk of myocardial infarction. (Early studies have been reviewed elsewhere.[48]) However, the present evidence for management of risk factors is based almost exclusively on unifactorial trials. To date, no trial has demonstrated convincingly the effectiveness of a wide, multi-risk factor intervention program, although the combination of several types of lifestyle modifications, as done in the Oslo Diet-Heart Trial, was beneficial.[49] The main existing trials of multiple risk factor intervention are the Multiple Risk Factor Intervention Trial (MRFIT),[44, 45] the European Collaborative Trial on Multifactorial Prevention of Coronary Heart Disease,[50] and the Oslo Diet-Heart Study.[49]

The European Collaborative Trial on Multifactorial Prevention of Coronary Heart Disease involved men aged 40–59 years who received dietary and anti-smoking advice and hypotensive treatment where appropriate. The combined incidence of nonfatal myocardial infarction and CHD death decreased by 10.2% after 6 years.[50]

MRFIT involved men aged 35–57 whose coronary risk factor score was in the upper 10–15% of population distribution.[45] The intervention period lasted 7 years. The risk factor assessment was based on total cholesterol concentration, blood pressure and smoking status. Intervention involved dietary and anti-smoking counseling and anti-hypertensive treatment. There was only a 2% decrease in cholesterol levels in the intervention group compared to the "usual care" group, and there was no difference in CHD or all-cause mortality. However, there was a 21% decrease in the CHD mortality in the subgroups of non-hypertensive nonsmokers and normotensive hypercholesterolemic smokers, respectively. At 10.5 years follow-up there was a 10.6% decrease in CHD mortality in the "special intervention" group.[45]

The Oslo Diet-Heart Study involved normotensive men aged 40–49, with high total cholesterol levels (mean, 328.9 mg/dL; 8.5 mmol/L). As many as 79% were smokers. Intervention included diet and anti-smoking advice. At 8.5–10 years follow-up there was a 42% decrease in combined nonfatal myocardial infarctions and CHD deaths.[49]

The ongoing Antihypertension and Lipid-lowering Treatment to Prevent Heart Attack Trial (ALLHAT) of more than 20,000 men and women will be an important stepping stone in our understanding of multiple risk factor interventions.[51]

RISK ASSESSMENT AND STRATIFICATION

Risk stratification in an individual patient is important for providing a guide to the intensity of preventive measures and is based on risk prediction. Such risk prediction needs to take into account not only risk of death, but also other events which affect quality of life, including risk of myocardial infarction, stroke, and unstable angina. The Framingham Study developed an algorithm for the assessment of total risk in individuals with multiple risk factors based on data from the Framingham Cohort and Offspring Studies.[52, 53] Risk tables based on these algorithms relate the presence of risk factors to an absolute risk of CHD or stroke.[54, 55] However, the tables include only the main risk factors: age, gender, total cholesterol/HDL-cholesterol ratio, hypertension, smoking, diabetes, and evidence of left ventricular hypertrophy on ECG. Risk-prediction algorithms are being constantly improved. The risk associated with elevated fibrinogen levels has recently been quantitated,[56] and other hemostatic risk factors also appear to be important.[57, 58]

The Adult Treatment Panel II (ATP II) of the National Cholesterol Education Program recommends an approach to risk management that takes total risk into account.[59, 60] Risk assessment and risk stratification are essential factors which determine therapy, particularly in patients with moderate hyperlipidemia. The ATP II recommends that dietary treatment precede drug treatment in the primary prevention setting, and that the intensity of drug therapy, when appropriate, should depend both on cholesterol level and on the presence or absence of other risk factors. The presence of two or more risk factors other than elevated cholesterol concentration is an important cutoff point for clinical decisions. These recommendations suggest application of clinical judgment in individual cases, particularly in multi-risk patients. Lifestyle changes such as diet, weight control, and physical activity are also addressed in ATP II recommendations. Importantly, ATP II recommends use of a health care team, including dietitians, nurses, and physician's assistants to reinforce lifestyle changes such as dietary compliance.

European guidelines have also focused on the concept of total cardiovascular risk. The risk tables are based on the Framingham algorithm.[42] The general target of risk management is the reduction of the 10-year absolute risk of an event to less than 5% in younger people and to less than 10% in older individuals.

In spite of the availability of recommendations, the management of cardiovascular risk is still inadequate. For instance, the recent British Cardiac Society survey of risk factor recording in medical records of patients with CHD, ASPIRE (Action on Secondary Prevention through Intervention to Reduce Events), demonstrated that information on cholesterol levels was much less completely recorded than details on blood pressure or smoking status.[61]

Most risk factor assessment algorithms are focused on primary prevention, and they often simply extend primary prevention issues to secondary prevention. Comprehensive risk assessment in patients with CHD needs to be combined with assessment of their cardiac status. Utilization of such full risk profiles will also help in determining how far to proceed with investigations of chest pain.[62] Comprehensive prevention of reinfarction includes not only lipid lowering and management of hypertension, but also antithrombotic treatment with aspirin or other agents, beta-blockade, and use of ACE-inhibitors in patients with compromised left ventricular function. Comprehensive recommendations for risk modification have been devised.[62, 63] Figure 3–2 illustrates the main components of cardiovascular risk assessment.

Patients with CHD represent a broad spectrum of risk. The magnitude of risk depends on the length of time from a preceding event. Patients immediately after infarction are at greatest risk due to susceptibility to sudden cardiac electrical instability and re-thrombosis. After re-vascularization, the risk of re-occlusion is greatest within 1–12 months, and after angioplasty, within the first 6 months. The severity of ischemic symptoms, the degree of left ventricular dysfunction, and the presence of arrhythmias further modify risk. The degree of congestive cardiac failure is a particularly strong

Figure 3–2 ✧ Main Determinants of Cardiovascular Risk

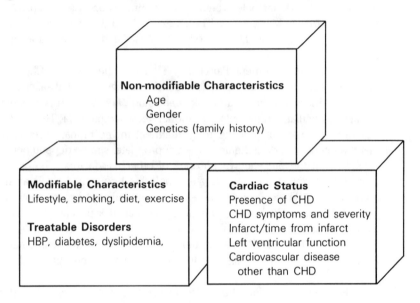

predictor of survival.[64] Also, the presence of peripheral vascular disease or cerebro-vascular disease increases risk of death by 25%. The value of non-invasive testing for risk stratification has recently been reviewed.[63] Due to the complexity of risk factor interactions, management of cardiovascular risk may differ considerably between individual patients and requires a "high standard of physician knowledge, skill, motivation, and performance."[65]

ONGOING ISSUES IN RISK STRATIFICATION

Age and Gender

Age is an independent risk factor for CHD. The present studies suggest that the benefit of cholesterol lowering is independent of age, at least in secondary prevention. Subgroup analysis of patients from the 4S study detected no difference in benefit between patients aged below and above 60 years.[6] In fact, pooled analysis of the Pravastatin Athero-sclerosis Intervention Program suggests that risk reduction, if anything, is greater in patients aged above 65 years.[66]

The issue of cardiovascular risk in women is more complex. There are important differences in the natural history of CHD in women as compared to men, but much less epidemiological data are available on women. Existing data indicate that women are generally at lower risk of myocardial infarction than men, except in the elderly. The total cholesterol/HDL-C ratio is a better predictor of CHD in women than total cholesterol.[67] Estrogen use in postmenopausal women is associated with a 50% risk reduction,[68] and clinical manifestations of CHD occur approximately 10 years later in women.[69–72] On the other hand, symptoms and prognosis after MI are worse for women. (See Fetters et al.[73] for a review.) Framingham Study results suggest that a random glucose level is an independent predictor of CHD in non-diabetic women but not in men.[74] Women who smoke are 3.6 times more likely to have MI than non-smokers,[75] while smoking combined with the use of oral contraceptives increases CHD risk by a factor of up to 20 times.

Diabetes

Diabetic patients are known to have a 2–3 times higher risk of CHD than non-diabetics.[76, 77] They often present with hyperlipidemia, characterized by elevated triglycerides, elevated IDL-C, and low HDL-C.[78] The protective effect of female gender is removed in diabetes. Of particular importance is the association of coronary mortality with diabetic nephropathy.[79] Atherosclerotic plaques in diabetics are similar to those in nondiabetics, and so the excess risk associated with diabetes remains unexplained. Diabetes involves widespread modification of proteins, including apolipoproteins, by glucose. This leads to modification of LDL metabolism[80] and to the formation of protein crosslinks, advanced glycosylation end products, which may contribute to atherogenesis.[81, 82] Although diabetic macroangiopathy is often referred to as equivalent to atherosclerosis, it is interesting to note that the original description of diabetic macroangiopathy[83] defined it as the non-atherosclerotic disease of large vessels in diabetes. Thus, the diabetes-induced changes in vessel metabolism or function may not be atherosclerotic in themselves, but may well produce a background for atherosclerotic disease.

No large-scale lipid intervention trials with diabetic patients have been completed. The ongoing Diabetes Atherosclerosis Intervention Study (DAIS), in which non-insulin-dependent diabetes mellitus (NIDDM) patients with coronary artery disease are treated with fenofibrate, should provide much-needed data on this patient group.[84]

Hypertension

Hypertension is an important risk factor for CHD. In several studies hypertension has been associated with dyslipidemia.[85] Endothelial dysfunction, induced by either native or oxidized LDL, may well be a link. Hypertension could be looked upon as a metabolically related disease associated with the abnormalities of carbohydrate metabolism, and in particular with insulin resistance.[86] There is an emerging picture of metabolic interrelationships between the different cardiovascular risk factors. This is illustrated in Figure 3-3. As is the case with plasma cholesterol, the relationship of diastolic blood pressure (DBP) to CHD risk is continuous and graded. A decrease in DBP of 5–6 mm Hg is associated with a risk reduction for stroke of 40%.[87] However, in contrast to decreasing the incidence of stroke, treating hypertension yields limited benefit in terms of reducing the incidence of coronary events.[88, 89] Hypertension is also a more important risk factor in women.[90–92]

Smoking

Smoking is an independent risk factor for CHD.[93–96] There is also an apparent synergistic effect, such that the risk associated with smoking is greatest when there are also other risk factors present. Smokers who have myocardial infarctions also have fewer other

Figure 3–3 ✧ The Metabolic Interrelationships between Cardiovascular Risk Factors

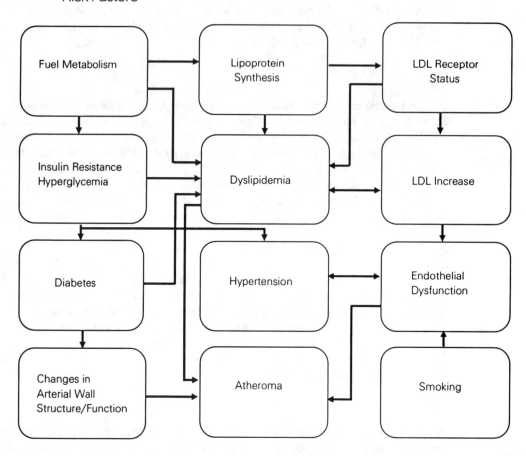

risk factors than non-smokers, which may indicate that coronary obstruction in smokers may be more thrombotic and less atherosclerotic in nature.[97] Apparently, smoking precipitates CHD events at an earlier age with a lesser degree of CHD.[98–100]

Diet

Primary prevention trials, using diets low in saturated fat and cholesterol, have shown a small benefit with respect to cardiovascular mortality, but the magnitude has been disappointing.[101] On the other hand, several secondary prevention trials involving dietary modification have yielded a significant benefit.[102] In the early Leiden Intervention Trial, dietary modification resulted in a decrease in CHD progression.[103] The STARS Trial, which involved a low-fat, low-cholesterol diet, resulted in a decrease in CHD progression.[17] In the Lifestyle Heart Trial, a 1-year trial of 28 patients treated with very low cholesterol diet (< 5 mg cholesterol per day), there was significant regression in stenosis in the treated group.[104]

The "new generation" of dietary trials, such as the Diet and Reinfarction Trial (DART),[105] the Lyon Trial,[106] and the Indian Study,[107] have focused on the general aspects of diets consumed by populations with lower incidence of coronary disease, such as Asian-vegetarian or Mediterranean diets, instead of fat and cholesterol content only. The decrease in the relative risk of combined cardiac deaths and non-fatal myocardial infarctions was 16% in the DART, 41% in the Indian Study, and 73% in the Lyon study. The overall risk of death decreased by 29%, 45%, and 70%, respectively. These trials suggest that total and saturated fat should not only be reduced, but should be replaced by a relative increase in omega-6 fatty acids, oleic acid, and omega-3 fatty acids, and that intake of natural antioxidants and oligoelements should be increased along with maintaining the intake of vegetable proteins.[102]

Exercise

Exercise programs target fuel metabolism rather than atherosclerotic plaque itself. Inactive lifestyle is a major contributor to obesity.[108, 109] There are associations between lipids and lipoproteins, exercise, and CHD mortality and morbidity.[110-112] Obesity, smoking, and excess fat intake are less prevalent in physically active individuals.[113, 114] Low energy expenditure may be more important to the development of obesity than overeating.[115] To get the most beneficial effect from an exercise program, a combination of frequency, duration, and intensity, as well as the type of resistance training program, are important. A moderate level of exercise is sufficient for cardiovascular benefit.[116]

Behavior Modification

Changes in diet, changes in exercise habits, and smoking cessation involve modification of behavior patterns. There is much to learn about the approach to behavior change from studies of diabetes care. The Diabetes Control and Complications Trial (DCCT) has demonstrated that intensive insulin therapy prevents or delays the development of microvascular and neuropathic complications in insulin-dependent diabetic patients.[117] The DCCT protocol required changes in behavior, such as insulin administration, diet modification, and physical activity.[118] The team involved in patient training and counseling included nursing, nutrition, clinical psychology, psychiatry, and social work professionals. Such a multidisciplinary team-based specialty approach is now being recommended for general diabetes care.[119] The DCCT results suggest that substantial behavioral change is possible but requires a carefully structured approach. This involves patient assessment to select candidates for intensive therapy and, conversely, the identification of patients with contraindications to intensive therapy such as those with personality disorders or severe family instability.

Patients' personal commitment to the therapeutic goal is essential. After selection, a negotiation of realistic treatment goals and planning of the optimal strategy for behavior change should take place.[118] Inducing behavioral change always depends to a large extent on patient self-care. Non-adherence to at least part of the regimen is common.[120] Interestingly for cardiovascular prevention, in complex diabetic regimens, implementing dietary change and exercise appear to be most difficult.[121, 122] Patient satisfaction also affects self-care. The patient's intentions to follow a treatment plan influence whether or not the plan is followed. How well the patient's regimen fits into his or her lifestyle also affects adherence to treatment.[122, 123]

For the maintenance of behavioral change, a comprehensive follow-up is necessary.[118] Frequent contacts between patient and health care providers are beneficial, particularly during the initial period of lifestyle change.

Finally, not all the pressure of inducing behavior change falls on the patient. Communication among the health care team is also essential, and this may require special training. To improve communication and adherence, behavioral interventions should be targeted both to patients and their physicians.[123]

LABORATORY ROLE IN CARDIOVASCULAR PREVENTION SERVICE

Lipoprotein testing plays an important role in the assessment of CHD risk,[42, 59, 125, 126] and therefore laboratory support is an essential component of a cardiovascular prevention system.[124] The main task of the lipid laboratory is the provision of precise and accurate measurements of lipid and lipoprotein concentrations to clinicians and patients, for use in the assessment of individual cardiovascular risk and for monitoring of lipid-lowering therapy.[125–127] There are three general tiers of lipoprotein testing complexity, all of which have an important role in identifying individuals at risk: screening, general clinical laboratory assessment, and specialty laboratory lipoprotein testing.

Screening

Lipoprotein screening for CHD risk is widely available in the United States, but is less frequently utilized elsewhere. The screening is a first level of testing and can be carried out in a variety of locations. Screening clinics and home testing frequently make it possible to reach segments of a population that may not otherwise have access to medical care, or may not take the time and effort to seek it. Clinics are frequently set up in shopping malls, elderly and subsidized living facilities, recreation facilities, and other public areas. From the individual's perspective, they involve a minimal amount of time, no prior preparation, and little or no cost.

Lipoprotein screening is most frequently performed in the nonfasting state, on blood obtained from fingersticks, using small compact analyzers or non-instrumented devices. Their use is convenient and can be applied to a relatively large number of people; however, they provide the potential for increased variability of results.[127–133] Therefore, every effort must be taken to ensure minimal error. As part of that effort, preanalytical sources of variation must be controlled to the extent possible.[134] (See Chapters 4 and 9 for details.)

The ATP II has recommended that lipid profiles that are outside the desirable range be repeated approximately 1–8 weeks after the first profile.[59] No such recommendations have been made for individuals with results in the desirable range. If the original screening results misclassify a person with abnormal values into the desirable category, the excess risk may go undetected for an extended period of time, since such individuals are only advised to have the tests repeated within five years.[59] It is important, therefore, when screening clinics are set up, that care be taken to ensure that the chosen equipment is capable of providing accurate and precise results, that the proper standardization and quality assurance procedures are in place, and that personnel are adequately trained to perform the testing and correctly interpret results.

The total cholesterol assay is the test most frequently performed in lipid screening clinics and is currently the only one available for home testing. HDL-C, the measurement of which has also been recommended by ATP II for screening, represents an independent risk factor for CHD. HDL-C is inversely associated with CHD and cannot be deduced from a total cholesterol value. Its measurement is currently offered at many screening clinics and physician offices in the United States. Measurement of LDL-C may eventually replace total cholesterol but is not currently applicable to screening equipment.[135-137] Screening clinics are also encouraged to provide guidance on dietary and physical activity habits and on risk factor reduction.

Individuals seen in screening clinics are generally not fasting. Total cholesterol, however, can be measured with quite good accuracy in the nonfasting state, since the increase in triglyceride-rich lipoprotein cholesterol is generally offset by decreased LDL- and HDL-C.[127] HDL-C can also be screened in the nonfasting state, with the realization that values will be slightly lower than those obtained in the fasting state.[127] In the average individual, after an average meal, HDL-C (and LDL-C) will be decreased by approximately 3–5%. These decreases are generally not of sufficient magnitude to negate their screening value, but those interpreting the results for patients must be aware of this fact and should query the patient regarding the magnitude of, and the time since, their last meal.

After a very high-fat meal (1 g/kg body weight), HDL-C and LDL-C values can drop by as much as 9–10%, and apo A-I and apo B values can decrease by approximately 6%, at 6 hours postprandially, the average time of maximal change.[127] Triglycerides should not be measured unless the individual has fasted for 12–14 hours, since the magnitude and variability of the postprandial triglyceride change is sufficient to preclude any extrapolation back to fasting values. For this reason, triglycerides are not commonly measured at screening facilities.

While screening only provides a cursory survey of lipoprotein status, if properly established to provide accurate results, it serves the purpose of alerting individuals at risk that they need follow-up care—information that they might otherwise not obtain.

Assessment of Lipoprotein Status in a General Clinical Laboratory

Most clinical laboratories, whether hospital-based or independent, are equipped to measure total cholesterol and HDL-C, triglycerides, and, in many cases, apo A-I and apo B. Typically, LDL-C values will be calculated using the formula of Friedewald et al.[138] The formula provides an adequate estimation of VLDL-C and LDL-C, provided that patients are truly fasting and provided that triglycerides are below 400 mg/dL (4.7 mmol/L), and preferably below 250 mg/dL (2.9 mmol/L). Currently, at the recommendation of the NCEP Working Group on Lipoprotein Measurement,[139] new methods to measure LDL-C directly, without the need for ultracentrifugation, are becoming available. These assays provide clinical laboratories with the capability of assessing LDL-C in hypertriglyceridemic and nonfasting samples.[135-137] (See also Chapter 8.)

It is essential that laboratories develop and monitor precision and accuracy for their assays. It is also important that values obtained in one laboratory, or at one point in time, be comparable to those obtained in another place, at another time. For these reasons, clinical laboratories and manufacturers of analytical systems for clinical laboratories should make use of precision and accuracy guidelines[139-141] and standardization programs that are available to ensure that results are accurate.[142] One such standardization option is the Cholesterol Reference Method Laboratory Network, coordinated by the Centers for Disease Control and Prevention (CDC) in Atlanta, which performs fresh sample comparisons between field methods and Abell-Kendall reference method for cholesterol for both manufacturers and individual laboratories.[143] (See also Chapters 11 and 12.) Other standardization and proficiency testing opportunities are also available for lipid, lipoprotein, and apolipoprotein assay evaluations.

From a practical perspective, it is important for general clinical laboratories to be able to process and provide meaningful results on a large number of samples, for both diagnostic and therapeutic purposes. Clinical laboratories cannot and should not be expected to perform all of the specialty tests that are ultimately possible. Lipoprotein tests that are not ordered routinely, or those that require exceptional expertise or costly equipment to perform, are better left to the lipoprotein specialty laboratory. But the tests that the clinical laboratory does offer, whether they be lipoprotein tests or otherwise, must be performed well.

Lipoprotein Specialty Laboratory Assessment

The lipoprotein specialty laboratory is the ultimate resource in the lipoprotein testing field. Samples with unusual profiles or from patients with rare diseases may require testing procedures that are not available in the average clinical laboratory. Typically, the lipoprotein specialty laboratories are research laboratories, frequently in an academic setting. Even these laboratories will have particular specialty procedures in use, depending on their research needs and interests. Of importance to clinical laboratories and private physicians that are seeking more comprehensive lipid profiles on dyslipidemic patients is the fact that most lipoprotein specialty laboratories perform ultracentrifugation to obtain reference method lipoprotein determinations.[144]

As with the screening and clinical laboratory settings, it is extremely important for a lipoprotein specialty laboratory to continuously monitor the precision and accuracy of the tests that they perform. Precision can be readily evaluated within the laboratory. Accuracy evaluations are more difficult, since no clearly defined reference points exist for many of the specialty assays. In many cases the normal ranges for these tests must be determined within the laboratory, after analyses have been completed in large normal populations. These ranges may or may not be transferable to similar tests performed in other research laboratories, unless some effort has been made to coordinate the test procedures. As an example, prior to the International Federation for Clinical Chemistry (IFCC) efforts to standardize apo A-I and apo B assays,[145-147] there was frequently no relationship between values for these tests from one laboratory to another. Each laboratory produced and purified its own antibodies, with different binding characteristics, and each used its own methodology with varying limitations. The IFCC Committee on Apolipoproteins, working with the CDC, developed a set of standard reference materials to be used by manufacturers for assay calibration. This allows different assay methodologies to be calibrated on the same basis, so that results among laboratories may be compared,[148, 149] (see also Chapter 10) and so that individual patients can have apo A-I and apo B levels meaningfully interpreted as part of the CHD risk evaluation. The end result of this process has been the transfer of research assays into the clinical laboratory arena, for wider utilization.

Lipoprotein specialty laboratories serve four major functions, all of which ultimately help individual patients through better preventive, diagnostic, and therapeutic interventions. One of the functions is the performance of sophisticated test procedures on patients already identified as having an abnormal lipoprotein status. The patient samples may have been forwarded from screening clinics, physician's offices, or clinical laboratories, or they may originate in specialty referral clinics, such as lipid, cardiology, diabetic, and endocrinology clinics. In this instance, the testing performed helps the patient directly by providing the physician with detailed test results to assist in diagnosis and/or specialized treatment.

A second function of lipoprotein laboratories is the participation in epidemiological studies. These studies provide the data base from which normal and high-risk values can be identified and analyzed. The Framingham Heart Study,[150] the US National Health and Nutrition Examination Survey,[151] and the Seven Countries Study[152] are just a few examples of large epidemiological studies that have had a major impact on the basic understanding of CHD risk factors.

A third function is the participation in clinical intervention trials for the evaluation of potential new therapeutic modalities. Also included in this category are the smaller, but extremely important, safety and efficacy studies of new medications and dietary intervention trials. The studies may be performed in normal individuals for primary prevention, such as the Lipid Research Clinics Primary Prevention Trial[153, 154] and the West of Scotland Coronary Prevention Study,[10] or in specific disease populations for secondary intervention purposes, such as the 4S Study[6] and the CARE Trial[5] described above. Assays performed can vary from standard lipid and lipoprotein assays that are already associated with risk, to new research assays that may become standard clinical laboratory tests of the future.

The fourth function associated with lipoprotein specialty laboratories is basic research. This area of study, although removed (in a direct and immediate sense) from the individual patient, is perhaps one of the most important aspects of investigation, as the basic research testing of today will lead to the epidemiological and intervention evaluations of tomorrow, and eventually to the preventive, diagnostic, and therapeutic interventions for helping individual patients. The lipid specialty laboratory has the additional objectives of providing training and development, and validation of new assays applicable to the assessment of cardiovascular risk.

SPECIALTY OUTPATIENT CLINICS

There is presently universal agreement that the optimal way to develop cardiovascular prevention programs, both as primary and as secondary prevention, involves modification of all existing risk factors. The concepts for the management of patients at risk have been developed in parallel by several specialties: hypertension, cardiology, and lipid specialists. Risk management by any single specialty has flaws. Lack of a coordinated approach could be one of the reasons for poor effectiveness of risk factor management, as illustrated by the ASPIRE Study described above.[61]

Effective cardiovascular prevention requires multiple skills which can only be obtained through a team approach.[155] Examples of coordinated approaches in other areas of medical care include provision of nutritional services[156] and, as described above, the treatment of diabetes. Figure 3–4 illustrates the organization of the cardiovascular prevention system currently operating in one of the authors' hospitals. It is based in two specialty outpatient clinics. The Lipid Clinic is run by a physician-lipid specialist. On-site cholesterol and triglyceride measurements are offered by the biochemistry laboratory using screening methods. This immediately reinforces the medical and dietetic advice. These results are later confirmed using conventional clinical laboratory methods. The dietetic service is another part of the clinic. At the first visit, patients are assigned a dietary score, which is then monitored at subsequent visits. And in addition, the Lipid Clinic specializes in intensive management of lipid disorders in patients with CHD and in individuals with familial lipoprotein disorders. It operates in close collaboration with the cardiology department.

Patients who require multi-specialist treatment are referred to the Cardiovascular Risk Factor Clinic, which involves a larger team comprising internists, hypertension and lipid specialists, dietitians, and nurse specialists. The Cardiovascular Risk Factor

Figure 3–4 ✧ The Lipid and Cardiovascular Risk Factor Specialist Clinic System

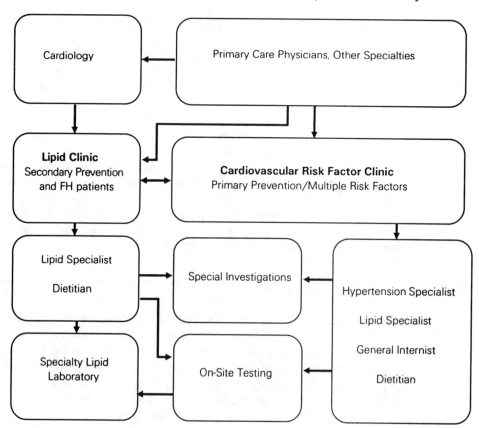

Clinic specializes in primary prevention in individuals with multiple risk factors. Both clinics have direct access to a range of procedures (ECG, exercise testing, cardiac ultrasound, cardiac imaging, 24-hour blood pressure monitoring, carotid Doppler, etc.). The multidisciplinary approach provides savings in the number of patient visits required for a comprehensive assessment.

RISK FACTOR MANAGEMENT IN PRIMARY CARE AND SPECIALTY CENTERS

Realization of the medical effectiveness of cholesterol lowering leads to increased numbers of patients undergoing lipid-lowering therapy which could overwhelm the specialty clinic system. The increased number of patients necessitates devolving the management of many of these patients to primary care, while maintaining close links with specialty centers. Shared-care arrangements involving specialty clinics and primary care physicians[119] allow treatment and monitoring of complicated patients in the specialty centers, whereas uncomplicated patients can be treated in the primary care setting using recommended regimens.[155] An arrangement allowing close communication, training, and information exchange is essential.

Effective cardiovascular prevention requires a modification of lifestyle in the majority of patients, and an effective collaboration between patients and health care professionals.[155] The non-pharmacological preventive interventions, such as smoking cessation, diet, and exercise are often underestimated.[157] Intensive lifestyle change requires professional, individualized advice, appropriate monitoring, and close follow-up. These measures include cardiac rehabilitation and exercise, smoking cessation, diet, and weight reduction advice. The components of such comprehensive program are shown in Figure 3–5.

Figure 3–5 ✧ The Components of a Comprehensive Cardiovascular Prevention Program

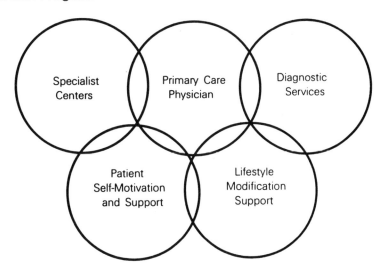

SPECIALIST TRAINING IN CARDIOVASCULAR PREVENTION

Most cardiology training programs do not have specialists in lipid disorders or risk factor management as members of the cardiology division.[155, 158] Traditionally, cardiovascular prevention has been biased towards lifestyle and public health measures. In the last 10 to 15 years, however, cardiovascular prevention has developed into a field which requires multidisciplinary expertise in both medical therapy and lifestyle modification. The suggested components of training for a specialist in cardiovascular prevention are illustrated in Figure 3–6. The cardiovascular prevention specialist does not need to match the depth of expertise of sub-specialties such as hypertension or cardiology, but must be trained to develop sufficient understanding of all the relevant sub-specialties to efficiently and safely manage multi-risk patients. In addition, part of the training needs to address the lifestyle and behavior modification. Cardiovascular prevention requires communication among a variety of specialists and primary care providers.

Training programs need to address the epidemiology of risk factors, as well as case management.[65] Metabolic aspects of lipid metabolism and hypertension need to be addressed. These issues are now being raised in the cardiology community.[155, 158] Presently many sub-specialties attempt the management of cardiovascular risk. In view of the extent of the problem and the present availability of validated therapies, now might well be the time for cardiovascular prevention to become a separate entity. ✧

Figure 3–6 ✧ Suggested Components of a Training Program in Cardiovascular Prevention

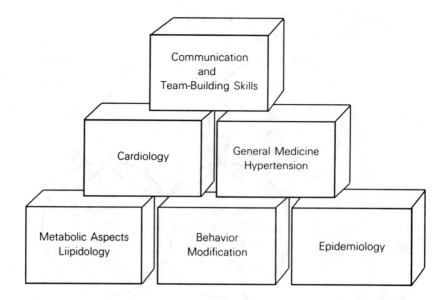

REFERENCES

1. Stamler J. Established major coronary risk factors. In: Marmot M, Elliot P, eds. Coronary heart disease epidemiology: From aetiology to public health. Oxford: Oxford Medical Publications, 1992:35-66.
2. Ross R, Glomset J. The pathogenesis of atherosclerosis, Part 1. N Engl J Med 1976; 295:369-77.
3. Ross R, Glomset J. The pathogenesis of atherosclerosis: part 2. N Engl J Med 1976; 295:420-28.
4. Ross R. The pathogenesis of atherosclerosis: a perspective for the 1990s. Nature 1993;362:801-13.
5. Sacks FM, Pfeffer MA, Moye LA, Rouleau JL, Rutherford JD, Cole TG, et al. The effect of pravastatin on coronary events after myocardial infarction in patients with average cholesterol levels. N Engl J Med 1996;335:1001-9.
6. Scandinavian Simvastatin Survival Study Group. Randomised trial of cholesterol lowering in 4444 patients with coronary heart disease: the Scandinavian Simvastatin Survival Study (4S). Lancet 1994;334:1383-9.
7. Canner PL, Berge KG, Wenger J, Stamler J, Friedman L, Prineas RJ, Friedewald W. Fifteen year mortality in coronary drug project patients: long term benefit with niacin. J Am Coll Cardiol 1986;8:1245-55.
8. The Post Coronary Artery Bypass Graft Trial Investigators. The effect of aggressive lowering of low-density lipoprotein cholesterol levels and low-dose anticoagulation on obstructive changes in saphenous-vein coronary-artery bypass grafts. N Engl J Med 1997;336:153-62.
9. Hokanson JE, Austin MA. Plasma triglyceride level is a risk factor for cardiovascular disease independent of high-density lipoprotein cholesterol level: a meta-analysis of population-based prospective studies. J Cardiovasc Risk 1996;3:213-19.
10. Shepherd J, Cobbe SM, Ford I, Isles CG, Lorimer AR, Macfarlane PW, et al. Prevention of coronary heart disease with pravastatin in men with hypercholesterolemia. N Engl J Med 1995;333:1301-7.
11. Ericsson C-G, Hamsten A, Nilsson J, Grip L, Svane B, de Faire U. Angiographic assessment of effects of bezafibrate on progression of coronary disease in young male postinfarction patients. Lancet 1996;347:849-53.
12. Blankenhorn DH, Nessim SA, Johnson RL, Sanmarco ME, Azen SP, Cashin-Hemphill L. Beneficial effects of combined colestipol-niacin therapy on coronary atherosclerosis and coronary venous bypass grafts. JAMA 1987;257:3233-40.
13. Pitt B, Mancini GBJ, Ellis SG, Rosman RS, Park J-S, McGovern M, et al., for the PLAC1 Investigators. Pravastatin limitation of atherosclerosis in the coronary arteries (PLAC1): Reduction in atherosclerosis progression and clinical events. J Am Coll Cardiol 1995; 26:1133-9.
14. MAAS Investigators. Effect of simvastatin on coronary atheroma: the Multicentre Anti-atheroma Study (MAAS). Lancet 1994;344:633-8.
15. Jukema JW, Bruschke AVG, van Boven AJ, Reiber JHC, Bal ET, Zwinderman AH, et al. Effects of lipid lowering by pravastatin on progression and regression of coronary artery disease in symptomatic men with normal to moderately elevated serum cholesterol levels. The Regression Growth Evaluation Statin Study (REGRESS). Circulation 1995;91:2528-40.
16. Brown G, Albers JJ, Fisher LD, Schaefer SM, Lin JT, Kaplan C, et al. Regression of coronary artery disease as a result of intensive lipid lowering therapy in men with high levels of apolipoprotein B. N Engl J Med 1990;323:1289-98.
17. Watts GF, Lewis B, Brunt JNH, Lewis ES, Coltart Dj, Smith LDR, et al. Effects on coronary artery disease of lipid-lowering diet, or diet plus cholestyramine in the St. Thomas Atherosclerosis Regression Study (STARS). Lancet 1992;339:563-9.
18. Buchwald H, Vargo RL, Matts JP, Long JM, Fitch LL, Campbell GS, et al. Effect of partial ileal bypass surgery on mortality and morbidity from coronary heart disease in patients with hypercholesterolemia. N Engl J Med 1990;323:946-55.

19. Selwyn AP, Kinlay S, Libby P, Ganz P. Atherogenic lipids, vascular dysfunction, and clinical signs of ischemic heart disease. Circulation 1997;95:5-7.

20. Burnett Jr JC. Coronary endothelial function in health and disease. Drugs 1997;53 (Suppl 1):20-29.

21. Glasser SP, Selwyn AP, Ganz P. Atherosclerosis: Risk factors and the vascular endothelium. Am Heart J 1996;131:379-84.

22. Rossi V, Breviario F, Ghezzi P Dejana E, Mantovani A. Prostacyclin synthesis induced in vascular cells by interleukin-1. Science 1985;229:174-6.

23. Furchgott RF, Zawadzki JV. The obligatory role of endothelial cells in the relaxation of arterial smooth muscle by acetylcholine. Nature 1980;288:373-6.

24. Nielsen LB. Transfer of low density lipoprotein into the arterial wall and risk of atherosclerosis. [Review]. Atherosclerosis 1996;123:1-15.

25. Libby P. Molecular bases of the acute coronary syndromes. Circulation 1995;91:2844-50.

26. Galis ZS, Sukhova GK, Lark MW, Libby P. Increased expression of matrix metallo-proteinases and matrix degrading activity in vulnerable regions of human atherosclerotic plaques. J Clin Invest 1994;94:2493-503.

27. Stary HC. Evolution and progression of atherosclerotic lesions in coronary arteries of children and young adults. Arteriosclerosis 1989;9(suppl 1):I-19-1-32.

28. Stary HC, Blankenhorn DH, Chandler AB, Glagov S, Insull W Jr, Richardson M, et al. A definition of the intima of human arteries and of its atherosclerosis-prone regions: a report from the Committee on Vascular Lesions of the Council on Arteriosclerosis, American Heart Association. Circulation 1992;85:391-405.

29. Stary HC, Chandler AB, Glagov S, Guyton JR, Insull W Jr, Rosenfeld ME, et al. A definition of initial, fatty streak and intermediate lesions of atherosclerosis: a report from the Committee on Vascular Lesions of the Council on Arteriosclerosis, American Heart Association. Circulation 1994;89:2462-78.

30. Stary HC, Chandler AB, Dinsmore RE, Fuster V, Glagov S, Insull W Jr, et al. A definition of advanced types of atherosclerotic lesions and a histological classification of atherosclerosis: a report from the Committee on Vascular Lesions of the Council on Arteriosclerosis, American Heart Association. Arterioscler Thromb Vasc Biol 1995; 15:1512-31.

31. Fuster V, Badimon L, Badimon JJ, Chesebro JH. The pathogenesis of coronary artery disease and the acute coronary syndromes (first of two parts). N Engl J Med 1992;326: 242-50.

32. Fuster V, Badimon L, Badimon JJ, Chesebro JH. The pathogenesis of coronary artery disease and the acute coronary syndromes (second of two parts). N Engl J Med 1992;326:310-18.

33. Fuster V. Elucidation of the role of plaque instability and rupture in acute coronary events. Am J Cardiol 1995;76:24C-33C.

34. Hackett D, Davies G, Maseri A. Pre-existing coronary stenoses in patients with first myocardial infarction are not necessarily severe. Eur Heart J 1988;9:1317-23.

35. Davies MJ, Thomas AC. Plaque fissuring: the cause of acute myocardial infarction, sudden ischemic death, and crescendo angina. Br Heart J 1985;53:363-73.

36. Davies MJ. A macro and micro view of coronary vascular insult in ischemic heart disease. Circulation 1990;82(suppl II):II-38-46.

37. Dominiczak MH. Atherogenesis. In: Colaco C, ed. The glycation hypothesis of atherosclerosis. Georgetown: Landes Bioscience, in press.

38. Andrews TC, Raby K, Barry J, Naimi CL, Allred E, Ganz P, Selwyn AP. Effect of cholesterol reduction on myocardial ischemia in patients with coronary disease. Circulation 1997; 95:324-8.

39. Tamai O, Matsuoka H, Itabe H, Wada Y, Kohno K, Imaizumi T. Single LDL apheresis improves endothelium-dependent vasodilation in hypercholesterolemic humans. Circulation 1997;95:76-82.

40. Treasure CB, Klein JL, Weintraub WS, Talley JD, Stillabower ME, Kosinski AS, et al. Beneficial effects of cholesterol-lowering therapy on the coronary endothelium in patients with coronary artery disease. N Engl J Med 1995;332:481-7.

41. Leung WH, Lau CP, Wong CK. Beneficial effects of cholesterol-lowering therapy on coronary endothelium-dependent relaxation in hypercholesterolemic patients. Lancet 1993;341:1496-500.

42. Pyorala K, De Backer G, Graham I, Poole-Wilson P, Wood D, on behalf of the Task Force. Prevention of coronary heart disease in clinical practice: recommendations of the Task Force of the European Society of Cardiology, European Atherosclerosis Society and European Society of Hypertension. Eur Heart J 1994;15:1300-31.

43. MacDonald S, Joffres MR, Stachenko S, Horlick L, Fodor G, Canadian Health Surveys Research Group. Multiple cardiovascular risk factors in Canadian adults. Can Med Assoc J 1992;142(suppl):48-56.

44. Multiple Risk Factor Intervention Trial Research Group. Multiple Risk Factor Intervention Trial: risk factor changes and mortality results. JAMA 1982;248:1465-77.

45. Multiple Risk Factor Intervention Trial Research Group. Mortality rates after 10½ years for participants of the Multiple Risk Factor Intervention Trial: findings related to the a priori hypotheses of the Trial. Circulation 1990;82:1616-28.

46. Assmann G, Schulte H. Relation of high-density lipoprotein cholesterol and triglycerides to incidence of atherosclerotic coronary artery disease: the PROCAM experience. Am J Cardiol 1992;70:733-7.

47. Assmann G, Schulte H. Modelling the Helsinki Heart Study by means of risk equations obtained from the PROCAM Study and the Framingham Heart Study. Drugs 1990;40 (Suppl 1):13-18.

48. Dominiczak MH, Packard CJ, Shepherd J. Hyperlipidaemia, its risks and treatment. In: Lorimer AR, Shepherd J, eds. Preventive cardiology. Oxford: Blackwell, 1991:54-86.

49. Hjerrman I, Velve-Byre DV, Holme I, Leren P. Effect of diet and smoking intervention on the incidence of coronary heart disease: report from the Oslo Study Group of a randomised trial of healthy men. Lancet 1981;ii:1303-10.

50. WHO (World Health Organization Collaborative Study Group). European collaborative trial of multifactorial prevention of coronary heart disease: final report on the 6-year results. Lancet 1986;I:869-72.

51. Davis BR, Cutler JA, Gordon DJ, Furberg CD, Wright JT, Cushman WC, et al. Rationale and design for the Antihypertensive and Lipid Lowering Treatment to Prevent Heart Attack Trial (ALLHAT). Am J Hypertens 1996;9:342-60.

52. Anderson KM, Wilson PWF, Odell PM, Kannel WB. An updated coronary risk profile: a statement for health professionals. Circulation 1991;83:356-62.

53. Kannel WB, Feinleib M, McNamara PM, Garrison RJ, Castelli P. An investigation of coronary disease in families: the Framingham Offspring Study. Am J Epidemiol 1979; 110:281-90.

54. Wilson PWF, Evans JC. Coronary artery disease prediction. Am J Hypertens 1993; 6:309S-13S.

55. Califf RM, Armstrong PW, Carver JR, D'Agostino RB, Strauss WE. Task force 5. Stratification of patients into high, medium and low risk subgroups for purposes of risk factor management. J Am Coll Cardiol 1996;27:964-1047.

56. Kannel WB, D'Agostino RB, Belanger AJ. Update on fibrinogen as a cardiovascular risk factor. Ann Epidemiol 1992;2:457-66.

57. Heinrich J, Balleisen L, Schulte H, Assman G, van de Loo J. Fibrinogen and factor VII in the prediction of coronary risk: results from PROCAM study in healthy men. Arterioscler Thromb 1994;14:54-59.

58. Meade TW, Brozovic M, Chakrabarti RR, Haines AP, Imeson JD, Mellow JN. Haemostatic function and ischaemic heart disease: principal results of the Northwick Park Heart Study. Lancet 1986;ii:533-7.

59. The Expert Panel. Summary of the second report of the National Cholesterol Education Program (NCEP) on detection, evaluation and treatment of high blood cholesterol in adults (Adult Treatment Panel II). JAMA 1993;269:3015-23.

60. Chait A. The high-risk strategy for adults. In: Rifkind BM, Ed. Lowering cholesterol in high-risk individuals and populations. New York: Marcel Dekker Inc., 1995;1-31.

61. ASPIRE Steering Group. A British Cardiac Society survey of the potential for the secondary prevention of coronary heart disease: ASPIRE (Action on Secondary Prevention through Intervention to Reduce Events). Heart 1996;75:334–42.

62. Smith SC, Blair SN, Criqui MH, Fletcher GF, Fuster V, Gersh BJ, et al. Preventing heart attack and death in patients with coronary disease. Circulation 1995;92:2–4.

63. Ryan TJ, Anderson JL, Antmann EM, Braniff BA, Brooks NH, Califf RM, et al. ACC/AHA guidelines for the management of patients with acute myocardial infarction: a report of the American College of Cardiology/American Heart Association Task Force on Practice Guidelines (Committee on Management of Acute Myocardial Infarction). J Am Coll Cardiol 1996;28:1328–428.

64. Emond M, Mock MB, Davis KB, Fisher LD, Holmes DR Jr, Chaitman BR, et al. Long-term survival of medically treated patients in the coronary artery surgery study (CASS) registry. Circulation 1994;90:2645–57.

65. Swan HJC. Gersh BJ, Graboys TB, Ullyot DJ. Task force 7. Evaluation and management of risk factors for the individual patient (case management). J Am Coll Cardiol 1996; 27:964–1047.

66. Byington Rp, Jukema JW, Salonen JT, Pitt B, Bruschke AV, Hoen H, et al. Reduction in cardiovascular events during pravastatin therapy: pooled analysis of clinical events of the Pravastatin Atherosclerosis Intervention Program. Circulation 1995;92:2419–25.

67. Hong MK, Romm PA, Reagan K, Green CE, Rackley CE. Usefulness of the total cholesterol to high-density lipoprotein cholesterol ratio in predicting angiographic coronary artery disease in women. Am J Cardiol 1991;68:1646–50.

68. Stampfer MJ, Colditz GA. Estrogen replacement therapy and coronary heart disease: a quantitative assessment of the epidemiologic evidence. Prev Med 1991;20:47–63.

69. Kannel WB, Feinleib M. Natural history of angina pectoris in the Framingham Study. Am J Cardiol 1972;29:154–63.

70. Stokes J III, Kannel WB, Wolf PA, Cupples LA, D'Agostino RB. The relative importance of selected risk factors for various manifestations of cardiovascular disease among women and men from 35–64 years: 30 years of follow-up in the Framingham Study. Circulation 1987;75:(suppl V):V65–73.

71. Lerner DJ, Kannel WB. Patterns of coronary heart disease morbidity and mortality in the sexes: a 26 year follow-up of the Framingham population. Am Heart J 1986: 111:383–90.

72. Castelli WP. Epidemiology of coronary heart disease: the Framingham Study. Am J Med 1984;76:4–12.

73. Fetters JK, Peterson ED, Shaw LJ, Newby LK, Califf RM. Sex-specific differences in coronary artery disease risk factors, evaluation and treatment: have they been adequately evaluated? Am Heart J 1996;131:796–813.

74. Wilson PW, Cupples LA, Kannel WB. Is hyperglycemia associated with cardiovascular disease?: the Framingham study. Am Heart J 1991;121:586–90.

75. American Heart Association. Heart and stroke facts: 1995 statistical supplement. Dallas: American Heart Association, 1994:10.

76. Kannel WB, McGee DL. Diabetes and cardiovascular disease: the Framingham Study. JAMA 1979;241:2035–8.

77. Krolewski AS, Kosinski EJ, Warram JH, Leland OS, Busick EJ, Asmal AC, et al. Magnitude and determinants of coronary artery disease in juvenile-onset insulin-dependent diabetes mellitus. Am J Cardiol 1987;14:55–60.

78. Steiner G. The dyslipoproteinemias of diabetes. Atherosclerosis 1994;110(Suppl);S27–33.

79. Manske CL. Coronary artery disease in diabetic patients with nephropathy. Am J Hypertens 1993;6:367S–374S.

80. Lyons TJ. Glycation and oxidation: a role in the pathogenesis of atherosclerosis. Am J Cardiol 1993:71:26B–31B.

81. Dominiczak MH. The significance of the products of the Maillard (browning) reaction in diabetes. Diabetic Med 1991;8:505–16.

82. Chappey O, Dosquet C, Wautier M-P, Wautier J-L. Advanced glycation end products, oxidant stress and vascular lesions. Eur J Clin Invest 1997;27:97-108.

83. Andresen JL, Rasmussen LM, Ledet T. Diabetic macroangiopathy and atherosclerosis. Diabetes 1996;45(Suppl. 3):S91-S94.

84. Steiner G, for the DAIS Project Group. The Diabetes Atherosclerosis Intervention Study (DAIS): a study conducted in cooperation with the World Health Organization. Diabetologia 1996;39:1655-61.

85. Goode GK, Miller JP, Heagerty AM. Hyperlipidaemia, hypertension and coronary heart disease. Lancet 1995;345:362-4.

86. De Fronzo RA, Ferranini E. Insulin resistance: a multifaceted syndrome responsible for NIDDM, obesity hypertension, dyslipidemia, and atherosclerotic cardiovascular disease. Diabetes Care 1991;14:173-94.

87. Lithell H. Hypertension and hyperlipidemia: a review. Am J Hypertens 1993;6:303S-308S.

88. Collins R, Peto R, Cutler JA, Collins R, Sorlie P, Neaton J. Blood pressure, stroke and coronary heart disease, Part 1. Prolonged differences in blood pressure: prospective observational studies corrected for the regression dilution bias. Lancet 1990;335:765-74.

89. Collins R, Peto R, MacMahon S, Herbert P, Fiebach NH, Eberlein KA, et al. Blood pressure, stroke and coronary heart disease, Part 2. Short-term reductions in blood pressure: overview of randomised drug trials in their epidemiological context. Lancet 1990;335:827-38.

90. Kitler ME. Differences in men and women in coronary heart disease, systemic hypertension and their treatment. Am J Cardiol 1992;70:1077-80.

91. Medical Research Working Party. MRC trial of mild hypertension: principal results. Br Med J 1985;291:197-204.

92. Hypertension Detection and Follow-up Program Cooperative Group. Five year findings of the hypertension detection and follow up program. II. Mortality by race, sex and age. JAMA 1979;242:2572-7.

93. Kannel WB. Update on the role of cigarette smoking in coronary artery disease. Am Heart J 1981;101:319-28.

94. Ramsdale DR, Faragher EB, Bray CL, Bennett DH, Ward C, Beton DC. Smoking and coronary artery disease assessed by routine coronary angiography. Brit Med J 1985; 290:197-200.

95. Nyboe J, Jensen G, Appleyard M, Schnohr P. Smoking and the risk of first acute myocardial infarction. Am Heart J 1991;122:438-47.

96. Yaznell JWG. Smoking and cardiovascular disease. Q J med 1996;89:493-98.

97. Gottlieb S, Boyko V, Zahger D, Balkin J, Hod H, Pelled B, et al. Smoking and prognosis after acute myocardial infarction in the thrombolytic era (Israeli Thrombolytic National Survey). J Am Coll Cardiol 1996;1506-13.

98. Mueller HS, Cohen LS, Braunwald E, Forman S, Feir F, Ross A, et al., for the TIMI investigators. Predictors of early morbidity and mortality after thrombolytic therapy of acute myocardial infarction: analyses of patients subgroups in the Thrombolysis in Myocardial Infarction (TIMI) trial, Phase II. Circulation 1992;85:1254-64.

99. Barbash G, Reiner J, White HD, Wilcox RG, Armstrong PW, Sadowski Z, et al. for the GUSTO-I investigators. Evaluation of paradoxic beneficial effects of smoking in patients receiving thrombolytic therapy for acute myocardial infarction: mechanism of "smoker's paradox" from the GUSTO-I trial, with angiographic insights. J Am Coll Cardiol 1995; 26:1222-9.

100. Kawachi J, Colditz GA, Stampfer MJ, Willett WC, Manson JE, Rosner B, et al. Smoking cessation in relation to total mortality rates in women. Ann Intern Med 1993;119:992-1000.

101. Corr LA, Olivier MF. The low fat/low cholesterol diet is ineffective. Eur Heart J 1997;18: 18-22.

102. de Lorgeril M, Salen P, Monjaud I, Delaye J. The "diet heart" hypothesis in secondary prevention of coronary heart disease. Eur Heart J 1997;18:13-18.

103. Arntzenius AC, Kromhout D, Barth JD, Reiber JHC, Bruschke AVG, Buis B, et al. Diet, lipoproteins and the progression of coronary atherosclerosis: The Leiden Intervention Trial. New Engl J Med 1985; 312:805–11.

104. Ornish D, Brown SE, Scherwitz LW, Billings JH, Armstrong WT, Perts TA, et al. Can lifestyle changes reverse coronary heart disease? Lancet 1990;336:129–33.

105. Burr ML, Fehily AM, Gilbert JF, Rogers S, Holliday RM, Sweetnam PM, et al. Effects of changes in fat, fish and fibre intakes on death and myocardial infarctions: diet and reinfarction trial (DART). Lancet 1989;2:757–61.

106. deLorgeril M, Renaud S, Mamelle N, Salen P, Martin J-L, Monjaud T, et al. Mediterranean alpha-linolenic acid-rich diet in secondary prevention of coronary heart disease. Lancet 1994;343:1454–9.

107. Singh RB, Rastogi SS, Verma R, Laxmi B, Singh R, Ghosh S, et al. Randomised controlled trial of cardioprotective diet in patients with acute myocardial infarction: results of one year follow-up. Brit Med J 1992;304:1015–19.

108. Kuczmarski RJ, Flegal KM, Campbell SM, Johnson CL. Increasing prevalence of over-weight among US adults: the National Health and Nutrition Examination Surveys 1960 to 1991. JAMA 1994;272:205–11.

109. Prentice AM, Jebb SA. Obesity in Britain: gluttony or sloth? Brit Med J 1995;311:437–39.

110. Paffenbarger RS, Hyde RT, Wing AL, Steinmetz CH. A natural history of athleticism and cardiovascular health. JAMA 1984;252:491–5.

111. Leon AS, Connett J, Jacobs DR, Rauramaa R. Leisure time physical activity levels and risk of coronary heart disease and death: The Multiple Risk Factor Intervention Trial. JAMA 1987;258:2388–95.

112. Ekelund LG, Haskell WL, Johnson JL, Whaley FS, Criqui MH, Sheps DS. Physical fitness as predictor of cardiovascular mortality in asymptomatic North American men: The Lipid Research Clinic Mortality Follow-Up Study. New Engl J Med 1988;319:1379–84.

113. Blair SN, Jacobs DR, Powell KE. Relationships between exercise or physical activity and other health behaviors. Public Health Rep 1985;100:172–180.

114. Escobedo LG, Marcus SE, Holzman D, Giovino GA. Sports participation, age and smok-ing initiation, and the risk of smoking among US high school students. JAMA 1993; 269:1391–5.

115. Eriksson J, Taimela S, Koivisto VA. Exercise and the metabolic syndrome. Diabetologia 1997;40:125–35.

116. Saltin B. Sedentary lifestyle: an underestimated health risk. J Intern Med 1992;232: 467–9.

117. DCCT Research Group. The effect of intensive treatment of diabetes on the develop-ment and progression of long-term complications of insulin-dependent diabetes mellitus. N Engl J Med 1993;329:977–86.

118. Lorenz RA, Bubb J, Davis D, Jacobson A, Jannasch K, Kramer J. Changing behavior: practical lessons from the Diabetes Control and Complications Trial. Diabetes Care 1996;19:648–52.

119. Scottish Intercollegiate Guidelines Network (SIGN). Report on good practice in the care of children and young people with diabetes. Edinburgh: SIGN, 1996:1–10.

120. Golin CE, DiMatteo MR, Gelberg L. The role of patient participation in the doctor visit: implications for adherence to diabetes care. Diabetes Care 1996;19:1153–64.

121. Goodall T. Self-management of diabetes mellitus; a critical review. Health Psychol 1991; 10:1–8.

122. Anderson L. Health care communication and selected psychological adherence in diabetes management. Diabetes Care 1990;13:66–67.

123. Hulka B, Cassel J, Kupper L, Burdette J. Communication, compliance, and concordance between physicians and patients with prescribed medications. Am J Public Health 1976;66:847–53.

124. Pearson TA, Fuster V. Matching the intensity of risk factor management with the hazard for coronary disease events: executive summary. 27th Bethesda Conference, September 14-15, 1995. J Am Coll Cardiol 1996;5:957–63.

125. The Bezafibrate Infarction Prevention (BIP) Study Group, Israel. Lipids and lipoproteins in symptomatic coronary heart disease: distribution, intercorrelations and significance for risk classification in 6,700 men and 1,500 women. Circulation 1992;86:839-48.
126. American College of Physicians. Guidelines for using serum cholesterol, high-density lipoprotein cholesterol, and triglyceride levels as screening tests for preventing coronary heart disease in adults. Ann Intern Med 1996;124:515-17.
127. Cohn JS, McNamara JR, Cohn SD, Ordovas JM, Schaefer EJ. Postprandial plasma lipoprotein changes in human subjects of different ages. J Lipid Res 1988;29:469-79.
128. Cohn JS, McNamara JR, Schaefer EJ. Lipoprotein cholesterol concentrations in the plasma of human subjects as measured in the fed and fasted states. Clin Chem 1988;34:2456-59.
129. Warnick GR, Leary ET, Ammirati EB, Allen MP. Cholesterol in fingerstick capillary specimens can be equivalent to conventional venous measurements. Arch Path Lab Med 1994;118:1110-14.
130. Koch TR, Mehta U, Lee H, Aziz K, Temel S, Donlon JA, Sherwin R. Bias and precision of cholesterol analysis by physicians office analyzers. Clin Chem 1987;33:2262-7.
131. Warnick GR. Measurement of cholesterol, triglycerides, and HDL using compact analysis systems. Clin Lab Med 1989;9:73-88.
132. Kaufman HW, McNamara JR, Anderson KM, Wilson PWF, Schaefer EJ. How reliably can compact chemistry analyzers measure lipids? JAMA 1990;263:1245-9.
133. McNamara JR, Warnick GR, Leary ET, Wittels E, Nelson FE, Pearl MF, Schaefer EJ. A multi-center evaluation of a patient-administered test for blood cholesterol measurement. Prev Med 1996;25:583-92.
134. Cooper GR, Myers GL, Smith SJ, Schlant RC. Blood lipid measurements: variations and practical utility. JAMA 1992;267:1652-60.
135. McNamara JR, Cole TG, Contois JH, Ferguson CA, Ordovas JM, Schaefer EJ. Immunoseparation method for measuring low-density lipoprotein cholesterol directly from serum evaluated. Clin Chem 1995;41:232-40.
136. Jialal I, Hirany SV, Devaraj S, Sherwood TA. Comparison of an immunoseparation method for direct measurement of LDL cholesterol with beta-quantification (ultracentrifugation). Am J Clin Path 1995;104:76-81.
137. Pisani T, Gebski CP, Leary ET, Warnick GR, Ollington JF. Accurate direct determination of low-density lipoprotein cholesterol using an immunoseparation reagent and enzymatic cholesterol assay. Arch Pathol Lab Med 1995;119:1127-35.
138. Friedewald WT, Levy RI, Fredrickson DS. Estimation of the concentration of low-density lipoprotein cholesterol in plasma, without use of the preparative ultracentrifuge. Clin Chem 1972;18:499-502.
139. Bachorik PS, Ross JW. National Cholesterol Education Program recommendations for measurement of low-density lipoprotein cholesterol: executive summary. Clin Chem 1995;41:1414-20.
140. Stein EA, Myers GL. National Cholesterol Education Program recommendations for triglyceride measurement: executive summary. Clin Chem 1995;41;1421-6.
141. Warnick GR, Wood PD. National Cholesterol Education Program recommendations for measurement of high-density lipoprotein cholesterol: executive summary. Clin Chem 1995;41:1427-33.
142. McNamara JR, Leary ET, Ceriotti F, Boersma-Cobbaert CM, Cole TG, Hassemer DJ, et al. Status of Lipid and lipoprotein standardization. Clin Chem, in press.
143. Abell LL, Levy BB, Brodie BB, Kendall FE. Simplified methods for the estimation of total cholesterol in serum and demonstration of its specificity. J Biol Chem 1953;195:357-66.
144. Manual of laboratory operations, Lipid Research Clinics Program. Lipid and lipoprotein analysis. Washington, DC: NIH, U.S. Dept. of Health and Human Services, 1982.
145. Albers JJ, Marcovina SM. Standardisation of apolipoprotein B and A-I measurements. Clin Chem 1989;35:1357-61.
146. Marcovina SM, Albers JJ, Henderson LO, Hannon WH. International Federation of Clinical Chemistry standardisation project for measurements of apolipoproteins A-I and

B. III. Comparability of apolipoprotein A-I values by use of international reference material. Clin Chem 1993;39:773–81.

147. Marcovina SM, Albers JJ, Henderson LO, Hannon WH. International Federation of Clinical Chemistry standardisation project for measurements of apolipoproteins A-I and B. IV. Comparability of apolipoprotein A-I values by use of international reference material. Clin Chem 1994;40:586–92.

148. Contois JH, McNamara JR, Lammi-Keefe CJ, Wilson PWF, Schaefer EJ. Reference intervals for plasma apolipoprotein AuI as determined with a commercially available immunoturbidometric assay: results from the Framingham Offspring Study. Clin Chem 1996;42:507–14.

149. Contois JH, McNamara JR, Lammi-Keefe CJ, Wilson PWF, Massor T, Schaefer EJ. Reference intervals for plasma apolipoprotein B as determined with a commercially available immunoturbidometric assay: results from the Framingham Offspring Study. Clin Chem 1996;42:515–23.

150. Wilson PWF, Garrison RJ, Abbott RD, Castelli WP. Factors associated with lipoprotein cholesterol levels: the Framingham Study. Arteriosclerosis 1983;3:273–81.

151. Sempos C, Fulwood R, Haines C, Carroll M, Anda R, Williamson DF, et al. The prevalence of high blood cholesterol levels among adults in the United States. JAMA 1989;262: 45–52.

152. Keys A, ed. Coronary heart disease in seven countries. Circulation 1970;41(Suppl I):1–198.

153. The Lipid Research Clinics Program. The Lipid Research Clinics Coronary Primary Prevention Trial. I. Reduction in incidence of coronary heart disease. JAMA 1984;251: 351–64.

154. The Lipid Research Clinics Program. The Lipid Research Clinics Coronary Primary Prevention Trial. II. The relationship of reduction in incidence of coronary heart disease to cholesterol lowering. JAMA 1984;251:365–74.

155. McBride PE, Houston Miller N, Smith SC. Task Force 8. Organization of preventive cardiology service. J Am Coll Cardiol 1996;27:964–1047.

156. Committee on Clinical Practice Issues in Health and Disease. The role and identity of physician nutrition specialists in medical school-affiliated hospitals. Am J Clin Nutr 1995;61:264–8.

157. Simon HB. Patient-directed, nonprescription approaches to cardiovascular disease. Arch Intern Med 1994;154:2283–93.

158. Gunnar RM, Williams RG. Future personnel needs for cardiovascular health care. Excerpt from conference program of the 25th Bethesda Conference, November 15–16, 1993. J Am Coll Cardiol 1994;24:280–81.

Preanalytical Variation in Lipid, Lipoprotein, and Apolipoprotein Testing

Nader Rifai, Robert Dufour, and Gerald R. Cooper

INTRODUCTION

❖ Accurate determination of serum lipids is dependent on control of both analytical and preanalytical factors. Preanalytical variation in subjects results from differences in lifestyle, altered lipid metabolism due to disease, the source of the specimen, and the conditions of sample collection. Variation can arise from biological, behavioral, and clinical factors, as well as variability in specimen collection and handling (see Figure 4–1). This chapter discusses the factors that contribute to preanalytical variations and addresses the importance of standardization of patient preparation for lipid testing.

BIOLOGICAL VARIATIONS

Intra-individual Variation

As for most laboratory tests, intra-individual variation in lipid values is generally smaller than person-to-person or inter-individual variation. An assessment of biological components of variation of total cholesterol (TC), high-density lipoprotein cholesterol (HDL-C), and apolipoproteins (apo) AI and B showed an index of individuality much less than 0.6.[1] (The index of individuality is calculated by dividing the intra-individual coefficient of variation [CV_B] by the inter-individual coefficient of variation [CV_P]). This finding indicates that the use of conventional population-based reference intervals in an interpretation is of little value and may be misleading.[2] Population-based reference ranges are not useful unless the index of individuality is greater than 1.4.[3] Therefore, health-based cutpoints from large population studies were derived by experts for the classification of hyperlipoproteinemia.

With recent improvements in analytical performance of lipid assays, it has become easier to define the day-to-day variations in lipid concentrations. Knowledge of such variations is important in that it provides both laboratorians and clinicians with a framework for comparing results to evaluate the efficacy of therapy. With improvement in methods, a major fraction of the variation in lipid measurements may be due to biological variability rather than analytical variability. One recent study attributed from 69% (for low-density lipoprotein cholesterol [LDL-C]) to 96% (for very-low-density lipo-

Figure 4–1 ✧ Components of Preanalytical Variation

BIOLOGICAL

Intra-individual	Gender
Age	Race

BEHAVIORAL

Diet	Alcohol Intake
Obesity	Caffeine Intake
Cigarette Smoking	Exercise

Stress

CLINICAL

Disease-Induced*

Endocrine & Metabolic
  Hypothyroidism
  Hypopituitarism
  Diabetes Mellitus
  Acute Intermittent Porphyria
  Pregnancy

Renal
  Nephrotic Syndrome
  Chronic Renal Failure

Hepatic
  Congenital Biliary Atresia

Storage Disease
  Gaucher Disease
  Glycogen Storage Disease
  Tay-Sachs Disease

Acute & Transient
  Burns
  Infections
  Myocardial Infarction

Others
Anorexia Nervosa
Systemic Lupus Erythematosus

Drug-Induced*

Antihypertensives	*Immunosuppressives*	*Sex Steroids*
Thiazides	Cyclosporine	Estrogen
Chlorothalidone	Tacrolimus	Progestin
Beta-blockers	Prednisolone	

SAMPLE COLLECTION & HANDLING

Fasting Status	Hemoconcentration
Anticoagulants & Preservatives	Specimen Storage
Capillary vs. Venous	

*Limited list

protein cholesterol [VLDL-C] and triglyceride [TG]) of total variance to biological variation.[4] Biological variation is similar in adults and children.[5]

Intra-individual variation (CV_I) is due to a combination of biological variation (CV_B), which includes collection variables (discussed below), diurnal variation, and other inherent changes in the person, as well as analytical imprecision (CV_A), which is dependent on the method and instrumentation used.[6] The total variability can be expressed mathematically as

$$CV_I = \left[\frac{CV_A{}^2}{(NR) \times (NS)} + \frac{CV_B{}^2}{(NS)} \right]^{1/2}$$

where NS is the number of specimens and NR is the number of replicate laboratory determinations per specimen.[7] Cooper et al. have proposed that the total intra-individual variation for TC should be less than 5% to reliably classify the risk of coronary heart disease (CHD).[7,8] If the total variation is more than 5%, then it will be necessary to obtain more than one sample to reduce the variation to the acceptable 5% level. Both analytical and biological variation must be reduced to allow estimates of risk of atherosclerosis to be made on the fewest number of specimens possible.

Table 4–1 shows the total individual variation obtained by varying the number of samples, the analytical variation, and by decreasing the biological variation from the average TC CV_B of 6.1%[7] through rigorous patient preparation. Although the table indicates the need for utilization of at least two specimens to reach this goal, which is also the recommendation of the National Cholesterol Education Program (NCEP),[9] single specimens may suffice for classification of patients whose TC values are far

Table 4–1 ❖ Effect of Multiple Specimens on Total Individual Variation (CV_I% of TC [200 mg/dL or 5.17 mmol/L])

Samples per person = K	CV_A = 5%		CV_A = 3%		CV_A = 2%		CV_A = 1%	
	n = 1	n = 2	n = 1	n = 2	n = 1	n = 2	n = 1	n = 2
CV_B 6.5%, Number of Replicate Measurements to Reach CV_I 5%								
1	7.9	7.1	6.8	6.4	6.4	6.3	6.2	6.1
2	5.6	5.0	4.8	4.6	4.5	4.4	4.4	4.3
3	4.6	4.1	3.9	3.7	3.7	3.6	3.6	3.6
4	3.9	3.5	3.4	3.2	3.2	3.1	3.1	3.1
CV_B 5.0%, Number of Replicate Measurements to Reach CV_I 5%								
1	7.1	6.1	5.8	5.4	5.4	5.2	5.1	5.0
2	5.0	4.3	4.1	3.8	3.8	3.7	3.6	3.6
3	4.1	3.5	3.4	3.1	3.1	3.0	2.9	2.9
4	3.5	3.1	2.9	2.7	2.7	2.6	2.5	2.5

CV_A = Analytical coefficient of variation.
CV_B = Biological coefficient of variation.
The thick line indicates the number of specimens required to meet the NCEP guideline of <5% total variability in cholesterol measurement. If biological variation is at the average value of 6.5%, this goal can be achieved with duplicate samples if the analytical CV is <2%, but requires 3 or 4 specimens if analytical variation is greater. If biological variation were only 5%, which may be achieved with careful patient preparation, duplicate measurements on a single specimen would be close to the guideline with a single specimen for methods with analytical CV <2%.

from the cutpoints. In a recent study, single samples resulted in accurate classification of risk category for patients with TC concentrations below 185 mg/dL (4.79 mmol/L), between 215 and 225 mg/dL (5.57–5.83 mmol/L), or over 255 mg/dL (6.60 mmol/L) when using a method with analytical variation of 1.3%.[10] Because of greater measurement imprecision (CV = 4.4%), LDL-C values could be correctly classified as to risk category with a single specimen for concentrations below 116 mg/dL (3.00 mmol/L) or above 174 mg/dL (4.51 mmol/L).[10] The new NCEP guidelines use a cutoff of 100 mg/dL (2.60 mmol/L) for clinical decision making in subjects with CHD. A single determination for this lower LDL-C value would no longer be reliable. Thus, two samples will continue to be needed for LDL-C, except for patients with the highest results. When CV_A is below 2%, there is virtually no effect of repeat analysis of the same specimen on total variation.

A simple method for estimating the degree of biological variability in an individual is to use the relative range (RR), defined as:

$$\text{Relative Range} = \frac{\text{Difference between highest and lowest result}}{\text{Average result}}$$

Cooper et al. have suggested that the CV_I for an individual should be below the average population CV_B and have calculated values of RR which satisfy this goal (Table 4-2).[7] In many individuals, CV_B is much greater than average. Maximum individual variation may range up to 10–15% for TC, LDL-C, HDL-C, apo AI and apo B, but up to 50% for Lp(a) and up to 75% for TG.[11, 12] Longitudinal data from the Framingham study suggest that patients with increased CV_B are at increased risk of cardiovascular disease.[13] If the individual's RR is below the cutoff values listed in Table 4-2, the average cholesterol can be used to estimate risk of CHD. If the RR is above the cutoff value, additional samples should be analyzed before a decision on risk is made.

Table 4–2 ✧ Maximum Allowable Relative Range (RR) to Conclude that Intraindividual Variation is Below Average Population Bilogical Variation at NCEP Target Values for Analyte Variation

	Maximum RR			
n	Total Cholesterol (CV_B 6.1%, CV_A 3.0%)	HDL Cholesterol (CV_B 7.4%, CV_A 6.0%)	LDL Cholesterol (CV_B 9.5%, CV_A 4.0%)	Triglyceride CV_B 22.6%, CV_A 5.0%
2	0.19	0.27	0.29	0.67
3	0.23	0.32	0.35	0.82
4	0.25	0.35	0.38	0.90
5	0.26	0.37	0.40	0.94

RR (Relative Range) = difference between highest and lowest results divided by mean of observed values; CV_A = analytical variation; CV_B = biological variation; *n* = number of samples analyzed from an indivudal subject.

The minimum time between repeated measurements needed to determine maximum variability has not been conclusively determined. While the NCEP recommends at least one week between serial measurements, recent studies have suggested that a period of two weeks provides a more reliable measure of variability.[14]

Serum TC is the most stable lipid analyte; day-to-day biological variation averages 6.1%,[6, 7] although some individuals may vary by up to 11%.[8] Time of day has little effect on TC concentration, as within-day variation is generally less than 3%.[8, 15] TC tends to be higher in winter than in summer by an average of 2.5%.[11, 16] In women, TC concentrations may fluctuate during the menstrual cycle, averaging 10–20% lower in the late luteal and menstrual phases.[17, 18] For the average woman, TC concentrations increase by about 14 mg/dL (0.36 mmol/L) around ovulation and fall to a nadir during menstruation.[19]

TG concentrations show marked intra-individual variation. Even excluding the known marked postprandial fluctuation, fasting TG concentrations differ by an average of 23% over one or more months, and in some persons may fluctuate as much as 40% around the mean value.[6, 8] During the day, TG concentrations typically rise from a nadir at 3:00 AM to reach peak values in mid-afternoon, then progressively fall throughout the evening; average diurnal variation is approximately 30%.[20] Because of this marked random variation, it is difficult to assess seasonal, menstrual, and other types of rhythmic fluctuations of TG.

HDL-C concentrations show an average intra-individual variation of 7% over one month to a year, but seldom differ by more than 12%. Seasonal variation in HDL-C is significantly higher but is slightly less than that of TC and LDL-C.[16]

Whether LDL-C concentration is measured directly or derived from measurements of TC, HDL-C, and TG, biological variability is similar at an average of 9.5%.[6, 21] As with TC, LDL-C concentration is approximately 2.5% higher in winter than in summer,[8, 16] and in women is lower in the late luteal phase and during menstruation.[18, 19]

A recent study has demonstrated that the CV_B of TC, TG, HDL-C and calculated LDL-C is the same in specimens collected by fingerstick or venipuncture.[22]

Data from apolipoprotein measurements show similar variability. Apo AI biological variation averages 7–8%; there are apparently no changes during the menstrual cycle.[18, 23] The intra-individual variation for both HDL-C and apo AI is greater in smokers than in non-smokers.[24] Apo AI concentrations tend to be highest in the evening and fall to a nadir at 6 AM.[25] It is not clear whether these differences are governed by sleep-wake or light-dark cycles.

Apo B has an average within-day biological variation of 6.5%, with a day-to-day variation of 8–10%.[23] Lipoprotein(a) [Lp(a)] shows an average biological variation of 8.6%.[26] There is no significant diurnal variation in apo B or Lp(a) concentrations.[25, 27] Lp(a) increases during the luteal phase in a minority of women; in most, it is unaffected by the menstrual cycle.[28]

Effects of Age, Sex, and Race on the Lipoprotein Profile

Numerous demographic factors within the population are correlated with differences in lipid and lipoprotein concentrations. In newborns, TC, TG, and most lipoprotein and apolipoprotein concentrations rise rapidly from the low values in cord blood to 80% of adult values by 4 days of age.[29] Lp(a) rises more slowly, continuing to increase gradually through at least the first 6 months of life.[30, 31] In children, lipid concentrations of both boys and girls remain stable until just before puberty, when a transient fall in TC, TG, HDL-C, and LDL-C occurs.[29] At puberty, lipid values begin to diverge; in boys, TC decreases slightly, due to a significant fall in HDL-C (and apo AI).[32, 33] After puberty, HDL-C and apo AI continue to decline through the early 20's, then remain stable, at least until age 55 y.[33, 34] In girls, HDL-C and apo AI increase gradually from menarche to the time of menopause.[32, 35] Lp(a) is similar in men and women of all ages, although it is slightly higher in young and adolescent girls.[36]

In black children, HDL-C, apo AI, Lp(a), and VLDL-C concentrations are noticeably higher than those of white children by about age 9 y, while LDL-C and apo B concentrations are lower.[37, 38] In adulthood, these sex- and race-related differences persist.[39] Little data exist on other minority groups in the population. In two studies, no differences were found in most lipid measurements between Hispanic and non-Hispanic whites.[40, 41] In contrast, Lp(a) is significantly lower in Hispanic whites, intermediate in Asians and non-Hispanic whites, and highest in blacks.[42-44] Similar plasma TC and TG changes were observed with respect to age and sex in the Lipid Research Clinics prevalence study of 60,502 participants in a survey of 11 separate and well-defined North American populations.[45]

In all individuals, TC concentrations gradually increase with age, although the magnitude of increase is not as great in more recent studies as it was 20 or more years ago.[46] In the Second National Health and Nutrition Examination Survey, mean TC concentration increased from approximately 180 mg/dL (4.66 mmol/L) at age 20 y to approximately 230 mg/dL (5.96 mmol/L) in men and 250 mg/dL (6.48 mmol/L) in women by age 65.[47] This increase is due primarily to increasing LDL-C concentration and is accompanied by an increase in apo B values. In the Framingham study, TC increases biannually by an average of 3.7% in men and 6.6% in women.[13] In women, there is a 14% increase in TC and a 19% increase in LDL-C in the five years surrounding menopause; TG and HDL-C are unaffected.[48] The TG concentration also increases with age.[32, 49] Lp(a) appears to rise slightly with age, and increases an average of 25% in women after menopause.[50, 51]

BEHAVIORAL VARIATIONS

The major behavioral factors that affect the lipid, lipoprotein, and apolipoprotein serum concentrations are diet, obesity, cigarette smoking, alcohol and caffeine intake, exercise, and stress. Since these lifestyle elements are controllable, it is imperative that subjects maintain their usual behavior for several days before blood specimens for lipid testing are obtained.

Diet

The effect of diet on lipid and lipoprotein concentrations is well established. The extent of this effect, however, varies among individuals. It has been shown that an increase in dietary intake of cholesterol can cause serum TC concentration to rise over 5% in only 30% of the studied population.[8] Various fatty acids appear to have different effects on the lipoprotein profile and CHD risk. In general, diets rich in mono- and polyunsaturated fatty acids cause serum TC, LDL-C, apo B, and TG to decrease, while diets rich in saturated fat, mainly palmitic acid, cause serum TC and LDL-C to increase.[52, 53] However, stearic acid, which is also a saturated fatty acid, does not appear to increase LDL-C.[53] Progression of CHD over 39 months measured by angiography was strongly related to intakes of long-chain saturates, especially 18:0, and trans-unsaturates such as t-18:1, apparently independent of plasma TC concentration.[54]

Omega-3 fatty acids, from fish oil, have been shown to consistently decrease TG and VLDL in both normal and hypertriglyceridemic subjects, possibly by inhibiting the hepatic synthesis of VLDL-apo B and VLDL-TG.[55] In contrast, the documented effects of fish oil on TC, LDL-C, and HDL-C have been inconsistent.

The Cholesterol Lowering Atherosclerosis Study observed that when total and saturated fat intakes are being reduced, protein and carbohydrate are preferred substitutes for fat calories rather than mono- or polyunsaturated fats.[56] Furthermore, the reduction in fat intake was reflected in a significant decrease in TC concentrations.[56]

The effect of dietary intake of fiber on serum lipids remains controversial.[57] However, water-soluble fibers were shown to reduce TC.[58, 59]

Vegetarians are known to have a healthier lipid profile than non-vegetarians. The Lifestyle Heart Trial studying the effect of comprehensive lifestyle changes (low-fat, vegetarian diet, stopping smoking, stress management training, and moderate exercise) observed regression of severe coronary atherosclerosis after only 1 y by angiography.[60] One study has demonstrated that LDL-C is 37% lower and HDL-C is 12% higher in strict vegetarians than in non-vegetarians.[61]

Changes in eating habits have been shown to significantly alter lipid and lipoprotein profiles within a relatively short period of time. When the low-fat and high-fiber diet of a group of Tarahumara Indians was substituted with an "affluent" diet for a period of 5 weeks, increases in TC and LDL-C (up to 39%) and TG concentrations (19%) as well as body weight (7%) were seen.[62]

Since diet modification can affect lipid concentrations, subjects should maintain customary dietary intake and eating habits before blood samples are collected for lipid and lipoprotein studies. When subjects have changed their dietary habits significantly, the NCEP guidelines suggest a waiting period of 3–6 months before performing any lipid testing.[9]

Obesity

Obesity has been shown to be associated with increased risk of CHD. In addition, obese individuals have higher TG, TC, and LDL-C and lower HDL-C compared to non-obese controls.[8] After weight loss, an obese individual will experience a decrease in TG of about 40%, a decrease in TC and LDL-C of about 10%, and an increase in HDL-C of about 10%.[63] In a study of identical twins, obesity was independently associated with TC, LDL-C, HDL-C, and TG, as well as systolic and diastolic blood pressure and glucose tolerance.[64]

Current evidence suggests that body fat distribution has a stronger association with various morbidities, such as hyperlipidemia, hypertension, diabetes, and CHD, than just body weight.[65] The intra-abdominal fat accumulation (waist-to-hip ratio) in obese women was associated with higher TG and VLDL-C and lower HDL-C, independent of total obesity.[66] Visceral abdominal fat measured independently by computed tomography is the most relevant positive obesity factor for TC, TG, and apo B-containing lipoproteins, and negative for HDL-C.[67]

Repeated weight gain and loss in obese individuals would precipitate significant variations in serum lipid and lipoprotein concentrations. Therefore, subjects should avoid any alterations in lifestyle that can cause weight changes at the time when blood specimens are collected.

Cigarette Smoking

Cigarette smoking is an established independent risk factor for CHD. Smoking-associated physiological changes that probably contribute to the high risk of heart disease include increased clotting factors and carboxyhemoglobin concentrations, increased blood viscosity, and altered lipoprotein profile.[68] The strong association of smoking with white blood cell count, hematocrit, and heart rate suggests that smoking-induced risk is more associated with occlusive thrombosis than with atherosclerosis.[69] In addition, oxidized LDL produced after exposure to cigarette smoke was shown to cause the accumulation of cholesterol ester in macrophages *in vitro*.[70] Therefore, oxidized LDL could also contribute to foam cell formation and atherosclerosis in smokers.

Compared to non-smokers, cigarette smokers have significantly higher serum TG, VLDL-C, and LDL-C and lower apo AI and HDL-C (mainly the HDL_3-C fraction).[71, 72] Furthermore, the relationship between smoking and HDL-C was shown to be dose-dependent in both men and women;[73] therefore, the extent of smoking will affect the degree of alteration in the lipoprotein profile. Passive smoking through multiple components of second-hand smoke affects platelet activity, accelerates atherosclerotic lesions, increases ischemic tissue damage,[74] and decreases HDL-C.[75]

Subjects should not change their smoking pattern at the time when blood specimens are collected.

Alcohol Intake

Several epidemiological studies have demonstrated a relationship between alcohol consumption, lipoprotein profile changes, and cardiovascular mortality.[76] The alcohol-induced alterations in the lipoprotein pattern depend on the amount of alcohol consumed, individual susceptibility, genetic variables, and dietary factors. Therefore, these changes differ among moderate and heavy drinkers. Moderate alcohol drinkers (1.2 oz/day; 34 g/day) have increased concentrations of HDL-C, apo AI, and apo AII compared to non-drinkers.[77, 78] Another study has shown that moderate alcohol intake increases total HDL-C, HDL_2-C, and HDL_3-C, increases TC, LDL-C, and VLDL-C, and decreases the risk of myocardial infarction.[79] In premenopausal women, moderate daily alcohol consumption has resulted in a 10% increase in HDL-C, an 8% decrease in LDL-C and unchanged Lp(a) concentrations.[80] However, moderate alcohol consumption in patients with primary hypertriglyceridemia usually results in a profound increase in TG.[81] With increased alcohol intake, LDL-C and HDL_2-C are reduced and

TG is increased.[78] In chronic alcoholic men with normal liver function and structure, TG is usually in the normal range, HDL-C is increased, and LDL-C is decreased.[78]

Lp(a) concentration appears to be influenced by alcohol differently from the other lipids. Lp(a) concentrations decrease by about 33% initially then return to baseline after 6 weeks of alcohol intake.[82]

Alcohol consumption has been shown to have a U-shaped relationship to heart disease.[8] The actual mechanism of that link and the molecular basis of the alcohol-induced lipid changes remain unclear.

Subjects should maintain their usual pattern of alcohol intake prior to blood specimen collection.

Caffeine Intake

Several epidemiological studies have investigated the link between coffee consumption, cardiovascular morbidity, and altered lipid concentrations. These correlations have been inconsistent and have been largely dismissed as being due to confounding variables. Intake of coffee in Norway has been associated with a trend toward an atherogenic diet and unhealthy lifestyle.[83] Recently it was suggested that the inconsistency in these findings may result from the coffee brewing methods used. The strongest evidence for a direct association between coffee consumption and increased TC and LDL-C values comes from Scandinavia, where coffee is normally brewed by boiling.[84] Consumption of filtered coffee was reported to have a substantially lesser effect on cholesterol values than consumption of coffee brewed by boiling. The serum concentrations of apo AI, apo AII, apo B, HDL-C, and VLDL-C appear to be unaffected by consumption of coffee, even when brewed by boiling.[85] However, in another study, boiled Scandinavian-style coffee was found to contain more lipid material than drip-filtered coffee, and this was reported to raise serum LDL-C and VLDL-C concentrations.[86] The diterpenes, cafestol, and kahweol present in the unfiltered coffee may be responsible for increasing TC, TG, and alanine transaminase.[87]

Replacing regular coffee with decaffeinated coffee did not alter TG, TC, or HDL-C in healthy men and women.[88] Coffee as consumed by U.S. women apparently causes no increased risk of subsequent CHD.[89] However, a randomized clinical trial found that consumption of filtered regular coffee led to a statistically significant increase in the plasma concentration of TC, which was due to increases in both LDL-C and HDL-C concentrations.[90]

Subjects should maintain their usual daily intake of caffeine during the days prior to lipid testing, but abstain from drinking coffee and cream 12 h prior to collecting blood specimens.

Exercise

Several epidemiological investigations have reported an association between a sedentary lifestyle and an increased risk of developing the clinical manifestations of CHD.[91] A lower level of physical fitness is associated with higher serum concentrations of LDL-C and TG and higher risk of death from cardiovascular disease.[92] Exercise exerts a preventive effect on the progression of coronary atherosclerosis, possibly by altering the lipoprotein profile. In hyperlipidemic subjects, additional favorable alteration in the lipoprotein profile was seen when physical exercise accompanied dietary treatment.[93, 94]

Strenuous exercise causes decreases in serum TG, LDL-C, and apo B and increases in HDL-C (mainly the HDL_2-C fraction) and apo AI.[8, 95] Furthermore, the extent of these changes may be dependent on the intensity and type of exercise training program.[95] Acute exercise causes a significant rise in HDL-C which is due to an increase in HDL_3-C.[96] Moderate and regular physical exercise also appears to have a favorable effect on serum lipids. Adults who walk 2.5 to 4 h each week have lower TC and higher HDL-C than those who do not walk regularly.[97] In previously sedentary women who walked briskly an average of 155 min each week for a period of 1 y, TC decreased by 6.5% and HDL-C increased by 27%.[98]

Subjects should maintain their usual level of exercise on days before lipid testing, but avoid any strenuous exercise 24 h prior to blood specimen collection.[8]

Stress

A high level of stress as well as a Type A personality have been linked to increased risk of CHD. Furthermore, several studies have demonstrated an increase in TC concentration during stressful situations,[99] which is possibly due to dietary changes that accompany stress.[100] The stressors employed in these trials were diverse and included both chronic stressors and acute challenges posed in the laboratory. Some evidence suggests that stress affects the lipid concentrations of males and females differently.[101] In addition, elective hospitalization was shown to cause HDL-C and apo AI to decrease by approximately 10%.[102]

The exact mechanism of the interplay of stress with CHD and lipid changes remains unclear. Therefore, it is not advisable to perform lipid testing for cardiac risk assessment in a stressful period such as during academic examinations or hospitalization, even for elective procedures.

To minimize the effect of acute stress on lipid testing, subjects who report to the laboratory should be encouraged to relax for at least 5 min prior to blood sample collection.

CLINICAL VARIATIONS

An individual's lipoprotein profile is markedly altered in acute infectious and metabolic diseases. In addition, drug-induced hyperlipidemia has been reported in several patient populations. To obtain the subject's usual lipid and lipoprotein concentrations, testing should preferably be performed in the absence of any secondary dyslipoproteinemia. Otherwise, the disorder or the medication causing the disruption in lipid values should be noted on the patient's analytical report.

Disease-Induced Secondary Lipid Alterations

Several endocrine, metabolic, renal, hepatic, and storage diseases precipitate secondary hyper- or hypolipidemia. Hypothyroidism and diabetes mellitus are perhaps the most common disorders to cause secondary hyperlipidemia. Serum TC and LDL-C are increased in 30% of patients with hypothyroidism because of increased production and decreased removal of LDL.[103] Variable degrees of hypertriglyceridemia are seen in patients with Type I and Type II diabetes mellitus.[8, 104] The CARDIA Study found that higher concentrations of insulin are associated positively with unfavorable values of TC and LDL-C, TG, apo B, and blood pressure, and negatively with HDL-C, HDL$_2$-C, HDL$_3$-C, and apo AI.[105] Insulin treatment of non-insulin-dependent diabetics usually results in a significant change toward normalization of TG, HDL-C, and LDL-C concentrations.[106] Lp(a) appears to be increased in both Type I and Type II patients.[107] Evidence suggests that a direct correlation might exist between diabetic control and Lp(a) concentrations.[107, 108]

The induction of the lipoprotein lipase by insulin is thought to be responsible for the hyperlipidemic status in the diabetic population.[109] Patients with nephrotic syndrome or chronic renal failure who are undergoing hemodialysis have significantly higher serum TC and LDL-C, TG, apo B, and Lp(a), and lower concentrations of apo AI compared to controls.[110–112] Furthermore, increases in Lp(a) concentrations were documented in patients with pronounced proteinuria of various origins.[113] The exact nature of these abnormalities remains uncertain. However, it has been recently suggested that lipid alterations in patients with nephrotic syndrome are attributable to reversible increases in VLDL production.[114] Obstructive biliary tract disease causes the production of the abnormal lipoprotein "lipoprotein X." Since this cholesterol-rich particle is poorly removed from circulation, TC concentrations in these patients are markedly increased (over 1000 mg/dL [25.90 mmol/L]).[115]

Cancer, in general, tends to lower TC and HDL-C.[116] The most profound decrease is usually noted in patients with hematological malignancies.[116, 117] These changes may be the reflection of active cell proliferation. In addition, long-term survivors of cancer have persistently low HDL-C and apo AI, despite resolution of their underlying disease.[117, 118]

Acute myocardial infarction is associated with variable decreases in TC, LDL-C, apo AI, and apo B and an increase in Lp(a).[119–121] The extent of the decrease is usually dependent on the original lipid values. For example, little change would be seen in TC when the original concentration is below 200 mg/dL (5.17 mmol/L). Lipid concentrations remain stable within 24 h after the infarction and then decrease gradually to a lower plateau at which they remain for 6–8 weeks.[8] Changes in serum lipids similar to those encountered after a myocardial infarction were reported after a stroke.[122]

Blood specimens should be obtained within 24 h after a myocardial or stroke or 3 months following the infarct in order to reflect accurately the person's usual lipid values.

Infections and inflammations cause TG and Lp(a) to increase and TC and HDL-C to decrease, independently of the infectious agent, the cause of the illness, and the clinical condition of the patient.[123, 124] Various forms of dyslipoproteinemia are produced by numerous other disorders, such as acute intermittent porphyria, glycogen storage disease, Gaucher disease, Tay-Sachs disease, rheumatoid arthritis, anorexia nervosa, and systemic lupus erythematosus. The treatment of the primary disorder (except inherited disorders) will usually result in the normalization of the lipoprotein profile. Therefore, serum lipid assessment should only be conducted after a complete recovery from illness.

Drug-Induced Secondary Lipid Alterations

Medications that alter lipoprotein metabolism and serum concentrations include diuretics, some beta-blockers, sex steroids, glucocorticoids, and cyclosporine, among others. Thiazides and chlorothalidone, the most commonly used diuretics in the treatment of mild essential hypertension, cause increases in serum TC (12%), LDL-C (20%), TG (7%), and apo B (20%) concentrations, and decreases in HDL-C (16%) and apo AI (6%) concentrations compared to controls.[125] Other diuretics are also known to disrupt the lipoprotein profile.[126] In addition, propranolol, a non-cardioselective beta-blocker which is also used in the treatment of hypertension, significantly increases serum TG and decreases HDL-C (mainly the HDL_2-C fraction).[127] Up to 50% of children receiving asparaginase for the treatment of acute lymphoblastic leukemia exhibit gross increase in TG concentrations (over 5,000 mg/dL [5.65 mmol/L]).[117] These increases subside after the treatment is discontinued.

Various investigators have reported conflicting findings concerning the effect of oral contraceptives on the lipid and lipoprotein concentrations. This discrepancy can be largely attributed to the variations in the hormonal content of the medications used in these studies, mainly differences in the estrogen to progestin ratio.[128, 129] Oral contraceptives with a high progestin content cause an increase in serum TC and LDL-C and a decrease in HDL-C.[130] Opposite changes can be expected in women taking oral contraceptives with a high estrogen content and in post-menopausal women receiving an estrogen supplement.[131] Estrogen treatment, both in women and in men suffering from prostatic carcinoma, appears to decrease Lp(a) concentration by as much as 50%.[132]

Immunosuppressive agents are also reported to alter lipid metabolism. Prednisolone increases serum TC, LDL-C, HDL-C, VLDL-C, TG, apo AI, and apo B, possibly by increasing lipoprotein production.[133] Cyclosporine markedly increases TC, LDL-C, and apo B, and decreases Lp(a).[134-135] However, hypertriglyceridemia is the most profound lipid change after prednisolone and azathioprine therapy, and hypercholesterolemia is the more common finding after cyclosporine therapy in transplant patients.[136] In contrast, tacrolimus (previously known as FK 506) appears to decrease TC concentration.[137] The actual mechanisms for the distinct effect of the two immunosuppressive agents, tacrolimus and cyclosporine, on lipoprotein metabolism are currently unknown.

Because of the effect of various pharmacological agents on lipoprotein metabolism, medications should be suspended, if possible, for several days or weeks, depending on the drug and its effects, before lipid studies are conducted. Otherwise, any medication that is known to alter lipid values should be noted on the laboratory report.

Pregnancy

Physiologic and endocrine systems are greatly affected during pregnancy, altering the concentration of several biochemical parameters. Serum TC, LDL-C, TG, apo AI, apo AII, apo B, and Lp(a) increase significantly during pregnancy, mainly in the second and third trimesters.[8, 138-140] The concentrations of these analytes usually return to normal within 10 weeks postpartum, unless the woman is breast feeding.[141] The increased mobilization of lipids probably reflects the rise in maternal metabolic demand as a result of pregnancy. Therefore, the assessment of the lipoprotein profile during pregnancy does not reflect the usual pattern of the subject.

Lipid studies should be performed at least 3 months postpartum or 3 months following cessation of lactation.

VARIATION DUE TO SPECIMEN COLLECTION AND HANDLING

Fasting versus Non-fasting

The effect of food ingestion on lipid measurements has long been established. A controlled dietary study showed that ingestion of a typical fat-containing meal caused a significant increase in TG that persisted for at least 9 h.[15] VLDL-C also increases, while LDL-C falls significantly; both changes persist for at least 9 h. The increased VLDL-C and decreased LDL-C are greater for calculated values than those obtained by ultracentrifugation. The changes, however, are significant regardless of the methodology used. For calculated LDL-C, the differences seen are the result of not only falsely increased VLDL-C, but also of changes in lipoprotein composition. Post-prandially, precipitation methods appear to cause a slight but significant decrease in HDL-C, while ultracentrifugation methods appear to cause a slight increase in HDL-C; the cause of this discrepancy is not yet known. With more prolonged fasting, profound changes occur in lipid concentrations. TC and TG increase an average of 25% after one week of fasting, falling to baseline after three weeks. Refeeding causes a 13% fall in TC but an 86% increase in TG.[142]

The second report of the NCEP Adult Treatment Panel recommends that initial screening for lipid disorders should include both TC and HDL-C. These measurements may be performed using non-fasting samples.[9] As a result, it is important for the laboratory to verify that the method used for HDL-C is not affected in the non-fasting state. TC, Lp(a), apo AI, and apo AII are unchanged after food ingestion.[15, 143] Some investigators have reported an increase in apo B after meals,[25] while others report no change; the latter finding is consistent with constancy of the sum of VLDL-C and LDL-C in the post-prandial state.[15, 143] Therefore, except for measurements of TC, Lp(a), apo AI, and apo AII, lipid measurements should be carried out only after a fast of at least 12 h.

Anticoagulants and Preservatives

The type of specimen collected is an important consideration in interpreting lipid values. Most laboratories use serum or EDTA plasma. At 4° C, TC and TG concentrations are stable for at least 4 days in either serum or plasma.[8] EDTA has a theoretical advantage in that metal-ion induced oxidation and enzymatic cleavage of lipoproteins is retarded, but this does not appear to be an issue in the routine laboratory. Current NCEP cutpoints are based on serum sample values. Because of its osmotic effect, EDTA causes a method-dependent artifactual fall in most lipid and lipoprotein concentrations, but a paradoxical rise in HDL-C.[144] In the past, most reports stated that this causes a reduction of 3% in TC;[8] however, a recent study reports that the average difference between plasma and serum using tubes with disodium EDTA is now 4.7%, because the EDTA concentration has been made 50% higher in blood collection tubes.[145] Since EDTA concentration is dependent on volume of blood added, the actual decrease in TC in underfilled tubes may be as much as 10%.[146] It would be prudent to insist on fully filled evacuated tubes to minimize the effect of differing anticoagulant concentration.

Use of other anticoagulants such as oxalate and citrate is associated with even greater osmotic fluid shifts.[8] Fluoride causes fluid shift and has an inhibitory effect on some enzymatic measurements of TC.[146] These anticoagulants are not recommended for use in lipid measurements. Heparin does not produce fluid shifts and appears to be an acceptable alternative for TC measurement;[147] however, heparin activates lipo-protein lipase both *in vitro* and *in vivo*.[148] TG concentration falls gradually in specimens containing heparin, including "serum" specimens from patients who are receiving ther-apeutic doses of heparin.[149] Most serum separator tubes do not appear to affect the results of lipid measurements.[146]

Capillary versus Venous Blood

The source of specimen appears to have some effect on TC concentration, which may be important in remote-site screening programs. Several studies have reported that TC is higher in capillary blood plasma than in venous serum, the average bias being approximately 3%.[150] Since heparin was utilized, this effect is not due to shifts in fluid from the anticoagulant. Other studies have reported no difference[151] or lower[152] concentrations of TC in capillary blood. It is unclear whether these conflicting results are due to variations in the site of collection, the puncture technique, the post-prandial state, or other variables. Further research is necessary to clarify this issue, since different measurement techniques may be a source of inaccurate classification of patients' risk factors.[153] Use of a standardized protocol for collecting capillary samples can produce results that agree closely with venous plasma.[154]

Hemoconcentration

Hemoconcentration from posture or other causes increases the relative concentration of proteins and protein-bound substances, which would produce a predictable change in all lipid and apolipoprotein measurements. A patient who stands for 5 min will experience an apparent increase in lipid concentration of 9%, and a further increase to 16% after 15 min.[155] This can be minimized by having a patient remain seated for at least 15 min before venipuncture.[8, 155, 156]

Use of a tourniquet can also cause significant hemoconcentration. After 1 min there is no significant change in TC or protein concentration; however, after 2 min the apparent TC concentration increases up to 5%, and after 5 min apparent increases of 10–15% can occur.[8] If a tourniquet remains for 15 min during phlebotomy, lipid measurements increase by 20–40%.[157]

Posture changes have also become associated with changes in plasma, nor-adrenaline concentrations, and apparent sympathetic activity, which may also indirectly alter lipid concentration.[158]

Specimen Storage

Specimens for most lipid testing are stable at 0–4° C for up to 4 days, with HDL-C and LDL-C being less stable. Serum specimens show some spontaneous hydrolysis of phospholipids and TG which is inhibited in EDTA plasma.[8] For longer storage of lipids, specimen stability is better at –70° C than at –20° C, since serum does not fully freeze until about –40° C. Apo B can decrease slightly when frozen,[159] but other lipid components appear stable when frozen for up to 6 months.[146] Distribution of lipids among lipoproteins changes during storage at 4° C or –20° C; ultracentrifugation should be performed as soon as possible after collection.[160] Alterations in apo B and apo(a) measurements after storage are method-dependent; if specimens are to be stored for long periods, the laboratory must verify that its method is not affected by specimen storage. Repeated freezing and thawing should be avoided, as it can affect results of lipid measurements after as few as two cycles.[161] This is a particular concern for specimens stored at –20° C, as most frost-free freezers regularly increase temperatures to melt accumulated frost, which may result in specimen thawing; specimens for lipid testing should not be stored in frost-free freezers.

RECOMMENDATIONS FOR MINIMIZING PREANALYTICAL VARIATION

Highlights from the NCEP Laboratory Standardization Panel recommendations for minimizing the effect of preanalytical factors on lipid and lipoprotein testing are presented in Figure 4-2.[162] No specific recommendations were made by the Panel concerning apolipoprotein testing. However, steps similar to those described should be taken to help minimize preanalytical sources of variation in apolipoprotein measurements.

CONCLUSION

Results of lipid measurements are affected by many biological, behavioral, and clinical factors, and by variability in sample collection and handling. Failure to control for these variables can lead to misclassification of patient risk. Therefore, standardization of preanalytical sources of variation to the fullest extent possible will improve the accuracy and utility of lipid testing in assessing the risk of CHD.　　❖

REFERENCES

1. Pagani F, Panteghini M. Significance of various parameters derived from biological variability for lipid and lipoprotein analyses. Clin Biochem 1993;26:415–20.
2. Harris EK. Statistical aspects of reference values in clinical pathology. Prog Clin Pathol 1981;8:45–66.
3. Ford RP. Essential data derived from biological variation for establishment and use of lipid analysis. Ann Clin Biochem 1989;26:281–5.
4. Mogadam M, Ahmed SW, Mensch AH, Godwin ID. Within-person fluctuations of serum cholesterol and lipoproteins. Arch Intern Med 1990;150:1645–8.
5. Kafonek SD, Derby CA, Bachorik PS. Biological variability of lipoproteins and apolipoproteins in patients referred to a lipid clinic. Clin Chem 1992;38:864–872.

Figure 4–2 ✧ Recommendations for Minimizing Preanalytical Variation

1. A subject's lipid and lipoprotein profile should only be measured when the individual is in a steady metabolic state.

2. Subjects should maintain their usual diet and weight for at least 2 weeks prior to the determination of their lipids or lipoproteins.

3. Multiple measurements should be performed within 2 months, at least 1 week apart, before making a medical decision about further action.

4. Subjects should not perform vigorous physical activity during the 24 h prior to testing.

5. Fasting or non-fasting specimens can be used for TC testing. However, a 12 h fasting specimen is required for TG and recommended for lipoproteins.

6. The subject should be seated for at least 5 min before specimen collection.

7. The tourniquet should not be kept on more than 1 min during venipuncture.

8. TC, TG, and HDL-C concentrations can be determined in either serum or plasma. When EDTA is used as the anticoagulant, plasma should be immediately cooled to 2–4° C to prevent changes in composition, and values should be multiplied by 1.03.

9. For TC testing, serum can be transported either at 4° C or frozen. Storage of specimens at –20° C is adequate for TC measurement. However, specimens must be stored frozen at –70° C or lower for TG and lipoprotein/apolipoprotein testing.

10. All blood specimens should be considered potentially infectious and handled accordingly.

6. Smith SJ, Cooper GR, Myers GL, Sampson EJ. Biological variability in concentrations of serum lipids: sources of variation among results from published studies and composite predicted values. Clin Chem 1993;39:1012-22.

7. Cooper GR, Smith SJ, Myers GL, Sampson EJ, Magid E. Estimating and minimizing effects of biologic sources of variation by relative range when measuring the mean of serum lipids and lipoproteins. Clin Chem 1994;40:227-32.

8. Cooper GR, Myers GL, Smith SJ, Sampson EJ. Standardization of lipid, lipoprotein, and apolipoprotein measurements. Clin Chem 1988;34:B95-B105.

9. Summary of the second report of the National Cholesterol Education Program (NCEP) Expert Panel on Detection, Evaluation and Treatment of High Blood Cholesterol in Adults (Adult Treatment Panel II). JAMA 1993;269:3015-23.

10. Bookstein L, Gidding SS, Donovan M, Smith FA. Day-to-day variability of serum cholesterol, triglyceride, and high density lipoprotein cholesterol levels: impact on the assessment of risk according to the National Cholesterol Education Program guidelines. Arch Intern Med 1990;150:1653-7.

11. Warnick GR, Albers JJ. Physiological and analytical variation in cholesterol and triglyceride. Lipids 1976;11:203-8.

12. Marcovina SM, Gaur VP, Albers JJ. Biological variability of cholesterol, triglyceride, low- and high-density lipoprotein cholesterol, lipoprotein(a), and apolipoproteins A-I and B. Clin Chem 1994;40:574-8.

13. Kreger BE, Odell PM, D'Agostino RB, Wilson PF. Long-term intraindividual cholesterol variability: natural course and adverse impact on morbidity and mortality—the Framingham Study. Am Heart J 1994;127:1607-14.

14. Choudhury N, Wall PM, Truswell AS. Effect of time between measurements on within-subject variability for total cholesterol and high-density lipoprotein cholesterol in women. Clin Chem 1994;40:710-5.

15. Cohn JS, McNamara JR, Schaefer EJ. Lipoprotein cholesterol concentrations in the plasma of human subjects as measured in the fed and fasted states. Clin Chem 1988;34:2456-9.

16. Gordon DJ, Trost DC, Hyde J, et al. Seasonal cholesterol cycles: the Lipid Research Clinics Coronary Primary Prevention Trial placebo group. Circulation 1987;76:1224-31.

17. Kim HJ, Kalkhoff RK. Changes in lipoprotein composition during the menstrual cycle. Metabolism 1979;28:663-8.

18. Lussier-Cacan S, Xhignesse M, Desmarais JL, et al. Cyclic fluctuations in human serum lipid and apolipoprotein levels during the normal menstrual cycle: comparison with changes occurring during oral contraceptive therapy. Metabolism 1991;40:849-54.

19. Tangney C, Brownie C, Wu SM. Impact of menstrual periodicity on serum lipid levels and estimates of dietary intakes. J Am Coll Nutr 1991;10:107-13.

20. Terstrat J, Hessel LW, Seepers J, Van Gent CM. The influence of meal frequency on diurnal lipid, glucose and cortisol levels in normal subjects. Eur J Clin Invest 1978;8:61-6.

21. Schectman G, Patsches M, Sasse EA. Variability in cholesterol measurements: comparison of calculated and direct LDL cholesterol determinations. Clin Chem 1996;42:732-7.

22. Kafonek SD, Donovan L, Lovejoy KL, Bachorik PS. Biological variation of lipids and lipoproteins in fingerstick blood. Clin Chem 1996;42:2002-7.

23. Fraser CG. Biological variation in clinical chemistry. An update: collected data, 1988-1991. Arch Path Lab Med 1992;116:916-23.

24. Haarbo J, Christiansen C. Treatment-induced cyclic variations in serum lipids, lipoproteins, and apolipoproteins after 2 years of combined hormone replacement therapy: exaggerated cyclic variations in smokers. Obstet Gynecol 1992;80:639-44.

25. Matuchansky C, Fabre J, Guillard O, Morechar-Beauchant M, Reinberg A. Effects of cyclic (nocturnal) total parenteral nutrition and continuous enteral nutrition on circadian rhythms of blood lipids, lipoproteins and apolipoproteins in humans. Am J Clin Nutr 1985;41:727-34.

26. Panteghini M, Pagani F. Pre-analytical, analytical and biological sources of variation of lipoprotein(a). Eur J Clin Chem Clin Biochem 1993;31:23-8.

27. Chandler WL, Loo SC. Lipoprotein (a) does not show circadian variations. Thromb Haemost 1990;63:151.

28. Tonolo G, Ciccarese M, Brizzi P, Milia S, Dessole S, Puddu L, Secchi G, Maioli M. Cyclical variation of plasma lipids, apolipoproteins, and lipoprotein(a) during menstrual cycle of normal women. Am J Physiol 1995;269:E1101-5.

29. Strobl W, Widhalm K. The natural history of serum lipids and apolipoproteins during childhood. In: Widhalm K, Naito HK (eds). Detection and treatment of lipid and lipoprotein disorders of childhood. New York: Alan R. Liss, 1985:101-21.

30. Rifai N, Heiss G, Doetsch K. Lipoprotein(a) at birth, in blacks and whites. Atherosclerosis 1992;92:123-9.

31. Van Biervliet JP, Labeur C, Michiels G, Usher DC, Rosseneu M. Lipoprotein(a) profiles and evolution in newborns. Atherosclerosis 1991;86:173-81.

32. Siest, G, Henny J, Schiele F, Young DB (eds.). Interpretation of clinical laboratory tests. Foster City, CA: Biomedical Publications, 1985.

33. Berenson GS, Srinivasan SR, Cresanta JL, Foster TA, Webber LS. Dynamic changes of serum lipoproteins in children during adolescence and sexual maturation. Am J Epidemiol 1981;113:157-70.

34. Twisk JW, Kemper HC, Mellenbergh GJ. Longitudinal development of lipoprotein levels in males and females aged 12-28 years: the Amsterdam Growth and Health Study. Int J Epidemiol 1995;24:69-77.

35. Steinmetz J, Choukaife A, Visvikis S, Henny J, Siest G. Biological factors affecting concentration of serum LpAI lipoprotein particles in serum, and determination of reference ranges. Clin Chem 1990;36:677-80.

36. Jenner JL, Ordovas JM, Lamon-Fava S, et al. Effects of age, sex, and menopausal status on plasma lipoprotein(a) levels: the Framingham Offspring Study. Circulation 1993;87:1135-41.

37. Srinivasan SR, Freedman DS, Webber LS, Berenson GS. Black-white differences in cholesterol levels of serum high-density lipoprotein subclasses among children: the Bogalusa Heart Study. Circulation 1987;76:272-9.

38. Srinivasan SR, Dahlen GH, Jarpa RA, Webber LS, Berenson GS. Racial (black-white) differences in serum lipoprotein(a) distribution and its relation to parental myocardial infarction in children: the Bogalusa Heart Study. Circulation 1991;84:160-7.

39. Tyroler HA, Heiss G, Schonfeld G, et al. Apolipoprotein A-I, A-II, and C-II in black and white residents of Evans county. Circulation 1980;62:249-54.

40. Webber LS, Harsha DW, Phillips GT, Srinivasan SR, Simpson JW, Berenson GS. Cardiovascular risk factors in Hispanic, white, and black children: the Brooks County and Bogalusa Heart studies. Am J Epidemiol 1991;133:704-14.

41. Fulton-Kehoe DL, Eckel RH, Shetterly SM, Hamman RF. Determinants of total high density lipoprotein cholesterol and high density lipoprotein subfraction levels among Hispanic and non-Hispanic white persons with normal glucose tolerance: the San Luis Valley Diabetes Study. J Clin Epidemiol 1992;45:1191-200.

42. Haffner SM, Gruber KK, Morales PA, et al. Lipoprotein(a) concentrations in Mexican Americans and non-Hispanic whites: the San Antonio Heart Study. Am J Epidemiol 1992;136:1060-8.

43. Cobbaert C, Kesteloot H. Serum lipoprotein(a) levels in racially different populations. Am J Epidemiol 1992;136:441-9.

44. Marcovina SM, Albers JJ, Jacobs DR Jr, et al. Lipoprotein(a) concentrations and apolipoprotein(a) phenotypes in Caucasians and African Americans: the CARDIA study. Arterioscler Thromb 1993;13:1037-45.

45. Lipid Research Clinics Population Studies Data Book. Volume 1. The Prevalence Study. Aggregate distributions of lipids, lipoproteins and selected variables in 11 North American Populations. (NIH publication No. 80-1527). Bethesda, MD: Public Health Service, National Institutes of Health, July 1980.

46. Johnson CL, Rifkind BM, Sempos CT, et al. Declining serum total cholesterol levels among U.S. adults. JAMA 1993;269:3002-8.

47. National Center for Health Statistics, National Heart, Lung, and Blood Institute Collaborative Lipid Group. Trends in serum cholesterol levels among US adults aged 20 to 74 years: data from the National Health and Nutrition Examination Surveys, 1960 to 1980. JAMA 1987;257:937-42.

47. Fukami K, Koike K, Hirota K, Yoshikawa H, Miyake A. Perimenopausal changes in serum lipids and lipoproteins: a 7-year longitudinal study. Maturitas 1995;22:193-7.

49. Cowan LD, Wilcosky T, Criqui MH, et al. Demographic behavioral, biochemical, and dietary correlates of plasma triglyceride. Arteriosclerosis 1985;5:466-80.

50. Slunga L, Asplund K, Johnson O, Dahlen GH. Lipoprotein (a) in a randomly selected 25-64 year old population: the Northern Sweden Monica Study. J Clin Epidemiol 1993;46:617-24.

50. Kim CJ, Ryu WS, Kwak JW, Park CT, Ryoo UH: Changes in Lp(a) lipoprotein and lipid levels after cessation of female sex hormone production and estrogen replacement therapy. Arch Intern Med 1996;156:500-4.

52. Kloer HU. Diet and coronary heart disease. Postgrad Med J 1989;65:S13-21.

53. Grundy SM, Denke MA. Dietary influences on serum lipids and lipoproteins. J Lipid Res 1990;31:1149-72.

54. Watts GF, Jackson P, Burke V, Lewis B. Dietary fatty acids and progression of coronary artery disease in men. Am J Clin Nutr 1996;64:202-9.

55. Harris WS, Connor WE, Illingworth DR, Rothrock DW, Foster DM. Effects of fish oil on VLDL triglyceride kinetics in humans. J Lipid Res 1990;31:1549-58.

56. Blankenhorn DH, Johnson RL, Mack WJ, El Zein HA, Vaillas LI. The influence of diet on the appearance of new lesions in human coronary arteries. JAMA 1990;263:1646-52.

57. Ripsin CM, Keenan JM, Jacobs DR, et al. Oat products and lipid lowering: a meta-analysis. JAMA 1992;267:3317-25.

58. Kris-Atherton DM, Krommel D, Russell ME, et al. The effects of diet on plasma lipids, lipoproteins and coronary heart disease. J Am Diet Assoc 1988;88:1373-400.

59. Cooper GR, Myers GL, Smith SJ, Sehlant RC. Dietary oat fiber sources and blood lipids. JAMA 1992;268:986.

60. Ornish D, Brown SE, Scherwitz LW, et al. Can lifestyle changes reverse coronary heart disease? Lancet 1990;336:129-33.

61. Sacks FM, Ornish D, Rosner B, et al. Plasma lipoprotein levels in vegetarians. JAMA 1985;524:1337-41.

62. McMurray MP, Cerqueira MT, Connor SL, Connor WE. Changes in lipid and lipoprotein levels and body weight in Tarahumara Indians after consumption of an affluent diet. N Engl J Med 1991;325:1704-8.

63. Wolf RN, Grundy SM. Influence of weight reduction on plasma lipoproteins in obese patients. Arteriosclerosis 1983;3:160-9.

64. Newman B, Selby JV, Quesenberry Jr., et al. Nongenetic influences of obesity on other cardiovascular disease risk factors: an analysis of identical twins. Am J Public Health 1990;80:675-8.

65. Kaplan NM. Obesity: location matters. Heart Dis Stroke 1992;1:148-50.

66. Despres JP, Moorjani S, Lupien PJ, et al. Regional distribution of body fat, plasma lipoproteins, and cardiovascular disease. Arteriosclerosis 1990:10:497-511.

67. Zamboni M, Armellini F, Cominacini L, et al. Obesity and regional body-fat distribution in men: separate and joint relationships to glucose tolerance and plasma lipoprotein. Am J Clin Nutr 1994;60:682-7.

68. McGill HC Jr. Potential mechanisms for the augmentation of atherosclerosis and atherosclerotic disease by cigarette smoking. Prev Med 1979;8:390-403.

69. Knoke JD, Hunninghake DB, Heiss G. Physiological markers of smoking and their relation to coronary heart disease. Arteriosclerosis 1987;7:477-82.

70. Yokode M, Kita T, Arai M, et al. Cholesteryl ester accumulation in macrophages incubated with low-density lipoprotein pretreated with cigarette smoke extract. Proc Natl Acad Sci USA 1988;85:2344-8.

71. Craig WY, Palomaki GE, Haddow JE. Cigarette smoking and serum lipid and lipoprotein levels: an analysis of published data. Br Med J 1989;298:784-8.

72. Craig WY, Palomaki GE, Johnson M, Haddow JE. Cigarette smoking-associated changes in blood lipid and lipoprotein levels in the 8- to 19-year-old age group: a meta-analysis. Pediatrics 1990;85:155-8.

73. Willet W, Hennekens CH, Castelli W, et al. Effects of cigarette smoking on fasting: triglyceride, total cholesterol, and HDL cholesterol in women. Am Heart J 1983;105:417-21.

74. Glantz SA, Parmley WW. Passive smoking and heart disease. Mechanisms and risk. JAMA 1995;273:1047-53.

75. Neufeld EJ, Meietus-Snyder M, Bieser A, Baker A, Newberger JW. Passive smoking is associated with reduced HDL-cholesterol levels in children with high-risk lipid profiles. [Abstract]. Circulation 1994;90:I-102.

76. Steinberg D, Pearson TA, Kuller LH. Alcohol and atherosclerosis. Ann Intern Med 1991; 114:967-76.

77. Haskell WL, Camargo C, Williams PT, et al. The effect of cessation and resumption of moderate alcohol intake on serum high density lipoprotein subfractions: a controlled study. N Engl J Med 1984;310:805-10.

78. Taskinen MR, Nikkila EA, Valimaki M, et al. Alcohol-induced changes in serum lipoproteins and in their metabolism. Am Heart J 1987;113:458-64.

79. Gaziano JM, Buring JE, Breslow JL, et al. Moderate alcohol intake, increased levels of high density lipoprotein and its subfractions, and decreased risk of myocardial infarction. N Engl J Med 1993;329:1829-34.

80. Clevidence BA, Reichman ME, Judd JT, et al. Effects of alcohol consumption on lipoproteins of premenopausal women. A controlled diet study. Arterioscler Throm Vasc Biol 1995;15:179-84.

81. Wilson DE, Schneibman PH, Brewster AC, Arky RA. The enhancement of alimentary lipemia by ethanol in man. J Lab Clin Med 1970;75:264-74.

82. Valimaki M, Laitinen K, Ylikahrit R, et al. The effect of moderate alcohol intake on serum apolipoprotein Al-containing lipoproteins and lipoprotein(a). Metabolism 1991; 40:1168-72.

83. Solvoll K, Selmer R, Loken EB, Foss OP, Trygg K. Coffee, dietary habits, and serum cholesterol among men and women 35-49 years of age. Am J Epidemiol 1989; 129:1277-88.

84. Thelle DS, Arnesen E, Forde OH. The Tromso Heart Study: Does coffee raise serum cholesterol? N Engl J Med 1983;308:1454-7.

85. Bak AAA, Grobbee DE. The effect on serum cholesterol levels of coffee brewed by filtering or boiling. N Engl J Med 1989;321:1423-7.

86. Zock PL, Katan MB, Merkus MP, Van Dusseldorp M, Harryvan JL. Effect of a lipid-rich fraction from boiled coffee on serum cholesterol. Lancet 1990;335:1235-37.

87. Urgert R, Schulz GM, Katan MB. Effects of cafestol and kahweol from coffee grounds on serum lipids and serum liver enzymes in humans. Am J Clin Nutr 1995;61:149-54.

88. Van Dusseldorp M, Katan MB, Demacker PNM. Effect of decaffeinated versus regular coffee on serum lipoproteins: a 12- week double-blind trial. Am J Epidemiol 1990; 132:33-40.

89. Willett WC, Stampfer MJ, Manson JE, et al. Coffee consumption and coronary heart disease in women. JAMA 1996;275:458-62.

90. Fried RE, Levine DM, Kwiterovich PO, et al. The effect of filtered-coffee consumption on plasma lipid levels: results of a randomized clinical trial. JAMA 1992;267:811-5.

91. Berlin JA, Colitz GA. A meta-analysis of physical activity in the prevention of coronary heart disease. Am J Epidemiol 1990;132:612-28.

92. Ekelund LG, Haskell WL, Johnson JL, et al. Physical fitness as a prediction of cardiovascular mortality in asymptomatic North American men. N Engl J Med 1988;319: 1379-84.

93. Wood PD, Stefanick ML, Williams PT, Haskell WL. The effects of plasma lipoproteins on a prudent weight reducing diet, with or without exercise, in overweight men and women. N Engl J Med 1991;325:461-6.

94. Lampman RM, Santinga JT, Hodge MF, Block WD, Flora JD, Bassett DR. Comparative effects of physical training and diet in normalizing serum lipids in men with type IV hyperlipoproteinemia. Circulation 1977;55:652-9.

95. Dufaux B, Assmann G, Hollmann W. Plasma lipoproteins and physical activity: a review. Int J Sports Med 1982;3:123-36.

96. Swank AM, Robertson RJ, Deitrich RW, Bates M. The effect of acute exercise on high density lipoprotein cholesterol and the subfractions in females. Atherosclerosis 1987; 63:187-92.

97. Tucker LA, Friedman GM. Walking and serum cholesterol in adults. Am J Public Health 1990;80:1111-3.

98. Hardman AE, Hudson A, Jones PRM, Norgan NG. Brisk walking and plasma high-density lipoprotein cholesterol concentration in previously sedentary women. Br Med J 1989; 299:1204-5.

99. McCann BS, Warnick GR, Knopp RH. Changes in plasma lipids and dietary intake accompanying shifts in perceived workload and stress. Psychosomatic Med 1990; 52:97-108.

100. Dimsdale JE, Herd JA. Variability of plasma lipids in response to emotional arousal. Psychosom Med 1982;44:413-30.

101. Stoney CM, Matthews KA, McDonald RH, Johnson CA. Sex differences in lipid, lipoprotein, cardiovascular and neuroendocrine responses to acute stress. Psychophysiology 1988;25:645-56.

102. Genest JJ, McNamara JR, Ordovas JM, et al. Effect of elective hospitalization on plasma lipoprotein cholesterol and apolipoproteins AI, B and Lp(a). Am J Cardiol 1990;65: 677-9.

103. Walton KW, Scott PJ, Dykes PW, Dawids JWL. The significance of alteration in serum lipids in thyroid dysfunction. II. Alteration of the metabolism and turnover of ^{131}I-low density lipoprotein in hypothyroidism and thyrotoxicosis. Clin Sci 1965;29:217-38.

104. Betteridge DJ. Lipids, diabetes and vascular disease: the time to act. Diabetic Med 1989;6:195-218.

105. Manolio TA, Savage PJ, Burke GL, et al. Association of fasting insulin with blood pressure and lipids in young adults. Arteriosclerosis 1990;10:430-6.

106. Hughes TA, Clements RS, Fairlough PK, Bell DSH, Segrest JP. Effects of insulin therapy on lipoproteins in non-insulin-dependent diabetes mellitus. Atherosclerosis 1987;67: 105-14.

107. Ruotolo G, Zoppo A, Parlavecchia M, Giberti B, Micossi P. Apolipoprotein(a) levels in Type I and Type 2 diabetes mellitus. Acta Diabetol 1991;28:158-61.

108. Haffner SM, Tuttle KR, Rainwater DL. Decrease of Lp(a) with improved metabolic control in subjects with insulin-dependent diabetes mellitus. Diabetes Care 1991;14: 302-7.

109. Pollare T, Vessby B, Lithell H. Lipoprotein lipase activity in skeletal muscle is related to insulin sensitivity. Arterioscler Thromb 1991;11:1192-203.

110. Wheeler DC, Varghese Z, Moorhead JF. Hyperlipidemia in nephrotic syndrome. Am J Nephrol 1989;9(Suppl 1):78-84.

111. Rifai N, King ME, Sica D. Effects of long-term hemodialysis on lipid, lipoprotein and apolipoprotein levels of black patients with chronic renal failure. Ann Clin Biochem 1988;25:242-5.

112. Murphy BG, McNamee, Duly E, et al. Increased serum apolipoprotein(a) in patients with chronic renal failure treated with continuous ambulatory peritoneal dialysis. Atherosclerosis 1992;93:53-5.

113. Karadi I. Romics L, Palos G, et al. Lp(a) lipoprotein concentration in serum of patients with heavy proteinuria of different origin. Clin Chem 1989;35:2121-3.

114. Joven J, Villabona C, Vilella E, et al. Abnormalities of lipoprotein metabolism in patients with the nephrotic syndrome. N Engl J Med 1990;323:579-84.

115. Levy RI. Cholesterol, lipoproteins, apolipoproteins and heart disease: present status and future prospects. Clin Chem 1981;27:653-62.

116. Dessi A, Batetta B, Spano O, et al. Clinical remission is associated with restoration of normal high-density lipoprotein cholesterol levels in children with malignancies. Clin Science 1995;89:505-10.

117. Parsons SK, Skapek SX, Neufeld EJ, et al. Asparaginase-associated lipid abnormalities in children with acute lymphoblastic leukemia. Blood 1997;89:1886-95.

118. Talvensaari KK, Laning M, Tapanainen P, et al. Long-term survivors of childhood cancer have an increased risk of manifesting the metabolic syndrome. J Clin Endo Met 1996; 81:505-10.

119. Gore JM, Goldberg RJ, Matsumoto AS, et al. Validity of serum total cholesterol level obtained within 24 hours of acute myocardial infarction. Am J Cardiol 1984;54:722-5.

120. Shephard MDS, Hester J, Walmsley RN, White GH. Variation in plasma apolipoprotein AI and B concentrations following myocardial infarction. Ann Clin Biochem 1990;27:9-14.

121. Rantapaa-Dahlqvist S, Wallberg-Jonsson S, Dahlen G. Lipoprotein(a), lipids and lipoproteins in patients with rheumatoid arthritis. Ann Rheum Dis 1991;50:366-8.

122. Mendez I, Hachinski V, Wolfe B. Serum lipids after stroke. Neurology 1987;37:507-11.

123. Alvarez C, Ramos A. Lipids, lipoprotein and apolipoproteins in serum during infection. Clin Chem 1986;32:142-5.

124. Maeda S, Abe A, Makino K, Noma A, Kawade M. Transient changes of serum lipoprotein(a) as an acute phase reactant. Clin Chem 1989;89:145-50.

125. McKenney JM, Wright JT, Goodman RP, et al. The effect of low dose of hydrochlorothiazide on blood pressure, serum potassium and lipoproteins. Pharmaco-therapy 1986;6:179-84.

126. Krone W, Nagele H. Effects of antihypertensives on plasma lipids and lipoprotein metabolism. Am Heart J 1988;116:1729-34.

127. Woodcock BG, Rietbrock N. Beta-blocker induced changes in the cholesterol: high density lipoprotein cholesterol ratio and risk of coronary heart disease. Klin Wochenschr 1984;62:843-9.

128. Goldsland IF, Crook D, Simpson R, Proudler T, Felton C. The effects of different formulations of oral contraceptive agents on lipid and carbohydrate metabolism. N Engl J Med 1990;323:1375-81.

129. Wahl P, Walder C, Knopp R, et al. Effects of estrogen/progestin potency on lipid/lipoprotein cholesterol. N Engl J Med 1983;308:862-7.

130. Bush TL, Fried LP, Barrett-Conner E. Cholesterol, lipoproteins and coronary heart disease in women. Clin Chem 1988;34:B60-B70.

131. Miller VT, Muesing RA, LaRosa JC, et al. Effects of conjugated estrogen with and without three different progestogens on lipoproteins, high density lipoprotein subfractions and apolipoprotein AI. Obstet Gynecol 1991;77:235-40.

132. Henriksson P, Angelin B, Berglund L. Hormonal regulation of serum Lp(a) levels. Opposite effects after estrogen treatment and orchidectomy in males with prostatic carcinoma. J Clin Invest 1992;89:1166-71.

133. Ilowite NT, Samuel P, Ginzler E, Jacobson MS. Dyslipoproteinemia in pediatric systemic lupus erythematosus. Arthritis and Rheumatism 1988;31:859-63.

134. Ballantyne CM, Podet EJ, Patsch WP, et al. Effects of cyclosporine therapy on plasma lipoprotein levels. JAMA 1989;262:53-6.

135. Farmer JA, Ballantyne CM, Franzier OH, et al. Lipoprotein(a) and apolipoprotein changes after cardiac transplantation. J AM Coll Cardiol 1991;18:926-30.

136. Markell MS, Friedman EA. Hyperlipidemia after organ transplantation. Am J Med 1989;87(suppl 5N):61-67.

137. Van Thiel DH, Iqbal M, Jaln I, Todo S, Starzl TE. Gastrointestinal and metabolic problems associated with immunosuppression with either CsA or FK 506 in liver transplantation. Transplant Proc 1990;22(Suppl 1):37-40.

138. Reichel R, Widhalm K. Lipids and lipoproteins during pregnancy. In: Widhalm K, Naito HK, eds. Recent aspects of diagnosis and treatment of lipoprotein disorders. New York: Alan R. Liss, 1988:125-133.

139. Rifai N, Pham Q, McMurray RG. Serum lipid and apolipoprotein changes in normal pregnancy. Clin Chem 1989;35:1066.

140. Panteghini M, Pagani F. Serum concentrations of lipoprotein(a) during normal pregnancy and postpartum. Clin Chem 1991;37:2009-10.

141. Knopp RH, Walden CE, Wahl PW, et al. Effect of postpartum lactation on lipoprotein lipids and apoproteins. J Clin Endocrinol Metab 1985;60:542-7.

142. Thampy KG. Hypercholesterolaemia of prolonged fasting and cholesterol lowering of refeeding in lean human subjects. Scand J Clin Lab Invest 1995;55:351-7.

143. Rifai N, Merrill JR, Holly RG. Postprandial effect of a high fat meal on plasma lipid, lipoprotein cholesterol and apolipoprotein measurements. Ann Clin Biochem 1990; 27:489-93.

144. Beheshti I, Wessels LM, Eckfeldt JH. EDTA-plasma vs. serum differences in cholesterol, high-density-lipoprotein cholesterol, and triglyceride as measured by several methods. Clin Chem 1994;40:2088-92.

145. Cloey T, Bachorik PS, Becker D, et al. Reevaluation of serum-plasma differences in total cholesterol concentration. JAMA 1990;263:2788-9.

146. Naito HK. Problems associated with lipid and lipoprotein analyses. In: Widhalm K, Naito HK, eds. Detection and treatment of lipid and lipoprotein disorders of childhood. New York: Alan R. Liss, 1985:19-60.

147. Lum G, Gambino R. A comparison of serum versus heparinized plasma for routine chemistry tests. Am J Clin Pathol 1974;61:108-13.

148. Ferlito S, Ricceri M, Ossino AM. Acute lipidemic effect of calcium heparin in normolipemic and hyperlipemic subjects. Int Angiol 1989;8:140-4.

149. Horton G, Cole TG, Gibson DW, Kessler G. Decreased stability of triglycerides and increased free glycerol in serum from heparin-treated patients. Clin Chem 1988;34: 1847-9.

150. Greenland P, Bowley NL, Meiklejohn B, Doane KL, Sparks CE. Blood cholesterol concentration: fingerstick plasma vs. venous serum sampling. Clin Chem 1990;36:628-30.

151. Ishikawa TT, Morrison J, Fallat R, Parsons D, Glueck CJ. Comparison of capillary and venous blood sampling for quantitation of plasma cholesterol. J Lab Clin Med 1974;84: 281-6.

152. Kupke IR, Zeugner S, Gottschalk A, Kather B. Differences in lipid and lipoprotein concentrations of capillary and venous blood samples. Clin Chim Acta 1979;97:279-83.

153. Naughton MJ, Luepker RU, Strickland D. The accuracy of portable cholesterol analyzers in public screening programs. JAMA 1990;283:1213-7.

154. Warnick GR, Leary ET, Ammirati EB, Allen MP. Cholesterol in fingerstick capillary specimens can be equivalent to conventional venous measurement. Arch Pathol Lab Med 1994;118:1110-14.

155. Tan MH, Wilmshurst EG, Gleason RE, Soldner JS. Effect of posture on serum lipids. N Engl J Med 1973;289:416-19.

156. Miller M, Bachorik PS, Cloey TA. Normal variation of plasma lipoproteins: postural effects on plasma concentrations of lipids, lipoproteins, and apolipoproteins. Clin Chem 1992;38:569-74.

157. Page IH, Moinuddin M. The effect of venous occlusion on serum cholesterol and total protein concentration: a warning. Circulation 1962;25:651-2.

158. Howes LC, Krum H, Louis WJ. Plasma cholesterol levels are dependent on sympathetic activity. J Hypertension 1987;5(Supp):S361-3.

159. Brown SA, Epps DF, Dunn JK, et al. Effect of blood collection and processing on radioimmunoassay results for apolipoprotein B in plasma. Clin Chem 1990;36:1662-6.

160. Evans K, Mitcheson J, Laker MF. Effect of storage at 4 degrees C and -20 degrees C on lipid, lipoprotein, and apolipoprotein concentrations. Clin Chem 1995;41:392-6.

161. Sgoutas DS, Tuten T. Effect of freezing and thawing of serum on the immunoassay of lipoprotein(a). Clin Chem 1992;28:1873-7.

162. National Cholesterol Education Program. Recommendations for improving cholesterol measurement: a report from the Laboratory Standardization Panel of the National Cholesterol Education Program. (NIH Publication No. 90-2964). Bethesda, MD: National Institutes of Health, 1990:28-9.

Measurement of Cholesterol Concentration

5

Joseph D. Artiss and Bennie Zak

INTRODUCTION

❖ Guidelines for the treatment of adults who have high blood serum total cholesterol (TC) concentrations have been released by the National Cholesterol Education Program's (NCEP) Expert Panel on the Detection, Evaluation, and Treatment of High Blood Cholesterol in Adults.[1] More recently the panel released it's findings for children and adolescents.[2, 3] The first of these reports succinctly outlined the current knowledge pertaining to the direct relationship between increased concentrations of serum TC and coronary heart disease, and explained that TC is a major component of a very complex pathophysiological process. The second of these reports confirms that there is a close relationship between juvenile and adult TC levels—that is, that children with elevated levels of TC tend to grow into adults with elevated levels of TC. Furthermore, the atherogenic processes leading to vascular disease in adults do, in fact, begin at a relatively young age. These reports have established standardized cutoff concentrations for blood serum TC: for adults, desirable < 200 mg/dL (5.17 mmol/L), borderline 200–239 mg/dL (5.17–6.19 mmol/L), and high ≥ 240 mg/dL (6.20 mmol/L); for children between the ages of 2 and 19 years, acceptable < 170 mg/dL (4.39 mmol/L), borderline 170–199 mg/dL (4.39–5.14 mmol/L), and high ≥ 200 mg/dL (5.17 mmol/L). Furthermore, both of these reports recommend that treatment decisions should be based on low-density lipoprotein cholesterol (LDL-C) values. (Please refer to Chapter 2 for further details on the two NCEP reports.)

To date, in order to determine LDL-C, accurate values for serum TC, triglyceride, and high-density lipoprotein cholesterol must be established, as all three are utilized for the calculation of an LDL-C value. Although this approach is still probably the most common, it is important to note that direct methods for the determination of serum LDL-C have become commercially available and are applicable to most clinical laboratories. (Please refer to Chapter 8 for additional information on the measurement of LDL-C.)

Concurrent with the report from the Adult Treatment Panel, the Laboratory Standardization Panel of the NCEP released its report on the status of the measurement of serum TC in the United States.[4] This report was unique in that, for the first time, guidelines were established for the accuracy and precision of serum TC determinations. As of 1992, laboratories were expected to be able to attain TC concentrations that

99

are within 3% of the "true value" as defined by the definitive method, and to have a total imprecision (CV) of ≤ 3%. These comparatively tight standards were established in order to minimize the possibility of inappropriately reporting a TC value which was two "cutoff" levels higher or lower. For example, if the total imprecision were 10%, a specimen in the range of 200 mg/dL (5.17 mmol/L) could be reported as > 240 mg/dL (6.20 mmol/L) and, conversely, a high TC level could be reported as acceptable (mean ± 250). Both possibilities have their own set of unpleasant ramifications.

The coincidental timing of the release of these reports was not an accident. They were part of a well-planned and executed program to decrease serum TC concentrations in the general population of the United States. It is of interest to note that at the time of the report, a full 40% of the adult population of the United States had unacceptably high levels of serum TC, by the definitions set forth by the NCEP. For the first time, the determination of TC had become the subject of a great deal of interest not only to the medical community, but also to the general population.

We describe the reference method for the determination of serum TC in this chapter; however, it should be remembered that this method is neither applicable nor transferable to most clinical laboratories. It is worthy of note that since the first report from the Laboratory Standardization Panel, many of the manufacturers of TC reagents have, through both their own efforts as well as those of the member organizations of the NCEP, brought their products into line with the recommended guidelines for accuracy and precision. We also discuss various aspects that should be considered in the evaluation and implementation of commercially available reagents.

METHODOLOGIES

Definitive Method

The underlying concept for a definitive method is that its levels of bias and imprecision are of a magnitude compatible with the method's stated purpose. That is, the mean value of the definitive method is considered to be the "true value."[5] For a method to be considered to be definitive, it must have been subjected to an extensive investigation and evaluation for sources of inaccuracy, including nonspecificity.[6] The definitive method for TC is an isotope dilution–mass spectrometric method, developed by the National Institute of Standards and Technology (NIST, formerly known as the National Bureau of Standards).[7] As definitive methods are generally very labor intensive, expensive, and require highly specialized instrumentation, they are not recommended for use in routine clinical laboratories.

Reference Method

A reference method is one which has been thoroughly investigated and which has exact and clear descriptions of the necessary conditions and procedures for the accurate determination of a substance. Furthermore, the accuracy and precision of the method are such that the method may be used for assessing other methods and assigning values to reference materials.[5] The currently accepted reference method for

TC is a Centers for Disease Control and Prevention (CDC) modification[8, 9] of the Abell modification[10] of the earlier method of Sperry and Brand.[11] The substance of this method rests in the hydrolysis of cholesterol esters prior to purification by organic solvent extraction and reaction of the purified cholesterol with a Liebermann-Burchard reagent.[12, 13] It should be noted that the reference method has been demonstrated to yield results that are, on average, 1.6% higher than the definitive method.[14, 15]

Although the reference method is intended to be technically and financially less demanding than the definitive method, it is still beyond the capabilities of all but a few clinical laboratories. As can be seen below, the reference method for TC, as performed by the Lipids Section of the CDC, is no exception to this rule. A more detailed protocol than the one described below is available from the CDC.[16]

Materials

The reagents are: cholesterol SRM 911b, absolute ethanol, glacial acetic acid, potassium hydroxide, acetic anhydride, and sulfuric acid; all are ACS reagent grade. Certified hexanes (boiling range 68–70° C or smaller) are also required, as well as reagent grade water (specific resistance ≥ 10 megohm/cm, specific conductivity ≥ 0.1 microhm/cm), Drierite™ indicating desiccant, and silica gel (for drying) 6–16 mesh.

Reagents

Aqueous Potassium Hydroxide (33%). Add 165 g of dry potassium hydroxide to about 400 mL of reagent grade water. Dissolve. Upon cooling to room temperature, transfer the solution to a graduated cylinder and make up to 500 mL with reagent grade water. Store in a Pyrex™, Teflon™, or polyethylene bottle with a lined screw cap. Prepare fresh monthly or whenever appreciable amounts of K_2CO_3 precipitate appear.

Alcoholic KOH (approximately 0.36 mol/L). Prepare immediately prior to use by transferring 6.0 ± 0.1 mL of 33% KOH (for each 10 mL of reagent) to a graduated cylinder and make up to 10 mL with absolute ethanol. Store stoppered in a glass or Teflon Erlenmeyer flask.

Liebermann-Burchard Reagent. Add 200 mL of acetic anhydride to a 1 L glass stoppered Erlenmeyer flask and cool to 5° C in the freezing compartment of a refrigerator. With constant mixing of the acetic anhydride, add steadily 10 mL of sulfuric acid. While gently swirling, add 100 mL of acetic acid and place the mixture in a 25° C water bath. The reagent should show no discoloration and should have an absorbance ≤ 0.003 at 620 nm.

Primary Standard Solution (stock standard). Dry cholesterol SRM 911b overnight at 55° C in an open bottle in a vacuum oven with a 250 mL evaporating dish full of silica gel. Allow the oven to drop to room temperature (approximately 4 h) while still under vacuum. Then allow the pressure to slowly increase to atmospheric. Immediately remove, cap, and store the bottle in a desiccator containing silica gel.

Cholesterol Standard Solution. Warm ethanol in a glass-stoppered Erlenmeyer flask to 55° C. Transfer 2.0000 ± 0.0002 g of recently dried cholesterol into a 200 mL volumetric flask and dissolve with the warm alcohol. Once the cholesterol is fully dissolved, allow the solution to cool to 25° C and dilute to the mark with ethanol at 25° C.

Working Standards

Dilute 5.0 mL of standard cholesterol solution to 200 mL with ethanol (0.25 g/L) to be used for HDL standard. Dilute 5.0, 10.0, 20.0, 30.0, and 40.0 mL to 100 mL with ethanol (0.50, 1.0, 2.0, 3.0, and 4.0 g/L). Label five screw-capped 20 × 150 mm test tubes for each set of standards and transfer about 20 mL of each working standard into each tube and cap tightly. Store in a desiccator, containing a 1 cm layer of ethanol, in a refrigerator at 4° C.

Preparation of Extracts

Transfer 2.0 mL of standards and samples into clean, dry and labeled vials with caps. Equilibrate standards and samples for approximately 15 min in a 25° C ± 1° C water bath. Deliver 0.5 mL of each standard, control, and sample into labeled tubes to which 5 mL of alcoholic KOH has been added. Cap the tubes, vortex, mix, and incubate at 50° C ± 2° C for 60 ± 5 min. Place all tubes in a 25° C water bath, add 5 mL of water, and equilibrate for 10 min. Add 10 mL of hexanes to each tube, cap firmly, and mix for 15 min in a mechanical shaker. Allow 5 min for phase separation. Transfer 2.0 mL of the organic phase to test tubes and deliver it with 3.0 mL of hexane into labeled clean and dry racked test tubes. Evaporate all tubes to dryness in a vacuum oven maintained at 55° C.

Color Development

Transfer freshly-prepared Liebermann-Burchard (L-B) reagent to a two- or three-necked Teflon-stoppered Pyrex flask which has connected to one neck a drying tube containing Drierite™, cotton, and fine mesh protecting the flask inlet. Add 3.25 mL of L-B reagent to each of the dried extracts from above at 20 sec intervals with vortex mixing, and place each tube in a 25° C ± 1° C water bath. Following a 30 min incubation, read each tube in sequence against a water blank at 620 nm. The concentrations of the unknowns are determined from the line of regression calculated from the standards run in duplicate. The correlation coefficient of the line of regression should be between 0.9998 and 1.0000. There are a number of criteria that are required to define an acceptable standard curve; the authors refer the reader to the more detailed description for a complete listing of these criteria.[16]

Enzymic Methods

Enzyme-based reagents for the determination of TC (Figure 5–1) have largely supplanted the older (strong acid) chemical approaches for routine laboratory measurements. The change to enzymic methods is due mainly to the better specificity afforded by the

Figure 5–1 ◈ Enzyme-Based Reagents for Determination of TC

Cholesterol Esters + H_2O $\xrightarrow{\text{Cholesterol Esterase}}$ Cholesterol + Fatty Acids

Cholesterol + O_2 $\xrightarrow{\text{Cholesterol Oxidase}}$ Δ^4-Cholestenone + H_2O_2

2 H_2O_2 + Phenolic + 4-Aminoantipyrine $\xrightarrow{\text{Peroxidase}}$ Red Chromogen + $4H_2O$

enzymes, their applicability to automation, and the elimination of some of the hazardous materials used in the older methods. However, as is often the case, the new enzymic methods frequently have problems with interferences that may not have been experienced with the older methods that involved extraction (purification) of the cholesterol prior to the reaction with the color forming reagents. Several articles[4, 17, 18] have discussed the determination of TC, but have made only passing mention of interferences. There have also been reports of interference studies carried out on several chemistry analyzers,[19-21] as well as a related review on glucose determinations[22] that includes interference effects that may be applicable due to similar indicator reactions. There has been but one review on TC determinations in this decade,[23] and prior to that article, there had not been a review in over a decade.[24, 25]

Space does not permit a thorough review of enzymic methods and all potential interferences. However, a brief description and various approaches for evaluating, the common substances that may interfere with enzymic TC procedures follows.

Enzyme Specificity

The specificity of the enzymes used in TC determinations–or for that matter, any other analytical procedure–may be considered by some to be suspect. One argument that is almost certainly valid is that the enzymes cannot be characterized to the same degree as other reagent chemicals. Furthermore, it is doubtful that in the foreseeable future we will be able to characterize enzymes to this degree. However, it may be that, unlike the wet chemical procedures, the enzyme preparations are much more forgiving and therefore do not require the same degree of characterization. The reason that these systems seem so robust is not at all clear. It may be simply because the enzymes behave as catalysts and therefore do not participate directly in the analytical process. Alternatively, perhaps it is that we have learned how to characterize and control their behavior in any given system. The use of recombinant sources for enzymes may facilitate more uniformity among preparations.

Cholesterol Esterase

At one time, the completeness or perhaps specificity of enzymic hydrolysis of cholesterol esters was considered to be a problem with totally enzymic procedures.[26] Even when the enzyme cocktail, which often included nonspecific lipases or proteases, hydrolyzed all of the serum cholesterol esters, discrepancies often manifested themselves when synthetic or short-chain fatty acid esters (e.g., acetate) of cholesterol were used to spike control or calibrator materials. However, it has been relatively well established that this is no longer a major problem.[27-30] The significant difference between earlier reagents and newer ones is the incorporation of esterase(s) of microbial rather than mammalian origin. Although the manufacturers of kits often protect their proprietary information, it would appear that the genus of this microbe is *Pseudomonas*[31, 32] and that the species is probably *fluorescens*. The Boehringer-Mannheim (Indianapolis, IN) claim of at least 99.5% hydrolysis seems to have been verified.[26, 27] Bateson et al.,[31] in comparing enzymic to chemical hydrolysis using an esterase from the above-mentioned genus and species, reported the efficiency of the enzyme(s) to be in excess of 99%. Therefore, it seems reasonable to conclude that the current generation of esterases provides quite an acceptable degree of hydrolysis. It is of some interest that, unlike the other enzymes in the typical TC reagent, specificity of the esterase is something which is undesirable.

Although surfactants do not participate directly in the hydrolytic reaction, and therefore do not have to be identified on the package insert, they are a critical component of the reagent. In the absence of the appropriate surfactant the esterase reaction, if it occurs at all, will be very slow and unlikely to reach completion. Various sources of esterases respond differently not only to different surfactants but also to the concentration of those surfactants.

Cholesterol Oxidase

Like the esterases, it is not always easy to identify the microbial source of the oxidases. However, Deeg and Ziegenhorn[26] have reported the use of an enzyme from a *Streptomyces* species as being ideal for Boehringer's kinetic TC procedure. Likewise they utilize an enzyme from *Nocardia erythropolis* for end-point determinations.[27] Bateson et al.[28] utilized an oxidase from a *Cellulomonas* genus; in this case it is not the authors but rather the enzyme producer who does not wish to exactly identify the specific species of microbe used to obtain the enzyme.

Almost certainly none of the above-mentioned sources of enzyme are totally specific to a 3,5-beta hydroxysterol such as cholesterol, but it might be concluded that this lack of specificity is not particularly important. We say this in light of the fact that all other reactive steroidal compounds that occur naturally in human blood are present in concentrations of at least several orders of magnitude less than cholesterol. Therefore, even if there were 100% cross-reactivity, the effects would normally not be appreciable.

Although cholesterol oxidase is quite specific to free cholesterol, it is worthy of note that the authors have found that, on occasion, impurities in the phenolic chemical used in the color reaction will inhibit the oxidase. It is unlikely that readers will encounter this problem unless they are preparing their own reagent.

Measurement

In order to complete the enzymic determination of TC, one final step is necessary. That step involves the detection and measurement of the product of the cholesterol oxidase reaction as a means of quantifying the amount of cholesterol that was present. Three general approaches have been taken as a means of quantifying the products of the cholesterol oxidase reaction. Each is discussed in the sections that follow.

Electrochemical Measurement of Oxygen Consumed

Methods have been described[31, 32] and made commercially available for measurement (by electrode) of oxygen consumption, in a manner similar to that used for some glucose oxidase methods. Noma and Nakayama[32] reported that bilirubin and ascorbic acid, at 10 mg/dL (171 μmol/L and 568 μmol/L, respectively), were without effect on either the amount or the rate of oxygen consumption. The oxygen consumption methods are not easily automated and generally require a substantial amount of cholesterol oxidase. Thus, these methods have not become widely used.

Ultraviolet Spectrophotometric Measurement of Cholest-4-en-3-one Produced

An early approach to quantitating the cholesterol oxidase reaction has been to measure the cholestenone produced during the oxidase reaction. Flegg[29] measured the absorption of this compound at 240 nm, and also measured the absorption of the 2,4-dinitrophenylhydrazone derivative at 390 nm. The procedure is time consuming and difficult to perform and is probably of use only in research applications; even there, it seems to have little utility when compared to the third approach to be discussed. Interference studies have not been reported, and it is quite unlikely that all other ultraviolet-absorbing species would be absent. Additionally, it almost certainly would not be able to achieve the analytical sensitivity of the peroxidase coupled reaction.

Measurement of Hydrogen Peroxide Produced by the Cholesterol Oxidase Reaction

Measurement of the hydrogen peroxide produced is the most common method of quantitating the cholesterol oxidase reaction. The measurement of hydrogen peroxide has been accomplished by use of several different approaches. Allain et al.[30] reported the first totally enzymic method of determining serum TC by measuring hydrogen peroxide. This method was based on the Trinder reaction previously used for the determination of glucose.[33] The hydrogen peroxide produced in the cholesterol oxidase reaction was used to oxidatively couple two chromogenic substrates by catalysis with horseradish peroxidase (EC 1.11.1.7). In this original procedure, the chromogenic compounds used were phenol and 4-aminoantipyrine (4AAP). The product of the reaction is presumed to be a quinoneimine dye that can be measured photometrically at a wavelength of about 500 nm. Compounds other than 4AAP and phenol represent variations of the same analytical theme. Their ease of use and ready applicability to automation has made numerous variations of this procedure very popular.

The peroxidase which is used in most clinical assays is derived from horseradish. Although new microbial sources are available which almost certainly exhibit different specificities, they are not in common use. The catalytic properties of peroxidase are very nonspecific; therefore, interferences are most common with this step in the reaction sequence.

The list of substances that may interfere with the peroxidase catalyzed measurements have been reported to include: ascorbic acid,[34, 35] bilirubin,[34-39] triglycerides,[34, 37] hemolysis,[35] and possibly unknown substances.[40] It is difficult to put absolute estimates on the degree of interference that may be exhibited. The magnitude of this difficulty is relatively obvious when one considers the numerous types of reagent formulations and instrument configurations that are available for use.

Evaluation of Interfering Substances

As mentioned above, space does not permit an in-depth discussion of all possible interfering substances and their effects on all possible combinations of instruments and reagents. In fact, this has never been done, and probably will never be done, due to the sheer magnitude of the task. Hence, we limit our discussion to the most common interfering substances—ascorbate, bilirubin(s), lipids, and hemolysis—and various approaches to assessing their effects on any given measurement system.

Ascorbic Acid

Ascorbic acid is well known for its properties as a reducing substance. It is these properties that allow it to interfere in peroxidase catalyzed reactions by competing with the intended chromogen substrates for generated peroxide. Thus, if sufficiently high levels of ascorbate are present in a sample, the measured TC value will be spuriously low. The interference caused by ascorbate must be considered to be insidious as it is invisible to the person making the measurement. Furthermore, it is somewhat difficult to assess experimentally, as in solution it is subject to air oxidation; thus, experiments must be carefully planned and quickly carried out or the interfering substance will have disappeared prior to initiation of the measurement process. It should be noted that this same phenomenon is probably what prevents ascorbate from being a bigger problem than it is. That is, by the time the sample reaches the laboratory and eventually the instrument, any ascorbate present may have already oxidized.

Although it is a common practice to include ascorbate oxidase in reagents for the determination of uric acid, we are not aware of the need for it in wet-chemistry reagent systems for cholesterol. This may not be the case with point-of-care testing. We need also to be wary of the current trend toward the use of self-prescribed doses of various "anti-oxidants." We know of no studies involving vitamin A and E supplements.

Bilirubin

From an academic point of view, the mechanism of interference by bilirubin in peroxidase coupled reactions is quite interesting in its complexity. As with ascorbate, bilirubin competes with the intended chromogenic substrates for peroxide. In addition, both the native and oxidized bilirubin contribute their spectral characteristics to the blank and/or final measurement.[41] To further complicate the issue, it must be remembered that what we commonly refer to as "bilirubin" is, in fact, a family of species of which some are water soluble while others are not, and some are protein bound while others are not. Furthermore, those that are water soluble may be either mono- or diconjugated. Thus, spiking a sample or standard with something from a bottle labeled "Bilirubin from bovine gall bladder" may not be an appropriate approach for evaluating its effects on enzymic reactions.

Recently, we have begun to use serial dilutions of pools of icteric samples with clear pools. Although this approach is not as neat and straightforward in appearance as simply dissolving some yellow/orange powder in a bit of base and then spiking samples with it, we believe that the results will better reflect reality. The premise underlying this approach is that there is no interference at low concentrations of the bilirubin, and that as the concentration of the bilirubin increases, a point will be reached where errors will begin to occur. By plotting the measured TC concentration versus the sample dilution factor, the point at which interference occurs should present itself as a deviation from linearity. Repeating the experiment several times with different pools should give the investigator more useful information as to the effects of the interfering substance. It should be noted that the effects of bilirubin may vary among reagents and instruments.

Lipids

The interference caused by the turbidity of hypertriglyceridemia is of particular concern with lipid measurements. Traditional approaches for clearing a specimen, such as ultracentrifugation or solvent extraction/precipitation, simply will not work in this case because some of the species of interest will be removed in the clearing process.

In the past, investigators,[20, 21] including ourselves,[42] have used total parenteral nutrition, solutions such as Intralipid™, to spike clear specimens in order to evaluate the effects of the turbidity caused by elevated levels of triglyceride. Although we knew that this artificial turbidity did not behave exactly the same as serum triglycerides, we believed that it was a reasonable approach in that it was a worst-case scenario for liquid reagents. In comparing instruments of traditional wet-chemistry and dry-film technologies, Cobbaert and Tricarico have reported that this is, in fact, a best-case scenario for the non-liquid systems.[43] For this reason we have adopted an approach similar to the one mentioned above for bilirubin: that is, serially diluting clear pools with turbid ones and plotting the measured TC against the sample dilution factor.

It is of note that the results of such experiments are valid for only one given reagent system on one given instrument. Reagents for the determination of lipids typically contain surfactants that have the effect of (partially) clearing turbid specimens. This clearing process is not likely to be immediate, so that small differences in the timing sequence and the blank measurement, for example, will have significant effects on the final concentration.[34]

Hemolysis

Hemoglobin, with its pseudo peroxidase-like activity, should have little effect on a peroxidase-coupled reaction sequence. However, the inherent color of the hemoglobin will be a problem if the instrument is not capable of blanking it out of the final measurement. For the most part, this does not cause a problem with the current equipment.

Although we tend to immediately think of hemoglobin when we see a hemolyzed sample, we must consider those cellular components that we cannot see that are spilled at the same time as the hemoglobin. Erythrocytes contain a relatively high concentration of catalase, which will compete for the generated peroxide with peroxidase. Liquid reagent systems usually have sufficient amounts of peroxidase present that it wins the competition for the peroxide. However, this may not be the case with all thin-film technologies.

STANDARDIZATION, CALIBRATION, AND CONTROL

We must first define the terms, "standard", "calibrator," and "control," as they are often interchanged, and in lipid determinations the distinctions become very important. A standard material is a pure material that can be accurately measured and prepared to some predetermined concentration. A calibrator, on the other hand, is a material that is typically provided by a manufacturer with an assigned concentration to be used for some specific application. It is very important to note that this assigned concentration often does not reflect the true concentration of the analyte of interest. A control material typically is processed serum of human or bovine source. The analyte concentration is usually presented as a range, and this, coupled with the fact that the material has been processed, makes it unsuitable for assessing the accuracy of an assay. This does not mean that the material is not suitable for the day-to-day assessment and monitoring of imprecision.

As reference ranges for TC have evolved, from population distributions (i.e., concentrations found in 95% of the population) to "optimal" target values with specific cutoff points above which intervention is recommended, extraordinary attention has been focused on the accuracy with which the laboratory measurement of TC must be performed. The initial goal put forward by the NCEP in 1988 was that levels of bias and imprecision for routine TC measurement should not exceed ± 5%. By 1992, these levels were to be no greater than ± 3% for bias and imprecision, and the NCEP suggested that all TC concentrations should be traceable to the Abell-Kendall reference method. The decrease in bias and imprecision from 5% to 3% leads to a concomitant decrease in total allowable error from 15% to 9%.

The standardization of lipid assays in general is not an easy process. The lipids are unlike other analytes (e.g., sodium, glucose, etc.) that are water soluble. Thus, by converting to enzymic reagents we have created a situation in which the reagents are dissolved in one phase and the analyte of interest is contained in a second phase (i.e., the lipoprotein particles which contain the lipids are not truly in aqueous solution). This is best exemplified by the chylous sample which, upon sitting in the refrigerator overnight, forms an obvious biphasic system. With this concept in mind it becomes easier to appreciate that standardization becomes a somewhat complicated process. We might pose the rhetorical question, "How do we dissolve our pure standard in a matrix that will mimic human serum?" The answer is simple: It has not been done. However, it is not important for all enzymic assays. The manual method which we describe below seems to respond well to the certified reference material NBS SRM 911b dissolved in an organic solvent matrix. It should not be construed that this is necessarily the case with the same method on an automated system, as the solvents may affect the instrument's pipetting system.

To avoid these problems, manufacturers tend to provide "calibrators" for their systems. Typically, the value on the label is not the "true" but rather the "assigned" concentration of the analyte. The manufacturer has, in its facility, measured the concentrations of species of interest numerous times and compared them (hopefully) to fresh serum results, as will be described below. If this is the case, one should not assume that the assigned value is transferable from one instrument to another, not even to a different model from the same manufacturer. Furthermore, one should be able to obtain documentation from manufacturers that they and their calibrator materials are indeed certified by the CDC Cholesterol Reference Method Laboratory Network for the particular application of interest.

The CDC Cholesterol Reference Method Laboratory Network has been established in order to allow both manufacturers and individual laboratories access to results from the established reference method for TC. A list of these laboratories is presented in Chapter 12. By sharing split samples with one of the network laboratories, laboratorians can establish the validity of their calibration. A typical approach would involve contacting one of the network laboratories and arranging for the delivery of the appropriate samples. Prior to the arrival of the fresh serum samples from the network laboratory (or vice versa, depending on the arrangements that are made), laboratorians would calibrate their instrument according to the manufacturer's directions. Once the fresh split samples are run and the results compared to those of the network laboratory, the calibration can be adjusted, if need be, and then the samples re-assayed to confirm the adjusted calibration.

Since there is a cost involved with this service, a laboratory may not wish to do this on a regular basis; however, it is a relatively convenient approach for resolving any concerns about calibration. It should be remembered that this approach has been adopted by many of the equipment manufacturers, and appropriate documentation to confirm the accuracy of their calibration material should be available.

Although it is good practice for clinical laboratories to subscribe to at least one proficiency testing program, the results of many programs must be interpreted with caution. Although a few programs are available that use fresh frozen serum pools as the control material, most control programs utilize processed serum. It cannot be over-emphasized that processed materials may or may not behave in a manner identical to serum with any given instrument/reagent system. Therefore, these programs are best suited for assessing imprecision and not accuracy.

Several commercial companies sell materials that are traceable to the CDC reference method for standardization purposes (refer to Chapter 12 for details). The CAP provides survey materials that are traceable to the CDC reference method as well as materials to test for linearity. Linearity checks are a sensitive technique to observe analytical problems before they have profound effects on accuracy.[44] Once again, it is important to note that the user may experience problems using these materials to establish accuracy if the system being standardized is sensitive to matrix effects (refer to Chapter 11 for additional information).

Even when a particular method, or a particular combination of method and instrument, is traceable to the CDC or NIST and has acceptable imprecision and inaccuracy, it is quite a different matter to say that the system in one's own laboratory meets the required limits if any modifications have been made. The NBS SRM911b and the CAP survey materials demonstrate marked matrix effects with some methods. As with all calibration and control materials, great care has to be exercised in extrapolating the values provided by the manufacturer to another situation unless all conditions are identical to those used by the manufacturer.

ENZYMIC METHOD

Materials

The following materials can be obtained from Genzyme Corporation (Cambridge, MA): cholesterol esterase (CHE), from *Pseudomonas sp.*, sterol-ester acylhydrolase (EC 3.1.1.13); cholesterol oxidase (COX), from *Cellulomonas sp.*, cholesterol: oxygen oxidoreductase (EC 1.1.3.6); lipase, from *Chromobacterium viscosum*, Triacylglycerol acylhydrolase (EC 3.1.13); and peroxidase (HRP), from horseradish (donor: hydrogen-peroxide oxidoreductase) (EC 1.11.1.7).

Triton X-100™, α-cyclodextrin (α-CD), magnesium acetate, and 4-aminoantipyrine may be obtained from Sigma Chemical Co. (St. Louis, MO).

Potassium ferrocyanide (reagent grade) may be obtained from Spectrum Chemical Manufacturing Co. (Redondo Beach, CA).

The sodium salt of 2-hydroxy-3,5-dichlorobenzenesulfonic acid (may also be listed as 3,5-dichloro-2-hydroxybenzenesulfonic acid [HDCBS]) may be obtained from Research Organics, Inc. (Cleveland, OH). (There are other sources.)

Cholesterol (NBS SRM911b) may be obtained from NIST, the U.S. Department of Commerce (Gaithersburg, MD).

Reagents

The TC reagent is prepared in TRIS-HCl buffer (50 mmol/L, pH 7.6) to contain per liter 0.5 g of Triton X-100™, 1.0 mmol of 4AAP, 2.0 mmol of HDCBS, 4.1 mmol of α-cyclodextrin, 50 μmol of potassium ferrocyanide, 400 U of CHE, 800 U of COX, 294 U (guaiacol) of HRP, and 200 kU of lipase.

Cholesterol standards are prepared with NBS SRM911b cholesterol which has been dried under vacuum over silica gel at 55° C for at least 12 h.[45] The appropriate amount of this material is dissolved in 2-methoxyethanol containing 200 g/L Triton X-100.

Specimen Collection and Storage

A detailed description of specimen collection is given in Chapter 4.

Blood is generally drawn from the patient's antecubital vein or other convenient arm vein.[46] Concentrations of TC in finger-stick samples of whole blood have been found to be comparable with venous plasma, providing the initial drop of blood which contains tissue fluid is discarded and excessive "milking" of the finger is minimized to prevent hemolysis.[47, 48]

TC concentrations in serum or plasma have been shown to be stable when subjected to various storage conditions. Although it is standard practice to separate serum from the blood clot by centrifugation within 1 h, a delay in this procedure for 48 h produced no significant change in measured TC.[49] However, when blood was collected, allowed to clot, centrifuged, and stored at 6–7° C in the same serum separator tube for 7 d, a slight increase (1.8%) was observed.[50]

After using a secondary serum standard in the long-term Lipid Research Clinics Program, no evidence was uncovered to suggest that cholesterol in pooled serum deteriorates while stored at –20° C.[51] Cholesterol was also shown to be stable in either frozen or lyophilized forms of pooled serum during nearly 5 y of storage at –20° C.[52]

When plasma is to be used for TC analysis, anticoagulant-treated blood should be centrifuged as soon as possible to prevent hemolysis of red blood cells. No change in TC was noted after storage of heparinized plasma for 4 d at 25° C.[53]

The patient need not be fasting if the sample is to be used for TC only.[54]

Procedure

Pipette 1.0 mL of reagent into the appropriate test tubes, add and mix 3 µL of sample, standard or control. Allow the reaction mixture to incubate for 12 min at 37° C. The absorbance is measured at 510 nm against a reagent blank.

Performance

The data collected with the manual procedure suggests that the within-run reproducibility of this reagent system should be less than 1.5% and that the between-run reproducibility should be less than 3%.[55] The reagent is linear to about 900 mg/dL (23 mmol/L) cholesterol. Interference studies conducted at the concentrations recommended by the National Committee for Clinical Laboratory Standards (NCCLS) illustrate minimal interference from ascorbate,[55] hemolysis,[55] and lipemia.[56] Bilirubin at a level of 20 mg/dL (342 µmol/L) will cause a negative interference of about 6% with this procedure.[55] It is of note that NCCLS recommends evaluation of ascorbate at concentrations up to 30 mg/dL (1.7 mmol/L). Although this is well above concentrations that are commonly encountered, extremely increased concentrations of ascorbate will almost certainly interfere.[57]

REFERENCE RANGES

Within the last decade, the reference ranges for serum TC filled the better part of two pages of most textbooks. There were different ranges for age (one per half-decade) and sex. In an attempt to simplify treatment decisions, the NCEP has recommended the use of two cutoff values for TC. Adult serum concentrations below 200 mg/dL (5.17 mmol/L) are considered desirable, concentrations between 200 and 239 mg/dL (5.17-6.19 mmol/L) are considered borderline, and concentrations of 240 mg/dL (6.20 mmol/L) and above are considered high. Thus, the clinician's decision as to whether follow-up studies are necessary is based solely upon two numbers: 200 and 240 mg/dL (5.17 and 6.20 mmol/L). Decisions concerning treatment are based on the patient's medical history and concentration of LDL-C. (For additional information, please refer to Chapters 2 and 3.)

Earlier in the chapter we discussed transferability–or the lack of it–of the Abell-Kendall method to the routine laboratories in which the method might be attempted. The fact that more complex procedures such as Abell-Kendall are designated as "accurate" does not guarantee accuracy in any or all cases. The time and care required to perform the tests, as well as to make up a reagent whose matrix is so critical to the quality of the measurement, are beyond the scope of many laboratories. The procedure proposed here does not suffer from the same problems as the Abell-Kendall method, in that it is easily carried out in any laboratory and offers certain features that are not available in the field methods it closely resembles. A critical aspect of its reagent matrix is that severely hypertriglyceridemic specimens are more amenable to measurement, owing to the lipolysis that occurs simultaneously with the sequence of enzyme reactions leading to the measured color. In addition, the fatty acids split off by the lipase are trapped as the transparent guests of the host molecule, α-cyclodextrin. As a result, interference by turbidity of the sample is avoided, as has been suggested in the past for both the sample and the sample blanking.   ◇

REFERENCES

1. Report of the National Cholesterol Education Program Expert Panel on the Detection, Evaluation, and Treatment of High Blood Cholesterol in Adults. Arch Intern Med 1988; 148:36-68.
2. National Cholesterol Education Program (NCEP). Highlights of the report of the Expert Panel on Blood Cholesterol Levels in Children and Adolescents. Pediatrics 1992;89: 495-501.
3. National Cholesterol Education Program. Report of the Expert Panel on Blood Cholesterol Levels in Children and Adolescents. Pediatrics 1992;89:525-76.
4. Current status of blood cholesterol measurement in clinical laboratories in the United States: a report from the Laboratory Standardization Panel of the National Cholesterol Education Program. Clin Chem 1988;34:193-201.
5. Development of definitive methods for the National Reference System for the Clinical Laboratory, NRSCL1-A. Villanova, PA: National Committee for Clinical Laboratory Standards, 1991.
6. Dorsey DB. How does the National Reference System for the clinical laboratory standardize results? Pathologist 1984;May:307.
7. Cohen A, Hertz HS, Mandel J, et al. Total serum cholesterol by isotope dilution/mass spectrometry: a candidate definitive method. Clin Chem 1980;26:854-60.

8. Duncan IW, Mather A, Cooper GR. The procedure for the proposed cholesterol reference method. Atlanta, GA: Centers for Disease Control, 1982.

9. Cooper GR, Smith SJ, Duncan IW, et al. Interlaboratory testing of the transferability of a candidate reference method for total cholesterol in serum. Clin Chem 1986;32: 921-9.

10. Abell LL, Levy BB, Brodie BB, Kendall FE. Simplified methods for the estimation of total cholesterol in serum and demonstration of its specificity. J Biol Chem 1951;195: 357-66.

11. Sperry WM, Brand FC. The colorimetric determination of cholesterol. J Biol Chem 1943;150:315-24.

12. Liebermann C. Ueber des Oxychinoterpen. Ber Dtsch Chem Ges 1885;18:1803-9

13. Burchard H. Beitrage Zur Kenntnis des Cholesterins. Chem Zentralbl 1890;61:25-7.

14. Ellerbe P, Myers GL, Cooper GR, et al. A comparison of results for cholesterol in human serum obtained by the reference method and by the definitive method of the national reference system for cholesterol. Clin Chem 1990;36:370-5.

15. Bernert JT, Akins JR, Cooper GR, et al. Factors influencing the accuracy of the National Reference System total cholesterol reference method. Clin Chem 1991; 37:2053-61.

16. Etheridge SF, Waynack, PP. The cholesterol reference method. Centers for Disease Control and Prevention, 1994:1-24.

17. Naito HK. Reliability of lipid, lipoprotein, and apolipoprotein measurements. Clin Chem 1988;34(suppl):B84-94.

18. Cooper GR, Myers GL, Smith SJ, Sampson EJ. Standardization of lipid, lipoprotein, and apolipoprotein measurements. Clin Chem 1988; 34(suppl):B95-105.

19. Joseph JC, Konishi R, Peterson D. Interference studies on four chemistry analyzers [Abstract]. Clin Chem 1984;30:949-50.

20. Glick MR, Ryder KW, Jackson SA. Graphical comparisons of interferences in clinical chemistry instrumentation. Clin Chem 1986;32:470-5.

21. Glick MR, Ryder, KW. Analytical systems ranked by freedom from interferences. Clin Chem 1987;33:1453-8.

22. Burrin JM, Price CP. Measurement of blood glucose [Review]. Ann Clin Biochem 1985; 22:327-42.

23. Zak B, Artiss JD. Some observations on cholesterol measurement in the clinical laboratory [Review]. Microchem J 1990;41:251-70.

24. Zak B. Cholesterol methodologies: a review. Clin Chem 1977;23:1201-14.

25. Witte DL, Brown LF, Feld RD. Enzymatic analysis of serum cholesterol and triglycerides: a brief review. Lab Med 1978;9:39-44.

26. Deeg R, Ziegenhorn J. Kinetic enzymatic method for automated determination of total cholesterol in serum. Clin Chem 1983;29:1798-802.

27. Siedel J, Rollinger W, Röschlau P, Ziegenhorn J. Total cholesterol, end-point and kinetic method. In: Bergmeyer HU, Bergmeyer J, Graßl, M, eds. Methods of enzymatic analysis, 3rd ed. Weinheim: VCH Verlagsgesellschaft GmbH, 1985:139-48.

28. Bateson J, Artiss JD, Zak B. Sensitive enzymic methods for HDL and HDL subclass cholesterol measurement. Clin Chem 1988;34:1230.

29. Flegg HM. An investigation of the determination of serum cholesterol by an enzymatic method. Ann Clin Biochem 1973;10:79-84.

30. Allain CC, Poon LS, Chan CSG, Richmond W, Fu PC. Enzymatic determination of total serum cholesterol. Clin Chem 1974;20:470-5.

31. Kumar A, Christian GD. Enzymatic assay of total cholesterol in serum or plasma by amperometric measurement of rate of oxygen depletion following saponification. Clin Chim Acta 1977;74:101-8.

32. Noma A, Nakayama K. Polarographic method for rapid microdetermination of cholesterol with cholesterol esterase and cholesterol oxidase. Clin Chem 1976; 22:336-40.

33. Trinder P. Determination of glucose in blood using glucose oxidase with an alternative oxygen acceptor. Ann Clin Biochem 1969;6:24-7.

34. Pesce MA, Bodourian SH. Interference with the enzymic measurement of cholesterol in serum by use of five reagent kits. Clin Chem 1977;23:757-60.

35. Garber CC, Feldbruegge D. Evaluation of the performance of the automated enzymatic cholesterol method on the SMAC [Abstract]. Clin Chem 1978;24:1020.

36. Pesce MA, Bodourian SH. Enzymic measurement of cholesterol in serum with the Centrifichem centrifugal analyzer. Clin Chem 1977;23:280-2.

37. Fingerhut B. Enzymic serum cholesterol measurement with a basic autoanalyzer and the DuPont ACA method. Clin Chem 1978;24:1624-7.

38. Witte DL, Brown LF, Feld RD. Effects of bilirubin on detection of hydrogen peroxide by use of peroxidase. Clin Chem 1978;24:1778-82.

39. McGowan MW, Artiss JD, Zak B. Spectrophotometric study on minimizing bilirubin interference in an enzyme reagent mediated cholesterol reaction. Microchem J 1982; 27:564-73.

40. James DR, Price CP. Interference in colorimetric reactions for measuring hydrogen peroxide. Ann Clin Biochem 1984;21:398-404.

41. Perlstein MT, Thibert RJ, Zak B. Bilirubin and hemoglobin interference in direct color-imetric cholesterol reactions using enzyme reagents. Microchem J 1977;22:403-19.

42. Sharma A, Artiss JD, Strandbergh DR, Zak B. The turbid specimen as an analytical medium: hemoglobin determination as a model. Clin Chim Acta 1985;147:7-14.

43. Cobbaert C, Tricarico A. Different effect of Intralipid™ and triacylglycerol rich lipopro-teins on the Kodak Ektachem serum cholesterol determination. Eur J Clin Chem Clin Biochem 1993;31:107-9.

44. Kroll MH, Emancipator K. A theoretical evaluation of linearity. Clin Chem 1993;39:405-13.

45. Deacon AC, Dawson JG. Enzymic assay for total cholesterol involving chemical or enzymic hydrolysis: a comparison of methods. Clin Chem 1979;25:976-84.

46. Bachorik PS, Albers JJ, Ellefson RD, Kane JP, Wood, PD. Collection of blood samples for lipoprotein analysis. Clin Chem 1982;28:1375-8.

47. Alzofon J, Tilton KA, Haley NJ. Enzymatic determination of cholesterol in plasma ob-tained by fingerstick. Clin Chem 1985;31:168.

48. Kaplan SA, Yuceoglu AM, Strauss J. Chemical microanalysis: analysis of capillary and venous blood. Pediatrics 1959;24:270.

49. Ono T, Kitaguchi K, Takehara M, Shiiba M, Hayami K. Serum constituents analyses: effect of duration and temperature of storage of clotted blood. Clin Chem 1981;27: 35-8.

50. Haider T, Per Foss O. The analytical variation and mean difference of serum lipid values in duplicate samples subjected to different times of storage. Scand J Clin Lab Invest 1983;43:439-43.

51. Hainline A, Karon JM, Winn CL, Gill JB. Accuracy and comparability of long-term measurements of cholesterol. Clin Chem 1986;32:611-15.

52. Kuchmak M, Taylor L, Olansky AS. Suitability of frozen and lyophilized reference sera for cholesterol and triglyceride determinations. Clin Chim Acta 1982;120:261-71.

53. Keller VH. Errors, resulting from storage, in the determination of eleven parameters in heparinized whole blood and plasma. Z Klin Chem Klin Biochem 1975,0.217-24.

54. Manual of laboratory operations for the Lipid Research Clinics Program. In: Hainline A, Karon J, Lippel K, eds. Lipid and lipoprotein analysis, 2nd ed. Bethesda MD: National Heart, Lung and Blood Institute, National Institutes of Health, 1982:5.

55. Bateson JE, Artiss, JD, Zak B. The development of an enzymic reference equivalent method for total cholesterol. Clin Chem 1989;35:1071-2.

56. Bateson JE, Artiss JD, Zak B. Cholesterol measurement in grossly lipemic specimens. Clin Chem 1989;35:1072.

57. Peddicord CH, Barnes WA. Ascorbic acid interferogram for cholesterol in the Demand and TDx. Clin Chem 1988;34:773-4.

Measurement of Triglyceride Concentration

6

Thomas G. Cole, Sigrid G. Klotzsch, Judith R. McNamara

INTRODUCTION AND CLINICAL SIGNIFICANCE

❖ Triglycerides (TG) are water-insoluble lipids, consisting of three fatty acids linked to one glycerol molecule. TG represent a concentrated source of metabolic energy, contributing 9 kcal/g, as opposed to 4 kcal/g for protein or carbohydrate. TG are transported in the blood as core constituents of all lipoproteins, but the greatest concentration of these molecules is carried in the TG-rich chylomicrons and very-low-density lipoproteins (VLDL). These two species of TG-rich lipoproteins are frequently combined into a single category called TG-rich lipoproteins (TRL), but they are synthesized in two separate metabolic pathways.

A major source of TG is dietary fat. Dietary fats are hydrolyzed in the gut into free fatty acids and mono- and diglycerides, in which form they are transported through the intestinal villi. After absorption through the gut, they are resynthesized into new TG, assembled into chylomicrons, and secreted into the lymph. Chylomicrons ultimately enter the blood compartment, where most of the TG are rapidly hydrolyzed in the capillary bed, by lipoprotein lipase, into glycerol and free fatty acids, which are absorbed by adipose tissue for storage or by other tissues requiring a source of energy. A peak concentration of chylomicron-associated TG occurs within 3–6 h after ingestion of a fat-rich meal; however, the rate of absorption of fats is highly variable, depending on the individual and the dietary composition of the fat.[1] Chylomicrons that have been hydrolyzed in the circulation are termed chylomicron remnants. They are taken up by the liver through a receptor-mediated process in which apolipoprotein (apo) E and/or apo B on the chylomicron remnant surface binds to the apo E receptor, LDL receptor, or LDL receptor-related protein (LRP)[2-4]. This entire absorptive process is termed the exogenous lipoprotein metabolic pathway (see Chapter 2, Figure 2-1).

Significant amounts of circulating TG are also transported in VLDL. VLDL are synthesized in the liver from constituents derived from the receptor-mediated uptake of chylomicron remnants. Following synthesis and secretion into the blood stream, they circulate, and are hydrolyzed by lipoprotein lipase into VLDL remnants, in much the same way that chylomicrons are hydrolyzed. A small portion of VLDL remnants are taken up directly by the liver and catabolized, but the majority continue the hydrolysis cascade through intermediate-density lipoproteins (IDL), to become low-density lipoproteins (LDL).[5-9] Synthesis and catabolism of lipoproteins originating in the liver are part of the endogenous lipoprotein metabolic pathway.

The rates of VLDL synthesis and hydrolysis are regulated by many factors, including substrate availability, hormonal status, hydrolytic enzyme activity, and the cofactor activity of specific apolipoproteins. While increased levels of circulating LDL have clearly been shown to be atherogenic, there is also a great deal of evidence to support the hypothesis that TRL, or perhaps, specific subspecies of TRL, are also atherogenic.[10, 11] Additional information on TRL is presented in Chapter 25.

Fasting serum TG concentrations below 200 mg/dL (2.3 mmol/L) are considered desirable. Concentrations between 200 and 400 mg/dL (2.3 and 4.5 mmol/L) are borderline high, and fasting concentrations above 400 mg/dL (4.5 mmol/L) are definitely elevated.[12] Both borderline and elevated concentrations require attention in the presence of other coronary heart disease (CHD) risk factors. Extremely elevated levels require attention, unrelated to CHD risk, as TG concentrations above 1000 mg/dL (11.3 mmol/L) can lead to abdominal pain and may be life-threatening due to chylomicron-induced pancreatitis.[13] Fasting TG concentrations are also indicators of postprandial response. Even within the desirable range, the magnitude of postprandial response is positively associated with fasting TG concentration, as well as with fat and total caloric intake.[1] Alcohol intake also increases serum TG concentration, and abstinence for 24 h is recommended before blood is drawn for a lipid profile.

Although the relationship between TG concentration and risk of CHD has not been firmly established, several studies have found increased TG concentrations to be positively correlated with increased risk for CHD in univariate analyses.[14-17] However, whether TG concentration represents an independent risk factor is not clear, since other independent risk factors, such as reduced concentrations of high-density lipoprotein cholesterol (HDL-C), are often associated with increased TG.[18] Estrogen replacement in postmenopausal women is associated with significant increases in TG, but is one of the rare instances where it is accompanied by significant increases in HDL-C and apolipoprotein A-I (apo A-I),[19] and is associated with decreased CHD risk.[20] When results from studies have been subjected to multivariate analysis that includes HDL-C, the independent significance of TG has generally been lost, with a few exceptions.[18, 21, 22]

Since TRL are a heterogeneous population of particles, however, there may be specific subspecies, such as remnants, that are atherogenic, while other subspecies are not. (For additional information on TRL, refer to Chapter 25.) Isolating separate subspecies for relative analysis of risk, however, has been extremely difficult, since there is much overlap in compositional constituents and particle size. Recently, however, a method developed to separate TRL remnants from nascent TRL was reported.[23] If separation of TRL subspecies can provide better evaluation of TG-associated CHD risk, similar to the separation of LDL and HDL, perhaps more sensitive risk analysis may be gained.

TG are measured in the clinical laboratory for three major purposes: to establish triglyceridemic status, to assess risk of CHD, and to calculate LDL-C concentration through use of the Friedewald equation,[24] when LDL-C cannot be determined directly:

LDL-C (mg/dL) = Total Cholesterol - Total TG/5 - HDL-C

For results in mmol/L, use Total TG/2.22.

Use of the Friedewald equation to approximate LDL-C concentration makes three assumptions: that all TRL are actually VLDL (i.e., no chylomicrons are present); that all serum TG is contained in VLDL, with none in any other lipoproteins; and that the relative proportion of cholesterol in VLDL is constant at 20% of VLDL mass. These assumptions, which are only partially true, are of increasing unreliability at TG concentrations above 250 mg/dL (2.8 mmol/L), and are completely unreliable at TG concentrations above 400 mg/dL (4.5 mmol/L), and in cases where individuals have chylomicrons or have Type III hyperlipoproteinemia.[25, 26]

The introduction of methodology to isolate and measure LDL-C directly, based on immunoseparation of non-LDL lipoproteins reduces the need to use the Friedewald calculation, since the methods are not affected by increased TG concentrations and do not depend on mathematical assumptions. For additional information on the limitations of calculations, and on direct methods for measuring LDL-C, refer to Chapter 8.

Methods for the determination of TG concentration involve the enzymatic measurement of total serum glycerol after hydrolysis of TG into glycerol and free fatty acids. Since glycerol is formed through normal metabolic processes, and is not specific to TG, and since each glycerol molecule is calculated to represent a triglyceride molecule, TG concentrations will be overestimated if endogenous unesterified glycerol is not subtracted through the use of a glycerol blank. Even then, it will be slightly overestimated by the presence of endogenous mono- and diglycerides, which will also be measured as TG. In normal individuals, endogenous glycerol represents the equivalent of 5–20 mg/dL (0.06–0.22 mmol/L) TG, which is a tolerable amount of error. In certain situations, however, endogenous, non-TG-associated glycerol concentrations may be much higher, confounding TG measurement. Such situations include diabetes mellitus, emotional stress, intravenous administration of drugs or nutrients containing glycerol, and contamination of blood collection devices or blood samples by glycerol. In addition, prolonged storage of whole blood under non-refrigerated conditions can cause increased concentrations of free glycerol liberated from erythrocyte membrane phospholipids. Although reagents and methods are currently available to eliminate the interference of glycerol, only about 5% of all American clinical laboratories blank TG measurements for endogenous glycerol.

REVIEW OF EXISTING METHODOLOGIES

Almost all clinical laboratories use enzymatic methods for the analysis of TG concentration. Although a multitude of variations have been developed, three basic steps are common to all the methods.[27, 28] These are illustrated in Figure 6–1. The first step uses lipases which are optimized for the hydrolysis of TG to glycerol and fatty acids. Earlier formulations were not always optimized to hydrolyze the TG commonly found in the circulation, i.e., those containing fatty acids of 16 or more carbon atoms. However, manufacturers are now aware of the importance of complete hydrolysis.

Figure 6–1 ❖ Generalized Scheme of Enzymatic TG Analyses

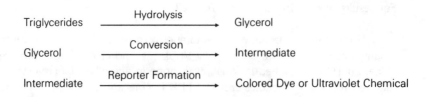

Although phospholipids are not hydrolyzed by current lipase mixtures, mono- and diglycerides are hydrolyzed and contribute to the amount of TG quantified. Since mono- and diglycerides represent only about 3% of the total plasma neutral glyceride concentration, and since a portion of the mono- and diglycerides arises from *in vivo* and *in vitro* hydrolysis of TG, they are included as part of the TG measurement. All enzymatic methods then quantify the amount of glycerol present after hydrolysis.

The conversion step commonly uses an enzyme, such as glycerol kinase, to phosphorylate glycerol for further enzymatic reactions, or may generate an intermediate which can be used directly for the quantification of TG.

The final step leads to the formation of either a colored dye (commonly quinone-imine or formazin) or an ultraviolet light-absorbing chemical whose concentration can be measured spectrophotometrically (appearance or disappearance of NADH) and which can then be related to the concentration of TG in the specimen.

The calibration of TG analyses is confounded by the lack of validated definitive and reference methods. A "reference" chromotropic acid method, as used by the Centers for Disease Control and Prevention (CDC), is considered to establish the accuracy base for TG. Calibrators should be traceable to this method. Glycerol solutions, although suitable as standards, should not be used alone for calibration, because the hydrolysis step of the analytical process is not evaluated. Since TG are a heterogeneous mixture of glycerides with various fatty acid moieties, the choice of analytical standard becomes critical. The CDC uses a standard composed of triolein and tripalmitin (2:1, w/w), as this ratio approximates the distribution of fatty acids in lipoprotein-associated TG; however, values are reported as triolein equivalents. Due to the difference in molecular weights, a disparity of approximately 10% occurs when values are reported as tripalmitin equivalents. Truly unambiguous values would result if the Systeme International d'Unites units (mmol/L) were adopted, as recommended by the International Federation of Clinical Chemistry; however, such a change does not appear to be close at hand for the United States.

Since all enzymatic methods measure TG as the quantity of glycerol in a specimen, the endogenous glycerol will cause an overestimation of TG concentration if it is not taken into consideration. Two methods for the elimination of this interference have been devised. The first, the "external blanking" method, requires the use of two assay reagent solutions, one containing all components necessary for the measurement of TG and endogenous glycerol and one which is similar but lacks the lipase enzymes and therefore measures only the endogenous glycerol. In practice, a specimen is run twice, once with each reagent, and the difference in values represents the true TG concentration. The major advantage of this method is that it can be used with most analytical systems; one need only set up a separate test for each reagent solution. In addition, if the system is arranged so that each test provides a value before calculation of the true TG concentration, the concentration of the endogenous glycerol will be known, which may have medical significance in some situations. A disadvantage is that this method does require the duplicate analysis of a specimen using two complete sets of reagents, cuvettes, and other consumable supplies, thereby increasing the cost and the time of the analysis.

An alternative method, the "internal blanking" method, uses a single reagent which is split into two components: the first contains all enzymes necessary to consume the endogenous glycerol without the generation of a measurable light-absorbing compound or with subtraction of the resulting absorbance as blank; the second contains lipase and any other chemicals necessary for the measurement of TG. In practice, the specimen is reacted with the first component of the reagent for a period of time sufficient for the removal of all the endogenous glycerol. At this point a baseline reading is made, the second component of the reagent is added, and the complete reaction, including the hydrolysis of TG, is carried to completion. The value obtained from the second reaction represents the true or net TG concentration. Advantages of this method are that it requires only a single test on the analyzer to be devoted to the analysis, and that it is economical, since only a single, but divided, reagent and a single cuvette per analysis are required. Disadvantages of this method are that it requires a versatile instrument capable of the addition of the second component of the reagent at the proper time, and not all instruments have this capability; that the time required for analysis is prolonged due to the sequential reactions taking place in a single cuvette; and that the actual value of the endogenous glycerol is not available. The measurement of free glycerol concentration may be desirable in some situations, such as when a patient has a high level of endogenous lipoprotein lipase activity in response to heparin therapy.[29]

Much discussion has been devoted to the issue of why and when to glycerol-blank TG measurements.[30] Ideally, if economical and convenient methods were available, a glycerol blank should be included in every TG measurement. In reality, such is not the case; glycerol blanking is not utilized in most clinical laboratories. Complicating the decision is the fact that excessively high concentrations of endogenous glycerol are a problem in only a very small percentage of specimens;[31] however, in these situations an inappropriate medically significant decision may be made. Therefore, if all specimens are not glycerol blanked, decisions must be made as to which specimens are to be blanked. Unfortunately, the lack of communication between the laboratory and the ordering physician often precludes proper decision-making, and any system that depended upon it probably would be in error a large part of the time. To reduce the potential for errors, the following recommendations are made:

1.   Clinical laboratories should use only systems and reagents with glycerol blanking capabilities and should have the reagent available at all times to be used as necessary.

2.   All hospital in-patient specimens should be glycerol-blanked, due to the higher incidence of endogenous glycerol in this population.

3. Specimens from hospital out-patients or from other sources generally need not be glycerol-blanked, unless specimens are from patients who may be expected to have increased concentrations of glycerol, such as patients from clinics that treat diabetes or other endocrine disorders.

4. All specimens must be kept refrigerated until analyzed. Improper storage or transport of specimens may cause an increase in free glycerol. At room temperature, lipases may continue to hydrolyze TG. In addition, unrefrigerated whole blood may have high concentrations of free glycerol from erythrocyte phospholipid hydrolysis.

5. Any specimen with TG concentration > 200 mg/dL (2.3 mmol/L) should be glycerol-blanked using a "reflex" ordering system.

6. Any suspicious specimen, such as one that has high TG concentrations but is not turbid, should also be glycerol-blanked.

Grossly lipemic specimens are often associated with other potential sources of error. One error is caused by the "clearing effect" of the lipase as it hydrolyzes TG. In systems which utilize a serum blank rather than a reagent blank, light scattering due to large-sized, TG-rich lipoproteins causes an artificially high baseline absorbance measurement. As the analysis progresses, the turbidity is reduced as the lipase hydrolyzes TG and reduces the size of lipoproteins. The overall effect is a slight underestimation of total TG concentration in an up-reaction (NADH appearance), or an overestimation in a down-reaction (NADH disappearance). Reagent-blanked systems are not affected by this phenomenon. Several methods have been devised to minimize the error. The inclusion of proper detergents in the reagent mixture will eliminate the problem in some, but not all, cases.[32] Fortunately, since the magnitude of the error is only a few percent and occurs only in specimens with increased TG concentrations, the error is usually acceptable.

In addition, grossly lipemic specimens, particularly those with a high chylomicron content, may become heterogenous as chylomicrons float to the top of the sample cup in an analyzer. Therefore, grossly lipemic specimens should be mixed thoroughly prior to analysis and the analysis must be carried out with minimal delay. The large amounts of fatty acids liberated by the hydrolysis of TG, particularly in lipemic specimens, can interfere in the analysis due to turbidity and the inactivation of some lipases by product inhibition. This situation is avoided by the inclusion in the reaction buffer of a chemical reservoir for the liberated fatty acids. Generally, bovine serum albumin or α-cyclodextrin is used for this purpose.[32]

As for all analytes, TG concentration should be measured as soon as possible after blood is drawn. In certain specimens containing high values of lipase activities, such as those obtained from heparinized patients, TG will become hydrolyzed upon standing.[28, 29] Over time, the glycerol blank concentration in these specimens will increase while the true TG concentration will decrease; however, apparent total TG concentration will remain stable. This process is temperature-dependent and persists at 4° C, but is minimized if the specimen is frozen at –20° C.

REFERENCE, DEFINITIVE, AND RECOMMENDED METHODS

At this time, no true definitive or reference method has been established for the measurement of TG. The National Institute of Standards and Technology (NIST) has published two candidate definitive methods for the measurement of TG.[33] Both methods are based on isotope dilution/mass spectrometry using $^{13}C_3$-triolein. One method measures only true TG and the other measures total glycerides (tri-, di-, and monoglycerides as well as free glycerol).

The chemical method that the CDC uses as its "in-house reference method" has been accepted by The National Committee for Clinical Laboratory Standards as the interim reference method for the U.S. National Reference System. The CDC uses this method to maintain the accuracy base for the CDC-NHLBI (National Heart, Lung and Blood Institute) Lipid Standardization Program, which requires precision consistent with a coefficient of variation of 5% and accuracy within 5% of the target values set on frozen serum specimens by the CDC. The method involves silicic acid-methylene chloride extraction, alkaline hydrolysis, and color formation with chromotropic acid.[34-37] Due to several technical factors, including the difficulty of transferring the method between laboratories, the CDC is investigating modifications of the method, as well as alternative candidate methods. The Cholesterol Reference Method Laboratory Network is currently evaluating a combination of the CDC extraction and hydrolysis steps with enzymatic detection of glycerol to produce a "designated comparison method" for the purpose of evaluating current and future TG assays.

Given the lack of true definitive and reference methods for the analysis of TG, it is difficult to recommend any particular method over another, beyond the recommendation of using a method which incorporates a form of glycerol blanking.

REFERENCE RANGES

The National Institutes of Health Consensus Development Conference on Treatment of Hypertriglyceridemia has set limits for evaluation of triglyceridemic status.[38] These limits, shown in Table 6–1, have been accepted by the National Cholesterol Education Program Expert Panel on Detection, Evaluation, and Treatment of High Blood Cholesterol in Adults,[39] with slight modification.[12] TG values of North American males and females are presented in the appendix to this book.

Table 6–1 ✦ Recommended Cutpoints for Evaluation of Fasting Triglyceridemic Status

Classification	mg/dL	mmol/L
Normal	TG < 200	TG < 2.3
Borderline High	TG 200–400	TG 2.3–4.5
Hypertriglyceridemic	TG > 400	TG > 4.5
High Risk for Pancreatitis	TG > 1000	TG > 11.3

INTERFERING SUBSTANCES AND CAUTIONS

The sources of potential interfering substances in the analysis of TG have been reviewed in depth,[27] and such reviews should be referred to for more detailed information. The limits of acceptable analytical performance in the presence of ascorbic acid, bilirubin, hemolysis, and gross lipemia need to be evaluated for each system.[40] In many situations, the inclusion of a serum blank may eliminate the effects of the interfering substances.

Glycerol

As discussed above, endogenous glycerol causes an overestimation of all enzymatic TG measurements. Methods are available to eliminate this interference and should be used whenever the inclusion of the endogenous glycerol concentration may lead to errors in medical judgment. However, when blanking is instituted, it is important to avoid conditions that would cause *in vitro* hydrolysis prior to analysis, since this would result in a falsely underestimated TG concentration.

Ascorbic Acid

As an antioxidant, ascorbic acid can interfere with oxidation/reduction reactions. Specimens from patients ingesting megadoses of Vitamin C may have improper analysis of TG and other analytes. Concentrations of ascorbic acid up to 20 mg/dL (1135 µmol/L) may be acceptable for most systems.

Bilirubin

Both chemical and spectral interference can be a serious problem with high concentrations of bilirubin in colorimetric methods. Concentrations of bilirubin up to 20 mg/dL (340 µmol/L) may be acceptable for most systems.

Hemolysis

Slight to moderate hemolysis may cause no interference, but gross hemolysis is unacceptable. The effects of hemoglobin interference will vary depending on the oxidative state of the hemoglobin, the type of reaction being performed, and the type of spectrophotometric system in use. In addition, the lysis of erythrocytes results in the dilution of lipid constituents.

Other Interferences

Carryover from reagent to reagent exists in all random-access analyzers and has been described for many instruments.[41-44] To avoid interference, the manufacturer's programmed test sequence or module use must be followed to take advantage of the software-controlled wash cycles.

Carryover errors can alter results by 10–15% in the first sample which follows a series of tests with another reagent. Reagents which are particularly prone to exhibit carryover problems into TG reagents are total protein and iron due to their concentrations of oxidizing/reducing substances affecting the Trinder sequence of reactions. If direct bilirubin is measured after TG, errors occur due to the carryover of surfactants.

Analytical errors in TG, as well as other analytes, can also be caused by increased TG due to plasma displacement, as described by McGowan et al.;[45] an impressive example is a dangerous exacerbation of pseudohypo values for electrolytes in the presence of severe hypertriglyceridemia.

SUMMARY

Although TG concentration is a less powerful indicator of cardiovascular risk than is cholesterol concentration in most circumstances, evolving evidence suggests that certain TG-rich lipoproteins and their remnant particles may be very important in the development of heart disease. With the availability of a definitive method for TG and the incorporation of a designated reference method into the Cholesterol Reference Method Laboratory Network program, manufacturers can calibrate TG assays with improved accuracy. However, due to the broad biologic variability of TG, the accuracy of measurement has not been of overwhelming importance in the clinical laboratory, except for the calculation of LDL-C through use of the Friedewald equation. With the emergence of direct measurements of LDL-C, the value of the measurement of TG may be lessened further. ❖

REFERENCES

1. Cohn JS, McNamara JR, Cohn SD, Ordovas JM, Schaefer EJ. Postprandial plasma lipoprotein changes in human subjects of different ages. J Lipid Res 1988;29:469–79.
2. Borensztajn J, Getz GS, Kotlar TJ. Uptake of chylomicron remnants by the liver: further evidence for the modulating role of phospholipids. J Lipid Res 1988;29:1087–96.
3. Brasaemle DL, Cornely-Moss K, Bensadoun A. Hepatic lipase treatment of chylomicron remnants increases exposure of apolipoprotein E. J Lipid Res 1993;34:455–65.
4. Hussain MM, Innerarity TL, Brecht WJ, Mahley RW. Chylomicron metabolism in normal, cholesterol-fed, and Watanabe heritable hyperlipidemic rabbits. J Biol Chem 1995;270: 8578–87.
5. Phair RD, Hammond MG, Bowden JA, et al. A preliminary model for human lipoprotein metabolism in hyperlipoproteinemia. Fed Proc 1975;34:2263–70.
6. Packard CJ, Munro A, Lorimer AR, Gotto AM, Shepherd J. Metabolism of apolipoprotein B in large triglyceride-rich very low density lipoproteins of normal and hypertriglyceridemic subjects. J Clin Invest 1983;74:2178–92.
7. Beltz WF, Kesaniemi YA, Howard BV, Grundy SM. Development of an integrated model for analysis of the kinetics of apolipoprotein B in plasma very low density lipoproteins, intermediate density lipoproteins, and low density lipoproteins. J Clin Invest 1985;76: 575–85.
8. Millar JS, Lichtenstein AH, Cuchel M, et al. Impact of age on the metabolism of VLDL, IDL, and LDL apolipoprotein B-100. J Lipid Research 1995;36:1155–67.9.
9. Welty FK, Lichtenstein AH, Barrett PHR, et al. Decreased production and increased catabolism of apolipoprotein B-100 in apolipoprotein B-67/B-100 heterozygotes. Arterioscler Thromb Vasc Biol 1997, in press.

10. Kane JP, Chen G, Hamilton RL, et al. Remnants of lipoproteins of intestinal and hepatic origin in familial dysbetalipoproteinemia. Arteriosclerosis 1983;3:47-56.

11. Karpe F, Steiner G, Uffelman K, Olivecrona T, Hamsten A. Postprandial lipoproteins and progression of coronary atherosclerosis. Atherosclerosis 1994;106:83-97.

12. National Cholesterol Education Program. Summary of the second report of the National Cholesterol Education Program Expert Panel on Detection, Evaluation, and Treatment of High Blood Cholesterol in Adults. (Adult Treatment Panel II). JAMA 1993;269: 3015-23.

13. Goldstein JL, Hobbs HH, Brown MS. Familial hypercholesterolemia. In Scriver CR, Beaudet AL, Sly WS, Valle D, eds. Metabolic and molecular bases of inherited diseases, 7th ed. New York: McGraw-Hill, 1995:1981-2030.

14. Brunzell, JD, Albers JJ, et al. Plasma lipoproteins in familial combined hyperlipidemia and monogenic familial hypertriglyceridemia. J Lipid Res 1983;24:147-55.

15. Genest J, Sniderman A, Cianfeone K, et al. Hyperapobetalipoproteinemia. Plasma lipoprotein responses to oral fat load. Arteriosclerosis 1986;6:297-304.

16. Carlson LA, Bottinger LE, Ahfeldt P-E. Risk factors for myocardial infarction in the Stockholm prospective study: a 14-year followup focusing on the role of plasma triglyceride and cholesterol. Acta Med Scand 1979;206:351-60.

17. Austin MA, Hokanson JE. Epidemiology of triglycerides, small dense low-density lipoprotein, and lipoprotein(a) as risk factors for coronary heart disease. Med Clinics of North America 1994;78:99-115.

18. Austin MA. Plasma triglyceride and coronary heart disease. Arterioscler Thromb 1991; 11:2-14.

19. Granfone A, Campos H, McNamara JR, et al. Effects of estrogen replacement on plasma lipoproteins and apolipoproteins in postmenopausal, dyslipidemic women. Metabolism 1992;41:1193-98.

20. Stampfer MJ, Colditz GA. Estrogen replacement therapy and coronary heart disease: a quantitative assessment of the epidemiologic evidence. Prev Med 1991;20:47-63.

21. Castelli WP. The triglyceride issue: a view from Framingham. Am Heart J 1986;112: 432-7.

22. Hokanson JE, Austin MA. Plasma triglyceride level as a risk factor for cardiovascular disease independent of high-density lipoprotein cholesterol level: a meta-analysis of population-based prospective studies. J Cardiovasc Risk 1996;1996:312-19.

23. Nakajima K, Saito T, Tamura A, et al. Cholesterol in remnant-like lipoproteins in human serum using monoclonal anti apo B-100 and anti apo A-I immunoaffinity mixed gels. Clin Chim Acta 1993;223:53-71.

24. Friedewald WT, Levy RI, Frederickson DS. Estimation of the concentration of low-density lipoprotein cholesterol in plasma, without use of the preparative ultracentrifuge. Clin Chem 1972;18:499-502.

25. Warnick GR, Knopp RH, Fitzpatrick V, Branson L. Estimating low-density lipoprotein cholesterol by the Friedewald equation is adequate for classifying patients on the basis of nationally recommended cutpoints. Clin Chem 1990;36:15-19.

26. McNamara JR, Cohn JS, Wilson PWF, Schaefer EJ. Calculated values for low-density lipoprotein cholesterol in the assessment of lipid abnormalities and coronary disease risk. Clin Chem 1990;36:36-42.

27. Klotzsch SG, McNamara JR. Triglyceride measurements: a review of methods and interferences. Clin Chem 1990;36:1605-13.

28. Naito HK, David JA. Laboratory considerations: determination of cholesterol, triglycerides, phospholipids and other lipids in blood and tissues. In: Story JB, ed. Lipid research methodology. New York: Alan R. Liss, 1984:31.

29. Hortin GL, Cole TG, Gibson DW, Kessler G. Decreased stability of triglycerides and increased free glycerol in serum for heparin-treated patients. Clin Chem 1988;34: 1847-9.

30. Cole TG, Glycerol blanking in triglyceride assays: is it necessary? Clin Chem 1990;36: 1267-8.

31. Jessen RH, Dass CJ, Eckfeldt JH. Do enzymatic analyses of serum triglycerides really need blanks of free glycerol? Clin Chem 1990;36:1372-5.

32. Artiss JD, Strandbergh DR, Zak B. Elimination of glycerol interference in a colorimetric enzymic triglyceride assay. Clin Chim Acta 1989;182:109-16.

33. Ellerbe P, Sniegoski LT, Welch MJ. Isotope dilution mass spectrometry as a candidate definitive method for determining total glycerides and triglycerides in serum. Clin Chem 1995;41:397-404.

34. Carlson LA, Wadstrom LB. Determination of glycerides in blood serum. Clin Chim Acta 1959;4:197-205.

35. Carlson LA. Determination of serum triglycerides. J Athero Res 1963;3:334-6.

36. Van Handel E. Zilversmit DB, Micromethod for the direct determination of triglycerides. J Lab Clin Med 1957;50:152-7.

37. Lofland Jr HB. A semiautomated procedure for the determination of triglycerides in serum. Anal Biochem 1964;9:393-400.

38. Consensus Development Conference. Treatment of hypertriglyceridemia. JAMA 1984; 251:1196-1200.

39. National Cholesterol Education Program. Report of the National Cholesterol Education Program Expert Panel on Detection, Evaluation, and Treatment of High Blood Cholesterol in Adults. Arch Intern Med 1988;148:36-69.

40. Glick JR, Ryder KW. Interferographs. User's guide to interferences in clinical chemistry instruments. Indianapolis: Science Enterprises, Inc., 1987.

41. Haeckel R. Carryover effects from reagent to reagent. J Clin Chem Clin Biochem 1985;23:255-6.

42. Bailey IR, McVittie JD. Gaseous diffusion as a source of carryover. Clin Chem 1986;32:5 (L).

43. DellAnna L, Morosini L, Franceschin A, Bortolussi A. Carryover in the TRAF technology: really impossible? Clin Chem 1986;32:7 (L).

44. Dixon K. A theoretical study of carryover in selective access analyzers. Ann Clin Biochem 1990;27:139-42.

45. McGowan MW, Artiss JD, Zak B. Description of analytical problems arising from elevated serum solids. Anal Biochem 1984;142:239-51.

Measurement of High-Density Lipoprotein Cholesterol

Donald A. Wiebe and G. Russell Warnick

INTRODUCTION AND CLINICAL SIGNIFICANCE

❖   High density lipoprotein cholesterol (HDL-C) is an integral part of the lipoprotein profile–cholesterol (TC), triglycerides (TG), HDL-C, and low-density lipoprotein cholesterol (LDL-C)—used to assess an individual's risk for developing coronary heart disease (CHD). Epidemiological studies have demonstrated the inverse relationship between HDL-C and CHD, such that individuals with low values of HDL-C have increased incidence of CHD. At the other extreme, individuals with high concentrations of HDL-C, as in familial hyperalpha-lipoproteinemia, seldom present with symptoms of CHD. The fact that pre-menopausal females tend to have higher HDL-C and less CHD compared to males and post-menopausal women supports the protective role of HDL-C. Thus, there has been substantial interest in HDL-C measurements to assess potential risk for CHD, and most clinical laboratories routinely perform HDL-C analysis.

In 1988, the National Cholesterol Education Program (NCEP) Adult Treatment Panel (ATP) developed uniform treatment guidelines for individuals with increased TC. HDL-C was given a limited role in the initial ATP guidelines, such that HDL-C levels < 35 mg/dL (0.91 mmol/L) were considered to be a risk factor for CHD.[1] Updated guidelines adopted by APT II and released in 1993 recognized HDL-C as an independent risk factor and placed greater importance on HDL-C by recommending measurement of HDL-C together with TC during the initial screen.[2] An HDL-C concentration of < 35 mg/dL (0.91 mmol/L) is still considered high risk for CHD, while ≥ 60 mg/dL (1.56 mmol/L) is considered protective. Thus, ATP II recognized that for reliable classifications of patients, clinical laboratories must have dependable HDL-C methods.

Physicians generally treat patients with lipid patterns associated with increased risk of developing CHD. Occasionally, patients have normal concentrations of total cholesterol (< 200 mg/dL; 5.18 mmol/L) with low HDL-C (< 35 mg/dL; 0.91 mmol/L). There are few therapeutic approaches available for increasing HDL-C; exercise, stopping smoking, and weight loss are perhaps the most effective. More often, patients present with increased TC or LDL-C concentrations and the intervention programs are primarily oriented to cholesterol lowering by diet and, if necessary, drug therapy. Some of the common cholesterol lowering drugs, such as niacin and the fibrates, tend to increase HDL-C. The newer statins may also be useful for increasing HDL-C. (For additional information, refer to Chapter 2.)[3] Thus, HDL-C remains part of the lipoprotein profile package, and for management of patients with cardiovascular disease, specifically those with hyperlipidemia, HDL-C is only one piece of the puzzle.

DEFINITION

High-density lipoprotein (HDL), the smallest in size of the lipoproteins, includes a complex family of lipoprotein particles. These lipoprotein particles exist in a constant state of dynamic flux as they interact with other HDL particles, low-density lipoprotein (LDL), and very low density lipoprotein (VLDL) particles. HDL has the highest proportion of protein relative to lipid compared to other lipoproteins, comprising > 50% protein. The major HDL proteins are designated apolipoproteins AI (apo A-I) and A-II, with small amounts of the C apolipoproteins (C-I, C-II, and C-III), E, A-IV, and D. Phospholipids are the principal lipid component of HDL, with lesser amounts of cholesterol esters, unesterified cholesterol, and TG (see Table 7–1). Since cholesterol esters are hydrolyzed to unesterified or free cholesterol in most analytical procedures, the esterified portion is usually quantified as unesterified cholesterol.

Table 7–1 ✧ Lipid Composition of HDL Particles	
Lipid	*% of Total Lipid*
Phospholipids	50
Cholesterol esters	30
Cholesterol	10
Triglycerides	10

Classically, HDL-C refers to the fraction of TC (both free cholesterol and cholesterol esters) associated with HDL as defined by ultracentrifugation (hydrated density). In common practice, these fractions, separated by chemical precipitation or electrophoretic (mobility) properties, are also referred to as HDL. Therefore, HDL is defined by the operation used to isolate the lipoprotein and includes a family of similar particles that vary in size, chemistry, and composition.

REVIEW OF EXISTING METHODS

Ultracentrifugation

Lipoproteins can be readily separated on the basis of their differing hydrated densities using ultracentrifugation techniques. The proportion of lipid, especially TG, associated with the proteins in a particular lipoprotein adds to the buoyancy of the total complex, allowing separation of the major classes by either equilibrium or rate methods.

The nomenclature for lipoproteins that is commonly used in the literature is based on their relative densities. Therefore, VLDL by definition includes particles with density < 1.006 Kg/L, the background density of serum. The density range of LDL particles is 1.006–1.063 Kg/L and of HDL particles is 1.063–1.210 Kg/L. (For additional information on the separation of lipoproteins by ultracentrifugation, refer to Chapter 29.) These classes are approximately comparable to electrophoretic fractions designated pre-beta, beta, and alpha lipoproteins, respectively.

Fractionation of the lipoproteins can be accomplished using ultracentrifugation following adjustment of the specimen density with salts, such as NaBr or KBr.[4] Figure 7–1 illustrates the 1.063 Kg/L separation of VLDL and LDL (top fraction) from HDL (bottom fraction).

The reliability of lipoprotein quantitations following separation by ultracentrifugation techniques depends on both the performance of the analytical method, such as cholesterol analysis, and the skills of the technologist performing accurate recovery and transfer of the lipoprotein fractions from the ultracentrifuge tube. Further adjustment of the 1.063 Kg/L bottom fraction to a density of 1.210 Kg/L followed by ultracentrifugation can be used to isolate the HDL from other serum proteins. However, for quantitative analysis, HDL is usually simply considered to be the fraction of density > 1.063 Kg/L.

Ultracentrifugation has long been considered the ultimate comparison method for the isolation and quantitation of lipoproteins. Unfortunately, ultracentrifugation cannot meet the stringent requirements for a reference method. Achieving complete and reproducible recovery is difficult, even for experienced technologists, and fractions may be cross-contaminated. In addition, fractions isolated by ultracentrifugation are heterogeneous, containing other functional particles. For example, the HDL fraction with density between 1.063 and 1.210 Kg/L may contain considerable amounts of Lp(a).

An interesting utilization of the ultracentrifuge is an automated approach to quantitate lipoprotein fractions from a single spin.[5] An aliquot (1.3 mL) of plasma adjusted to a density of 1.21 Kg/L with solid KBr is overlaid with 3.5 mL of normal saline and

Figure 7–1 ✧ Ultracentrifugation at 1.063 Kg/L

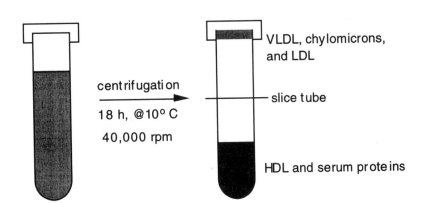

Figure 7-2 ✧ Separations by Electrophoretic Systems

The left panel illustrates the typical pattern observed for serum proteins, with immunoglobulins at the origin in the gamma region and albumin migrating past the alpha region. The middle and right panels demonstrate differences observed for lipoproteins separated on cellulose acetate or agarose media compared to polyacrylamide. Polyacrylamide separates the lipoproteins on the basis of size.

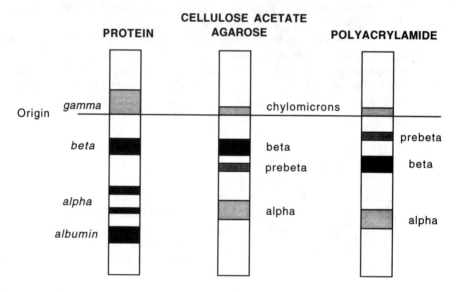

centrifuged in a vertical rotor (DuPont-Sorvall rotor TV865) for 45 min at 64,000 rpm. The bottom of the centrifuged sample tube is punctured and cholesterol concentration of the effluent is monitored continuously. A computer is used to analyze the profile and generate values for cholesterol associated with HDL, LDL, VLDL, and Lp(a). This single-spin vertical autoprofiler (VAP) approach is capable of accurate and reproducible lipoprotein quantitation.

Electrophoresis

Historically, lipoproteins were isolated using electrophoretic techniques and the lipoproteins, visualized with lipophilic dyes, were named on the basis of mobility by comparison to mobilities of common serum proteins. Thus, lipoprotein classes were commonly referred to as alpha, pre-beta, and beta lipoproteins (see Figure 7–2). Lipoproteins can be separated using a variety of electrophoretic media, such as paper, agarose gel, cellulose acetate, and polyacrylamide with numerous buffers.[6] Lipid stains, such as Oil Red O, Fat Red 7B, or Sudan Black, have been used to detect lipoproteins after electrophoresis. Alpha lipoproteins which have mobility comparable to alpha-proteins are approximately comparable to the HDL class.

Electrophoresis has proven primarily useful for qualitative analysis of lipoproteins and has not been considered appropriate for quantitation. The lipophilic dyes are not specific for a class of lipid, such as cholesterol, TG, or phospholipids, and as result cannot be used to accurately quantitate lipoproteins. Staining electrophoretic plates with specific enzyme reagents, such as cholesterol esterase and oxidase for cholesterol coupled with a peroxidase indicator, is an interesting approach.[7] However, the system must be reproducible to achieve the precision or accuracy necessary for HDL-C quantitation for clinical purposes. Recent studies suggest newer automated electrophoretic systems may be made suitable for accurate HDL-C quantitation.[8] For additional information on electrophoresis of lipoproteins, refer to Chapter 27.

Precipitation

Selective chemical precipitation techniques were reported by Burstein and Samaille in 1960 as a rapid method to measure cholesterol associated with the lipoproteins.[9] Selective precipitation of lipoproteins can occur by mixing polyanions and divalent cations or other chemicals with the serum/plasma specimens to precipitate VLDL and LDL which are sedimented by low-speed centrifugation.[10-12] Cholesterol in the supernate is quantitated by a conventional enzymic or other assay. Table 7–2 lists several of the common reagents available for selective isolation of lipoproteins.[13-17]

Table 7–2 ✧ The Most Common Precipitation Procedures for the Isolation of Lipoproteins
✧   Heparin-Manganese Chloride[13]
✧   Heparin-Calcium Chloride[14]
✧   Dextran Sulfate-Magnesium Chloride[15]
✧   Sodium Phosphotungstate-Magnesium Chloride[16]
✧   Polyethylene glycol[17]

Each of the chemical precipitation methods has several modifications or variations which reportedly improve the selectivity or performance of the system. For example, heparin-manganese chloride methods are reported with 1.0 and 2.0 mol/L $MnCl_2$, where the lower concentration is the preferred reagent with serum and the latter with EDTA plasma. The higher concentration with plasma is required to compensate for the chelation of some of the divalent cations by EDTA and avoid incomplete precipitation of apo B-containing lipoproteins. Dextran sulfate-$MgCl_2$ precipitation has been reported with both 500,000 and 50,000 molecular weight materials; the HDL-C values are significantly lower with the first reagent. The sodium phosphotungstate procedures have been used with or without $MgCl_2$, adjusted for pH and at several concentrations. Similarly, a variety of polyethylene glycol concentrations and pH conditions have been reported for HDL-C analysis.

Quantitation of HDL-C in routine laboratories is performed almost exclusively by one of the precipitation techniques. There are several reasons for this:

1. There is high demand for routine quantitation of HDL-C as a CHD risk factor and the estimation of LDL-C by the Friedewald calculation.

2. Expensive equipment, such as the ultracentrifuge, is not required.

3. Cholesterol analysis is performed directly on supernate.

4. The technique can be partially automated for high-volume laboratories.

Therefore, HDL-C was more easily quantitated by the relatively simple and inexpensive selective precipitation techniques compared to either ultracentrifugation or electrophoresis methods.

Selection of the most suitable HDL reagent for a given laboratory is not a simple decision. Inordinate effort would be required to perform an in-depth evaluation of each method to assess all the possible performance characteristics and optimize the procedures to ensure that the cholesterol in the supernate accurately represents the patient's HDL-C. Most laboratories rely on commercial reagents, with the majority using either dextran sulfate or sodium phosphotungstate procedures. Two methods, representative of typical assays with these two reagents, are described in some detail in the following sections.

Dextran Sulfate[15]

This method was reported as a selected method for clinical chemistry.[18]

Reagents:

Dextran sulfate (50,000 MW) is manufactured by Sochibo (Meudon-La-Foret, France) and distributed by Genzyme (Boston, MA) in the USA. Reagent-grade magnesium chloride hexahydrate crystalline material is available from several sources.

Solutions:

Stock dextran sulfate solution is prepared with 2.0 g dextran sulfate in 100 mL deionized water. Stock 1.0 mol/L magnesium chloride is prepared with the dry hexahydrated salt using 20.3 g $MgCl_2$ in 100 mL deionized water. Combined working solution is prepared by mixing equal volumes of the two stock solutions to obtain a 10 g/L solution of dextran sulfate and 0.5 mol/L $MgCl_2$. Alternatively, the combined reagent can be prepared directly. With the addition of 0.05% sodium azide (NaN_3), this reagent is stable for at least one year at room temperature.

Precipitation Sequence:

1. Equilibrate specimens and reagents to room temperature.

2. Transfer an accurate and reproducible volume of specimen (either plasma or serum) to a suitable tube, e.g., 10 × 75 mm. The user may select a volume based upon the analytical requirements for cholesterol analysis. The original document suggests a 2.0 mL sample size; however, 500 μL should be more than sufficient for most enzymic cholesterol assays.

3. Add the combined working reagent at the amount of 10% of the volume of specimen used, such that a 1.0 mL specimen should have 100 µL of precipitation reagent. Thoroughly mix the tube immediately, preferably using a vortex mixer, for a minimum of 3 sec.

4. Allow the tubes to sit for 10 min at room temperature before centrifugation.

5. Centrifugation for sedimentation of the precipitate was originally recommended at 1500 ×g at 4° C for 30 min. More recent studies[19] suggest that centrifugation between 10–12,000 ×g for 5 min gives equivalent results on normolipidemic specimens and better sedimentation for hyperlipidemic specimens.

6. Carefully remove the supernate by pipeting from the pellet for cholesterol analysis. The use of conical-shaped rather than round-bottom tubes may facilitate the removal of the supernate without disturbing the pellet.

   Note: Incomplete separation of apo B-containing lipoproteins may be observed by the presence of cloudy or turbid supernates in hypertriglyceridemic specimens. Cloudy supernates may be cleared by ultrafiltration with a 0.22 µm filter or by repeat precipitation procedure with the original specimen diluted 1:1 with saline. Alternatively, the dilution can be made subsequently on turbid supernates. Simply mix equal volumes of the turbid supernate with an equal volume of saline containing precipitation reagent at the same concentration originally added to the specimen.

7. Perform the cholesterol analysis on the supernate.

   Note: The cholesterol assay should be optimized for high performance in the low cholesterol concentration range. The cholesterol result is corrected for dilution by multiplying by 1.1. In the case of turbid supernates diluted with saline, multiply by the additional dilution factor times 2.

Sodium Phosphotungstate[16,20]

Reagents:

Reagent-grade phosphotungstate-free acid crystals and magnesium acetate (tetrahydrate) are available from several chemical suppliers.

Solutions:

Stock 4% sodium phosphotungstate is prepared with 10.0 g of the free acid dissolved in 125 mL deionized water mixed with 40 mL 1.0 mol/L NaOH. The resulting solution is adjusted to pH 7.6 and brought to a total volume of 250 mL. The pH of the stock solution should be checked for stability and adjusted as required with dilute NaOH. Stock 2.0 mol/L magnesium acetate is prepared with 42.89 g of magnesium acetate [$(CH_3CO_2)_2Mg \cdot 4H_2O$] dissolved in 100 mL deionized water in a volumetric flask. The magnesium acetate solution should be checked by the laboratory's routine Mg assay to insure proper concentration (see instructions below). Combined working reagent is prepared by mixing 4 parts of the 4% sodium phosphotungstate with 1 part 2.0 mol/L magnesium acetate.

Analysis to Confirm the Concentration of the
Stock 2.0 M Magnesium Acetate Solution:

Transfer 1.0 mL of the stock solution to a 250 mL volumetric flask and bring to volume with deionized water for a 0.008 mmol/L solution that contains 19.45 mg/dL Mg. Analysis of the diluted magnesium acetate solution by the laboratory's routine Mg procedure should range from 19.25–19.65 mg/dL.

The stock magnesium acetate can be easily diluted with deionized water or adjusted with solid magnesium acetate to compensate for overly concentrated or dilute reagent, respectively.

Note: With this reagent it is important to be consistent in batch-to-batch preparation.

1. Prepare fresh, combined working reagent for a batch of specimens.

2. Allow the specimens to equilibrate to room temperature. Label the conical centrifuge tubes with appropriate identification marks for the specimens and controls.

3. Using a precision dispenser/dilutor, transfer 500 µL of serum and 63 µL of combined working reagent to a conical shaped centrifuge tube.

4. Vortex the resultant mixture for 15 sec.

5. Centrifuge the specimens at 1500 xg (2900 rpm with the Beckman Accuspin FR) at 4° C for 45 min.

   Note: To achieve reproducibility with this reagent, it is important to standardize and be consistent in the timing and temperature of the measuring, mixing, and centrifugation steps.

6. Carefully remove the supernate and transfer to proper container for cholesterol analysis without disturbing the pellet.

7. Analyze the supernatant for cholesterol content and correct the result for dilution by multiplying by 1.126.

CDC Reference Method

The following procedure is used at Centers for Disease and Prevention (CDC) to assign HDL-C target values for human-based serum pools.[21] Although there is no validated reference method for HDL-C now, the CDC HDL-C procedure can be considered the best current accuracy target because most of the major epidemiologic/population studies have used CDC pools as the reference target for analyses. Since the accepted NCEP cutpoints for HDL-C are derived from such population studies, appropriate patient classification is dependent on obtaining routine results in agreement with the CDC method. Therefore, the CDC HDL-C method is considered the reference method for calibrating and checking the accuracy of routine methods.

There are three key components to the CDC HDL-C method, outlined below and illustrated in Figure 7–3.

Figure 7–3 ✧ CDC HDL-C Reference Method

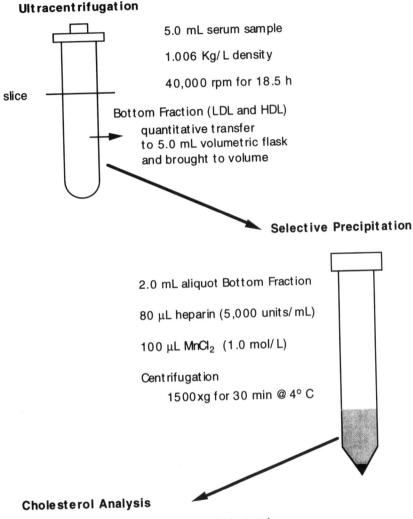

Ultracentrifugation

5.0 mL serum sample

1.006 Kg/L density

40,000 rpm for 18.5 h

slice

Bottom Fraction (LDL and HDL)
quantitative transfer
to 5.0 mL volumetric flask
and brought to volume

Selective Precipitation

2.0 mL aliquot Bottom Fraction

80 µL heparin (5,000 units/mL)

100 µL $MnCl_2$ (1.0 mol/L)

Centrifugation
1500xg for 30 min @ 4° C

Cholesterol Analysis

Modified Abell-Kendall procedure for cholesterol
optimized for the low range of HDL-C values

1. Ultracentrifuge at density 1.006 Kg/L to isolate HDL and LDL from chylomicrons and VLDL.[21] Selective precipitation procedures for HDL may be falsely elevated when increased triglyceride-rich lipoproteins (chylomicrons and VLDL) prevent their sedimentation. Therefore, ultracentrifugation eliminates these lipoproteins as potential interferences.

2. Perform selective precipitation of LDL with heparin/$MnCl_2$. CDC uses the same precipitation reagent as that used for the Lipid Research Clinics studies.

a. *Reagents:* Pharmaceutical-grade heparin (Lipo-Hepin, Riker Laboratories, Minneapolis, MN) (40,000 units/mL) and reagent-grade $MnCl_2.4H_2O$ (available from several chemical suppliers) are used for the HDL procedure.

b. *Solutions:* Working heparin solution (5,000 units/mL). Mix 1.0 mL heparin with 7.0 mL saline (0.15 mol/L NaCl). The solution is stable for at least 1 month when stored at 4° C. A 1.0 mol/L $MnCl_2$ solution is prepared by dissolving 197.91 g of the tetrahydrate in water and bringing to volume in a 1.0 L volumetric flask.

c. *Precipitation:* Add 80 µL heparin solution and 100 µL $MnCl_2$ to 2.0 mL of 1.006 bottom fraction in an ice bucket, mixing thoroughly after each addition. Allow to stand for 30 min in the ice bucket and centrifuge for 30 min at 1500 xg and at 4° C. Recover supernates by pipeting for subsequent cholesterol analysis.

3. Analyze cholesterol in the HDL supernate by the CDC reference method, a modified Abell-Kendall assay. The Abell-Kendall reference method for TC is the accepted accuracy target for any cholesterol tests in specific lipoproteins, including HDL-C. The HDL supernate aliquot required for cholesterol analysis is twice the amount required for TC to increase the sensitivity of the procedure in the lower HDL-C range.

Designated Comparison Method[22]

Few laboratories have an ultracentrifuge available to perform the CDC reference method for HDL-C. In addition, ultracentrifugation requires a sample volume greater than 5.0 mL, which exceeds the amount laboratories receive for a total lipid panel. Therefore, the Network Laboratories developed the following dextran sulfate procedure to be used with lesser volumes of either serum or plasma samples. The Network Laboratories established this method for a comparative analysis with HDL-C procedures used in outside laboratories that require a critical analysis of their accuracy.[23, 24] Thus, all laboratories are able to perform the assay within their laboratory. Note the slight but important variations in this method from the dextran sulfate procedure listed previously. (For additional information on Network Laboratories, refer to Chapter 12.)

Solutions:

Stock dextran sulfate solution is prepared with 2.0 g dextran sulfate (Dextralip 50, Cat #70-5800, available from Genzyme) and 50 mg NaN_3 (sodium azide) in 100 mL deionized water. Store at 2–8° C. Prepare stock 0.7 mol/L magnesium chloride with dry 14.22 g $MgCl_2$ hexahydrated salt and 50 mg NaN_3 in 100 mL deionized water. Store at 2–8° C. Prepare combined working solution by mixing equal volumes of the two stock solutions to obtain a solution of 10 g/L dextran sulfate and 0.35 mol/L $MgCl_2$.

Precipitation sequence:

1. Equilibrate specimens and reagents to room temperature. It is recommended that HDL separation be performed on the same day the specimen is collected;

otherwise the sample off the cells may be stored up to 48 h at 4° C or frozen at –70° C. (Frozen samples at –15° C are probably acceptable.)

Note: The method states the samples should be collected from fasting individuals, 12–14 h. Also, samples must have triglycerides < 200 mg/dL (2.26 mmol/L).

2. Transfer an accurate and reproducible volume of specimen (either plasma or serum) to a 4.5 mL tube. Pipette 1000 µL of well-mixed sample and add 100 µL of the combined reagent into the tube. Cap the tube with parafilm and vortex for 5 sec.

3. Incubate the tubes for 10 min starting from the time the last tube in the rack is vortexed.

4. Centrifuge the tubes at the highest speed for 32 min in a Beckman TJ-3 refrigerated centrifuge (or equivalent) set at 10° C.

5. Transfer clear supernates, without disturbing the pellet, to a suitably labeled tube. Place cloudy supernates on a low-speed centrifuge with 0.22 µm filters (Millipore Corp., catalog #AP20 29325). If supernate is not clear, do not assay.

6. Assay the supernates by enzymic or Abell-Kendall method on the same day as precipitated, or freeze at –20° C.

NEW HDL-C METHODS

Second-Generation HDL-C Assays

As of this writing, manufacturers have provided few alternate approaches for HDL-C analysis that lessen the labor-intensive aspects of the separation methods listed above. Cholesterol analysis can be performed with automated chemistry analyzers, but the HDL precipitation step requires pipeting, mixing, and centrifugation, which are difficult to automate. Efforts have been made to streamline the pre-treatment and improve the efficiency of the quantitation. Some users have adapted robotic pipeting stations to achieve similar results. These labor-intensive procedures include the volume transfer of both the patient specimen and precipitation reagent, and the transfer of the HDL supernate for cholesterol analysis. Both of these steps require a technologist's time and, if the processes are not performed properly, significant error can be introduced into the HDL-C result.

The following sections describe several attempts by manufacturers to provide laboratories with more user-friendly methods for performing HDL-C analysis. One alternative commercial approach employs a plastic device (Spin-Pro) containing pre-measured precipitation reagent.[25] The user simply adds an unmeasured volume of serum or plasma in the top of the plastic tube and centrifuges the device. During centrifugation, a measured portion of the sample mixes with the precipitation reagent and the resultant precipitate sediments. After centrifugation, the supernate rises into the central well and the device can be placed in the sample tray of a chemistry analyzer for direct sampling. This device streamlines and standardizes the HDL separation.

A second commercial variation involves the use of magnetized dextran sulfate particles to circumvent centrifugation.[26] The magnetic reagent approach allows for the separation of the complexed lipoproteins (VLDL and LDL) from HDL-containing supernate with a magnet rather than a centrifuge—a possible advantage for small laboratories.

Both of these approaches achieve the benefit of requiring less labor-intensive sample processing for HDL measurement. Serendipitously, both of these HDL procedures have been reported to work with hypertriglyceridemic specimens, samples which are difficult to process with most conventional HDL methods.[27, 28] In addition, the magnetic approach may offer a streamlined separation in conjunction with automated chemistry analyses. Finally, there are also compact analyzers with integrated HDL separation schemes which use whole blood and eliminate the need for pre-treatment steps. (See Chapter 9 for additional discussion of these methods).[29, 30] These last two techniques are attractive to clinics that lack centrifuges to perform the more traditional HDL-C assays. But a new generation of HDL-C methods are available.

Third-Generation HDL-C Assays

The newer approaches to HDL-C analysis provides the user with highly automated and reproducible methods that require minimal sample handing.[31-33] In fact, the only sample handing required may be as simple as placing a bar-coded specimen on the automated analyzer and letting the system do the rest of the work. Such is the case with two recently released commercial methods. The specimen (less than 10 μL) is incubated with one reagent, which forms stable complexes with all apo B-containing lipoproteins. Unlike previous HDL methods, these complexed particles remain soluble in the reaction mixture. However, as in the previous methods, HDL remains free of the complexing agents. The second step is the addition of the enzymic reagents, cholesterol oxidase and esterase (see Figure 7–4). These enzymes may either be modified with molecules that inhibit their interaction with the complexed lipoproteins and leave only HDL as their substrate, or mixed with detergents that enhance their enzymic activity towards the uncomplexed HDL particles. Either approach can be readily adapted to highly automated systems and provide substantial cost savings by reducing labor cost. An advantage of these newer methods is the improved precision gained from the automation of the method, which may allow future HDL-C methods to achieve the NCEP performance goals for 1998 and beyond. The reduced complexity of these new HDL approaches will result in rapid acceptance by clinical laboratories within the next few years. HDL precipitation techniques will be replaced in many routine applications.

Polyethylene glycol (PEG), modified cholesterol esterase and oxidase are the key aspects of the new HDL approach reported in 1995.[31] The authors found the 6,000 dalton form of PEG to be the most efficient to maintain functional activity towards cholesterol and cholesterol esters with intact HDL. Sulfated α-cyclodextrin in the presence of 2 mol $MgCl_2$ was added to the final reaction mixture to reduce the activity of the modified enzymes with both VLDL and chylomicrons. The cyclodextrin-lipoprotein interactions resulted in soluble complexes that do not react and do not interfere with the absorbance readings of the enzyme cholesterol reagents.

Figure 7-4 ✧ General Third-Generation HDL-C Schemes

The left panel illustrates the addition of the α-cyclodextrin and magnesium, which forms soluble complexes with the chylomicrons, VLDL, and LDL. The right panel represents the addition of modified cholesterol esterase (CE) and oxidase (CO), which have limited reactivity towards the complexed lipoproteins.

PHASE 1 - Selective Inactivation   Phase 2 - Modified Enzymic Activity

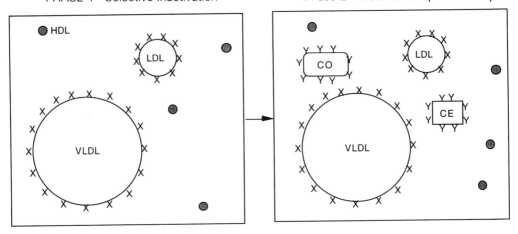

Preliminary evaluations of these new HDL-C methods suggests that they will achieve the performance standards required by NCEP. In addition, these assays seem to work well with hypertriglyceridemic specimens. Thus, these new third-generation HDL-C assays will likely impact the procedures by which clinical laboratories perform HDL-C analysis.

Assessment of HDL-C Method Performance

Regardless of which method a laboratory selects to measure HDL-C on patient specimens, the procedure should be capable of achieving acceptable analytical performance. Analytical performance goals for precision, accuracy, and total error in HDL-C measurement have been developed by the NCEP (see Table 7–3).[34] Most of the common precipitation techniques can provide acceptable results when performed with an accurate and reproducible cholesterol assay. Precision can be assessed by replicate analysis of commercial controls or frozen serum pools. Currently the only reliable approach for ensuring the accuracy of a routine HDL-C assay is a comparison of actual patient specimens with a Network laboratory using the Designated Comparison Method. Reference materials for HDL-C that behave as patient materials for the transfer of accuracy from laboratory to laboratory are not available through the usual commercial sources.

Table 7–3 ❖ NCEP HDL-C Analytical Goals	
INTERIM GOALS	
Precision	HDL-C ≥42 mg/dL (1.09 mmol/L): CV ≤ 6% < 42 mg/dL: SD ≤ 2.5 mg/dL (0.065 mmol/L)
Accuracy*	bias ≤ ± 10%
Total Allowable Error	≤ 22%
1998 GOALS	
Precision	HDL-C ≥ 42 mg/dL (1.09 mmol/L): CV ≤ 4% < 42 mg/dL: SD ≤ 1.7 mg/dL (0.044 mmol/L)
Accuracy*	bias ≤ ± 5%
Total Allowable Error	≤ 13%
* Bias compared to CDC three-step reference method.	

Standardization of TC measurements has been improved by the activities of the Cholesterol Reference Method Laboratory Network, which was organized by CDC to make reference methods readily available for direct comparison on fresh patient specimens. Recently, the Network has established a similar program for standardizing HDL-C measurement using the Designated Comparison Method mentioned above. The Network laboratories will be available to manufacturers and clinical laboratories to verify the accuracy of their HDL-C methods. A detailed protocol for conducting a comparison study is available through the Network program. (See Chapter 12 for additional information on the Network Laboratories).

In addition to participating in the Network program, manufacturers and laboratories may wish to perform additional validation. The following set of universal evaluation and performance considerations is presented to enable a laboratory to check its own HDL procedure.

1.   Optimize cholesterol method.
    a. Linearity from 0–120 mg/dL (0–3.11 mmol/L).
    b. Reproducibility with 1SD = 2 mg/dL (0.05 mmol/L) or less.

2.   Establish reproducible specimen and reagent transfers using precise pipettes. Methods maybe automated using programmable dispensing apparatus. For example, the Beckman Accu-Prep or Micromedic systems are capable of high precision. High-volume laboratories may automate this process to the extent of achieving a "walk-away" system.

3.   Establish specific conditions for specimen processing.
    a. Length of time for mixing (vortexing)
    b. Time and temperature for incubation
    c. Time, temperature, and force of centrifugation

4.   Compare HDL-C results on fresh patient specimen with a reliable laboratory using accurate methods.

a. The Cholesterol Reference Method Laboratory Network sponsored by CDC is available for such comparisons (phone 770-488-4126 for additional information).

b. Patient specimens should be distributed throughout the usual assay range of 20–100 mg/dL (0.52–2.59 mmol/L).

c. Analyze specimens stored or shipped under similar conditions at about the same time to minimize confounding effects of specimen deterioration.

The following experiments can be performed to assess the specificity and separation characteristics of any given HDL-C procedure:

1. Lipoprotein electrophoresis of the supernates and resolubilized precipitates provides an indication of the specificity of the separation. The HDL precipitates should be washed with saline/precipitation reagent solution and dissolved with 0.6 mol/L NaCl prior to electrophoresis. The supernate should have an HDL or alpha band only and no beta or pre-beta band, and the precipitate should have no HDL band. The sensitivity of this technique depends upon the characteristics of the stain used with the particular electrophoresis method.

2. Analysis of both the supernates and solubilized precipitates for apolipoprotein AI and B (apo AI and apo B) can assess the possible inadequate separation of lipoproteins; for example, apo B in the supernate would suggest the presence of non-HDL contamination. High levels of apo AI in the precipitate suggests precipitation of HDL.

3. Select several patient specimens with varying amounts of TG to compare the performance of the HDL-C assay at low and increased concentrations of TG. Some, HDL-C methods experience incomplete sedimentation and supernatant turbidity when TG exceed 400–500 mg/dL (4.52–5.65 mmol/L). Specimens with chylomicrons can give erroneous values, often yielding cloudy supernates and overestimation of HDL. Such specimens should be re-precipitated after dilution or the supernates filtered to obtain reliable results.

Population Frequency Distribution for HDL-C

Lipid Research Clinics (LRC) data[35] from a prevalence study has reported the HDL-C values for plasma using the heparin/$MnCl_2$ precipitation procedure and Technicon AutoAnalyzer cholesterol method. Keep in mind that the LRC HDL-C method required the use of 0.046 mol/L $MnCl_2$ and heparin with EDTA plasma specimens. If the study were repeated today, the method would use a higher (0.092 mol/L) concentration of $MnCl_2$ and have slightly lower HDL-C values. Refer to the appendix for the LRC HDL-C values in various populations.

NECP guidelines for interpreting HDL-C data have simplified the matter for clinicians. Simply, serum HDL-C values < 35 mg/dL (0.91 mmol/L) are associated with increased risk for CHD for both males and females. In addition, HDL-C values ≥60 mg/dL (1.56 mmol/L) are a positive healthy indicator for the patient. As HDL-C values increase above 35 mg/dL (0.91 mmol/L), TC to HDL-C ratios tend to decrease, which is also considered a healthy indicator. In general, ratios, whether HDL or otherwise, have interesting statistical significance concerning a patient's risk toward a given disease.

However, ratios are unitless values and NCEP guidelines suggest the physician make decisions based on the individual TC or LDL-C to HDL-C values rather than the ratios.

SUMMARY REMARKS

HDL-C analysis has been routine for almost twenty years, and yet there is still a need to improve analytical performance to ensure that HDL-C results meet the clinical requirements. The analytical goals for accuracy and precision developed by the NCEP provide a performance target for clinical laboratories. The CDC reference method network program which has been effective in standardizing TC provides a similar service for HDL-C, which will facilitate improvements in accuracy. Development and widespread availability of HDL-C reference materials that behave as patient specimens (no matrix effects) for use in comparing other HDL-C assays to the consensus reference procedure would make the standardization process more efficient. Priority should be given to encouraging manufacturers to take advantage of the opportunity to validate and standardize their methods, as this will have the effect of improving performance in many laboratories.

The importance of accurate HDL-C measurements was emphasized by Robert Levy, M.D., past director of the National Heart Lung and Blood Institute, who made the following statement concerning HDL-C performance requirements in a paper in *Clinical Chemistry:*[36]

> One has to be able to measure accurately in the range below 50 mg/dL (1.30 mmol/L) a difference of less than 5 mg/dL (0.13 mmol/L) if the HDL determination is to be used to define an individual's risk.

The newer generation HDL-C assays will facilitate the ability of laboratories to achieve this lofty performance standard. The new automated procedures will likely provide better precision in HDL-C measurements, which in turn will lead to better comparison studies to resolve biases that may exist between the different approaches. Development of better HDL reference materials that can be used to transfer accuracy among methods is a critical component that would facilitate this process. ✦

REFERENCES

1. Current status of blood cholesterol measurements in clinical chemistry laboratories in the United States: a report from the Laboratory Standardization Panel of the National Cholesterol Education Program. Clin Chem 1988;34:193-201.

2. The Expert Panel. Summary of the second report of the National Cholesterol Education Program (NCEP) expert panel on detection, evaluation, and treatment of high blood cholesterol in adults (Adult Treatment Panel II). JAMA 1993;269:3015-23.

3. Fuster V, Badimon L, Badimon JJ, Chesbro JH. The pathogenesis of coronary artery disease and the acute coronary symptoms. N Eng J Med 1992;326:242-56, 310-18.

4. Lindgren FT, Jensen LC, Hatch FT. The isolation and quantitative analysis of serum lipoproteins. In: Nelson GF (ed.), Blood lipids and lipoproteins: quantitation, composition, and metabolism. Wiley Interscience, 1972:181-274.

5. Cone JT, Segrest JP, Chung BH, Ragland JB, Sabesin SM, Glasscock A. Computerized rapid high resolution quantitative analysis of plasma lipoproteins based upon a single vertical spin centrifugation. J Lipid Res 1982;23:923-35.

6. Lewis LA and Opplt JJ (eds.). CRC handbook of electrophoresis, Vol 1. CRC Press, Boca Raton, 1980.

7. Conlon DR, Blankstein LA, Pasakarins PA, Steinberg CM, D'Amelio JE. Quantitative determination of high-density lipoprotein cholesterol by agarose gel electrophoresis. Clin Chem 1979:25:1965–9.

8. Warnick GR, Leary ET, Goetsch J, Hicks D. Electrophoretic quantitation of LDL-cholesterol using the Helena REP. Clin Chem 1993;39:1122.

9. Burstein M, Samaille J. Sur un dosage rapide du cholesterol lie aux a- et aux b-lipoproteins du serum. Clin Chem Acta 1960;5:609.

10. Levin SJ. High-density lipoprotein cholesterol: review of methods. American Society of Clinical Pathologists. Core Chemistry No. PTS 89-2 (PTS-36) 5/2, 1989.

11. Warnick GR, Cheung MC, Albers JJ. Comparison of current methods for high-density lipoprotein cholesterol quantitation. Clin Chem 1979;25:596–604.

12. Denmacker PNM, Hijmans AGM, Vos-Janssen HE, Van't Laar A, Jansen AP. Measurement of high-density lipoprotein cholesterol in serum: comparison of six isolation methods combined with enzymic cholesterol analysis. Clin Chem 1980;26:1780–6.

13. Warnick GR, Albers JJ. A comprehensive evaluation of the heparin-manganese precipitation procedure for estimating high density lipoprotein. J Lipid Res 1978;19:65–76.

14. Srinivasan SR, Radhakrishnamurthy B, Berenson GS. Studies on the interaction of heparin with serum lipoproteins in the presence of Ca^{++}, Mg^{++}, and Mn^{++}. Arch Biochem Biophys 1975;170:334–40.

15. Warnick GR, Benderson J, Albers JJ. Dextran sulfate-Mg^{2+} precipitation for quantitation of high-density lipoprotein cholesterol. Clin Chem 1982;28:1379–88.

16. Lopes-Virella MF, Stone P, Ellis S, Colwell JA. Cholesterol determination in high-density lipoproteins separated by three different methods. Clin Chem 1977;23:882–4.

17. Brigg CJ, Anderson D, Johnson P, Deegan T. Evaluation of the polyethylene glycol precipitation method for the estimation of high-density lipoprotein cholesterol. Ann Clin Biochem 1981;18:177–81.

18. Warnick GR, Benderson J, Albers JJ. Dextran sulfate-Mg^{2+} precipitation procedure for quantitation of high density lipoprotein cholesterol. In: Cooper, GR, ed. Selected methods of clinical chemistry, Vol. 10. Washington, DC: American Association for Clinical Chemistry, 1983:91–99.

19. Nguyen T, Warnick GR. Improved methods for the quantitation of total HDL and subclasses. Clin Chem 1989;35:1086.

20. Davies C, Fahie-Wilson MN. Use of magnesium acetate in high-density lipoprotein cholesterol assay. Clin Chem 1979;25:1510.

21. Hainline A, Karon J, Lippel K., eds. Manual of laboratory operations. In: Lipid Research Clinics Program, Lipid and lipoprotein analysis, 2nd ed. Bethesda, MD: U.S. Dept. Health and Human Services, 1982.

22. Warnick, GR, Pacific Biometrics, Inc., Seattle WA. Personal communication.

23. Kimberly MM, Waymack PP, Myers GL, et al. Comparison of precipitation methods for determination of HDL cholesterol in the Cholesterol Reference Method Laboratory Network. Clin Chem 1994;40:1105.

24. Kimberly MM, Waymack PP, Smith SJ. Evaluation of frozen vs. fresh serum samples using the Designated Comparison Method for HDL cholesterol in the Cholesterol Reference Method Laboratory Network. Clin Chem 1995;41:S136.

25. Tjersland G, Warnick GR, Cole TG. SPINPRO-HDL qualifies for certification from the CDC Cholesterol Reference Method Laboratory Network. Clin Chem 1996;42:S289.

26. Naito HK, Kwak YS. The evaluation of a new high-density lipoprotein cholesterol (HDL-C) technology: selective separation of lipoproteins by magnetic separation. Clin Chem 1995;41:S135.

27. Harris N, Galpchian, Rifai, N. Three routine methods for high-density lipoprotein cholesterol compared with the Reference Method. Clin Chem 1996;42:738–43.

28. Harris N, Galpchian V, Thomas J, Lannotti E, Law T, Rifai, N. Three generations of high-density lipoprotein cholesterol assays compared with ultracentrifugation/dextran sulfate-Mg^{2+} method. Clin Chem, in press.

29. Beranek J, Carlson C, Roberts P, Feld R. Evaluation of the Cholestech LDX lipid analyzer for cholesterol, triglyceride and HDL cholesterol (HDL-C) using whole blood. Clin Chem 1994;40:1104.

30. Bodwell J, Roberts K. An evaluation of three lots of Reflotron HDL-cholesterol. Clin Chem 1992;38:1062.

31. Sugiuchi H, Uji Y, Okabe H, et al. Direct measurement of high-density lipoprotein cholesterol in serum with polyethylene glycol-modified enzymes and sulfated α-cyclo-dextrin. Clin Chem 1995;41:717-23.

32. Hino K, Nakamura M, Nakanishi K, Manabe M. A new method for the homogeneous assay of serum HDL-cholesterol. Clin Chem 1996;42:S298.

33. Pisani T, Krassnoff, Long S. A homogeneous assay for the measurement of HDL-cholesterol in serum. Clin Chem 1996;42:S294.

34. Warnick GR, Wood P. National Cholesterol Education Program recommendations for measurement of high-density lipoprotein cholesterol: Executive summary. Clin Chem 1995;41:1427-33.

35. The Lipid Research Clinics population studies data book. Vol. 1: The prevalence study. (NIH Publication No. 80-1527). National Institute of Health, 1980.

36. Levy RI. Cholesterol, lipoproteins, apoproteins, and heart disease: present status and future prospects. Clin Chem 1981;27:653-62.

Measurement of Low-Density Lipoprotein Cholesterol

8

Paul S. Bachorik

INTRODUCTION

❖   In serum or plasma from normal fasting individuals, cholesterol is associated with three major classes of lipoproteins: very-low-density lipoprotein (VLDL, $d < 1.006$ kg/L), low-density lipoprotein (LDL, d 1.019–1.063 kg/L), and high-density lipoprotein (HDL, d 1.063–1.21 kg/L). About two-thirds of this cholesterol is associated with LDL and most of the remainder is carried by the other two lipoproteins. A small amount of cholesterol (20–40 mg/L [0.50–1.0 mmol/L], on average) is also found in intermediate density lipoprotein (IDL, d 1.006–1.019 kg/L) and (Lp(a) (d 1.045–1.080 kg/L), although the concentrations of both of these lipoproteins can be considerably higher in certain individuals. In addition, patients with Type III hyperlipoproteinemia manifest an unusual lipoprotein called beta-VLDL, or "floating beta" lipoprotein, which is not present in normal individuals.[1]

LDL is formed in the circulation as the end product of VLDL catabolism. During this process, VLDL-triglycerides are hydrolyzed, and apolipoproteins other than apolipoprotein B (apo B) are removed. Intermediates in this process include VLDL remnants, part of which are removed by the liver, and IDL, which arise from the further catabolism of VLDL remnants.

LDL is a spherical molecule consisting of a hydrophobic core of cholesteryl esters and triglycerides (TG) surrounded by an amphipathic coat composed of phospholipids, unesterified cholesterol, and B-100. Each LDL molecule contains one mole of apo B-100. Small amounts of apo C-III (0.34–1.90 molecules) and apo E (0.08–0.74 molecules)[2] are also present on LDL. The lipids, as a percentage of the total mass of the LDL particle, consists of about 38% cholesterol ester, 22% phospholipid (principally phosphatidyl choline and sphingomyelin), 11% TG, and 8% unesterified cholesterol.[3] Protein makes up about 21% of the lipoprotein mass, and of this, 95% or more is apo B.

LDL-cholesterol (LDL-C) plays a causal role in the development of atherosclerosis. In 1988, The National Cholesterol Education Program Adult Treatment Panel (NCEP-ATP) developed recommendations for the diagnosis and treatment of patients with hypercholesterolemia.[4] These recommendations define hypercholesterolemia and use LDL-C as the primary criterion for treatment. The treatment recommendations are based on the patient's LDL-C concentration and also take account of a number of other risk factors. The ATP recommendations were updated in 1993.[5] The revised guidelines still use LDL-C concentration and risk factor profile as the primary treatment criteria, but additional emphasis was placed on the measurement of HDL-cholesterol (HDL-C) (see Chapter 2). The NCEP has also issued recommendations for the classification of children and adolescents;[6] these are given in Table 8-1.

Table 8–1 ✦ NCEP Guidelines for Adults and Classification for Children and Adolescents		
*Revised NCEP Guidelines for Adults: Initiation of Therapy**		
	Initiation Concentration	*Goal of Therapy*
Without 2 or more CHD risk factors	LDL-C ≥ 160 mg/dL (4.14 mmol/L)	LDL-C < 160 mg/dL (4.14 mmol/L)
With 2 or more CHD risk factors	LDL-C ≥ 130 mg/dL (3.36 mmol/L)	LDL-C < 130 mg/dL (3.36 mmol/L)
*Revised NCEP Guidelines for Adults: Initiation of Drug Therapy after Diet Therapy**		
Without 2 or more CHD risk factors	LDL-C ≥ 190 mg/dL (4.92 mmol/L)	LDL-C < 160 mg/dL (4.14 mmol/L)
With 2 or more CHD risk factors	LDL-C ≥ 160 mg/dL (4.14 mmol/L)	LDL-C < 130 mg/dL (3.36 mmol/L)
With CHD	LDL-C ≥ 130 mg/dL (3.36 mmol/L)	LDL-C < 100 mg/dL (2.59 mmol/L)
NCEP Classification for Children and Adolescents		
Desirable: LDL-C < 110 mg/dL (2.85 mmol/L)		
Borderline: LDL-C 110–129 mg/dL (2.85-3.34 mmol/L)		
High: LDL-C > 130 mg/dL (3.36 mmol/L)		
*See Chapter 2 for a list of risk factors.		

METHODOLOGY

General

Measurement of LDL-C requires the *separation* of LDL particles in serum from other lipoproteins, followed by the *measurement* of cholesterol in the LDL fraction. LDL can be separated from VLDL and HDL based on physical characteristics such as density, size, charge, or apolipoprotein composition. Some of the approaches that have been used are described briefly here.

Because of their lipid content, the densities of the lipoproteins are lower than those of the other serum proteins, and the lipoproteins can be separated from them, and from each other, using the ultracentrifuge. Methods for lipoprotein separation with the analytical ultracentrifuge were developed in the 1950s[7-9] and continue to be used today in some research laboratories. In this technique, the lipoproteins are separated according to their rates of flotation under defined conditions of density, temperature, and ultracentrifugal force. The migration of the lipoproteins is followed by measuring the changes in optical refraction as the lipoproteins migrate. The method measures the total mass of lipoproteins but does not provide information about their lipid or protein compositions. Analytical ultracentrifugation is useful for certain kinds of physical chemical studies and is the basis for the original definition of the lipoproteins in terms of their flotation rates and densities. Because of the complexity of the method, however, it is not suitable for use in the routine clinical laboratory or even in most research laboratories.

Sequential ultracentrifugation was developed by Havel, Eder, and Bragdon[10] in 1955. In this technique, the sample is ultracentrifuged at an appropriate density (e.g., *d* 1.006 kg/L for VLDL), and the floating layer is collected. The infranatant is then adjusted to the next density (e.g., *d* 1.019 kg/L), ultracentrifuged again, and the lipoproteins that float at the new density, in this case IDL, are recovered. The process is repeated until all lipoprotein fractions of interest have been isolated.[10, 11] Lipoproteins can be isolated within any desired density interval and in sufficient quantities to allow for multiple chemical analyses. Sequential ultracentrifugation continues to be used today for preparing lipoproteins, and for clinical purposes in certain circumstances (see discussion below).

Equilibrium density gradient ultracentrifugation evolved from sequential ultracentrifugation.[12-22] In this approach, the sample is placed onto a density gradient. The gradient is generally constructed using solutions of a dense salt, such as KBr, for density adjustment. A smooth density gradient can be constructed with the aid of a gradient maker, or alternatively, a series of solutions of different density can be layered onto each other to produce a gradient that is discontinuous initially, but which becomes smooth during ultracentrifugation. When ultracentrifuged, each lipoprotein migrates to its isopycnic (equilibrium) density, and the separated lipoproteins are collected for analysis. Depending on the density gradient used, this method can be used either to separate the major classes of lipoproteins from each other, or to separate each lipoprotein class into several subfractions whose densities and sizes differ slightly. Once collected, the lipoproteins or their subfractions can then be quantitated by measuring their cholesterol (or other compositional component) content. The technique is labor intensive, however, and its throughput is limited compared to the more commonly used methods (see discussion below). For this reason, its use is confined primarily to the research laboratory, although a commercial lipoprotein analytical service is available that uses a procedure based on density gradient ultracentrifugation (VAP Atherotech, Inc., Birmingham, AL). For additional information refer to Chapter 29.

Other methods for separating LDL-C include: gel filtration and other types of chromatography, electrophoresis, and precipitation or binding with appropriate reagents. The gel filtration methods include agarose column chromatography,[23] high-performance gel filtration chromatography,[24, 25] and fast-flow gel filtration.[26] Affinity chromatography using heparin, dextran sulfate, or antibodies to apo B, linked to Sepharose gels has also been used to isolate LDL. Chromatographic methods can exhibit considerable biases for LDL and HDL.[25] For additional information, refer to Chapter 30.

Electrophoretic methods separate the lipoproteins according to their charge and size. They are primarily used for the qualitative assessment of the presence of beta-VLDL, characteristic of Type III hyperlipoproteinemia (see discussion below). Electrophoretic methods are available from commercial sources as kits containing pre-formed agarose gels, buffer, and stain. A small quantity of the sample, typically 1–2 μL, is applied to the gel and electrophoresis is conducted at pH 8.6. The separated lipoproteins are visualized using lipophilic stains such as Oil Red O or Sudan Black B or with enzymatic cholesterol reagents. Because the lipoproteins contain essentially all the circulating lipids, the use of lipid stains precludes the need to separate the lipoproteins from the other plasma proteins. Figure 8–1 illustrates the migration of LDL and other lipoproteins using agarose gel electrophoresis.

Figure 8–1 ✧ Electrophoretic Patterns Observed in Normal and Type III Plasma

Representation of agarose gel electrophoresis of normal plasma (A) and plasma from patient with Type III hyperlipoproteinemia (B). Left to right: patterns observed in unfractionated plasma; ultracentrifugal top fraction; ultracentrifugal bottom fraction. When present, beta-VLDL appears in the ultracentrifugal top fraction as a band with the mobility of LDL. Note: When Lp(a) is present in sufficiently high concentration, it is observed in the ultracentrifugal bottom fraction as a band with a mobility similar to VLDL (not shown in diagram).

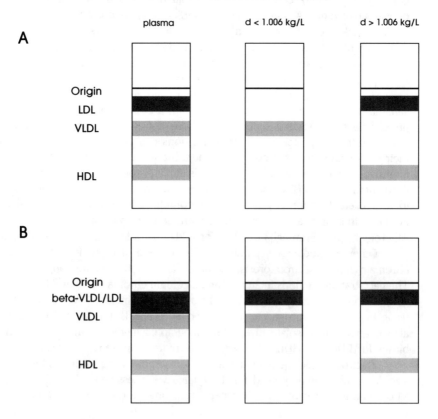

Although attempts have been made to quantitate the separated lipoproteins by densitometry or by measuring lipoprotein cholesterol enzymatically in the separated fractions, these methods have not been widely accepted for this purpose for several reasons. First, the apo-B-containing lipoproteins cannot be completely resolved from each other. For example, in paper or agarose gel, IDL can run as a smear overlapping LDL and VLDL; Lp(a) generally migrates with or near VLDL; and beta-VLDL, when present, co-migrates with LDL. Second, electrophoretic methods can be imprecise because of lot-to-lot and gel-to-gel variations in the gels themselves. Third, depending on their lipid composition, the intensity of staining per mole of lipoprotein differs among the lipoproteins. An extreme example of this occurs with samples from patients with biliary cirrhosis, who have high concentrations of unesterified cholesterol. Because unesterified cholesterol is not well visualized with lipophilic stains, electropherograms from such patients can appear normal despite the presence of cholesterol in concentrations above 1,000 mg/dL (25.9 mmol/L).[27] For additional information on electrophoretic separations, refer to Chapter 27.

Various methods for selective chemical precipitation have been reported.[28-34] In these methods, LDL-C is calculated as the difference between TC and that which remains soluble after precipitating LDL. Such methods can be reasonably accurate in samples with low TG concentrations, but can be quite inaccurate in samples with high TG concentrations.[28, 29, 33-37] In general, precipitation methods have been most successfully applied to remove the apo-B-containing lipoproteins from HDL rather than to separate apo-B-containing lipoproteins from each other, because they can also precipitate some of the remnants and IDL present in many samples with high TG concentrations.

Finally, using immunochemical techniques, LDL can be separated from the other lipoproteins using specific antibodies to particular apolipoproteins found in HDL and the other apo-B-containing lipoproteins. This approach is the basis for a promising new method, described later in this chapter.

Common Methods for LDL-C Measurement

The following discussion describes the most commonly used methods for LDL-C measurement, as well as an innovative and relatively new immunochemical method for direct LDL-C measurement.

Clinical LDL-C measurements, and those in most large-scale clinical and epidemiological studies, particularly those from which the relationships between LDL-C concentration and risk for coronary heart disease (CHD) were established, were made using one of two methods.[38] The first method combines ultracentrifugation and polyanion precipitation and is generally referred to as "beta quantification." Because the method is somewhat involved, it is not generally used for routine clinical measurements. Rather, beta quantification is primarily used in the initial diagnosis of hyperlipoproteinemia to rule out Type III hyperlipoproteinemia, and in circumstances where the second method cannot be used. The second, and by far the most commonly used method for routine clinical purposes and large-scale studies, is one in which LDL-C is estimated from primary measurements of TC, TG, and HDL-C using the Friedewald equation.[39]

Both of these methods have been studied and used extensively and are described below.

Beta Quantification

The beta quantification method assumes that virtually all cholesterol (TC) is contained in the three major lipoprotein classes:

    a. TC = VLDL-C + LDL-C + HDL-C

In addition to measuring LDL-C, the method also evaluates the presence of beta-VLDL. The procedure requires several kinds of measurements (TC, TG, and HDL-C) that are described elsewhere in this book. This discussion focuses on those manipulations that are specific to the beta quantification method.

An aliquot of plasma is ultracentrifuged at d 1.006 kg/L (i.e., at its own density) for at least 18 h at 105,000 ×g. Under these conditions, the VLDL accumulates as a floating layer at the top of the tube. The floating layer also contains chylomicrons and beta-VLDL, if present. The infranate contains primarily LDL and HDL, but also contains any IDL and Lp(a) that may be present.

The VLDL fraction (top fraction) is removed. The bottom fraction is collected quantitatively, reconstituted to known volume, and its cholesterol concentration is measured. LDL-C is calculated as the difference between that in the d 1.006 bottom fraction and HDL-C:

    b. LDL-C = [d 1.006 kg/L bottom-C] – HDL-C

Because the TG rich lipoproteins are removed from the sample, neither high TG concentrations nor chylomicrons or beta-VLDL affect the measured d 1.006 kg/L bottom C.

VLDL-C is calculated as the difference between TC and that in the ultracentrifugal bottom fraction:

    c. VLDL-C = TC – [d 1.006 kg/L bottom-C]

It should be noted that VLDL-C is not generally quantitated directly in the d 1.006 kg/L supernate because it can be difficult to recover the top fraction quantitatively, particularly in samples with high TG concentrations.

What is referred to as "LDL-C" actually contains the contributions of IDL-C and Lp(a)-C also. Since IDL and Lp(a) are both thought to be atherogenic,[40–43] the "LDL-C" measurement actually represents the amount of cholesterol being transported in potentially atherogenic particles. In normal individuals, IDL concentrations contribute only about 2 mg/dL (0.05 mmol/L) to the LDL-C measurement, but IDL-C concentrations may be considerably higher in certain patients with high TG concentrations in whom IDL may be overproduced or not cleared normally. On average, Lp(a) also contributes only about 3–4 mg/dL (0.08–0.1 mmol/L) to the measured LDL-C.[38] Lp(a) concentrations, however, are largely genetically determined and are independent of the concentrations of the other plasma lipoproteins. Therefore, the contribution of Lp(a)-C to the measurement cannot be readily evaluated without actually measuring Lp(a). It has been estimated that Lp(a) would contribute about 7% to the LDL-C measurement in a patient with a measured LDL-C concentration of 130 mg/dL (3.37 mmol/L) and an Lp(a) concentration of 30 mg/dL (expressed as total Lp(a) mass).[38]

A more accurate estimation of the concentration or LDL-C itself could be made by adjusting the observed LDL-C value for the contribution of Lp(a). This can be done using the following relationship:[43, 44]

   d.   LDL-C_{corr} = LDL-C_{obs} − [0.3 × Lp(a) mass]

where LDL-C_{obs} is the measured LDL-C concentration and the factor 0.3 × Lp(a) mass represents the average sterol content of Lp(a).

It should be kept in mind, however, that the current risk cutoffs relating "LDL-C" levels to cardiovascular disease[4, 5] include the contributions of both IDL-C and Lp(a)-C. It is possible that correcting the measured LDL-C value for the contribution of either IDL or Lp(a) could decrease the sensitivity of the LDL-C measurement as a risk indicator because it would not include all of the potentially atherogenic lipoproteins. Furthermore, patients who are at risk for CHD can, as a group, be expected to have higher concentrations of both IDL-C and Lp(a)-C. Adjusting the LDL-C measurements in this group would be expected to invalidate, to some extent, the current risk-based cutoffs for LDL-C. After considering these factors, the NCEP Working Group on Lipoprotein Measurement recommended that LDL-C measurements not be corrected for the contribution of Lp(a)-C.[38]

Type III hyperlipoproteinemia, a rare genetic disorder, is characterized in part by the presence of beta-VLDL, an unusual lipoprotein that when present is found in the ultracentrifugal top fraction, but migrates electrophoretically with LDL (beta lipoprotein) rather than VLDL (pre-beta lipoprotein)[1] (see Figure 8–1). When present, beta-VLDL can be observed electrophoretically as a beta migrating band in the ultracentrifugal top fraction, and for this reason has been called "floating beta" lipoprotein. Because it is richer in cholesterol than normal VLDL, it increases the amount of cholesterol in the VLDL fraction. Thus, the ratio of cholesterol to TG in the VLDL-containing fraction is higher in Type III hyperlipoproteinemia than in normal individuals or patients with other lipoprotein disorders. The beta quantification method includes two assessments for the presence of beta-VLDL, one quantitative and the other qualitative.

The quantitative indicator is to determine the ratio of VLDL-C to plasma TG. This assumes that most of the plasma TG is carried on VLDL. This ratio is < 0.3 in normal patients or those with other forms of hyperlipoproteinemia. Because beta-VLDL is enriched in cholesterol compared to normal VLDL, the Type III pattern is indicated when the ratio exceeds 0.3. It is not unusual for the VLDL-C:plasma TG ratio to be 0.4 or higher in Type III patients.

The qualitative indicator is the observation of beta-VLDL in the ultracentrifugal top fraction when examined electrophoretically. The procedure is performed as follows. Aliquots of unfractionated plasma, and the two ultracentrifugal fractions are subjected to agarose gel electrophoresis at pH 8.6. In this evaluation, focus is on the top fraction.

The unfractionated plasma and the ultracentrifugal bottom fraction serve to help mark the position of the LDL band, i.e., each sample serves as its own control. VLDL migrates with pre-beta mobility and is observed in the ultracentrifugal top fraction (see Figure 8–1). LDL and HDL have beta and alpha mobility, respectively, and are found in the bottom fraction (see Figure 8–1). When present, beta VLDL is also observed in the top fraction, but as a band with LDL mobility. The observation of a VLDL-C:plasma TG ratio > 0.3 and beta-VLDL in the ultracentrifugal top fraction defines the Type III pattern. This pattern tends to persist even in treated Type III patients. The interpretation of the electrophoretic pattern, however, requires skill and can be equivocal in some samples.

LDL-C Estimation Using the Friedewald Equation

This method also assumes that TC is distributed among the three major lipoprotein classes. Using measurements of TC, TG, and HDL-C, the empirical equation of Friedewald, et al.[39] is used to calculate LDL-C as follows:

e. LDL-C = TC – HDL-C – TG/5

where the factor TG/5 is an estimate of VLDL-C. As with beta quantification, "LDL-C" estimated in this way also contains the contributions of IDL-C and Lp(a)-C.

The Friedewald equation gives LDL-C values within about 2 mg/dL (0.05 mmol/L) of those determined by beta quantification when the samples have TG values up to about 200 mg/dL (2.26 mmol/L), and in practice the equation can be used with samples having TG concentrations up to 400 mg/dL (4.52 mmol/L).

The equation cannot be used in certain cases. It cannot be used in samples with TG > 400 mg/dL (4.52 mmol/L) or in samples with significant amounts of chylomicrons, as occurs in non-fasting samples. The TG:cholesterol ratio of normal VLDL is about 5:1. In samples with high TG or significant chylomicrons, however, the VLDL fraction can contain more TG than normal VLDL, and the factor plasma TG/5 will not give a sufficiently accurate estimate of cholesterol associated with this lipoprotein fraction. For example, the TG:cholesterol ratio of chylomicrons can be 15:1 or higher. Thus, the factor TG/5 simply does not apply, and use of the Friedewald equation in such cases will over-estimate the amount of cholesterol associated with the VLDL fraction. This produces an under-estimate of LDL-C.

The error is in the opposite direction if the equation is applied to the Type III patient. In this case, the TG:cholesterol ratio of the VLDL fraction will be 3:1 or lower due to the presence of beta-VLDL, which is richer in cholesterol than normal VLDL. Use of the Friedewald formula in this case under-estimates the amount of cholesterol in the VLDL fraction and therefore over-estimates LDL-C. Thus, a Type III patient can be misdiagnosed as having a high LDL-C concentration (Type II hyperlipoproteinemia), and since the two disorders are managed differently, such a misdiagnosis can lead to inappropriate treatment.

It is for this reason that beta quantification is used in the initial evaluation of Type III hyperlipoproteinemia, and thereafter whenever an accurate LDL-C measurement is needed.

These considerations normally do not preclude the use of the Friedewald equation for most clinical or research purposes. First, chylomicrons are not normally present in plasma from fasting patients, and when present in significant amounts are visible as a floating layer when plasma is allowed to stand in the refrigerator overnight. Second, samples with TG exceeding 400 mg/dL (4.52 mmol/L) are generally turbid, although the author has occasionally observed a clear sample with a TG concentration in the 400–500 mg/dL (4.52–5.65 mmol/L) range. Third, the 99th percentile for TG is under 300 mg/dL (3.39 mmol/L), even in women taking estrogens.[45] Finally, the prevalence of Type III hyperlipoproteinemia is about 1–2 per thousand in the general population.[46] Thus, the Friedewald equation generally can be used with most individuals, and most samples for which it is not appropriate can be detected simply by observing whether the sample is turbid or contains significant amounts of chylomicrons after standing in the refrigerator overnight. Such samples would then be referred for analysis by beta quantification, if necessary.

Immunochemical Direct LDL-C Measurement

Efforts have been made to develop methods capable of measuring LDL-C directly, rather than calculating it from several primary measurements. The desirability of using a direct LDL method might be considered, in view of the fact that it would produce *only* an LDL-C measurement. However, for diagnostic purposes, and in many cases for follow-up as well, both TG and HDL-C concentrations must also be considered.[4, 5] Since the Friedewald equation requires both of these measurements anyway, one might question the advantage of using a separate method to determine LDL-C.

Nonetheless, a fairly simple direct LDL-C method, developed by Genzyme Corporation, is available as a kit from Sigma Chemical Company, (St. Louis, MO) and other distributors. This method uses polyclonal antibodies to apo AI and apo E, which are attached to latex beads, to remove lipoproteins other than LDL. LDL-C is then measured directly in the resulting supernatant. This is a promising new approach when only an LDL-C measurement is needed, but currently only limited information is available on its performance, and not all findings have been consistent.

For example, Leary et al.[47] presented data indicating that the direct method tended to run 7–10% high compared with beta quantification, but displayed a fairly high correlation with the beta quantification method ($r = 0.96$). On the other hand, Devaraj et al.[48] reported no significant difference in LDL-C values of samples from 249 patients when measured with the direct method compared to beta quantification, but the correlation between the two methods was only about 0.89. This is fairly low for two methods that should be measuring the same thing in the same samples. Harris et al.[49] found average biases of about –6% in samples from 96 fasting patients and +14% in 42 samples from non-fasting, hypertriglyceridemic patients, compared with beta quantification. Bias was related to both TG and LDL-C concentration, and the correlation between the two methods was only 0.86 when the two groups were combined, although it was a little better (0.93) in samples from fasting patients. On the other hand, McNamara et al.[50] also found very little bias between the two methods in samples from 115 patients, and reported a very good correlation ($r = 0.97$) between the direct LDL method and beta quantification. However, the reproducibility (i.e., analytical co-efficient of variation) of the direct LDL method was found to be in the same range as for conventional LDL-C measurements,[49-51] despite the fact that it requires less sample handling and only a single cholesterol measurement. The direct LDL-C method appears to offer no clear advantage over the conventional methods in terms of precision.[51]

This particular method has several intriguing characteristics that deserve further study. First, some workers found no significant difference in LDL-C concentrations in samples from fasting or non-fasting patients.[50] Since it is known that following a fat-containing meal LDL-C undergoes actual compositional changes that transiently lower LDL-C values,[52-54] it is not clear why this was not observed with the direct method. It might be noted that other researchers using this method did observe a postprandial decrease of about 5%,[48] about as expected.

Second, the method cannot be used in frozen samples, since freezing has been found to *reduce* the measured LDL-C values by up to 25%.[48-50] The loss of LDL-C increases with storage time.[50] Again, it is not clear why this should occur. Indeed, assuming complete removal of lipoproteins containing apo A-I and apo E in fresh samples, one might expect that if freezing had any effect at all, it would be to change the immunochemical properties of those lipoproteins containing apo A-I and apo E such that they might not be completely precipitated, leading to an *increase* rather than a decrease in measured LDL-C values. The observed decrease in LDL-C values implies that some of the LDL itself may become bound after freezing. Such large decreases have not been observed with the conventional methods, however, and it is not apparent why losses of this magnitude occur using antibodies that are specific for apo A-I and apo E, since neither apolipoprotein is found in LDL.

Finally, apparently neither immunochemical nor chemical precipitation methods for LDL-C can be used in lyophilized samples either, as evidenced by the 50–75% negative biases observed for these methods among laboratories participating in the College of American Pathologists Chemistry Proficiency Surveys.[55] The large losses observed in both frozen and lyophilized samples makes the present versions of these methods unsuitable for long-term clinical or epidemiological studies because they preclude the assessment of analytical bias or long-term analytical trends. They also complicate quality control monitoring of routine clinical measurements, since frozen or lyophilized serum pools cannot be used for this purpose. Thus, further study is needed to develop reagents that overcome these difficulties.

REFERENCE METHOD FOR LDL CHOLESTEROL DETERMINATION

Since LDL does not have a unique chemical structure, it has not been possible to develop a true reference method for LDL-C measurement. For this reason, "accuracy" must be defined functionally, i.e., in terms of the methods used for the measurement.[38] The method being developed for this purpose by CDC is based on beta quantification, but differs from that described above in two ways. First, in order to eliminate interference with the HDL-C measurement in samples with high TG (see discussion of HDL measurement in Chapter 7), the HDL-containing fraction is prepared by precipitating the IDL, LDL, and Lp(a) from the ultracentrifugal bottom fraction rather than from unfractionated serum. Second, cholesterol in both the ultracentrifugal bottom fraction and HDL fraction is measured with the CDC reference method for cholesterol.[56] LDL-C is then calculated as indicated in equation b. above. The method is performed under highly controlled conditions and provides a basis for judging the accuracy of LDL-C measurements.

NCEP Recommendations for LDL-C Measurement

The NCEP Working Group on Lipoprotein Measurement recently published recommendations for reliable LDL-C measurements. These recommendations cover a variety of issues related to LDL-C measurement, and the interested reader is referred to the Working Group's full report,[38] and the Executive Summary for LDL-C measurement, which has been published separately.[57] Some of the issues considered by the Working Group were discussed above. Following is a summary of some of the main points of the recommendations.

1. The Working Group *did not* recommend that any particular method be used to measure LDL-C. Rather, the recommendation was for the user to understand exactly which lipoproteins are included in the LDL-C measurement, and that the method be capable of giving results equivalent to those used to establish the epidemiological database from which the relationship between LDL-C concentration and risk for CHD was established.

2. Because it was necessary to define accuracy in functional terms, the Working Group recommended that the ultracentrifugation-polyanion precipitation (i.e., beta quantification) method, modified to incorporate the use of reference methods for TC and HDL-C, should be used to afford a single setpoint from which to judge accuracy. The reference method should include both IDL and Lp(a) in the "LDL-measurement," and the HDL-C method should provide values equivalent to those obtained with the heparin-$MnCl_2$ method (see discussion of HDL measurement in Chapter 7).

3. Since plasma values can be lower than serum values, depending on the anticoagulant used, accuracy should be based on serum-equivalent values. EDTA plasma values are converted to serum-equivalent values by multiplying the LDL-C value by the factor 1.03.

4. Blood samples should be drawn after a 12 h fasting period. A 9 h fasting period, as recommended by the ATP II,[5] can be used, but will produce a 2–4% underestimate of LDL-C, on average.

5. Lipid and lipoprotein concentrations are subject to postural changes due primarily to the redistribution of water between the vascular and extravascular space as an individual changes from the standing to sitting or supine positions. TC and lipoprotein-C concentrations decrease about 5% when a standing person sits, and about 10% when a person moves from the standing to supine position.[58] The change for TG is almost twice as great.[58] If possible, blood sampling should be standardized to the sitting position, after allowing the patient to sit quietly for at least 5 min. If it is necessary to use the supine position, the patient should be sampled in the same position on each occasion in order to minimize this source of within-individual physiological variation.

6. Serum or plasma should be removed from cells within 3 h of venipuncture. Specimens can be stored at 4° C for up to 3 days, at –20° C for up to several weeks in a non-self-defrosting freezer, and at –70° C for longer periods.

7. Lipoprotein concentrations are not constant; they normally fluctuate about some mean value during the normal course of day-to-day activity, even when the patient is in a steady state, i.e., in good health, of stable weight, and observing usual patterns of diet and exercise. When the patient is treated with diet or lipid-lowering medications, lipid levels decrease (i.e., the patients physiological state changes) until a new steady state is attained, after which normal physiological fluctuation resumes. Based on the results of a number of studies, the co-efficient of normal physiological variation is assumed to be 8.2%. Assuming a maximum total analytical error of 12% (see item 8, below), when determining the patient's usual average LDL-C concentration, measurements should be made in two or three serial samples and the measurements averaged. The difference between *sequential* individual measurements in the series should not exceed 25%. If they do, the patient's physiological state may have changed or a laboratory error may have occurred; hence, an additional sample should be considered.

8. With respect to the laboratory measurements themselves, the recommendation for acceptable LDL-C measurements is set in terms of total analytical error, rather than specifying separate criteria for accuracy and precision. The total error specification accounts for *both* accuracy and imprecision at the same time, rather than considering them separately. The recommendation is that LDL-C be measured with an average total error not exceeding 12%. In order to frame this guideline in more familiar terms, the Working Group noted that the total error criterion could be met in a laboratory that operated within a bias limit of ±4%, and with an imprecision, reflected by coefficient of variation, no greater than 4%. For example, if the bias exceeds 4%, the CV must be smaller by an amount that restricts the total error to no more than 12%, and vise versa. A fairly accurate estimate of total error can be obtained using the following equation.

f. TE = % bias + 1.96 × % CV

where TE is total error and bias is the average laboratory bias.

The usefulness of the current risk tables relating lipid and lipoprotein concentrations to risk for CHD depends in part on how accurately the measurements are made. The ultimate purpose of establishing standard conditions for patient handling and uniform criteria for reliable measurements is that the same values would be obtained regardless of where or how the measurements are made. Table 8–2 illustrates the results obtained in several serum pools provided in the CAP Chemistry Proficiency Surveys.[55] The data in the table reflect the results from over 2800 participating laboratories using the Friedewald equation to calculate LDL-C values, compared to CDC confirming values in the same pools using the Friedewald and CDC reference methods to measure TC, TG, and HDL-C. The results indicate an average bias of about 5.7%, and an *among-laboratory* CV of about 8%, for an overall total error of about 20%. While this exceeds the NCEP recommendation, the results are remarkable and quite encouraging considering that (a) the recommendation for total error was directed at measurements in *individual* laboratories; (b) a variety of different methods and variations of methods are used in different laboratories for TC, TG, and HDL-C measurement; and (c) the CAP surveys use lyophilized serum pools, which are not ideal for HDL-C measurement.

Table 8–2 ❖ Accuracy and Imprecision of LDL-C Measurements				
Pool	*CDC Confirming Value[2] (mg/dL)*	*Mean[3] (mg/dL)*	*Mean Bias[4]*	*CV[5] (%)*
LP-01	80.4	73.9	9.9	–8.1
LP-02	100.7	93.9	9.0	–6.8
LP-11	91.4	87.2	7.6	–4.6
LP-12	150.1	143.6	6.1	–4.3

[1] Data from CAP Clinical Chemistry Surveys, 1995, College of American Pathologists, Northfield, IL.
[2] CDC confirming values were calculated by CAP from CDC confirming values for TC, TG, and HDL-C using the equation: LDL-C = TC – HDL-C – TG/5. To convert to mmol/L, multiply by 0.0259.
[3] Results from 2800 to 2841 participating laboratories
[4] Bias with respect to CDC confirming values.
[5] CV, co-efficient of variation, calculated as SD/mean × 100.

SUMMARY

LDL-C measurement is important for the diagnosis and treatment of hyperlipidemia, and for these purposes the ability to standardize LDL-C methods is essential. While a number of different methods are available, beta quantification and LDL-C estimation by the Friedewald equation have been most widely used and investigated. These remain the best characterized and most common methods presently in use. In both methods, the measured LDL-C values include the contributions of the other atherogenic apo B-containing lipoproteins.

As new methods are developed, it will be necessary to define exactly which lipoproteins they measure and to what extent atherogenic lipoproteins other than LDL contribute to the observed LDL-C values. It will also be necessary to assess how the new methods compare with those used to generate the risk cutoffs for LDL-C. New LDL-C methods must both satisfy the criteria for reliable LDL-C measurement and offer the capability of appropriate long-term monitoring for quality-control purposes.   ❖

REFERENCES

1. Mahley RW, Rall SC. Type III hyperlipoproteinemia (dysbetalipoproteinemia): the role of apolipoprotein E in normal and abnormal lipoprotein metabolism. In Scriver CR, Beaudet AL, Sly WS, Valle D (eds.), The metabolic and molecular basis of inherited disease, Vol. II, 7th ed. New York: McGraw Hill, 1995:1953–80.
2. Lee DM, Alaupovic P. Apolipoproteins B, C-III and E in two major subpopulations of low-density lipoproteins. Biochim Biophys Acta 1986;879:126–33.

3. Chapman J. Comparative analysis of mammalian plasma lipoproteins. Methods in Enzymology 1986;128:70-143.
4. The Expert Panel. Report of the National Cholesterol Education Program Expert Panel on Detection, Evaluation, and Treatment of High Blood Cholesterol in Adults. Arch Intern Med 1988;148:36-69.
5. The Expert Panel. Summary of the second report of the National Cholesterol Education Panel (NCEP) Expert Panel on Detection, Evaluation, and Treatment of High Blood Cholesterol in Adults (Adult Treatment Panel II). JAMA 1993;269:3015-23.
6. NCEP Expert Panel on Blood Cholesterol Levels in Children and Adolescents. National Cholesterol Education Program (NCEP): Highlights of the report of the Expert Panel on Blood Cholesterol Levels in Children and Adolescents. Pediatrics 1992;89:495-501.
7. Lindgren FT, Elliott HA, Gofman JW. The ultracentrifugal characterization and isolation of human blood lipids and lipoproteins, with applications to the study of atherosclerosis. J Phys & Colloid Chem 1951;55:80.
8. Lewis LA, Green AA, Page IH. Ultracentrifuge lipoprotein pattern of serum of normal, hypertensive and hypothyroid animals. Am J Physiol 1952;171:391.
9. de Lalla OF, Gofman JW. Ultracentrifugal analysis of serum lipoproteins. Methods of Biochemical Analysis 1954;1:459-78.
10. Havel RJ, Eder HA, Bragdon JH. The distribution and chemical composition of ultracentrifugally separated lipoproteins in human serum. J Clin Invest 1955;34:1345-53.
11. Schumaker VN, Puppione DL. Sequential flotation ultracentrifugation. Methods in Enzymology 1986;128:155-70.
12. Lindgren FT, Nichols AV, Upham FT, et al. Subfractionation of the S_f 20-10^5 lipoproteins in a swinging bucket rotor. J Phys Chem 1962;66:2007-11.
13. Lossow WJ, Lindgren FT, Murchio JC, et al. Particle size and protein content of six fractions of the $S_f > 20$ plasma lipoproteins isolated by density gradient centrifugation. J Lipid Res 1969;10:68-76.
14. Hinton RH, Kowalski AJ, Mallinson A. Choice of conditions for the gradient flotation of serum lipoproteins in swing-out rotors. Clin Chim Acta 1973;44:267-70.
15. Redgrave TG, Roberts DCK, West CE. Separation of plasma lipoproteins by density-gradient ultracentrifugation. Anal Biochem 1975;65:42-49.
16. Foreman JR, Karlin JB, Edelstein C, et al. Fractionation of human serum lipoproteins by single-spin gradient ultracentrifugation: quantification of apolipoproteins B and A-I and lipid components. J Lipid Res 1977;18:759-67.
17. Nilsson J, Mannickarottu V, Edelstein C, et al. An improved detection system applied to the study of serum lipoproteins after single-step density gradient ultracentrifugation. Anal Biochem 1981;110:342-48.
18. Belcher JD, Egan JO, Bridgmen G, Baker R, Flack J. A micro-enzymatic method to measure cholesterol and triglyceride in lipoprotein subfractions separated by density gradient ultracentrifugation from 200 microliters of plasma or serum. J Lipid Res 1991;32:359-70.
19. Chung BH, Wilkinson T, Geer JC, et al. Preparative and quantitative isolation of plasma lipoproteins: rapid, single discontinuous density gradient ultracentrifugation in a vertical rotor. J Lipid Res 1980;21:284-91.
20. Cone JT, Segrest JP, Chung BH, et al. Computerized rapid high resolution quantitative analysis of plasma lipoproteins based upon single vertical spin centrifugation. J Lipid Res 1982;23:923-35.
21. Campos E, McConathy WJ. Distribution of lipids and apolipoproteins in human plasma by vertical spin ultracentrifugation. Arch Biochem Biophys 1986;249:455-63.
22. Chung BH, Segrest JP, Ray MJ, et al. Single vertical spin density gradient ultracentrifugation. Methods in Enzymology 1986;128:181-209.
23. Rudel LL, Lee JA, Morris MD, et al. Characterization of plasma lipoproteins separated and purified by agarose-column chromatography. Biochem J 1974;139:89-95.
24. Williams MC, Stenoien CG, Kushwaha RS. Rapid method for measuring plasma low density lipoprotein turnover using high performance gel exclusion chromatography. J Chromatogr 1986;375:233-43.

25. Krause BR, Shork NH, Kieft KA, Smith MP, Maciejko JJ. High correlation but lack of agreement between direct high-performance gel chromatography analysis and conventional indirect methods for determining lipoprotein cholesterol. Clin Chem 1996;42: 1996-2001.
26. März W, Siekmeier R, Scharnagl H, Seiffert UB, Gross W. Fast lipoprotein chromatography: new method of analysis for plasma lipoproteins. Clin Chem 1993;39:2276-81.
27. Levy RI. Cholesterol, lipoproteins, apoproteins, and heart disease; present status and future prospects. Clin Chem 1981;27:653-62.
28. Weiland H, Seidel D. A simple specific method for precipitation of low density lipoproteins. J Lipid Res 1983;24:904-9.
29. Kersher L, Schiefer S, Draeger B, Maier J, Ziegenhorn J. Precipitation methods for the determination of LDL cholesterol. Clin Biochem 1985;18:118-225.
30. Maier J, Draeger B, Wehmeyer G, Gloger M, Ziegenhorn J. Method for the quantitation of serum low density lipoprotein cholesterol (LDL-CH) [Abstract]. Clin Chem 1983; 29:1173.
31. Assmann G, Jabs H-U, Kohnert U, Nolte W, Schriewer H. LDL-cholesterol determination in blood serum following precipitation of LDL with polyvinyl sulfate. Clin Chim Acta 1984;140:77-83.
32. Moss MA, Wong CSY, Tan MH, et al. Determination of low density lipoprotein cholesterol (LDL-C) in serum by Biomerieux cholesterol/-phospholipids polyanion precipitation method and comparison with preparative ultracentrifugation. [Abstract]. Clin Chem 1986;32:1096-7.
33. Mainard F, Madec Y. Are "precipitated LDL" really low density lipoproteins? Clin Chim Acta 1987;162:141-6.
34. Shaikh M, Miller NE. Evaluation of a commercial reagent for precipitating human serum low-density lipoprotein. Clin Chim Acta 1985;152:213-17.
35. Demacker PN, Hijmans AG, Brenninkmeijer BJ, et al. Five methods for determining low-density lipoprotein cholesterol compared. Clin Chem 1984;30:1797-1800.
36. Assmann G, Jabs HU, Nolte W, Schriewer H. Precipitation of LDL with sulphopolyanions: a comparison of two methods for LDL cholesterol determination. J Clin Chem Clin Biochem 1984;22:781-5.
37. Mulder K, van Leeuwen C, Schouten JA, et al. An evaluation of three commercial methods for the determination of LDL-cholesterol. Clin Chim Acta 1984;143:29-35.
38. National Cholesterol Education Program Working Group on Lipoprotein Measurement. Recommendations on lipoprotein measurement (NIH Publication No. 95-3044) Bethesda, MD: National Institutes of Health, September, 1995.
39. Friedewald WT, Levy RI, Fredrickson DS. Estimation of the concentration of low density lipoprotein cholesterol in plasma without use of the ultracentrifuge. Clin Chem 1972; 18:449-502.
40. Austin MA. Plasma triglyceride as a risk factor for coronary heart disease: the epidemiological evidence and beyond. Amer J Epi 1989;129:249-59.
41. Simons LA, Dwyer T, Simons J, et al. Chylomicrons and chylomicron remnants in coronary artery disease: a case-control study. Atherosclerosis 1987;65:181-9.
42. Krauss RM, Williams PT, Brensike J, et al. Intermediate-density lipoproteins and progression of coronary artery disease in hypercholesterolaemic men. Lancet 1987;11: 62-66.
43. Sandkamp M, Funke H, Schulte H, Kohler E, Assmann G. Lipoprotein(a) is an independent risk factor for myocardial infarction at a young age. Clin Chem 1990;36:20-23.
44. Jurgens G, Koltringer P. Lipoprotein (a) in ischemic cerebrovascular disease: a new approach to the assessment of risk for stroke. Neurology 1987;37:513-15.
45. The Lipid Research Clinics Population Studies Data Book. Volume I, The Prevalence Study (NIH Publication No. 80-1527). Bethesda, MD: National Institutes of Health, July 1980.
46. LaRosa JC, Chambless LE, Criqui MH, et al. Patterns of dyslipoproteinemia in selected North American populations: The Lipid Research Clinics Program Prevalence Study. Circulation 1986;73(I):12-29.

47. Leary ET, Tjersland G, Warnick GR. Evaluation of the Genzyme immunoseparation reagent for direct quantitation of LDL cholesterol. [Abstract]. Clin Chem 1993;39: 1124.

48. Devaraj S, Hirany SV, Sherwood TA, Jialal I. Comparison of an immunoprecipitation method for direct measurement of LDL-cholesterol with beta quantification. [Abstract]. Clin Chem 1995;41:S141.

49. Harris N, Neufeld EJ, Newburger JW, Tich B, Baker A, Ginsburg GS, Rimm E, Rifai N. Analytical performance and clinical utility of a direct LDL-cholesterol assay in a hyper-lipidemic pediatric population. Clin Chem 1996;42:1182-8.

50. McNamara JR, Cole TG, Contois JH, Furguson CA, Ordovas JM, Schaefer EJ. Immunoseparation method for measuring low-density lipoprotein cholesterol directly from serum evaluated. Clin Chem 1995;41:232-40.

51. Schectman G, Patsches M, Sasse EA. Variability in cholesterol measurements: comparison of calculated and direct LDL-cholesterol determinations. Clin Chem 1996;42: 732-7.

52. Cohn JS, McNamara JR, Cohn SD, Ordovas JM, Schaefer EJ. Postprandial plasma lipoprotein changes in human subjects of different ages. J Lipid Res 1988;29:469-79.

53. Cohn JS, McNamara JR, Schaefer EJ. Lipoprotein cholesterol concentrations in the plasma of human subjects measured in the fed and fasted states. Clin Chem 1988;34: 2556-9.

54. Wilder LB, Bachorik PS, Finney CA, Moy TF, Becker DM. The effect of fasting status on the determination of low density and high density lipoprotein cholesterol. Am J Med 1995;99:374-7.

55. College of American Pathologists Clinical Chemistry Proficiency Surveys. Northfield, IL: College of American Pathologists, 1995.

56. Ellerbe P, Myers GL, Cooper GR, et al. A comparison of results for cholesterol in human serum by the reference method and by the definitive method of the National Reference System for Cholesterol. Clin Chem 1990;36:370-5.

57. Bachorik PS, Ross JW, for the National Cholesterol Education Program Working Group on Lipoprotein Measurement. Guidelines on the measurement of low density lipoprotein cholesterol: executive summary. Clin Chem 1995;44:1414-20.

58. Miller MM, Bachorik PS, Cloey TC. Normal variation of plasma lipoproteins: postural effects on plasma lipid, lipoprotein and apolipoprotein concentrations. Clin Chem 1992; 38:569-74.

Lipid and Lipoprotein Analysis with Desk-Top Analyzers

Paul S. Bachorik

INTRODUCTION

❖   Cholesterol is transported in the circulation by plasma lipoproteins, primarily by low-density lipoproteins (LDL), which account for about two-thirds, and high-density lipoproteins (HDL), which carry about 20–25% of the circulating cholesterol in humans. An increased concentration of LDL cholesterol (LDL-C) is a well-established risk factor for the development of premature coronary heart disease (CHD),[1] and over the past few years it has been established that lowering plasma LDL-C concentrations reduces the risk of CHD.[2-7] Total cholesterol (TC) is an effective surrogate measure of LDL-C in adults, and therefore TC measurement has assumed increasing importance in identifying patients with high LDL-C concentrations. TC measurement is performed in various kinds of screening operations and in follow-up analyses used to evaluate the progress of patients being treated for hypercholesterolemia. A low concentration of HDL cholesterol (HDL-C) is independently associated with increased risk of CHD,[8-10] although it has not yet been demonstrated that raising HDL-C reduces risk.

The National Cholesterol Education Program Adult Treatment Panel (NCEP-ATP) recently updated[11] its original[12] recommendations concerning the diagnosis and treatment of hypercholesterolemia in adults. (Refer to Chapter 2 for additional information.) While the original recommendations focused primarily on TC and LDL-C, the updated report places increased emphasis on HDL-C by recognizing a high HDL-C concentration as a protective factor and recommending the measurement of HDL-C whenever TC is measured.

Technical developments over the past 15 years have increased the speed and accuracy of clinical measurements of lipids and lipoproteins and, to some extent, have moved the performance of these measurements from the conventional laboratory to the physician's office and to other nontraditional settings. The first of these developments was the introduction into the laboratory of completely enzyme-based methods for cholesterol and triglyceride (TG) measurement.[13-16] Such methods have virtually replaced the older, more involved and technically demanding chemical methods. The second development was the adaptation of this methodology to small, portable analyzers, commonly called desk-top analyzers. These analyzers were originally designed to be used in the physician's office, but they have also been widely used for TC screening in non-medical settings,[17-20] and are capable of measuring TC, TG, and HDL-C.

In this chapter we discuss the use of desk-top analyzers for lipid and lipoprotein measurements in non-laboratory settings.

PRINCIPLES OF OPERATION

Total Cholesterol

Virtually all of the desk-top analytical systems currently available are based on the same kinds of enzymatic methods used in laboratory settings. For measurement of TC, they employ a single, combined reagent mixture which contains all of the necessary enzymes, buffers, and other cofactors required for the test. An aliquot of serum or plasma, usually 10–30 µL, is mixed with the combined reagent and allowed to incubate under controlled conditions for a short period, generally about 3–8 min, during which a colored reaction product forms. The intensity of the color is related to the cholesterol concentration. The results are read from a digital display on the instrument and a paper printout. The chemical reactions involved are as follows:

1. Cholesteryl Esters + H_2O $\xrightarrow{\text{Cholesteryl Esterase}}$ Cholesterol + Fatty Acid

2. Cholesterol + O_2 $\xrightarrow{\text{Cholesterol Oxidase}}$ Cholestanone + H_2O_2

3. H_2O_2 + Dye $\xrightarrow{\text{Peroxidase}}$ Colored Dye Product

Cholesteryl esters are hydrolyzed and then cholesterol is oxidized to produce cholestanone and hydrogen peroxide. The amount of hydrogen peroxide produced is proportional to the amount of cholesterol in the sample. The concentration of H_2O_2 is then measured through a peroxidase catalyzed reaction in which a colored dye product is formed.

Triglycerides

TG are similarly measured through a series of enzyme reactions.

4. Triglyceride + H_2O $\xrightarrow{\text{Bacterial Lipase}}$ Fatty Acid + Glycerol

5. Glycerol + ATP $\xrightarrow{\text{Glycerokinase}}$ Glycerophosphate + ADP

The glycerophosphate formed is most commonly measured using glycerophosphate oxidase.

6. Glycerophosphate + O_2 $\xrightarrow{\text{Glycerophosphate Oxidase}}$ Dihydroxyacetone + H_2O_2

The H_2O_2 produced is generally measured as in reaction 3 above.

In general, all of the reactions occur once the sample has been placed into the instrument. The instrument controls the time and conditions of the incubation, reads the color intensity, converts the readings to units of concentration, and displays the results. The entire analysis can be accomplished in 10 minutes or less.

HDL Cholesterol

Desk-top analyzer methods have also become available for HDL-C measurement.[21-23] These tests rely on the removal of the lipoproteins containing apolipoprotein B (apo B): very-low-density lipoproteins (VLDL), intermediate density lipoproteins (IDL, LDL, and lipoprotein(a) [Lp(a)]. This is generally done by precipitation with a polyanion in the presence of a divalent cation, under conditions in which HDL remains soluble. Precipitants such as phosphotungstate or dextran sulfate-Mg^{++} have been used. The cholesterol content of the HDL-containing fraction is then measured as described above, but with test strips or cassettes for which the cholesterol measurements have been optimized for use in the HDL-C concentration range. With some desk-top analyzers, the apo-B-containing lipoproteins must be precipitated from the sample before the HDL supernate is placed into the analyzer, while in others both the precipitation and cholesterol measurement steps are performed automatically.

LDL Cholesterol

For analyzers that measure TC, TG, and HDL-C, LDL-C can be calculated using the empirical relationship of Friedewald et al.:[24]

$$LDL\text{-}C = TC - HDL\text{-}C - TG/5$$

where the factor TG/5 is an estimate of VLDL-C concentrations when given in mg/dL. The factor TG/2.22 is used when concentrations are expressed in mmol/L.

INSTRUMENTS

The desk-top instruments available differ in their simplicity and ease of use. These instruments can be separated into two broad categories: those based on dry reagent chemistry and those for which reagents are furnished in a liquid form. Here we discuss the principles of operation of several of the more commonly used analyzers.

One of the simplest of the instruments to use is the Reflotron (Boehringer-Mannheim Corp., Indianapolis, IN). This is one of the so-called whole-blood analyzers, capable of making TC and TG measurements using either serum, plasma, or whole blood. The sample (30 µL) is applied to the sample application zone of a reagent strip. The sample moves downward into an absorbent pad through a glass fiber mesh which removes the red cells. The cell-free sample then moves into the reagent-containing zone, an area of the strip that has been impregnated with the enzymes and other reagents needed for the test. The reagents dissolve in the sample, allowing the reaction to proceed.

Once the sample is applied, the strip is inserted into the instrument. The reaction proceeds for about 3 min, during which time the color develops. At the end of this period, the intensity of the color is measured by reflectance photometry. A light beam is shined on the sample and the amount of light reflected is inversely related to the TC or TG concentration in the sample. The reflectance is converted to units of concentration and the results are displayed either in mg/dL or in mmol/L. The strip is then removed and the next test can be performed. The instrument is capable of analyzing one sample at a time.

The identity of the test, conditions for analysis, and the calibration curve are coded on a magnetic tape on the back of the strip, and this information is read by the instrument when the strip is inserted. This configuration makes the test very simple to use, since the operator need only verify the operation of the optics of the instrument and then perform the tests. Because of its simplicity, the Reflotron has been widely used for large-scale TC screening operations in various field settings.[17-20, 25]

Reflotron test strips are also available for HDL-C. For HDL-C, EDTA plasma (not whole blood) (30 µL) is applied to the strip. The sample then moves through a layer impregnated with dextran sulfate (M_r 50,000) and magnesium acetate, which precipitates the apo-B-containing lipoproteins. The HDL-containing fraction then moves to the reagent zone, where HDL-C is measured.

The Johnson & Johnson Vitros DT60 (Johnson & Johnson Clinical Diagnostics, Rochester, NY; formerly available from Kodak, Rochester, NY) is another example of a dry chemistry analyzer. With this instrument, however, the configuration of the test is somewhat different. The DT60 is something of a cross between a sequential analyzer and a batch analyzer. Reagents for the test are contained on a test slide in which the reagents are impregnated into a pad immediately below the sample application zone. The slide is also printed with a bar code that identifies the test and test conditions.

The slide is first inserted into the instrument, after which the sample (10 µL) is injected onto the slide through a port in the top of the instrument using a small, battery-powered, motorized pipet. After the sample has been applied, the slide moves automatically to an incubation chamber, where color development takes place. The reflectance of the sample is then measured and converted to units of concentration, and the results are printed on a paper tape. The entire analysis takes about 8 min. The incubation chamber, however, can accommodate a number of slides, so that samples can be continuously fed into the instrument. Once in operation, the results are printed about every 30 seconds. Separate test slides are available for TC, TG, and HDL-C.

The HDL-C assay requires the preliminary manual removal of apo-B-containing lipoproteins. The method uses dextran sulfate (M_r 50,000) and $MgSO_4$ as the precipitating reagent, and the reagent is provided with the HDL test kit.

The DT60 differs from the Reflotron in several other respects. First, it is not a whole-blood analyzer; blood cells must be removed before the sample is analyzed. Second, the instrument is calibrated by the user at intervals of about 30 days using lyophilized reference sera provided by the manufacturer. Three levels of reference sera are used, and the calibration curves are calculated and stored automatically by the instrument.

Since the introduction of these instruments, this technology has been developed further to allow several tests to be performed simultaneously on a single sample. This is accomplished by providing a channel through which the cell-free blood filtrate moves from the filter toward the reagent zones. The channel is split to allow portions of the sample to move to different test reagent zones. Using such an arrangement, the Cholestech LDX (Cholestech Corporation, Hayward, CA) can simultaneously measure TC, TG, and HDL-C. This analyzer has been optimized for use with whole blood.

The test parameters are contained in a magnetic strip on the test cassette and are used when the cassette is inserted into the instrument. Serum or plasma can also be used, although the results are slightly less accurate than those obtained with whole blood.[23, 26] The instrument completes all three measurements in about 4 min and is capable of analyzing one specimen at a time. The volume of sample applied must exceed 35 µL, but need not be measured accurately since the test cassette automatically meters the appropriate volumes of sample to the reagent zones.

The Abbott VISION (Abbott Laboratories, North Chicago, IL) is an example of a wet-chemistry, batch-type, whole-blood analyzer. The VISION analyzer uses a some-what different principle of analysis. First, the liquid reagent mixture is contained in a small plastic cassette. A sample of whole blood is injected into the cassette with the aid of a pipet. The cassette is then placed into the instrument, where it is centrifuged to sediment red cells. After centrifugation, the position of the cassette is automatically changed such that an accurately measured volume of the plasma spills into the chamber containing the reagent and is mixed. After an appropriate period, the absorbance of the mixture is measured and the absorbance readings are converted to units of con-centration and displayed on a printed tape. The instrument can accommodate up to 10 cassettes at one time, and the entire analysis takes about 10 min. Test cassettes are available for measuring TC, TG, and HDL-C, but for HDL the apo-B-containing lipoproteins must first be separated by a conventional pretreatment step before loading the supernate into the HDL test cassette.

Because the instrument incorporates a centrifuge, it is physically larger than the other analyzers and is therefore less mobile. Furthermore, the absorbance rather than the reflectance of the sample is measured.

Type of Sample Used

When using these instruments, it is necessary to consider the kind of sample that is used. The analyzers can be used with either venous or capillary samples, although in mass-screening settings, capillary samples are usually used. In general, the results obtained with the two kinds of samples are similar but not identical. In some studies, the values in capillary samples appear to be lower than those in venous samples; in other studies, the opposite was observed.[23, 27-29] On average, the differences between venous and capillary samples are fairly minor, on the order of a few percentage points. However, the values in capillary samples from individual patients can occasionally vary considerably from those in venous samples collected at the same time.[17] The reasons for these differences have not been investigated in any detail, but possibilities may include, among others, the temperature of the patient's finger, differential rates of posture related concentration changes on capillary and venous samples, and the ease with which blood flows from the finger puncture.

It is important to note that while the overall coefficients of normal biological variation (CV_b) for TC, TG, HDL-C, and LDL-C are about the same in capillary and venous blood[23] (Table 9-1), the differences observed within an individual on a given occasion will depend on the magnitude and direction of the concentration changes in the serial and capillary venous specimens. These are generally parallel, but this may not hold on a particular occasion.

Table 9–1 ✧ Comparison of Coefficients of Biological Variation for Lipid and Lipoproteins in Venous and Capillary Samples[1,2]

Specimen	Median CV_b3 (%)			
	TC	TG	HDL-C	LDL-C
Venous	5.1	15.8	6.5	7.5
Capillary	5.2	14.7	7.2	5.4

[1]Data taken from Kafonek et al.[23]
[2]Paired venous serum and heparinized capillary blood samples were drawn from each of 83 normal fasting (12 h) adults once each month for 3 months. The study population was sampled over a 7 month period. Capillary blood was analyzed immediately and venous serum about 60 min later after the blood had clotted and serum recovered. All analyses were performed on the Cholestech desktop analyzer using test cassettes that allowed the simultaneous analysis of TC, TG, and HDL-C. LDL-C was calculated using the Friedewald equation.[24] Analytical and biological components of within-individual variance and the median coefficients of biological variation were calculated as described in Kafonek et al.[23]
[3]CV_b, coefficient of biological variation.

Serum-plasma differences are another consideration. Certain anticoagulants exert an osmotic effect, resulting in the movement of water from the cells to the plasma. This causes dilution of the plasma lipoproteins, the degree of which depends on the osmotic activity of the anticoagulant used.[30] This difference was estimated to be about 3%,[31] and, according to the NCEP-ATP guidelines,[12] multiplication of plasma values by the factor 1.03 is recommended when evaluating patients. It must be kept in mind, however, that the term "plasma" used in this context refers specifically to EDTA plasma. Some agents, such as citrate, exert much larger osmotic effects, and lipids and lipoproteins should not be measured in samples that contain such anticoagulants. Heparin, on the other hand, exerts no detectable osmotic effect in concentrations used for blood collection, and TC values in heparinized plasma are indistinguishable from those in serum.[32] Capillary blood samples are generally collected into heparinized capillary tubes, and measurements in capillary blood need not be converted to serum values. Nonetheless, it is well to bear in mind possible differences between serum and plasma, since the NCEP-ATP guidelines are based on serum.[11, 12]

It might be worthy of mention that the factor 1.03 was determined at a time when blood-drawing tubes containing EDTA were supplied with sufficient EDTA to produce an anticoagulant concentration of 1 mg/mL.[31] Tubes supplied currently, however, contain 1.5 mg/mL EDTA, and the resulting hema-dilution is a little greater, at about 4.5%.[32]

RELIABILITY OF LIPID AND LIPOPROTEIN-CHOLESTEROL MEASUREMENTS

The NCEP Lipid Standardization Panel (LSP) established guidelines for acceptable TC measurement in the United States (Table 9–2).[33] These guidelines specify minimum standards for accuracy and precision and are consistent with a total analytical error of 8.9, or approximately 9%.

Table 9–2 ❖ NCEP Guidelines for Accuracy and Precision of Cholesterol Measurements	
Bias[1, 2]	≤ 3%
Coefficient of variation (CV)[2]	≤ 3%
[1]With respect to CDC reference method. [2]These limits for bias and imprecision are consistant with a total error of < 9%.	

The NCEP Working Group on Lipoprotein Measurement subsequently developed additional guidelines for reliable TG, HDL-C, and LDL-C measurements[34] (Table 9–3). The recommendations for lipoprotein and TG measurement are cast in terms of total error in order to account for both bias and imprecision at the same time; thus, the larger the method bias, the more precise the methods must be to satisfy the recommendations for total error.

Table 9–3 ❖ NCEP Recommendations for Reliable Triglyceride, HDL-C, and LDL-C Measurements[1]		
Analyte	*Total Error*	*Consistent with*[2]
Triglyceride	≤ 15%	bias ≤ 5% CV[3] ≤ 5%
HDL-C[3]	≤ 22%	bias ≤ 10% CV ≤ 6%[4]
LDL-C	≤ 12%	bias ≤ 4% CV ≤ 4%
[1]Data taken from NCEP Recommendations on Lipoprotein Measurement.[34] [2]The primary recommendations are cast in terms of total error. The bias and CV shown for each analyte is one example that will satisfy the criterion for that analyte. [3]CV, coefficient of variation [4]CV shown applies at HDL-C concentrations ≥ 42 mg/dL (1.09 mmol/L). At lower concentrations, use SD ≤ 2.5 mg/dL (1.065 mm/L). [5]Interim recommendations. More stringent criteria (total error < 13%) are recommended by 1998, providing technology capable of meeting this goal is available at that time.		

The NCEP guidelines do not distinguish between analyses performed in the laboratory and those performed in non-laboratory settings, nor do they establish separate guidelines for desk-top analyzers, since medically the impact of such measurements on the patient is generally the same regardless of how or where the measurements are made. A number of studies have evaluated the reliability of lipid and lipoprotein measurements with desk-top analyzers. In general, desk-top analyzers give fairly accurate measurements on average, but the measurements tend to be somewhat more variable than those obtained with laboratory-based methods.[22, 23, 26] The use of desk-top instruments with finger-stick blood specimens may contribute to this variability. In one study, the distribution of the difference between measurements of finger-stick samples with the Reflotron analyzer and with standardized laboratory measurements of venous samples taken at the same time was about twice as great as that for venous samples analyzed with both methods.[17] The reasons for the difference are not clear, but may derive, in part, from one or more physiological differences in venous and capillary samples.

It has also been found that one type of desk-top analyzer provided more reliable results when operated by trained laboratory technologists than by operators lacking formal laboratory training.[35] Desk-top analyzers operated under field conditions, in which the instruments must be transported frequently and may be operated in climates of varying temperature and humidity, generally provide more variable results than instruments operated at a fixed location.

In individual samples, however, even when venous samples are used, there can be substantial differences between measurements made with desk-top and laboratory-based systems. A comparison is given in Table 9–4. The data were collected in the author's laboratory in a split-sample comparison conducted over a 9-month period. The analyses were conducted on the DT60 using venous EDTA plasma. The comparison measurements were standardized according to the criteria established by the National Heart, Lung and Blood Institute (NHLBI) and the Centers for Disease Control and Prevention (CDC) for lipid and HDL standardization and were made on a Hitachi 704 analyzer (Boehringer-Mannheim Corp., Indianapolis, IN). There were no significant differences in group mean between the DT60 and laboratory measurements for TC, TG, or HDL-C. However, 15% percent of the TC values, 20% of the HDL-C values, and 26% of the TG values obtained from the DT60 differed by more than 10% from those derived from laboratory measurements. For TC, TG, and HDL-C values, 5–6% of the DT60's measurements differed from the laboratory measurements by more than 20%. For TC and HDL-C, there was no relationship between the magnitude of the differences and concentrations; for TG, the differences tended to decrease at higher concentrations (p = 0.003). Such differences can be of concern when dealing with individual patients, particularly those whose lipid and lipoprotein concentrations are not already known; in such cases, the error might not be suspected and the patient might be misclassified.

Table 9–4 ❖ Comparison of Total Cholesterol (TC), Triglyceride (TG), and HDL-Cholesterol (HDL-C) Values Measured with a Desk-Top Analyzer and Standard Laboratory Procedures

Analyte	n	DT60 mean (SD)[1] (mg/dL)[4]	Laboratory mean (SD)[2] (mg/dL)[4]	Difference (DT60-Lab) %	p	Percentage of Samples with Difference Exceeding:[3] 10%	20%
TC	115	210.5 (53.7)	216.3 (53.3)	−2.7	NS[5]	15	5
TG	117	142.7 (79.7)	142.3 (76.2)	+0.3	NS	26	6
HDL-C	114	47.3 (13.1)	46.0	+0.9	NS	20	5

[1]Measurements were made with the DT60.
[2]Measurements were make with the Hitachi 704 and were standardized through the CDC-NHLBI Lipid Standardization Program.
[3]Refers to the absolute values of the differences between methods.
[4]To convert to mmol/L, divide TC or HDL-C by 38.7 and TG by 88.5.
[5]NS, not significant (p > 0.05, Mann-Whitney Rank Sum Test).

The higher variability of desk-top analyzers can also be observed in several other ways. Table 9–5 summarizes data from the authors laboratory and indicates the variation in TC, TG, HDL-C, and LDL-C values as reflected by measurements in quality-control pools over a 1-year period using laboratory methods, and over a 7-month period using the DT60 analyzer. The control pools used with the DT60 were those supplied by the manufacturer. In all cases except one, the coefficients of variation (CVs) obtained with the desk-top analyzer were several times higher than those obtained from laboratory-based measurements. The one exception was a CV of 1.5% for the TG measurements obtained in one of the manufacturer's pools. Recent reports of studies using other desk-top analyzers also indicate greater analytical variation for these instruments.[21-23, 26]

Table 9–5 ✧ Accuracy and Precision of Lipid and Lipoprotein Measurements Made in the Laboratory and with a Desk-top Analyzer[1]

Analyte	Pool	CDC Reference Value (mg/dL)[2]	Laboratory Mean (SD) (mg/dL)	CV[3] (%)	Pool	DT60 Mean (SD) (mg/dL)	CV (%)
TC	Q17	166.8	165.2 (1.9)	1.2	I	158.2 (5.5)	3.5
	Q20	261.0	259.4 (4.0)	1.5	II	245.8 (10.2)	4.2
TG	Q18	103.4	103.5 (2.4)	2.3	I	132.9 (2.0)	1.5
	Q20	195.0	193.7 (4.5)	2.3	II	262.5 (23.3)	8.9
HDL-C	AQ13	51.9	49.7 (1.3)	2.6	I	29.4 (2.3)	7.8
	AQ14	43.2	44.3 (1.1)	2.5	II	41.9 (2.9)	6.9
LDL-C	AQ17/AQ13	94.2[4]	94.8 (2.4)[4,5]	2.5[5]	I	102.4 (6.0)[4]	5.95
	Q20/AQ13	170.1	171.0 (4.3)	2.5	II	151.3 (11.6)	7.7
	Q17/AQ14	102.9	100.2 (2.3)	2.2			
	Q20/AQ14	178.8	176.4 (4.2)	2.4			

[1]Data from the author's laboratory collected over a 1-y period. Desk-top analyzer data collected over a 7-m period on controls provided by the manufacturer.
[2]To convert to mmol/L, divide TC or HDL by 38.7 and TG by 88.5.
[3]CV, coefficient of variation.
[4]Reference values calculated from TC, TG, and HDL-C reference values for the pools indicated, using the Friedewald equation: LDL-C = TC – HDL-C – TG/5. (Use TG/2.2 for mmol/L.) Laboratory and desk-top analyzer LDL-C means were similarly calculated using the respective means for the three analytes.
[5]Variances for LDL-C were calculated from the variances for the three analytes as follows: $LDL_{var} = TC_{var} + HDL_{var} + TG_{var}/25$. SDs and CVs were calculated from the LDL variances.

The data in Table 9–6 illustrate the results of TC, TG, and HDL-C analyses performed in survey pools distributed by the College of American Pathologists for two commonly used desk-top analyzers. For comparison, data for the same survey pools for several common laboratory-based analyzers are shown in Table 9–7.

Overall, the desk-top analyzers were again slightly more variable than laboratory-based measurements for TC. For TC, among-laboratory CVs of 2.5–2.9% were obtained by the laboratory-based systems (Table 9–7) versus 3.1–3.9% for the desk-top analyzers (Table 9–6). In general, the biases of the desk-top analyzers for TC were about the same as for the laboratory-based systems (Table 9–8). The Abbott VISION desk-top analyzer had and overall negative bias of about 3% for TC compared to the CDC-confirming values for the survey pools. The Johnson & Johnson Vitros DT systems had about a 1% positive bias for TC. In comparison with laboratory-based systems the, biases averaged about +1% for two of the systems and about –3.5% for the third.

Table 9–6 ✦ Performance for Total Cholesterol (TC), HDL-Cholesterol (HDL-C), and Triglyceride (TG) Measurements with Two Desk-Top Analyzer Systems[1]						
			Abbott Vision		*Johnson & Johnson Vitros DT/DTII*	
Analyte	*Pool*	*CDC Confirming Value (mg/dL)*[2]	*Mean (mg/dL)*[2]	*Among-Laboratory CV (%)*	*Mean (mg/dL)*[2]	*Among-Laboratory CV (%)*
TC[3, 4]	LP-01	287	283	3.1	290	4.3
	LP-02	152	146	3.7	154	3.9
	LP-03	151	146	3.3	154	4.2
	LP-04	183	177	3.3	184	4.5
	LP-05	241	236	3.3	250	4.4
HDL-C[4]	LP-01	54.2	—	—	53.8	7.1
	LP-02	36.0	—	—	36.9	6.5
	LP-03	35.3	—	—	36.1	6.5
	LP-04	41.6	—	—	42.8	6.5
	LP-06	62.7	—	—	67.6	5.0
TG[3, 4]	LP-01	101	110	7.2	119	3.5
	LP-02	76	87	3.1	98	3.8
	LP-03	85	96	5.1	108	4.0
	LP-04	93	104	5.9	115	4.3
	LP-05	139	152	6.9	161	3.5

[1]Data from 1996 CAP Chemistry Survey Sets C1, C2, C6, C7 A and B, College of American Pathologists, Chicago, IL.
[2]To convert to mmol/L, divide TC or HDL-C by 38.7 and TG by 88.5.
[3]Data for TC and TG have been rounded to nearest 1 mg/dL.
[4]Results were reported from 17–26 participants for TC and from 10–14 participants for TG.
[5]Results for HDL-C were reported from 17–19 participants.

For TG, among laboratory CVs of 3.2–3.9% were obtained by the laboratory-based systems (Table 9–7), compared to 3.1–7.2 percent for the desk-top analyzers (Table 9–6). The biases for TG were about the same for the desk-top analyzers and laboratory-based systems (Table 9–8). In the examples shown, the percent biases are fairly large, primarily because the CDC confirming values do not include the TG blanks and none of the systems shown in Table 9–8 corrected for TG blanks.

Table 9-7 ❖ Performance for Total Cholesterol (TC), HDL-Cholesterol (HDL-C), and Triglyceride (TG) Measurements with Three Laboratory-Based Systems[1]

Analyte	Pool	CDC Confirming Value (mg/dL)	Abbott Spectrum		Johnson & Johnson Vitros		Hitachi 717	
			Mean (mg/dL)[2]	Among-Laboratory CV (%)	Mean (mg/dL)[2]	Among-Laboratory CV (%)	Mean (mg/dL)[2]	Among-Laboratory CV (%)
TC[3]	LP-01	287	282	4.0	278	3.2	292	2.9
	LP-02	152	150	3.6	145	3.0	153	2.7
	LP-03	151	151	3.7	145	3.0	153	2.7
	LP-04	183	181	3.9	178	3.0	184	2.5
	LP-05	241	241	3.4	238	3.1	245	2.5
HDL-C	LP-01	54.2	49.6	7.3	53.3	6.8	51.5	6.1
	LP-02	36.0	34.7	5.5	37.5	6.1	36.6	4.9
	LP-03	35.3	34.4	6.0	37.1	6.7	35.9	6.0
	LP-04	41.6	40.1	5.8	44.6	5.4	42.0	5.1
	LP-06	62.7	56.5	5.7	62.9	4.7	64.5	6.6
TG[3]	LP-01	101	103	6.4	124	2.2	117	3.8
	LP-02	76	89	6.2	103	2.3	96	3.9
	LP-03	85	96	5.7	113	2.3	105	3.7
	LP-04	93	102	5.5	120	2.3	112	3.2
	LP-05	139	148	4.6	167	2.2	169	3.3

[1]Data from 1996 CAP Chemistry Survey Sets C1, C2, C6, C7 A and B, College of American Pathologists, Chicago, IL.
[2]To convert to mmol/L, divide TC or HDL-C by 38.7 and TG by 88.5.
[3]Data for TC and TG have been rounded to nearest 1 mg/dL.

HDL-C measurements had among-laboratory CVs of 5–7% with the laboratory-based systems, and 5–7% for the desk-top analyzer system for which data were reported. This appears to be a major improvement inasmuch as these CVs are about two- to three-fold lower than was noted in the previous edition of this volume. The biases with the desk-top analyzer were well within the range of those with the laboratory based systems (Table 9–8). Since substantive "matrix effects" can occur with HDL-C measurement in lyophilized pools, these data probably underestimate the reliability of HDL-C measurements with both laboratory-based and desk-top analyzer systems. The fresh-specimen data shown in Table 9–4 support this conclusion.

Although the apparent improvement of desk-top analyzer measurements is encouraging, it cannot be readily generalized because survey data for these systems are considerably more limited that those available for laboratory based systems.

Table 9-8 ❖ Bias of Total Cholesterol (TC), HDL-Cholesterol (HDL-C), and Triglyceride (TG) Measurements with Various Analytical Systems[1]

Analyte	Pool	CDC Confirming Value mg/dL	Abbott Vision		Johnson & Johnson DT60II		Abbott Spectrum		Johnson & Johnson Vitros		Hitachi	
		mg/dL	mg/dL	bias	mg/dL	bias	mg/dL	bias	mg/dL	bias	mg/dL	bias
TC[2]	LP-01	287	283	-1.4%	290	1.0%	282	-1.7%	278	-3.1%	292	1.7%
	LP-02	152	146	-3.9%	154	1.3%	150	-1.3%	145	-4.6%	153	0.7%
	LP-03	151	146	-3.3%	154	2.0%	151	0.0%	145	-4.0%	153	1.3%
	LP-04	183	177	-3.3%	184	0.5%	181	-1.1%	178	-2.7%	184	0.5%
	LP-05	247	239	-3.2%	250	1.2%	241	-2.4%	238	-3.6%	245	-0.8%
	mean			-3.0%		1.2%		-1.3%		-3.6%		0.7%
HDL-C	LP-01	54.2	—	—	53.8	-0.7%	49.6	-8.5%	53.3	-1.7%	51.5	-5.0%
	LP-02	36.0	—	—	36.9	2.5%	34.7	-3.6%	37.5	4.2%	36.6	1.7%
	LP-03	35.3	—	—	36.1	2.3%	34.4	-2.5%	37.1	5.1%	35.9	1.7%
	LP-04	41.6	—	—	42.8	2.9%	40.1	-3.6%	44.6	7.2%	42.0	1.0%
	LP-06	62.7	—	—	67.4	7.5%	56.5	-9.9%	62.9	0.3%	64.5	2.9%
	mean					2.9%		-5.6%		3.0%		-0.1%
TG[2]	LP-01	101	110	8.9%	119	17.8%	103	2.0%	124	22.8%	117	15.8%
	LP-02	76	87	14.5%	98	28.9%	89	17.1%	103	35.5%	96	26.3%
	LP-03	85	96	12.9%	108	27.1%	96	12.9%	113	32.9%	105	23.5%
	LP-04	93	104	11.8%	115	23.7%	102	9.7%	120	29.0%	112	20.4%
	LP-05	139	152	9.4%	161	15.8%	148	6.5%	167	20.1%	169	21.6%
	mean			11.5%		22.7%		9.6%		28.1%		21.5%

[1]Data from 1996 CAP Chemistry Survey Sets C1, C2, C6, C7 A and B, College of American Pathologists, Chicago, IL.
[2]Data for TC and TG have been rounded to nearest 1 mg/dL.

RECOMMENDATIONS

The use of desk-top analyzers for TC measurement has been discussed in detail in the literature.[31, 36] The following sections represent, for the most part, a summary of the recommendations emanating from these discussions, and they can also be usefully applied to the measurement of TG and HDL-C.

Use an accurate system.

Select an instrument-reagent system for which the manufacturer has documented how the measurements were standardized and for which the measurements are traceable to the CDC reference values. This will help to ensure that at least on average, the instrument is capable of providing accurate values.

Use a precise instrument.

Select a system that is precise; that is, repeat measurements made in the same sample should be reproducible. Within individual clinical laboratories, CVs of 2% or less can generally be obtained for TC and TG, and 3% or less for HDL-C. With desk-top analyzers, however, CVs are generally higher, in the range of 4–5% for TC.

Use properly trained operators.

The measurements should be made by trained operators. Ideally, the operator should be a trained medical technician who is familiar with clinical chemical measurements and quality-control procedures. Before using the measurements for clinical purposes, the operator should be trained in the proper procedures for patient preparation, instrument operation, and regularly scheduled instrument maintenance according to the manufacturer's recommended procedures. Maintenance should be documented and records kept current.

Use a quality-control system.

Establish a formal quality-control system using quality-control pools that are available in sufficient quantities to be analyzed for a minimum period of 6 months. Quality-control pools should cover the clinically significant range. Two levels of controls should be used. Recommended concentrations are as follows:

> TC: 180–200 mg/dL (4.66–5.18 mmol/L) and 240–270 mg/dL (6.22–6.99 mmol/L)
> TG: 125–150 mg/dL (1.41–1.69 mmol/L) and 200–250 mg/dL (2.26–2.82 mmol/L)
> HDL-C: 35 mg/dL (0.90 mmol/L) and 60 mg/dL (1.55 mmol/L).

When first setting up the analytical system, these materials should be analyzed in duplicate on 5–10 different days during a 2-week period, and appropriate quality-control limits should be established for each. If assistance in calculating these limits is needed, a qualified local laboratory should be consulted.

New quality-control pools should be introduced before the current pools are exhausted and should similarly be analyzed to establish control limits for those pools before the original pools are discontinued. Quality-control records should be maintained and kept current.

In the laboratory, the results for patient samples are not used when the quality-control measurements are outside control limits; instead, the analyses are repeated. Such a procedure is not feasible with desk-top analysis because the results may have been reported before it was known that they were "out of control." For this reason, it is recommended that quality-control pools be analyzed at the beginning of the day to establish that the analyses are adequate, and again after every 20 samples (or every few hours if less than 20 samples are analyzed) to document that the instrument continues to function properly. If quality-control values are unacceptable, subsequent measurements should not be accepted, and appropriate corrective measures should be taken.

Setting up an adequate quality-control system for desk-top analyzers can be difficult. The main constraint is the difficulty of obtaining sufficient quantities of control materials to allow single lots to be used for extended periods. Test kits may be supplied with quantities sufficient only for that kit, and different lots of control materials may be supplied with subsequent kits. While manufacturers define the acceptable operating ranges of the control, these ranges can be considerably wider than can be routinely obtained with the particular instrument being used. This can make it difficult to determine when the system is behaving abnormally. If possible, it is best to purchase a sufficient quantity of test kits for a 6-month period and specify that all the control materials for the kits are from the same lots of control materials. Furthermore, it is essential to set up a formal system of split-sample analysis with a qualified, preferably CDC-standardized, laboratory (see discussion below).

Use a system of split-sample analysis.

Measurements in quality-control pools can be influenced by factors arising from the way the pools are prepared, and quality-control pools may not accurately reflect the reliability of measurements in freshly drawn patient specimens. It is *not advisable* to rely solely on such pools for quality control. Rather, the accuracy of the results should be monitored by comparing values generated by the desk-top analyzer to those in a qualified laboratory which is either CDC standardized or whose methods are ultimately traceable to reference values. This can be done in 5–10% of the samples by submitting aliquots of those samples to the laboratory. When desk-top analyzer measurements are made in capillary specimens obtained by finger stick, it is preferable that the split-sample comparison be performed in concurrently collected venous serum, since it may not be feasible to use split capillary specimens for laboratory-based measurements. The author prefers to use at least 100 split-sample measurements spaced evenly throughout the year. The data obtained provide a reasonable indication of the long-term accuracy and precision of the measurements.

Follow proper patient preparation procedures.

Blood collection should be performed in a standard way to minimize changes that can lead to inaccurate measurements. For further details on patient preparation and specimen collection and handling, refer to Chapter 4.

SUMMARY

In general, desk-top analyzers tend to be fairly accurate in fresh specimens but less precise than laboratory-based analyses. These instruments can be useful for lipid screening or for following the progress of a patient being treated for hyperlipidemia once the lipoprotein abnormality has been diagnosed using the appropriate medical procedures and lipoprotein measurements. TC concentrations can be measured in samples from non-fasting patients, if necessary. HDL-C measured in fasting samples can be expected to be lower than in non-fasting samples by a few percentage points. TG should not be measured in non-fasting samples. The analyses can be performed in either venous or capillary samples, but if capillary samples are used, it is well to be aware that in individual cases values may differ substantially from venous values.

Desk-top analyzers can be useful when they are operated by properly trained personnel, when adequate quality-control procedures are followed, and when the individuals charged with interpreting the results are aware of the limitations of the technology.   ✧

Acknowledgments: This work was supported in part by an NIH Grant (SCOR-A Grant No. HL 47212, NIH Grant No. RO1 HD 32193) and a grant from Merck and Co. and the Johns Hopkins Lipid Research Unit, Department of Pediatrics, of The Johns Hopkins University School of Medicine. The author wishes to thank Kathleen Lovejoy for assisting with the assembly and analysis of split-sample and quality-control data.

REFERENCES

1. Castelli WP, Garrison RJ, Wilson PWF, et al. Incidence of coronary heart disease and lipoprotein levels: the Framingham Study. JAMA 1986;256:2835–8.
2. Lipid Research Clinics Program. The Lipid Research Clinics Coronary Primary Prevention Trial results. I. Reduction in incidence of coronary heart disease. JAMA 1984;251:351–64.
3. Lipid Research Clinics Program. The Lipid Research Clinics Coronary Primary Prevention Trial results. II. The relation of reduction in incidence of coronary heart disease to cholesterol lowering. JAMA 1984;251:365–74.
4. Stamler J, Wentworth D, Neaton JD, for the MRFIT Research Group. Is the relationship between cholesterol and risk of premature death from coronary heart disease continuous and graded? Findings in 356,222 primary screenees of the Multiple Risk Factor Intervention Trial (MRFIT). JAMA 1986;256:2823–8.
5. Blankenhorn DH, Nessim SA, Johnson RL, et al. Beneficial effects of combined colestipol-niacin therapy on coronary atherosclerosis and coronary venous by-pass grafts. JAMA 1987;257:3233–40.
6. Frick MH, Elo O, Haapa et al. Helsinki Heart Study: primary prevention trial with gemfibrozil in middle-aged men with dyslipidemia. N Engl J Med 1987;317:1237–45.
7. Brensike EJ, Levy RJ, Kelsey SF, et al. Effects of therapy with cholestyramine on progression of coronary arteriosclerosis: results of the NHLBI Type II Coronary Intervention Study. Circulation 1984;69:313–24.
8. Gordon T, Castelli WP, Hjortland MC, Kannel WB, Dawber TR. High density lipoprotein as a protective factor against coronary heart disease: the Framingham Study. Am J Med 1977;62:707–14.
9. Castelli WP, Doyle JT, Gordon T, et al. HDL cholesterol and other lipids in coronary heart disease: the co-operative lipoprotein phenotyping study. Circulation 1972;55:767–72.
10. Miller NE, Forde OH, Thelle DS, Mjos OD. The Tromso Heart Study. High density lipoprotein and coronary heart disease: a prospective case-control study. Lancet 1977;1:965–7.
11. Summary of the Second Report of the National Cholesterol Education Program (NCEP) Expert Panel on Detection, Evaluation and Treatment of High Blood Cholesterol in Adults (Adult Treatment Panel II). JAMA 1993;269:3015–23.
12. Report of the National Cholesterol Education Program Expert Panel on Detection Evaluation and Treatment of High Blood Cholesterol in Adults. Arch Intern Med 1988;148:36–69.
13. Allain CC, Poon LS, Chan CSG, Richmond W, Fu PC. Enzymatic determination of total serum cholesterol. Clin Chem 1974;20:470–6.
14. Demaker PNM, Boerma GJM, Baadenhuijsen H, et al. Evaluation of accuracy of 20 different test kits for the enzymatic determination of cholesterol. Clin Chem 1983;29:1916–22.

15. Bucolo G, David H. Quantitative determination of serum triglycerides by the use of enzymes. Clin Chem 1973;19:476–82.

16. Bachorik PS, Levy RI, Rifkind BM. Lipids and dyslipoproteinemia. In: Henry JB, ed. Clinical diagnosis and management by laboratory methods, 18th ed. Philadelphia: WB Saunders, 1991:188–214.

17. Bachorik PS, Rock R, Cloey T, et al. Cholesterol screening: comparative evaluation of on-site and laboratory-based measurements. Clin Chem 1990;36:255–60.

18. Sedor FA, Holleman CM, Heyden S, Schneider KA. Reflotron cholesterol measurement evaluated as a screening technique. Clin Chem 1988;34:2542–4.

19. Bachorik PS, Bradford RH, Cole T, et al. Accuracy and precision of analyses for total cholesterol as measured with the Reflotron cholesterol method. Clin Chem 1989;35:1734–9.

20. von Schenck H, Treichl L, Tilling B, Olsson AG. Laboratory and field evaluation of three desktop instruments for assay of cholesterol and triglyceride. Clin Chem 1987;33:1230–2.

21. Ng RH, Sparks KM, Statland BE. Direct measurement of high-density lipoprotein cholesterol by the Reflotron Assay with no manual precipitation step. Clin Chem 1991;37:435–7.

22. Warnick GR, Boerma GJM, Assmann G, Endler AT, Gerique G, Gotto AM, et al. Multi-center evaluation of Reflotron direct dry-chemistry assay of high density lipoprotein cholesterol in venous and fingerstick specimens. Clin Chem 1993;39:271–7.

23. Kafonek SD, Donovan L, Lovejoy KL, Bachorik PS. Biological variation of lipids and lipoproteins in fingerstick blood. Clin Chem 1996;42:2002–7.

24. Friedewald WT, Levy RI, Fredrickson DS. Estimation of the concentration of low density lipoprotein cholesterol in plasma without use of the preparative ultracentrifuge. Clin Chem 1972;18:499–502.

25. Koch TR, Mehtu U, Lee H, et al. Bias and precision of cholesterol analysis by physicians office analyzers. Clin Chem 1987;33:2262–7.

26. Rogers EJ, Misner L, Ockene IS, Nicolosi RJ. Evaluation of seven cholestech LDX analyzers for total cholesterol determinations. Clin Chem 1993;39:860–4.

27. Kupke IR, Zeugner S, Gottschalk A, Kather B. Differences in lipid and lipoprotein concentrations of capillary and venous blood samples. Clin Chim Acta 1979;97:279–83.

28. Kaplan SA, Yuceoglu AM, Strauss J. Chemical microanalysis: analysis of capillary and venous blood. Pediatrics 1959;24:270–4.

29. Greenland P, Bowley NL, Melklejohn B, Doane KL, Sparks CE. Blood cholesterol concentration: fingerstick plasma vs. venous serum sampling. Clin Chem 1990;36:628–30.

30. Bachorik PS. Collection of blood samples for lipoprotein analysis. Clin Chem 1982;28:1375–8.

31. Laboratory Methods Committee, Lipid Research Clinics Program. Cholesterol and triglyceride concentrations in serum plasma pairs. Clin Chem 1977;26:60–3.

32. Cloey T, Bachorik PS, Becker D, Finney C, Lowry D, Sigmund W. Re-evaluation of serum-plasma differences in total cholesterol concentration. JAMA 1990;263:2788–9.

33. Laboratory Standardization Panel. Recommendations for improving cholesterol measurement: a report from the Laboratory Standardization Panel of the National Cholesterol Education Program, NIH Publication No. 90-2964. Executive Summary, NIH Publication No. 90-2964A. Bethesda, MD: NIH, 1990.

34. National Cholesterol Education Program Recommendations on Lipoprotein Measurement. From the Working Group on Lipoprotein Measurement, NIH Publication No. 95-3044. Bethesda, MD: NHLBI, Sept. 1995.

35. Belsey R, Vandenbark M, Goitein RK, Baer DM. Evaluation of a laboratory system intended for use in physicians' offices. II. Reliability of results produced by health care workers without formal or professional laboratory training. JAMA 1987;258:357–63.

36. Recommendations regarding public screening for measuring blood cholesterol: a summary of a National Heart, Lung and Blood Institute workshop, NIH Publication No. 89-3045. Bethesda, MD: NIH, 1989.

Measurement and Clinical Significance of Apolipoproteins A-I and B

10

Deepak Bhatnagar and Paul N. Durrington

GENERAL INTRODUCTION

✧   Apolipoproteins (apo) A-I and B are both integral parts of lipoprotein particles that play an important role in cholesterol transport. Apo B plays an essential role in the delivery of cholesterol to the tissues. Apo A-I has a role in the removal of excess cholesterol from the tissues and is the main apolipoprotein in the interstitial space. Both apo B and apo A-I have a role in the diagnosis and monitoring of disease and in the assessment of coronary risk, but further studies are needed to refine their clinical use.

APOLIPOPROTEIN A-I

Background

The principal apolipoproteins of high-density lipoproteins (HDL) are the A apolipo-proteins, so called because HDL was formerly called alpha lipoprotein.[1] In man, the two major A apolipoproteins are A-I and A-II. Apo A-I is the most abundant. Indeed, it is present in plasma in health at mass concentrations which generally exceed those of apo B. In the tissue fluid, A-I is the apolipoprotein present at the greatest concen-tration.[2]

Apo A-I and apo A-II originate from both the gut and the liver, from where they are secreted as phospholipid-rich discs called nascent HDL.[3] The gene for apo A-I is located on chromosome 11, where it occurs in close proximity to the genes for apo C-III and apo A-IV.[4] In common with many of the other apolipoprotein genes, it consists of four exons with three intervening introns. The exons code for a 267 amino acid precursor known as preproapo A. The prepeptide at the N-terminal end of this molecule is 18 amino acids long and is cleaved co-translationally, leaving the proapo A-I, which is the form secreted.[5] The six amino acid N-terminal propeptide is then removed in the circulation by a specific calcium-dependent protease. This results in the mature 243 amino acid apo A-I.[6] The residence time of proapo A-I in the circulation is approximately 4.5 h, whereas the half-life of mature A-I is of the order of 5–6 days. Proapo A-I comprises 4% of the total fasting serum apo A-I, but increases transiently after meals.

Most of the C terminal 200 amino acids of the mature apo A-I are coded for by the fourth exon, which is the largest.[7] In this part of the molecule are six repeated sequences each of 22 amino acids, each ending with proline. In between the prolines is an alpha-helical structure with polar and non-polar faces. This confers upon the A-I molecule powerful detergent properties, the non-polar groups being directed towards the hydrophobic core lipids and the polar groups interfacing with water molecules outside.[8] Most of the apo A-I is present in plasma and extravascular tissue fluid in HDL. There is, however, a small percentage of apo A-I which is not present in lipoproteins and which is generally referred to as pre-beta HDL, which accurately describes its electrophoretic mobility but wrongly describes its hydrated density, which is greater than that of HDL.[9] Use of the term "free apo A-I" to describe this fraction is also misleading because it contains phospholipid. A discoidal form termed pre-beta-2 HDL also exists in addition to the spherical form of alpha or mature HDL.[10] Recent evidence suggests that pre-beta HDL may be released from larger HDL particles as they circulate through peripheral tissues by the actions of lipoprotein lipase.[11] Studies of epitope mapping[12] indicate that the conformation of apo A-I differs in the various species of HDL (Figure 10-1). *In vitro* evidence suggests it is both an acceptor of cholesterol

Figure 10-1 ✧ The Conformation of Apolipoprotein A-I Differs in the Three Main HDL Subspecies

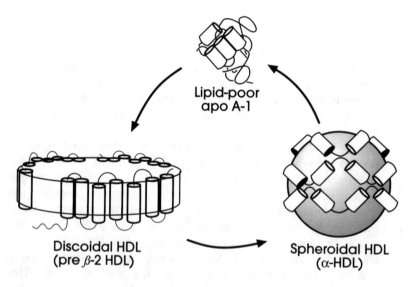

Lipid-poor
apo A-1

Discoidal HDL
(pre *β*-2 HDL)

Spheroidal HDL
(α-HDL)

Source: Fielding CJ, Fielding PE. Molecular physiology of reverse cholesterol transport. J Lipid Res 1995;36:211-28. Reprinted by permission.

and promotes cholesterol efflux. Besides its structural role, apo A-I is the major activator of the enzyme lecithin:cholesterol acyltransferase (LCAT).[13]

Apo A-I has six polymorphic isoforms designated 1–6, of which 4 and 5 are the most common. In addition, there are genetic mutations of apo A-I referred to as apo A-I$_{Tangier}$, apo A-I$_{Milano}$, apo A-I$_{Marburg}$, and so on (see discussion below). Apo A-I is unusual among the apolipoproteins in that carbohydrate is absent as a component of its mature form.

Clinical Relevance of Apo A-I Measurement

Presently apo A-I measurements are of most use in characterizing patients with genetic disorders that lead to low HDL-cholesterol (HDL-C) concentrations. Several disorders of HDL are associated with low apo A-I levels, but only some patients with these disorders will have mutations of apo A-I. The benefits of determining coronary heart disease (CHD) risk through apo A-I assays rather than with HDL-C measurements is unclear. There are few prospective studies of apo A-I in CHD prediction, and in some of them HDL-C was found to be superior to apo A-I.[14-17] Furthermore, until recently issues of standardization of assays remained unresolved. Moreover, data from genetic studies of HDL deficiency syndromes, many of which are not associated with CHD, are at odds with data from case-control studies where low apo A-I is often a marker of CHD risk.

Familial Low HDL Concentration

Familial low HDL appears to be quite common and is often associated with elevated plasma triglyceride levels. HDL-C levels below the 10th percentile are often associated with an increased risk of CHD.[18] In the United States, the 10th percentile in men between 20–69 years was 33 mg/dL (0.8 mmol/L) and in women between 25–55 years was 39 mg/dL (1.0 mmol/L).[19] No specific defects have been described in these patients, but it is thought that they have an increased turnover of apo A-I and other HDL proteins.[20] Apo A-I measurements are rarely required in these patients unless there is a strong suspicion of apo A-I deficiency disorders.

Familial Apo A-I Deficiency

There have been several reports of patients with apo A-I deficiency, all of whom are characterized by particularly low HDL-C levels.[21] The low apo A-I arises from mutations that result in incomplete forms of apo A-I. These deficiency syndromes are inherited as an autosomal-dominant trait and the associated phenotypes vary greatly. Not all patients develop CHD. Some have corneal clouding and others have planar xanthomata. Some patients with apo A-I deficiency syndromes also have a deficiency of apo C-III or of C-III and apo A-IV. Plasma lipid levels also show variation in phenotype. Mild hypertriglyceridemia is commonly present, but most patients do not have high plasma cholesterol concentrations.

Apo A-I Variants

In contrast to deficiency syndromes, many apo A-I variants have been reported in the literature. However, not all patients with these variants have low HDL-C levels.[22] Often these have been discovered on isoelectric focussing of apo A-I. Some like A-I_Milano are associated with longevity.[23]

Tangier Disease

This is a rare autosomal-recessive disorder characterized by low plasma total cholesterol and HDL-C levels and accumulation of cholesteryl esters in many tissues, particularly the reticuloendothelial system.[24] A typical presentation is the presence of hyperplastic yellowish-orange tonsils. In homozygotes, plasma apo A-I levels are usually 1–3% of normal; in heterozygotes, apo A-I levels are half that of normal. The exact biochemical defect is not known, but the accumulation of cholesteryl ester and low HDL levels suggest a problem with cellular cholesterol storage and processing.[25]

Familial Lecithin:Cholesterol Acyltransferase (LCAT) Deficiency

This is due to a deficiency of the enzyme lecithin:cholesterol acyltransferase.[26] Both alpha and beta LCAT activities are decreased. Plasma apo A-I levels are decreased to 15–30% of normal and HDL-C concentrations are 10% of normal. Most patients develop corneal opacities and anemia. Proteinuria and renal failure develop over time.

Fish Eye Disease

Fish eye disease is also characterized by LCAT deficiency, but it is mainly alpha LCAT activity that is decreased.[27] As in familial LCAT deficiency, patients typically have corneal opacities, but proteinuria and renal failure do not develop. Apo A-I levels are reduced to 15–30% of normal and HDL-C levels are 10% of normal.

Hyperalphalipoproteinemia

Hyperalphalipoproteinemia occurs in some families in whom HDL-C levels are consistently greater than the highest decile for the population.[28] The genetics of the condition are not clear, but it is important to exclude secondary causes for an increase in HDL-C. Apo A-I levels are elevated in parallel to HDL-C levels.

Familial Cholesteryl Ester Transfer Protein (CETP) Deficiency

CETP is a glycoprotein that transfers cholesteryl ester out of HDL to triglyceride-rich lipoproteins with a reciprocal exchange of triglycerides into HDL.[29] Families with CETP deficiency have been described recently.[30] Homozygotes have HDL-C levels that are markedly elevated with a doubling of the apo A-I concentration. Heterozygotes may have normal or high HDL-C, but apo A-I levels are increased. The small number of homozygotes discovered seem to be protected from CHD, but converse data linking CHD and high CETP levels are more convincing.[31]

Apo A-I and Coronary Risk

Many studies have confirmed the ability of HDL-C levels to predict coronary risk.[32-35] It therefore would seem logical that apo A-I levels should behave in a similar fashion, but it is generally thought that they offer little advantage over HDL-C levels. However, apo A-I assays have the theoretical advantage of better precision than HDL-C assays. Issues relating to standardization and antibody specificity have been addressed only recently, and prospective studies are needed to show firm benefit over the cheaper HDL-C assays currently in use.

Most case-control studies show an inverse relationship between apo A-I and CHD, similar to that seen with HDL-C. Of the four prospective studies to date,[14-17] one study, in which HDL-C was not measured, showed apo A-I to be a discriminator between subjects with and without CHD. Of the other three studies, two did not find that apo A-I contributed more than HDL-C, and the fourth found that apo A-I added to the value of apo B in predicting CHD.

APOLIPOPROTEIN B

Background

Apo B is central to the lipoprotein transport system. It is essential for the secretion of triglyceride-rich lipoproteins both from the liver and gut. (For further details see Chapters 1 and 2.) A single molecule of apo B is present in each chylomicron, very-low-density lipoprotein (VLDL), or low-density lipoprotein (LDL) particle from its assembly, its secretion, its metabolic transformation within the circulation, to its ultimate catabolism.[36] Apo B does not exchange between lipoprotein particles. It is for this reason that it has been possible, by labelling apo B with isotopes, to study the metabolic fate of apo-B-containing lipoproteins.[37] A similar approach, such as labelling apo A-I, can give only a limited insight into HDL metabolism.

Apo B is the most abundant protein in LDL. It acquired its name because it was formerly known as beta lipoprotein. Its serum concentration in Northern European and American populations is in the range of 50–180 mg/dL.[38] More than 90% of this is in LDL and the rest in VLDL (Table 10-1).[39] In conditions associated with a raised serum concentration of LDL-C, serum apo B is generally also raised, even when increased LDL-C concentrations are not accompanied by hypercholesterolemia (hyper-apobetalipoproteinemia; see below). It has long been realized that many of the hyper-lipoproteinemias leading to premature atherosclerosis are those in which serum apo B levels are high. In 1974, Fredrickson, commenting about apo B, wrote: "Its resistance to characterisation, its seeming essentiality for glyceride transport, and perhaps the added suspicion that it has something to do with atherogenesis have all transformed apo B into one of the central mysteries of lipoprotein physiology."[40]

Table 10–1 ◆ Apolipoprotein B Concentrations in LDL from Patients with Hyperlipidemia						
		WHO PHENOTYPE				
		Normal $n = 18$	IIa $n = 15$	IIb $n = 5$	IV $n = 6$	V $n = 4$
		SERUM				
Apolipoprotein B	mg/dL	92 ± 21	223 ± 47	289 ± 149	231 ± 104	130 ± 16
Cholesterol	mg/dL	182 ± 35	340 ± 46	321 ± 31	286 ± 43	552 ± 243
	mmol/L	4.7 ± 0.9	8.8 ± 1.2	8.3 ± 0.8	7.4 ± 1.1	14.3 ± 6.3
Triglyceride	mg/dL	80 ± 18	133 ± 27	327 ± 106	496 ± 274	2540 ± 1407
	mmol/L	0.9 ± 0.2	1.5 ± 0.3	3.7 ± 1.2	5.6 ± 3.1	28.7 ± 15.9
		LDL				
Apolipoprotein B	mg/dL	80 ± 18	206 ± 49	235 ± 125	160 ± 73	65 ± 10
% total serum apolipoprotein B		93 ± 9	93 ± 9	91 ± 1	81 ± 9	52 ± 8
Source: Adapted from Durrington, Bolton & Hartog[39]						

Since that time, evidence has progressively accumulated for a close association between serum apo B and premature coronary atheroma.[41] Until recently, the structure and properties of the apo B molecule remained a mystery because its enormous size, insolubility even when only partially delipidated, and tendency to aggregate make it resistant to many biochemical techniques. Now, as a result of advances in immunochemistry, in the study of specific proteolytic fragments, and molecular genetic techniques, fascinating details of its biochemistry have emerged. The apo B gene is situated on chromosome 2.[42] Its messenger RNA (mRNA) contains 14,121 nucleotides and is thus the largest mRNA known. It codes for a 4563 amino acid protein, the N-terminal 27 amino acids of which are cleaved, resulting in a 4536 amino acid native apo B-100.[43] The 27 residue terminal portion is hydrophobic and large enough to span a biological membrane. Thus, the apo B gene may be important in the membrane transport and anchoring of the apo B during the synthesis and secretion of the apo B-containing lipoproteins.[44] Apo B is synthesized in the smooth endoplasmic reticulum. Triglycerides may be stored before becoming bound to the apo B and appearing in the Golgi complex.[45] The binding of triglycerides to apo B is facilitated by microsomal triglyceride transfer protein (MTP).[46] The inheritance of defective MTP is the basis of abetalipoproteinemia (see discussion below). Carbohydrate is acquired in the Golgi complex before secretion of the nascent VLDL. N-linked oligosaccharides comprise some 8–10% of the mass of apo B.

The primary sequence of apo B-100 is unlike that of other apolipoproteins such as the apo A and apo C. It is a much larger molecule. Estimates of its molecular weight from the amino acids present are around 500,000 daltons which, allowing for the presence of carbohydrate, would suggest an actual mass as high as 550,000 daltons.[47] Therefore, from our knowledge of the protein content of LDL, there can be only one molecule of apo B-100 per molecule of LDL. Typically, apolipoproteins consist largely of alpha helices and beta structure. They bind to lipid through amphipathic sequences in the classical detergent-style. Apo B is different. It is very much more hydrophobic. Long hydrophobic sequences interspersed with hydrophilic ones characterize much of its structure, which is only 43% alpha helix, with the rest comprising about equally beta sheet, beta turn, and random structures. About 11 hydrophobic regions are thus strung out along the apo B molecule, and these probably bury themselves in the triglycerides and cholesteryl esters of the lipoprotein core, leaving the more hydrophilic intervening sections at the surface or within the outer phospholipid, free cholesterol, and apo-C-containing regions of the lipoprotein particle. There are several points in the apo B structure where disulfide bonds could either form internally or with another protein such as the apolipoprotein (a) of Lp(a) (see Chapter 15).

Despite its enormous size, apo B, like apo E, has only one receptor-binding site per molecule. It is in a region about one-quarter of the way from the C-terminal of the apo B molecule, which is rich in basic amino acids, homologous with the receptor-binding site of the apo E.[48] It is assumed that during the removal of the lipid core from VLDL in its conversion to LDL, conformational changes occur in the apo B which allow the receptor site to bind to the LDL receptor. Perhaps during the conversion of VLDL to LDL some of the hydrophobic regions of apo B become less deeply embedded in the diminishing lipid core and the surface parts of the molecule crowd closer together and project out further, allowing the receptor binding site to become more prominently exposed and to assume its most active shape. The removal of VLDL from the circulation via the LDL receptor is thus prevented until it has shed its triglyceride load.

In man, apo B-48 is the apo B produced by the gut but not by the liver.[49] It is estimated to have about 48% of the molecular weight of apo B (hence its name). It does not bind to lipoprotein receptors. Both apo B-100 and apo B-48 appear to arise from an identical gene (Figure 10–2). Apolipoprotein B-48 consists of the N-terminal 2152 amino acids of apo B-100.[50] Examination of the genome shows that it terminates in about the middle of the largest exon, meaning that transcription of the message is unlikely to be broken at this point. However, in the RNAs from gut and liver, codon 2153 is different.[51] In that codon, cytosine is present in hepatic mRNA, whereas uracil is present in intestinal mRNA. This makes the codon read CAA in the liver, which translates as glutamine, and UAA in the gut, which is an order to terminate translation. The intestine proves to possess a highly specific enzyme which changes the cytosine (perhaps by deamination) in codon 2153 of apo B mRNA.[52] The effect of the two types of apo B produced in the liver and gut is of fundamental importance to lipoprotein metabolism. Because the receptor-binding site of apo B-100 is in the C-terminal half not present in apo B-48, the triglyceride-rich lipoproteins from the gut are dependent on apo E for their clearance from the circulation. Mutations of the apo B gene also occur which lead to the premature termination of its translation leading to truncation of the apo B molecule.[53] This leads to an unexplained decrease in the production of apo B from the unmutated gene and to dominant inheritance of hypobetalipoproteinemia (discussed below).

It is also becoming clear that apo B-100 is highly polymorphic. This has been demonstrated by molecular biology techniques, and by individual variation in the bind-

Figure 10–2 ✧ Structure and Organization of the Apolipoprotein B Gene

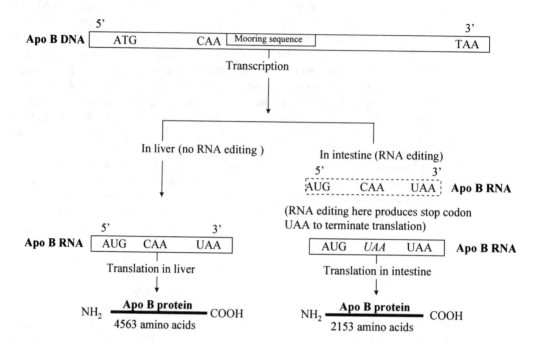

ing affinities of apo-B-containing lipoproteins to monoclonal antibodies directed at different parts of the apo B molecule.[54] The present interest in that area of research focuses on which of these polymorphisms influence the metabolism of apo-B-containing lipoproteins sufficiently to have a clinically significant impact on their serum concentration and their involvement in atherogenesis. There are also mutations of apo B, the most extensively studied of which has been the apo B-3500 mutation, which affects binding to the LDL receptor (familial defective apo B [FDB]).[55]

The hypothesis that macrophage uptake of LDL is important in atherogenesis has led to a further heightening of interest in apo B, because of evidence that it is its apo B moiety which allows the rapid uptake of LDL crossing the arterial endothelium by macrophages to form foam cells.[56] Macrophages do not possess a particularly active physiological LDL receptor, and macrophage uptake of unmodified LDL cannot account for the generation of foam cells. Modification of LDL, can, however, greatly increase the rate at which it is bound and internalized by macrophages via receptors which are quite distinct from the physiological LDL receptor.[57] The modification of LDL permitting this rapid uptake, which has attracted much attention, is oxidation.[58] This is because it is plausible that lipid-peroxidation could occur *in vivo*. Macrophage receptors which allow the uptake of oxidized LDL do so by binding to apo B which has been damaged by the breakdown products of the LDL lipids which are peroxidized, particularly the unsaturated fatty acyl groups in the Sn-2 position of phosphatidylcholine.[59] Aldehydes are produced by the schism following the introduction of oxygen free radicals at sites of double bonds. These aldehydes form adducts with the lysine groups of apo B, leading to its fragmentation.[60] LDL then loses its capacity to bind to the LDL receptor, but binds to the macrophage receptors. (For additional information on this topic, refer to Chapter 18.) The most extensively studied of these has been the acetyl-LDL receptor (so-named because the modification of LDL, which led to its discovery, was acetylation) or scavenger receptor.[61] However, there are undoubtedly other classes of receptors which can be involved, and have been termed oxidized LDL receptors.

Glycation is another modification of LDL which accelerates macrophage uptake.[62] This process involves the addition of glucose to lysine residue on apo B. This may in itself make the LDL more susceptible to fragmentation by products of lipid peroxidation, which may themselves be formed as a consequence of free radical generation during glycation.[63] It is not clear whether glycation might lead directly to foam cell generation by the same mechanism as oxidative modification. Glycated apo B comprises some 4% of the total circulating apo B in non-diabetic people and about twice that amount in diabetic patients with reasonable glycemic control.[64] In normolipidemic non-diabetic people, typical serum levels of glycated apo B are 2–6 mg/dL. Because of the high concentration of LDL in, for example, heterozygous familial hypercholesterolemia, the concentration of glycated apo B may be similar to that in diabetes even though the percentage glycated is not increased.[65] In contrast, oxidatively modified LDL is present only at substantially lower concentrations. It is difficult to be confident that such levels are present *in vivo* and are not generated during subsequent processing of the blood sample. Because oxidized LDL is antigenic, its generation may be detected by measuring titres of antibodies to modified LDL, and this may prove to be a more reliable method of detecting individuals' increased oxidized LDL production. The usefulness of titres of antibodies to various modifications of LDL in predicting the extent of oxidation is currently undergoing evaluation. Malondialdehyde modification has been most extensively studied thus far.[66]

Clinical Relevance of Apo B

A large body of experimental evidence implicates apo-B-containing plasma lipoproteins in the causation of atherosclerosis. In contrast, epidemiological data relating plasma apo B concentrations to coronary risk are not so numerous. Some of the reasons for this discrepancy probably arise from difficulties in standardization of assays for plasma apo B determination, but may also be due to a failure of assays to recognize the heterogeneity of apo B which is present in atherogenic particles such as intermediate-density lipoproteins (IDL) and small, dense LDL, and also in the relatively less atherogenic LDL-I and LDL-II subfractions.

In the last few years, progress has been made in standardization of apo B assays, and data on reference ranges based on population studies and case control studies is now becoming available . At present, the main utility of plasma apo B determination lies in the diagnosis of certain primary disorders of lipoprotein metabolism and as a research tool in the investigation of lipoprotein metabolism. Its role in the assessment of coronary risk remains unclear and needs to be investigated further.

Abetalipoproteinemia

Abetalipoproteinemia is an autosomal-recessive disorder due to a deficiency of apo B in the intestine and the liver.[67] As a consequence, dietary fat is malabsorbed and accumulates in the intestine to produce intestinal malabsorption. The apo B deficiency also results characteristically in acanthocytosis, retinitis pigmentosa, and ataxia due to spinocerebellar degeneration. The latter two conditions respond at least partially to supplementation of vitamins A and E, suggesting that a deficiency of fat-soluble vitamins may be the cause of the neurological features.

Apo B mRNA in the liver is increased. Hepatic steatosis also occurs, although this indicates that the defect does not lie in the gene, but in the assembly and secretion of triglyceride-rich lipoproteins, both by the gut and liver. Recent evidence indicates that abetalipoproteinemia may be due to a defect in the microsomal lipid transfer protein.[68]

Biochemically, patients with abetalipoproteinemia have markedly decreased serum cholesterol and triglycerides, and a firm diagnosis is made on clinical grounds, characteristic changes in gut mucosa, and absent plasma apo B.

Hypobetalipoproteinemia

Hypobetalipoproteinemia is usually an autosomal-dominant disorder which, like abetalipoproteinemia, also results in low plasma apo B concentrations, but not usually as low as in abetalipoproteinemia unless the patient is a homozygote.[69] Several features distinguish the two disorders. In hypobetalipoproteinemia, a defect in the apo B gene results in the production of a truncated apo B which is unable to associate with lipids. In heterozygotes, plasma apo B concentrations are no more than a quarter to half of normal concentrations. The homozygous state produces a clinical phenotype that is indistinguishable from abetalipoproteinemia. Both heterozygotes and homozygotes can be identified by measuring plasma apo B levels, but it is possible that certain mutations may lead to truncated forms of apo B that are not detected by conventional apo B assays. Family studies are often helpful in establishing the diagnosis of hypobetalipoproteinemia, since, unlike abetalipoproteinemia, the affected relatives are frequently found.

Hyperapobetalipoproteinemia (HABL)

HABL is a condition in which LDL-cholesterol (LDL-C) levels are within the accepted reference range but plasma apo B and LDL apo B concentrations are increased.[70] Patients with HABL generally have mild to moderate hypertriglyceridemia[71] or delayed postprandial triglyceride clearance,[72] and an increased risk of developing CHD.[73] These features of HABL are not dissimilar to those of familial combined hyperlipidemia in which, by definition, serum total and LDL-cholesterol are also elevated. Thus, the measurement of apo B becomes essential if the two conditions are to be differentiated. The prevalence of HABL has not been firmly established. The true frequency of the condition will only be known when both serum total and LDL-cholesterol measurements and apo B assays are carried out simultaneously in laboratories. Genest et al. found the prevalence of HABL to be around 30% in patients with premature CHD and 5% in the relatives of these probands.[74] In a case-control study, 19.8% of patients with CHD had HABL, compared to 8.4% in controls without CHD.[75]

Apo B and Coronary Risk

In case-control studies in patients with coronary heart disease (CHD), plasma apo B concentrations have been found to be more discriminating than other plasma lipids and lipoproteins.[76–78] In some of these studies, it is very likely that apo B would have been an even better predictor of IHD if the effect of myocardial ischemia and usage of beta-blockers, both of which can lower apo B and apo A-I levels, had been taken into account.[79] Many prospective studies also confirm the utility of plasma apo B levels in determining coronary risk, although the extent to which plasma apo B concentrations were better than serum lipids in predicting risk was variable.[80–83] This is perhaps due to the differing entry criteria and populations in these studies. These data would suggest that the case for measuring plasma apo B is strong, but the reality is that there is a complex biological (and hence statistical) interaction between the various biochemical parameters that predict coronary risk. Plasma apo B measurements perhaps have an inherent advantage over LDL-C levels which are often calculated, and the results have to rely on the patient being truly fasting.

Increasing recognition of the heterogeneity of LDL also introduces difficulties in distinguishing which LDL subfraction is associated with coronary risk.[84] While it is known that small, dense LDL and enrichment of LDL with cholesteryl ester are more atherogenic,[85] there is no easy way of identifying these abnormalities in routine laboratories. Since every particle of VLDL secreted from the liver has one molecule of apo B, plasma apo B concentrations provide not only a measure of risk associated with VLDL, IDL, and LDL, but also a measure of LDL particle number. Many of the primary and secondary coronary prevention studies and angiographic regression studies of cholesterol-lowering confirm the need to have a direct measure of a decrease in LDL particle number. This may explain why in some studies apo B does not compare well with total or LDL cholesterol as a measure of coronary risk.

So how should a laboratory use plasma apo B assays? At present, many laboratories are reluctant to introduce the test, mainly due to the cost of analysis, and until recently the difficulties in standardization also made the assay unsuitable for routine screening of patients. The value of plasma apo B lies in the diagnosis of disorders of lipoprotein metabolism and in the estimation of coronary risk and response to lipid-lowering therapy in most patients other than those with obviously elevated serum cholesterol levels. In particular, plasma apo B can provide a measure of risk in patients with hypertriglyceridemia, who may or may not have low HDL-C values.[86] Hypertriglyceridemia has been shown to be associated with CHD in several studies, but its heterogeneity makes it difficult to use serum triglycerides as a marker of CHD with any confidence.[87] Apo B measurements can further refine the assessment of coronary risk in patients with hypertriglyceridemia, as elevated apo B in this situation indicates the presence of small, dense LDL. At present, LDL subfractions measurements are carried out either by electrophoresis or by ultracentrifugation, neither of which can be automated. (For additional information, refer to Chapter 14.)

Another group of patients for whom apo B measurements can be of value are those with impaired glucose tolerance and type II diabetes mellitus. In both of these conditions, coronary morbidity is markedly increased and often patients have hypertriglyceridemia and low HDL-C along with serum cholesterol values that are not dissimilar to the non-diabetic general population.[88] In a recent prospective study, where serum insulin was shown to be an independent risk factor for IHD, the odds ratio was greatest for those with the highest plasma apo B levels.[89]

Many laboratories are now able to use molecular biology techniques in the diagnosis of disease. Several studies have suggested that genetic variation at the apo B gene locus can predict atherosclerosis through increasing serum cholesterol concentrations or altering dietary responsiveness to fat.[90] These effects only explain a small proportion of the variation in serum cholesterol and are therefore of limited use.[91] The variation of the apo B gene also does not help in the diagnosis of conditions such as HABL or familial combined hyperlipidemia, in which there is an overproduction of apo B. There is perhaps a role for genetic studies in identifying patients with familial defective apo B. This mutation in the ligand for the LDL receptor can present with a clinical phenotype similar to that of heterozygous familial hypercholesterolemia.[55]

ANALYTICAL ASPECTS OF APOLIPOPROTEIN MEASUREMENT

The analysis of apo B and apo A-I is carried out by immunochemical techniques. In the early years of apolipoprotein investigations, electroimmunoassay (EIA), radial immunodiffusion (RID), and radioimmunoassay (RIA) were widely used. However, the former two methods were difficult to automate for the measurement of large numbers of samples and consumed large amounts of antisera. RIA, on the other hand, has a greater sensitivity and is more precise than either EIA or RID.[92] It also overcomes the need for large amounts of specific antisera and avoids matrix problems seen with EIA and RID. Automation of RIA remains relatively difficult and has the inherent disadvantages of the use of radioactivity and short reagent half-lives.

Advances in the production of monospecific and monoclonal antibodies and the development of enzymic labels led to the development of enzyme-linked immunosorbent assays (ELISA) and better nephelometric and turbidimetric assays.[93] A great advantage of these assays, particularly the latter two, was the potential for automation and thus the capability to assay large numbers of samples. Immunonephelometry requires dedicated instrumentation and achieves better precision than immunoturbidimetric assay, but both methods require large amounts of specific antisera and are prone to matrix effects. Apolipoprotein analysis by ELISA is highly sensitive and moderately precise, but requires the use of large dilutions. Automated and electronic dispensers have improved the precision of pipetting of both small and large volumes of liquid, but automation of ELISA techniques is not fully achievable in routine clinical laboratories.

Recently, an particle-concentration fluorescence immunoassay (PCFIA) technique has been applied to the determination of apo B.[94] Another method has adapted a time-resolved immunofluorometric assay for apo B measurement in cerebrospinal fluid.[95]

Both these methods use fluorescent labels, are extremely sensitive, and their potential for automation makes the measurement of small amounts of apolipoprotein in large numbers a reality.

In most routine laboratories the choice of assay method for apolipoprotein measurement is immunonephelometry or immunoturbidimetry. Both are amenable to automation and have the ability to handle large numbers of samples. The need for sample manipulation is minimal, and with modern instruments precision is quite acceptable. The results are generally accurate and assays now can be calibrated against internationally acceptable reference materials for both apo A-I and B.[96, 97] Both nephelometric and turbidimetric assays can suffer from interference due to lipemia.[98] There is also the possibility of unstable immune complex formation, and in apo A-I assays the variation in HDL size may produce variable results.[99] Some of the inherent disadvantages of nephelometry and turbidimetry can be partially overcome by adding reagents to increase the reaction rate, which also aids the formation of more stable immune complexes.[100]

The pros and cons of analytical methods notwithstanding, until recently the main issue was perhaps the standardization of apolipoprotein measurements. Lack of standardization was, and to some extent still is, one of the major causes of analytical variation between laboratories.[101] The standardization issue was addressed in 1994 with the adoption of international reference materials endorsed by the World Health Organization for both apo A-I and B. (For further information, see Chapters 11 and 12.) The standardization problems arise from the close association between the lipid moiety and apolipoproteins and the influence this has on immunoreactivity of apolipoproteins. Antibodies raised against whole lipoproteins do not necessarily react against delipidated apolipoproteins. Moreover, antibodies to synthetic apolipoprotein peptides do not always react with apolipoproteins associated with lipids in lipoproteins. Essentially masking of apo B in triglyceride-rich lipoproteins is a potential problem, but most assays seem unaffected. The assay of apo B is greatly helped because each molecule of apo B is in a discrete, separate particle. On the other hand, more than one apo A-I molecule can be associated with a single HDL particle. Storage and preanalytical factors can lead to release of apo A-I molecules from HDL particles which have multiple apo A-I molecules associated with them; in an assay sensitive to particle number, these additional molecules will lead to inaccuracy. It is important to note that early well-validated apo A-I assays using rocket electrophoresis employed urea disruption or disruption by heating to release all the apo A-I loosely associated with the HDL particles. This step is now generally omitted.

Issues involving the conformation of apolipoproteins in the native lipoproteins are even more relevant than the technical aspects of antibody-antigen reactions. At present it is unclear whether particular epitopes are associated with disease or with coronary risk. It is not certain whether these considerations were taken into account when the International Federation of Clinical Chemistry (IFCC) was preparing candidate reference materials in association with commercial manufacturers.[102]

Apo B and apo A-I present different problems in the development of primary standards and reference methods. With apo B, a particular challenge has been the production of stable lyophilized reference material.[103] Apo B tends to self-associate, producing aggregates. The way around this has been to produce a primary standard based on ultracentrifugally separated LDL of density between 1.030 and 1.050 kg/L. Based on this standard, a secondary standard consisting of a liquid reference material has been produced. The above procedure succeeded in producing a standard material as standard, but when this was analyzed by different methods, marked variation between assay methods was found. Immunoturbidimetric and immunonephelometric assays produced higher apo B values than ELISA and RIA.

The purification of apo A-I to produce a stable lyophilized standard has been much less problematical compared to obtaining apo B reference material. There are difficulties, however, in obtaining suitable antisera for plasma apo A-I measurements.[104] Because of the close association of apo A-I with lipids, many of the protein's immunoreactive sites remain hidden. It is, therefore, desirable that assays for apo A-I include a step in which the immunoreactive sites are exposed via pre-treatment with detergents such as Tween 20 or Triton X-100 and chelating or denaturing agents such as guanidine and urea.

Direct LDL assays recently have been introduced for the easier determination of LDL-C. However, this does not necessarily overcome the main problem of the inability of LDL-C to fully reflect the atherogenic risk associated with the apo B component within the LDL particle. The LDL assays are relatively new, seem to require very large dilutions, and in some situations may be affected by serum triglycerides greater than 400 mg/dL (4.5 mmol/L).[105] Experience with these methods is limited. It is unclear whether they provide a true estimate of LDL in all disease states, especially in patients with renal disease or diabetes mellitus. (For additional information, refer to Chapter 8.) An assay has recently been described that measures apo B by immunonephelometry in LDL separated by a direct LDL assay (immunoseparation).[106]

Direct HDL methods avoiding the need for precipitation of apo-B-containing lipoproteins also have been introduced. Again, there have been few comparisons with apo A-I assays, and their performance in different disease states remains untested. (Refer to Chapter 7 for additional information.)

Several pre-analytical aspects need to be taken into account when interpreting the results of apolipoprotein measurement.[107] As with serum lipid determination, apolipoproteins are influenced by biological variation and other intra-individual factors. These are summarized in Table 10–2. (For additional information, refer to Chapter 3.)

Utility of Assays for Apo B-48

With a resurgence of interest in the relationship between postprandial lipemia and atherogenesis there has been an effort to develop assays for apo B-48 for the investigation of lipoproteins of intestinal origin. Antibodies that recognize apo B-100 often do not detect apo B-48 in triglyceride-rich lipoproteins. One way to determine apo B-48 is by separating it from apo B-100 by SDS-PAGE gel electrophoresis and obtaining a measure of apo B-48 by densitometric scanning.[108] The method is imprecise and not amenable to routine use. Recently, an antibody has been raised to the C-terminal end of apo B-48[109] which forms the basis of an ELISA technique that can be used to estimate apo B-48 in triglyceride-rich lipoproteins.[110] A recently described assay for determination of remnant-like particles in human serum that uses immunoprecipitation of apo B-100 and apo A-I seems to provide an indirect measure of chylomicron-remnant particles containing apo B-48.[111]

Table 10–2 ✦ Preanalytical Factors Affecting Plasma Apo B and Apo A-I Levels

	Effect on Plasma Apo B	*Effect on Plasma Apo A-I*
Diurnal variation	Approx. 5%. Peaks at midday and midnight	Approx. 4%. Peaks in late evening
Seasonal variation	Not known	Not known
Gender	Males > females	Females > males
Age	Increases with age	Probably unaffected. Some reports indicate decrease with age
Menstrual cycle	Lower values or no change	Lower values or no change
Pregnancy	Increase by 60%	Increase by 30%, sustained until delivery
Diet	Acute change: no effect Chronic change: decrease	Acute change: no effect Chronic change: increase
Exercise	Not known	Not known
Alcohol	Not known	Increased values
Smoking	Not known	Decreased values
Coffee	Probable increase by 15%	No change
Posture	5% decrease	9% decrease
Venous occlusion	5% increase	5% increase
Storage at –70° C	7% decrease*	No effect*
Storage at 4° C	5% increase*	No effect or increase*

* method dependent

REFERENCE RANGES AND CUTOFF POINTS

Many of the larger epidemiological studies carried out in the past did not measure plasma apolipoproteins. Therefore, few data or reference intervals exist for either apo B or Apo A-I. Laker and Evans have recently summarized reference data for both apo B and apo A-I on studies that included more than 100 subjects,[112] shown in Tables 10–3 and 10–4. The variability in the data are no doubt due to differences in standardization and is method-related. Recently, reference ranges on apo B and apo A-I have become available on a Finnish population[113] and from the Framingham Offspring Study.[114, 115] The latter study has larger numbers, but more importantly, both studies provide reference data for apo B and apo A-I based on WHO–IFCC standardized immunoturbidimetric assays that are commercially available. Despite the similarity of methods and standardization in both surveys, the advice on cutoff values for assigning coronary risk is slightly different (see Table 10–5). This is largely because the apo A-I values below the 10th percentile and apo B values above the 75th percentile, which are thought to indicate increased coronary risk, differ between the two studies. The cutoff points suggested by the Framingham group for apo B have been decided on the basis of comparability with the 75th percentile for LDL-C for the Framingham population.

Table 10–3 ✧ Reference Data for Apolipoprotein A-I from Studies Including at Least 100 Normolipidemic Subjects

Technique	Subjects (age in years)	Sample	Reference Data (mg/dL)
Radial immunodiffusion	263 males (20–65) 257 females (20–65)	EDTA plasma	119 (mean) 132 (mean)*
Radial immunodiffusion	95 males (40–49) 104 females (40–49)	Serum	91-183 91-183
Radial immunodiffusion	128 normolipidemic adults	EDTA plasma	118 (mean)
Radial immunodiffusion	1355 subjects (3–18)	Serum	102-202
Radioimmunoassay	4858 adults (18–30)	EDTA plasma	Effects of gender, ethnic group, and age compared
Immunoturbidimetry	193 adults	Serum	110-210 Men 124-240 Women
Immunoturbidimetry	135 adults	EDTA plasma	89-198
Immunoturbidimetry	1202 subjects (9–24)	Serum	104-196
Immunoturbidimetry	1145 (mean age 53)	Serum	145 (SD 28)

Adapted with permission from Laker & Evans[112]
*Higher mean values found in women receiving hormone preparations (mean 141 mg/dL) compared with those receiving no therapy (mean 129 mg/dL).

Table 10–4 ✧ Reference Data for Apolipoproteins B from Studies Including at Least 100 Normolipidemic Subjects

Technique	Subjects (age in years)	Sample	Reference Data (mg/dL)
Radial immunodiffusion	1355 subjects (3–18)	Serum	50-138
Enzyme immunoassay	146 adults	Plasma	90 (mean)
Radioimmunoassay	349 adults (20–65)	EDTA plasma	41-121
Radioimmunoassay	128 adults (16–60)	Plasma	27-146
Radioimmunoassay	107 adults (15–75)	Serum	91 (mean)* 59-123 (3rd to 97th percentile)
Radioimmunoassay	4858 adults (18–30)	EDTA plasma	Effects of gender, ethnic group, and age compared
Immunoturbidimetry	193 adults	Serum	63-138
Immunoturbidimetry	135 adults	EDTA plasma	30-95
Immunoturbidimetry	1188 subjects (9–24)	Serum	43-135
Immunoturbidimetry	1145 (mean age 53)	Serum	91 (SD 20)

Adapted with permission from Laker & Evans[112]
*From Durrington, Bolton & Hartog[39]

The effect of gender was apparent in reference ranges for both apo B and apo A-I, with women having lower apo B and higher apo A-I. The effect of age was mainly apparent for apo B, with increases in concentrations with age. The influence of age on apo A-I is complex and variable. Some studies show a fall in plasma apo A-I levels in men but not in women, and others have generally found no effect. Postmenopausal women tend to have lower plasma apo A-I levels.   ❖

Table 10–5 ❖ Cutoff Points (in mg/dL) for Apolipoproteins A-I and B				
	MEN		WOMEN	
	*Framingham Population**	*Finnish Population***	*Framingham Population**	*Finnish Population***
Apo A-I	10th Percentile			
	107	109	122	125
Apo B[†]	75th Percentile: Desired Value			
	118	141	< 111	129
	75th to 90th Percentile: Increased Risk			
	118–133	141–159	118–130	129–155
	Above 90th Percentile: High Risk			
	> 133	> 159	> 130	> 155

*Source: Contois et al.[114] and Contois et al.[115]
**Source: Leino et al.[113]
†The Framingham group suggests a single cutoff point of 120 mg/dL

REFERENCES

1. Schaefer EJ, Eisenberg S, Levy RI. Lipoprotein apoprotein metabolism. J Lipid Res 1978;19:667–87.
2. Sloop CH, Roheim PS. Interstitial fluid lipoproteins. J Lipid Res 1987;28:225–37.
3. Assman G, von Eckardstein A, Funke H. Mutations in apolipoprotein genes and HDL metabolism. In: Rosseneu M, ed. Structure and function of apolipoproteins. Boca Raton: CRC Press 1992:85–122.
4. Cheung P, Kno FT, Law ML, et al. Localization of the structural gene for human apolipoprotein A-I on the long arm of human chromosome 11. Proc Natl Acad Sci USA 1984;81:508–11.
5. Scanu AM. Proapolipoprotein-converting enzymes and high-density lipoprotein early events in biogenesis. Am Heart J 1987;113:527–32.
6. Edelstein C, Scanu AM. Extracellular posttranslational proteolytic processing of apolipoproteins. In: Scanu AM, Spector A, eds. Biochemistry of plasma lipoproteins. New York: Marcel Dekker 1986:53.
7. Karathanasis SK, Zannis VI, Breslow JL. Isolation and characterization of the human apolipoprotein A-I gene. Proc Natl Acad Sci USA 1983;80:6147–51.
8. Segrest JP, Jones MK, De Loof CG, et al. The amphipathic helix in the exchangable apolipoproteins: a review of secondary structure and function. J Lipid Res 1992;33:141–66.

9. Castro GR, Fielding CJ. Early incorporation of cell-derived cholesterol into pre-beta migrating high density lipoprotein. Biochemistry 1988;27:25–29.

10. Fielding CJ, Fielding PE. Molecular physiology of reverse cholesterol transport. J Lipid Res 1995;36:211–28.

11. Neary R, Bhatnagar D, Durrington PN, Ishola M, Arrol S, Mackness MI. An investigation of the role of lecithin:cholesterol acyl transferase and triglyceride-rich lipoproteins in the metabolism of pre-beta high density lipoproteins. Atherosclerosis 1991;85:34–48.

12. Fielding PE, Kawano M, Catapano AL, et al. Unique epitope of apolipoprotein A-I expressed in prebeta-1 high density lipoprotein and its role in the catalysed efflux of cellular cholesterol. Biochemistry 1994;33:6981–5.

13. Chen C-H, Albers JJ. Interspecies activation of lecithin:cholesterol acyl transferase by apolipoprotein A-I isolated from the plasmas of humans, horses, sheep, goats and rabbits. Biochim Biophys Acta 1983;753:40–46.

14. Cremer P, Elster H, Labrot B, et al. Incidence rates of fatal and non-fatal myocardial infarction in relation to the lipoprotein profile: first prospective results from the Gottingen Risk Incidence and Prevalence Study (GRIPS). Klin Wochenschrift 1988;66(suppl 11): 42–49.

15. Ishikawa T, Fidge N, Thelle DS, et al. The Tromso Heart Study: serum apolipoprotein A-I concentration in relation to future coronary heart disease. Eur J Clin Invest 1978; 8:179–82.

16. Salonen JT, Salonen R, Pentilla I, et al. Serum fatty acids, apolipoproteins, selenium and vitamin antioxidants and risk of death from coronary artery disease. Am J Cardiol 1985;56:226–31.

17. Wald NJ, Law M, Watt HC, et al. Apolipoproteins and ischaemic heart disease: implications for screening. Lancet 1994;343:75–79.

18. Heiss G, Johnson NJ, Reiland S, et al. The epidemiology of plasma high-density lipoprotein cholesterol levels. The Lipid Clinics Research Program Prevalence Study Summary. Circulation 1980;62(suppl iv):116–36.

19. Rifkind BM, Segal P. Lipid Clinics Research Program reference values for hyperlipidemia. JAMA 1983;250:1869–72.

20. Schaefer EJ, Zech LA, Jenkins LL, et al. Human apolipoprotein A-I and A-II metabolism. J Lipid Res 1982;23:850–62.

21. Ng DS, Vezina C, Wolever T, Kukis A, et al. Apolipoprotein A-I deficiency: biochemical and metabolic characteristics. Arterioscler Thromb Vascl Biol 1995;15:2157–64.

22. Rader DJ, Ikewaki K. Unravelling high density lipoprotein-apolipoprotein metabolism in human mutants and animal models. Curr Opin Lipidol 1996;7:117–23.

23. Franceschini G, Sirtori CR, Capruso A, et al. A-I milano apoprotein: decreased HDL cholesterol levels with significant lipoprotein modifications and without clinical atherosclerosis in an Italian family. J Clin Invest 1980;66:892–900.

24. Assman G, von Eckardstein A, Brewer HB. Familial HDL deficiency: Tangier disease. In: Scriver C, Beaudet A, Sly W, Valle D. The metabolic and molecular bases of inherited disease. New York: McGraw-Hill, 1995:2053–72.

25. Francis GA, Knopp RH, Oram JF. Defective removal of cellular cholesterol and phospholipids by apolipoprotein A-I in Tangier disease. J Clin Invest 1995;96:78–87.

26. Norum KR. Familial lecithin:cholesterol acyltransferase deficiency. In: Miller NE, Miller GJ, eds. Clinical and metabolic aspects of high density lipoproteins. Amsterdam: Elsevier, 1984:297–432.

27. Carlson LA. Fish Eye Disease. A new familial condition with massive corneal opacities and dyslipoproteinemia. Eur J Clin Invest 1981;12:41–53.

28. Glueck CJ, Fallat RW, Millett F, et al. Familial hyperalphalipoproteinemia: studies on 18 kindreds. Metabolism 1975;24:1243–65.

29. Fielding CJ, Havel RJ. Cholesteryl ester transfer protein: friend or foe? [Editorial; Comment]. J Clin Invest 1996;97:2687–8.

30. Koizumi J, Mabuchi H, Yoshimura A, et al. Deficiency of serum cholesteryl-ester transfer activity in patients with familial hyperalphalipoproteinemia. Atherosclerosis 1985;58: 175–86.

31. Anonymous. Cholesteryl ester transfer protein. Lancet 1991;338:666-7.
32. Gordon T, Castelli WP, Hjortland MC, Kannel WB, Dawber TR. High density lipoprotein as a protective factor against coronary heart disease: The Framingham Study. Am J Med 1977:62:707-14.
33. Kannel WB, Neaton JO, Wentworth O, Thomas HE, Stamler J, Hulley SB, Kjelsberg MO, for the MRFIT Research Group. Overall and coronary heart disease mortality rates in relation to major risk factors in 325,348 men screened for the MRFIT Multiple Risk Factor Intervention Trial. Am Heart J 1986;112:82-36.
34. Gordon DJ, Knoke J, Probstfield JL, Superko R, Tyroler HA, for the LRC Program. High density lipoprotein cholesterol and coronary heart disease in hypercholesterolemic men: The Lipid Research Clinics Coronary Primary Prevention Trial. Circulation 1986;74.
35. Manninen V, Tenkanen L, Koskinen P, Huttunen JK, Manttari M, Heinonen OP, Frick MH. Joint effects of serum triglyceride and LDL cholesterol and HDL cholesterol concentrations on coronary heart disease risk in The Helsinki Heart Study: implications for treatment. Circulation 1992;85:37-45.
36. Berman M, Eisenberg S, Hall M, et al. Metabolism of apo B and apo C apoproteins in man: kinetic studies in normal and hyperlipoproteinemic subjects. J Lipid Res 1978; 19:38-56.
37. Gaw A, Demant T. Apolipoprotein B metabolism in primary and secondary hyperlipidaemias. Curr Opin Lipidol 1996;7:149-57.
38. Rosseneu M, Vercaerist R, Steinberg KK, et al. Some considerations of methodology and standardisation of apolipoprotein B immunoassays. Clin Chem 1983;29:427-33.
39. Durrington PN, Bolton CH, Hartog M. Serum and lipoprotein apolipoprotein B levels in normal subjects and patients with hyperlipoproteinaemia. Clin Chim Acta 1978;82: 151-60.
40. Fredrickson DS. Plasma lipoproteins and apolipoproteins. The Harvey Lectures 1972-3, Series 68. London: Academic Press, 1974:185.
41. Durrington PN, Ishola M, Hunt L, Arrol S, Bhatnagar D. Apolipoproteins (a), A-I and B and parental history in men with early onset ischaemic heart disease. Lancet 1988;I: 1070-73.
42. Chan L, VanTunien P, Ledbetter DH, et al. The human apo B-100 gene: a highly polymorphic gene that maps to the short arm of chromosome 2. Biochem Biophys Res Commun 1985;133:248-55.
43. Brewer HB, Higuchi K, Hospattankar A, et al. Recent advances in the structure and biosynthesis of apolipoproteins B100 and B48. In: Suckling KE, Groot PHE. Hyperlipidaemia and atherosclerosis. London: Academic Press, 1988:33-44.
44. Yang C-Y, Pownall HJ. Structure and function of apolipoprotein B. In: Rosseneu M, ed. Structure and function of apolipoproteins. Boca Raton: CRC Press, 1992:63-84.
45. Young SG. Recent progress in understanding apolipoprotein B. Circulation 1990;82: 1574-94.
46. Pease RJ, Leiper JM. Regulation of hepatic apolipoprotein-B-containing lipoprotein secretion. Curr Opin Lipidol 1996;7:132-8.
47. Knott TJ, Pease RJ, Powell LM, et al. Complete protein sequence and identification of structural domains of human apolipoprotein B. Nature 1986;323:734-8.
48. Beisiegel U. Apolipoproteins as ligands for lipoprotein receptors. In: Rosseneu M, ed. Structure and function of apolipoproteins. Boca Raton: CRC Press, 1992:269-94.
49. Scott J, Wallis SC, Pease RJ, et al. Apolipoprotein B: a novel mechanism for deriving two proteins from one gene. In: Suckling KE, Groot PHE. Hyperlipidaemia and atherosclerosis. London: Academic Press, 1988:347-64.
50. Chen S-H, Yang C-H, Chem P-F, et al. The complete cDNA and amino acid sequence of human apolipoprotein B-100. J Biol Chem 1986;261:12918-21.
51. Powell LM, Wallis SC, Pease RJ, et al. A novel form of tissue specific RNA processing produces apolipoprotein B-48 in intestines. Cell 1987;50:831-40.
52. Chan L, Seeburg PH. RNA editing. Scientific American Science and Medicine 1995;2: 68-77.

53. Collins DR, Knott TJ, Pease RJ, et al. Truncated variants of apolipoprotein B cause hypobetalipoproteinemia. Nucleic Acid Res 1988;16:8361-75.

54. Pease RJ, Milne RW, Jessup WK, et al. Use of bacterial expression cloning to localise the epitopes for a series of monoclonal antibodies against apolipoprotein B-100. J Biol Chem 1990;265:553-68.

55. Myant NB. Familial defective apolipoprotein B-100: a review, including some comparisons with familial hypercholesterolaemia. Atherosclerosis 1993;104:1-19.

56. Durrington PN. Lipoproteins and their metabolism. In: Durrington PN. Hyperlipidaemia: diagnosis and management. Oxford: Butterworth-Heinneman, 1995:25-71.

57. Henriksen T, Mahoney EM, Steinberg D. Enhanced macrophage degradation of low density lipoprotein previously incubated with cultured endothelial cells: recognition by the receptor for acetylated low density lipoproteins. Proc Natl Acad Sci USA 1981;78: 6499-503.

58. Esterbauer H, Gebicki J, Puhl H, Jurgens G. The role of lipid peroxidation and antioxidants in oxidative modification of LDL. Free Radical Biol Med 1992;13:341-90.

59. Streinbecher UP, Lougheed M, Kwan W-C, Dirks M. Recognition of oxidised low density lipoprotein by the scavenger receptor of macrophages results from derivatization of apolipoprotein B by products of fatty acid peroxidation. J Biol Chem 1989;264: 15216-23.

60. Esterbauer H, Wag G, Puhl H. Lipid peroxidation and its role in atherosclerosis. Br Med Bull 1993;49:566-76.

61. Witzum JL, Steinberg D. Role of oxidised low density lipoprotein in atherogenesis. J Clin Invest 1991;88:1785-92.

62. Witzum JL, Mahoney EM, Branks MJ, et al. Nonenzymatic glycosylation of low density lipoprotein alters its biologic activity. Diabetes 1982;31:283-91.

63. Hunt JV, Smith CCT, Wolff SP. Autoxidative glycosylation and possible involvement of peroxides and free radicals in LDL modification by glucose. Diabetes 1990;39:1420-24.

64. Tames FJ, Mackness MI, Arrol S, et al. Non-enzymatic glycation of apolipoprotein B in the sera of diabetic and non-diabetic subjects. Atherosclerosis 1992;93:227-44.

65. Durrington PN. Familial hypercholesterolaemia. In: Durrington PN. Hyperlipidaemia: diagnosis and management. Oxford: Butterworth-Heinneman, 1995:108-39.

66. Parums DV, Brown DL, Mitchinson MJ. Serum antibodies to oxidized low-density lipoproteins and ceroid in chronic periaortitis. Arch Pathol Lab Med 1990;114:383-7.

67. Kane JP, Havel RJ. Disorders of the biogenesis and secretion of lipoproteins containing the B apolipoproteins. In: Scriver C, Beaudet A, Sly W, Valle D, eds. The metabolic and molecular bases of inherited disease. New York: McGraw-Hill, 1995:1860-66.

68. Wetterau JR, Aggerbeck LP, Bouma M-E, et al. Absence of microsomal triglyceride transfer protein in individuals with abetalipoproteinaemia. Science 1992;258:999-1001.

69. Kane JP, Havel RJ. Disorders of the biogenesis and secretion of lipoproteins containing the B apolipoproteins. In: Scriver C, Beaudet A, Sly W, Valle D, eds. The metabolic and molecular bases of inherited disease. New York: McGraw-Hill, 1995:1866-71.

70. Durrington PN, Bolton CH, Hartog M. Serum and lipoprotein apolipoprotein B levels in normal subjects and patients with hyperlipoproteinaemia. Clin Chim Acta 1978;82: 151-60.

71. Teng B, Thompson GR, Sniderman AD, et al. Composition and distribution of low density lipoprotein fractions in hyperapobetalipoproteinaemia, normolipidaemia and familial hypercholesterolaemia. Proc Natl Acad Sci USA 1983;80:6662-6.

72. Bhatnagar D, Durrington PN, Arrol S. Postprandial plasma lipoprotein responses to a mixed meal in subjects with hyperapobetalipoproteinaemia. Clin Biochem 1992;25: 341-43.

73. Sniderman AD, Shapiro S, Marpole D, et al. Association of coronary atherosclerosis with hyperapobetalipoproteinaemia (increased protein, but normal cholesterol levels in human plasma low density lipoproteins). Proc Natl Acad Sci USA 1980;77:604-8.

74. Genest J, Marlin-Munley SS, McNamara JR, et al. Familial lipoprotein disorders in patients with premature coronary artery disease. Circulation 1992;85:2025-33.

75. Kwiterovich PO Jr, Coresh J, Bachorik, PS. Prevalence of hyperapobetalipoproteinemia and other lipoprotein phenotypes in men (aged < 50 years) and women (< 60 years) with coronary artery disease. Am J Cardiol 1993;71:631-9.

76. Durrington PN, Hunt L, Ishola M, Kane J, Stephens WP. Serum apolipoproteins A-I and B in middle aged men with and without previous myocardial infarction. Br Heart J 1986;56:206-12.

77. Kwiterovich PO Jr, Coresh 3, Smith HH, et al. Comparison of the plasma levels of apolipoprotein B and AI, and other risk factors in men and women with premature coronary artery disease. Am J Cardiol 1992;69:1015-21.

78. Tornvall P, Bavenholm P, Landou C, de Faire U, Hamsten A. Relation of plasma levels and composition of apolipoprotein B-containing lipoproteins to angiographically defined coronary artery disease in young patients with myocardial infarction. Circulation 1993; 88:2180-89.

79. Genest J, McNamara JR, Ordovas JM, et al. Effect of elective hospitalization on plasma lipoprotein cholesterol and apolipoproteins A-I, B and Lp(a). Am J Cardiol 1990;65: 677-9.

80. Stampfer MJ, Sacks FM, Salvini S, et al. A prospective study of cholesterol, apolipoproteins and the risk of myocardial infarction. N Engl J Med 1991;325:373-81.

81. Cremer P, Nagel D, Labrot B, et al. Lipoprotein Lp(a) as a predictor of myocardial infarction in comparison to fibrinogen, LDL cholesterol and other risk factors: results from the Gottingen Risk Incidence and Prevalence Study (GRIPS). Eur J Clin Invest 1994;24:444-53.

82. Coleman MP, Key TJ, Wang DY, et al. A prospective study of obesity, lipids, apolipoproteins and ischemic heart disease in women. Atherosclerosis 1992;92:177-85.

83. Sigurdsson G, Baldursdottir A, Sigvaldason H, et al. Predictive value of apolipoproteins in a prospective survey of coronary artery disease in men. Am J Cardiol 1992;69: 1251-4.

84. Griffin BA. Low density lipoprotein heterogeneity. Ballieres Clin Endocrinol Metab 1995; 9:687-704.

85. Austin MA, Breslow JL, Hennekens CH, et al. Low density lipoprotein subclass patterns and risk of myocardial infarction. JAMA 1988;260:1917-21.

86. Sniderman AD, Cianlone K. Measurement of apoproteins: time to improve the diagnosis and treatment of atherogenic dyslipidemias. Clin Chem 1996;42:489-91.

87. Austin MA. Plasma triglyceride and coronary heart disease. Arterioscler Thromb 1990; 11:1-14.

88. Durrington PN. Secondary hyperlipidaemia. Br Med Bull 1990;46:1005-24.

89. Despres J-P, Lamarche B, Mauriege P, et al. Hyperinsulinemia as a risk factor for ischemic heart disease. N Engl J Med 1996;334:952-7.

90. Talmud PJ, Boerwinkle E, Xu CF, Tikkanen MJ, Pietinen P, Huttunen JK, Humphries S. Dietary intake and gene variation influence the response of plasma lipids to dietary intervention. Genet Epidem 1992;9:249-60.

91. Durrington PN. Genetics of lipoprotein disorders and coronary atheroma. In: Durrington PN. Hyperlipidaemia: diagnosis and management. Oxford: Butterworth-Heinneman, 1995:361-84.

92. Durrington PN, Whicher JT, Warren C, et al. A comparison of methods for the immunoassay of serum apolipoprotein B in man. Clin Chim Acta 1976;71:95-108.

93. Albers JJ, Marcovina SM. Apolipoprotein measurements. In: Kreisberg RA, Segrest JA, eds. Plasma lipoproteins and coronary artery disease. Boston: Blackwell Scientific Publications, 1992:265-88.

94. Hallaway BJ, Rastogi A, Kottke BA. Apolipoprotein B quantified by particle-concentration fluorescence immunoassay. Clin Chem 1992;38:2387-91.

95. Osman I, Gaillard O, Meillet D, et al. A sensitive time-resolved immunofluorometric assay for the measurement of apolipoprotein B in cerebrospinal fluid: application to

multiple sclerosis and other neurological diseases. Eur J Clin Chem Biochem 1995; 33:53-58.

96. Marcovina SM, Albers JJ, Henderson LO, Hannon WH. International Federation of Clinical Chemistry standardization project for measurements of apolipoproteins A-I and B. III. Comparability of apolipoprotein A-I values by use of international reference material. Clin Chem 1993;39:773-8.

97. Marcovina SM, Albers JJ, Kennedy H, Mei JV, Henderson LO, Hannon WH. International Federation of Clinical Chemistry standardization project for measurements of apolipoproteins A-I and B. IV. Comparability of apolipoprotein B values by use of international reference material. Clin Chem 1994;40:586-92.

98. DaCol P, Kostner G. Immunoquantification of total apolipoprotein B in serum by nephelometry: influence of lipase treatment and detergents. Clin Chem 1983;29:1045-50.

99. Levinson SS. Problems with the measurement of apolipoproteins A-I and AII. Ann Clin Lab Sci 1990;20:307-18.

100. Kricka LJ. Principles of immunochemical techniques. In: Burtis CA, Ashwood ER, eds. Tietz textbook of clinical chemistry. Philadelphia: WB Saunders, 1994:297.

101. Bhatnagar D, Durrington PN. Clinical value of apolipoprotein measurements. Ann Clin Biochem 1991;28:427-37.

102. Albers JJ, Marcovina SM. Standardization of apolipoprotein B and A-I measurements. Clin Chem 1989;35:1357-61.

103. Marcovina SM, Adolphson JL, Parlavecchia M, Albers JJ. Effects of lyophilization of apolipoproteins A-I and B. Clin Chem 1990;36:366-9.

104. Marcovina SM, Curtiss LK, Milne R, Albers JJ. Selection and characterization of monoclonal antibodies for measuring plasma levels of apolipoprotein A-I and B. J Aut Chem 1990;12:195-98.

105. Cole TG. The role of immunochemistry in the direct measurement of low density lipoprotein cholesterol. J Clin Ligand Assay 1996;19:168-71.

106. Vrga L, Contacos C, Li SCH, Sullivan DR. Comparison of methods for measurement of apolipoprotein B and cholesterol in low-density lipoproteins. Clin Chem 1997;43: 390-93.

107. Evans K, Laker MF. Intra-individual factors affecting lipid, lipoprotein and apolipoprotein measurement: a review. Ann Clin Biochem 1995;32:261-80.

108. Bergeron N, Kotite L, Havel RJ. Simultaneous quantification of apolipoproteins B-100, B-48, and E separated by SDS-PAGE. Meth Enzym 1996;263:82-94.

109. Peel AS, Zampelas A, Williams CM, Gould B. A novel antiserum specific to apolipoprotein B-48: application in the investigation of postprandial lipaemia in humans. Clin Sci 1993;85:521-4.

110. Lovegrove JA, Isherwood SG, Jackson KG, et al. Quantitation of apolipoprotein B-48 in triacylglycerol-rich lipoproteins by specific enzyme-linked immunosorbent assay. Biochim Biophys Acta 1996;1301:221-9.

111. Nakajima K, Okazaki M, Tanaka A, et al. Separation and determination of remnant-like particles in human serum using monoclonal antibodies to apo B-100 and apo A-I. J Clin Ligand Assay 1996;19:177-83.

112. Laker MF, Evans K. Analysis of apolipoproteins. Ann Clin Biochem 1996;33:5-22.

113. Leino A, Impivaara O, Kaitsaari M, Jarvisalo J. Serum concentrations of apolipoprotein A-I, apolipoprotein B and lipoprotein (a) in a population sample. Clin Chem 1995;41: 1633-6.

114. Contois JH, McNamara JR, Lammi-Keefe CJ, Wilson PW, Massov T, Schaefer EJ. Reference intervals for plasma apolipoprotein B determined with a standardized commercial immunoturbidimetric assay: results from The Framingham Offspring Study. Clin Chem 1996;42:515-23.

115. Contois J, McNamara JR, Lammi-Keefe C, Wilson PW, Massov T, Schaefer EJ. Reference intervals for plasma apolipoprotein A-1 determined with a standardized commercial immunoturbidimetric assay: results from The Framingham Offspring Study. Clin Chem 1996;42:507-14.

Matrix Effects in the Measurement and Standardization of Lipids and Lipoproteins

W. Greg Miller

11

INTRODUCTION

❖ The goal of clinical laboratory testing is to produce reliable information about an individual patient's clinical condition. Standardization of test method results is critically important for lipid testing because epidemiologically derived national guidelines are used to interpret laboratory results. Standardized test results require a calibration process that produces equivalent results irrespective of the testing method or location performing the assay.

Current routine methods for lipid and lipoprotein analysis are almost exclusively based on enzymatic or immunological reactions. Because pure total cholesterol (TC) or triglyceride (TG) molecules are only soluble in organic solvents, these primary standard materials are not suitable for calibration of routine assay methods. Lipoproteins can be purified, but their tertiary and quaternary structures are usually altered in the process, so preparation of primary aqueous standards with these compounds has not been practical. Routine laboratory methods for lipid testing are designed to recover analyte from human serum specimens. Consequently, serum-based secondary standards are commonly used for calibration of routine laboratory methods. The methodological and technological requirements for stable, high throughput assay systems can produce accurate measurements for human serum but inadequate performance for serum-based secondary standards containing matrix modified lipoprotein components.

The term "commutability" was used in 1973 by Fasce et al.[1] to refer to the ability of a processed material to show inter-assay analytical properties comparable to authentic clinical specimens. Ideally, processed materials used for routine calibration and for standardization and verification of accuracy among laboratories should be commutable with freshly collected serum specimens. Unfortunately, processed materials frequently have assay properties that are different from those of fresh patient specimens.

If an analysis system is sensitive to the difference between an analyte's reactive properties in a processed material and in fresh human specimens, the change in measured response to that analyte is referred to as a method/material-specific matrix interaction or matrix effect.[2] The matrix effect produces a matrix-related bias in the analyte result for that processed material, which precludes using that result to establish or evaluate accuracy of results for patient specimens. Matrix effects can be unique to a single lot of processed material and a single lot of reagents used in an analytical system. It is more common that matrix effects are consistently observed between an analytical measurement system and a processed serum-based material, although the magnitude of the matrix bias may be unique to each lot of material or reagent.

The matrix of a specimen or material has had various definitions in different contexts. The National Committee for Clinical Laboratory Standards (NCCLS) has defined matrix as the "milieu of the analyte"[3] and is developing a more specific definition applicable to serum-based reference materials.[4] The American Society for Testing and Materials defines matrix as "the principal element or elements in a sample" and defines an interference as "an effect due to the presence of a constituent or characteristic that influences the measurement of another constituent or characteristic."[5] Rej has provided a comprehensive definition of matrix as "the entire milieu or environment in which an analyte resides and all components (other than the analyte) or attributes."[6]

With these broad definitions, a matrix interference or effect could be ascribed to any processing induced or physiologically derived component of the material. Rej cautions that "matrix effects are often ascribed to interferences due to unknown or uncharacterized substance(s) or factor(s) in the biological specimen."[6] He prefers to consider matrix interferences as the result of lack of analytical specificity for the analyte, but notes that at some point a processed material may "differ so fundamentally from the normally encountered clinical specimen that the specificity of even the most robust method is unfairly challenged."[6]

In the context of this chapter, matrix effects are considered to be analytical interferences caused by alterations in the human serum material induced by preparation and processing of that material. Processing includes human and non-human additives to the material as well as any physical or chemical changes that occur as a result of the preparation or manufacturing procedure. Matrix effects in this context do not include interferences from physiological or drug-induced metabolic substances present in normal or abnormal concentrations. However, such physiological interferences are significant issues and represent analytical challenges that must be solved by acceptable field methods. Matrix effects may be caused by undefined substances in the material, but this phenomenon should not be used to arbitrarily dismiss inadequate methodologic specificity for the analyte of interest.

Although commutability between pooled-serum materials and fresh individual specimens is desirable, it is not necessary for all aspects of calibration. Secondary standard calibration materials used by a manufacturer solely to calibrate a unique analytical system do not need to be commutable with any other analytical system nor with patient specimens. In this case, any matrix bias in the calibration materials can be accommodated by assignment of a nominal analyte value such that the analytical system's response is set to produce accurate results for individual patient specimens. The process for value assignment of the secondary standard and verification of accurate results for those specimens must be linked to a credentialed reference system such as the National Reference System for the Clinical Laboratory (NRSCL) of the NCCLS (see Chapter 12).

SOURCE OF MATRIX MODIFICATIONS: TYPICAL PREPARATION OF SERUM-BASED REFERENCE MATERIALS

Serum-based reference materials can undergo a substantial number of processes during their manufacture that can change the matrix from that of native serum.[7-10] The starting material is commonly plasma collected at a commercial donor center. The plasma may be stored in liquid form or, more typically, frozen for several months prior to use. Off-the-clot serum can be used to obtain the base material, but it is considerably more expensive than plasma due to the time delay for clotting and its special handling requirements. Plasma is defibrinated and converted to serum by addition of calcium and clotting agents. The recovered serum may undergo various additional processes such as filtration, dialysis, ion exchange, reverse osmosis, charcoal adsorption, or lipid stripping[11] to reduce endogenous constituents to low levels.

Various spiking materials are added back to the base serum pool to produce the desired composition and concentrations of analytes. Other additives may also be added to prevent microbial growth, to enhance product stability, or to enhance compatibility with an analytical system. In the case of lipid products, the common spiking materials are low-density lipoprotein (LDL) rich and high-density lipoprotein (HDL) rich fractions from human serum obtained by various modifications of the ethanol and pH precipitation procedures originally described by Cohn.[8, 12] TG-rich additives are typically obtained from hen egg yolk.[9, 10] Ultracentrifugation can be used to obtain concentrated lipoprotein fractions from serum when smaller quantities of additive are required.[13]

Once the pool is prepared and analytes adjusted to desired concentrations, the material is filtered to 0.22 μm to remove bacteria, mixed to homogeneity, and dispensed into vials. The vials can be frozen or freeze-dried for storage and distribution. Freezing below $-50°$ C is necessary to fully crystallize water[14] and provide maximum stability of serum materials. Freeze-drying is commonly used because the materials can be stored, packaged, and shipped (usually at ambient temperatures) considerably more economically than when frozen. Additives such as sucrose are sometimes added to confer cryoprotection to lipid molecules during freeze-drying cycles.[15]

The freeze-drying process has been shown to alter the physical properties of serum materials. Rej[6, 16] reported that lyophilization of an aliquot of serum produced moderate changes in osmolality, surface tension, and viscosity, and produced large changes in pH, number and size of particles, and absorbance. It is well accepted that freeze-drying produces denaturation of lipoprotein particles, which makes them difficult to resolubilize in water and increases turbidity in reconstituted specimens. Kroll et al.[17] showed that freeze-drying two serum pools decreased the recovery of TC for four routine enzymatic methods compared to freezing at $-20°$ C or $-70°$ C. Marcovina et al.[18] showed a systematic decrease in recovery of apolipoprotein B by seven immunological methods after lyophilization of six human serum pools. Kroll and Chesler[19] further reported that five commercial and two in-house lyophilized pooled serum materials, including National Institute for Standards and Technology (NIST) Standard Reference Material (SRM) 909, had decreased recovery of TC with the duPont ACA due to a decreased reaction rate for the enzymatic hydrolysis of TC esters in these materials. The reaction time allowed by the analyzer was adequate for fresh human specimens but too short for complete hydrolysis of the matrix-altered lipoproteins in the lyophilized materials. Noel et al.[20] and Wiebe and Bernert[21] reported that cholesteryl esterases used in some enzymatic reagents did not completely hydrolyze cholesterol arachidonate present in some processed serum materials.

An NCCLS subcommittee is currently developing a guideline for preparation of serum cholesterol reference material. This subcommittee has documented a protocol for preparation of freshly collected off-the-clot frozen human serum pools. Two pools were prepared and demonstrated to have excellent commutability among 26 routine methods for TC[22]. Performance data for TG are under evaluation. Unfortunately, commutability was not tested for high-density lipoprotein cholesterol (HDL-C), low-density lipoprotein cholesterol (LDL-C), or other lipid analytes.

Myers et al.[23] described a new College of American Pathologists (CAP) Lipid Survey material formulation which more closely resembled the characteristics of native serum. The current CAP lipid product is prepared from off-the-clot human serum with low free glycerol which is assayed for TC, HDL-C, and TG and blended into pools to achieve the desired analyte concentrations. Supplementation is generally avoided. However, a human LDL concentrate is added to achieve elevated TC concentrations in some pools. The pools are freeze-dried but have shown good inter-method comparability in Survey results.

Stabilized liquid lipid reference materials have been developed by several vendors using proprietary stabilization processes. The convenience of liquid materials for quality control and proficiency testing (PT) applications will stimulate further development of these products. The matrix-related non-specificity of any new reference material requires careful investigation to establish its suitability for analytical usefulness.

IDENTIFICATION OF MATRIX LIMITATIONS IN MATERIALS AND METHODS

Commutability of a reference material must be evaluated by comparison of a material's results to those for individual patients' specimens for the methods of interest. Each individual's serum has variability in many components, including the distribution of lipoproteins. This variability becomes greater when sera from diseased persons are included to evaluate the full analytical range for a method. Thus, a group of freshly collected patient sera will have physiological differences in composition, and these sera may exhibit some variability in chemical reactivity when assayed by a routine method with limitations in chemical specificity. When comparing the analytical performance of clinical specimens between routine and reference methods, any observations of "outliers" must be evaluated carefully, as they may represent methodological limitations of the routine method when used with patients' specimens. Because of inherent physiological variability and the analytical imprecision of measurement, an adequate number of representative freshly collected patients' specimens is essential for evaluation of a material's or method's performance.

Any inference about the presence of matrix bias in a processed material must be based on a statistically sound evaluation protocol. The CAP has developed a protocol to detect the presence of matrix effects in processed materials when a reliable accuracy comparison method is available.[24] Briefly, the protocol selects 20 or more freshly collected individual human specimens and assays them along with the processed materials under evaluation using the test method and a suitable comparison method. The comparison method should be the most robust method available, ideally a NRSCL-credentialed reference method, such as Abell-Kendall for TC, or the best-characterized consensus method available for the analyte, such as a Centers for Disease Control and Prevention (CDC) standardized laboratory method for HDL-cholesterol (HDL-C) or TG. Regression analysis on the patients' results from each method is used to establish a 95% prediction interval, and the processed materials are evaluated for conformance to that interval.

This protocol identifies commutability of a material but does not specifically quantitate the magnitude of any matrix bias that may be present. When used with a chemically specific reference method, this procedure can also validate the accuracy of a routine method for patients' specimens and determine whether processed materials can be used for assessment of the method's accuracy. When used with a non-credentialed comparison method, this procedure can only confirm commutability of a material between the two methods. The NCCLS is currently developing a similar protocol for determining the presence of matrix effects in materials.[4]

Rej et al.[6] have described use of correspondence analysis[25] as a statistical tool to evaluate the commutability of processed materials with authentic clinical specimens. This technique does not require an accuracy-based reference method and does not quantitate matrix bias or calibration bias. The approach is useful for evaluating commutability among materials by simultaneously comparing reactivity characteristics among several materials assayed by several analytical methods. This procedure uses a multivariate statistical analysis and produces a two-dimensional projection of the most significant analytical components. Materials and methods that have commutable reactivity characteristics cluster in the same region as clinical specimens, while materials and methods with matrix interactions are located elsewhere.

EXAMPLES OF MATRIX RELATED LIMITATIONS AND DEVELOPMENT OF SOLUTIONS

Koch et al. demonstrated matrix-related limitations in reference materials in 1988.[26] They documented that the accuracy of four routine TC methods for freshly collected non-frozen individual patient's sera had an average bias of < 2.7% compared to the Abell-Kendall reference method.[27] Also assayed with each of the four methods were processed, freeze-dried serum materials intended for calibration of TC: NIST SRM 909 and three CAP Lipid Reference Materials. When the results for the reference materials were compared to the Abell-Kendall assigned target values, two of the routine methods had insignificant apparent biases ranging from –1.1% to +2.3%, while the other two routine methods had significant apparent biases ranging from –9.8% to –4.8%. Two of the routine methods had chemical non-specificity for the matrix-modified reference materials, which resulted in incorrect recovery of the TC. Consequently if the materials had been used for calibration of those methods, the patients' specimens results would have been incorrect.

A CAP-sponsored conference in 1992 titled "Matrix Effects and Accuracy Assessment in Clinical Chemistry"[28] reviewed the state of the art in understanding and controlling matrix effects and developed recommendations for future improvement of accuracy transfer and assessment. At this conference, Naito et al.[29] demonstrated the possible errors in interpretation of PT results for TC with processed serum materials. They described the Veterans Administration National Center for Laboratory Accuracy Standardization (VANCLAS) program for TC. Target values for the materials used were set by the CDC using the Abell-Kendall method. This standardization program included 174 VA medical centers and outpatient clinics, each of which received six fresh, non-frozen, non-supplemented, pooled human serum samples and five freeze-dried, human Cohn fraction supplemented, pooled human serum-based materials as used in the 1990 CAP PT program. The fresh, non-frozen serum pools were assumed to be free of any matrix interactions with the routine methods used by the participants.

Based on the fresh serum results, 112 laboratories (63%) met the ± 3% analytical bias specifications of the National Cholesterol Education Program (NCEP), and their results were used to evaluate matrix biases in the freeze-dried processed materials. In the laboratories that met the NCEP bias goal, six of eight routine methods had interactions with the matrix-modified processed materials which resulted in matrix-induced apparent biases that ranged from –8.9% to +4.4%. Figure 11–1, reprinted from Natio et al.,[29] illustrates the insidious nature of matrix bias using the duPont Dimension as an example. In this case, although results for patient specimens were correct, the PT results incorrectly indicated an apparent bias in results. The results from PT materials could not be used to judge the performance of a laboratory for patient specimens.

At the CAP conference, Ross et al.[30] reported results from an extensive evaluation of matrix effects in 37 routine method peer groups in the 1989 CAP Survey PT program. A sample of 915 participants out of approximately 5,000 assayed a single, freshly collected, off-the-clot, non-supplemented, frozen, pooled serum specimen as well as the two freeze-dried, human Cohn fraction supplemented, pooled human serum-based materials used in the PT program at that time. The fresh-frozen material was assumed to be free of matrix interactions with the various methods. Target values for TC were assigned to the fresh-frozen serum and the freeze-dried survey materials by both the NIST using the definitive isotope dilution mass spectrometry method[31] and the CDC using the Abell-Kendall reference method. Method calibration bias was determined as the difference between the reported result and the target value for the fresh-frozen specimen. Method matrix bias was determined as the difference between the mean result for a freeze-dried survey material and its target value minus the calibration bias. The freeze-dried PT material chosen to determine method matrix bias had a reference method TC of 204 mg/dL (5.29 mmol/L), which closely matched the fresh-frozen serum value of 198 mg/dL (5.11 mmol/L).

The participants were divided into 37 unique method groups based on instrumentation and reagent source. Table 11–1, which is adapted from Ross et al.,[30] indicates that 70% of the method groups exhibited a significant matrix bias with the freeze-dried survey material. The data in Table 11–1 used the NIST definitive method as the basis for accuracy evaluation. At that time, the definitive method results were on average 1.6% lower than the CDC reference method.[32] Thus, if the reference method were used for evaluation, the calibration bias in Table 11–1 would be decreased by approx-

Figure 11–1 ✧ Example of Matrix Effects between duPont Dimension and CAP Proficiency Testing Materials

The ideal line is the line of identity. The patient-regression line represents mean values of triplicate measurements on each of the five fresh human specimens plotted against CDC reference-method values (duplicate measurements). The CAP-regression line represents triplicate measurements on each of the five 1990 CAP Comprehensive Chemistry Survey specimens plotted against the CDC reference-method values. Data also indicate the laboratory's overall precision, mean bias on measurement of fresh human materials, and mean bias on measurement of CAP Survey materials. CV = Coefficient of variation. *Source:* Naito et al.[29] Reprinted by permission.

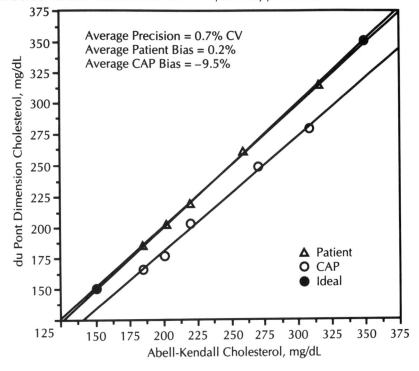

(To convert mg/dL to mmol/L, multiply by 0.0259.)

imately 1.6 and the matrix bias would be increased by approximately 1.6 for each method group.

Because matrix modifications and specific method/material interactions are somewhat unique to each production lot of materials and reagents, results for one specific combination cannot be extrapolated to other lots of reagents or materials. In 1994, the CAP extended the 1989 PT evaluation using a fresh/frozen serum specimen to assess calibration bias and quantify matrix bias in several PT materials for 15 peer groups and 11 analytes including HDL-C and TG.[33] The results supported the earlier conclusions that matrix bias was fairly common and was unique to specific method/material combinations.

Table 11–1 ◆ Instrument/Reagent System Specific Mean Survey Bias, Calibration Bias, and Matrix Bias versus the Definitive Method for one 1989 CAP Cholesterol Proficiency Testing Material[a]

Instrument/Reagent System, Manufacturer	Survey Bias (%)	Calibration Bias (%)	Matrix Bias (%)
Am Monitor Perspective/Am Monitor	1.6	8.2	−6.5
Olympus Demand/Technicon	−1.5	7.2	−8.7
Roche Cobas Mira/Roche	2.2	6.6	−4.4
Kone Progress/Kone	1.8	6.3	−4.5
Am Monitor KDA/Am Monitor	1.7	6.3	−4.7
Baker Encore/Baker	−1.9	5.8	−7.7
Roche Cobas/Roche	0.5	5.7	−5.2
Abbott TDX/Abbott	−4.7	4.8	−9.5
Baker Centrifichem/Baker	−0.1	4.1	−4.2
duPont Dimension/duPont	−0.6	4.1	−4.6
Gilford Impact 400/Ciba	3.6	3.9	•
Boehringer Mannheim 736, 737/BMD	1.3	3.6	−2.3
Baxter Paramax/Paramax	1.9	3.4	−1.5
Technicon SMAC/Technicon	2.3	3.2	•
Instrumentation Lab Monarch/Inst Lab	−3.0	2.8	−5.8
Olympus 5000/Olympus	1.5	2.6	−1.1
Technicon 12-60/Technicon	−0.6	2.1[†]	•
Technicon RA-1000/Technicon	0.5	2.0	−1.5
Abbott Spectrum/Abbott	−0.4	1.9	−2.2
Olympus Demand/Olympus	0.7	1.7[†]	−1.0
Ciba 550 Express/Ciba	−0.9	1.5[†]	•
Technicon RA-1000/Sigma	−1.4	1.5[†]	•
Technicon Chem 1/Technicon	1.1	1.0[†]	•
Am Monitor Parallel/Am Monitor	−2.9	0.7[†]	−3.6
duPont aca/duPont	−11.0	0.6[†]	−11.6
Boehringer Mannheim 8700/BMD	0.1	0.5	•
Boehringer Mannheim 704, 705/BMD	0.0	0.2[†]	•
Am Monitor Parallel/Behring	−0.2	0.1[†]	•
Boehringer Mannheim 717/BMD	−0.3	−0.3[†]	•
Ektachem DT 60/Kodak	0.9	−0.9[†]	−1.7

(Continues on next page)

Table 11–1 ✧ (Continued)			
Instrument/Reagent System, Manufacturer	*Survey Bias (%)*	*Calibration Bias (%)*	*Matrix Bias (%)*
Coulter Dacos/Coulter	-3.1	-1.3	-1.8
Beckman Synchron CX4,5/Beckman	-5.1	-1.5[†]	-3.6
Abbott VP/Abbott	-5.8	-1.5[†]	-4.4
Beckman Astra 4,8 Ideal/Beckman	-12.3	-1.5[†]	-10.9
Instrumentation Lab Multistat III/Beckman	-11.9	-1.9[†]	-10.1
Ektachem 400, 700/Kodak	-1.1	-3.2	2.1
Electronuclear Gemini/Electro	-6.6	-3.9[†]	*

*Matrix bias not significant, $P < 0.05$.
[†]Calibration bias not significant, $P < 0.05$.
[a]Adapted from Table 3 in Ross et al. Arch Pathol Lab Med 1993;117:393–400.

Proficiency testing results are not a reliable indicator of the true accuracy of a laboratory's results for patients' specimens. Inappropriate interpretation of PT results as an assessment of accuracy can have a detrimental effect on the true accuracy of results for patients' specimens. Several of the analytical systems listed in Table 11–1 had an apparently small Survey bias. However, because of the method/material matrix bias, some methods actually had a significant calibration bias for the fresh-frozen serum specimen.

Ferrero et al.[34] reported a regional assessment of 32 laboratories using two off-the-clot frozen serum pools and two commercially prepared experimental lyophilized serum-based materials. For TC assay, six routine methodologies were represented. The group average bias to the Abell-Kendall reference method was equivalent for either frozen pools or lyophilized materials. However, individual lab results were not tabulated and plots of bias by material type showed a range of results which may have been influenced by matrix interactions.

Lasky et al.[35] evaluated the matrix bias of PT materials used for TC assessment in eight different survey programs from four countries. They used frozen human serum pools, some of which were supplemented with human serum cholesterol concentrates, as the basis for evaluation of the highly processed freeze-dried materials. The Abell-Kendall reference method was used for target value assignment. Ten routine methods had acceptable performance with frozen serum pools; however, based on the Clinical Laboratory Improvement Amendments of 1988 (CLIA) ± 10% criterion, nine methods would have failed PT with one or more materials.

Franzini and Luraschi[36] evaluated the commutability of 24 lyophilized commercial control materials from 11 manufacturers with 107 individual patients' sera assayed by two methods using Boehringer Mannheim enzymatic TC reagents. They showed that if the lyophilized materials had been used as calibrators, seven of the materials had a matrix interaction which would have introduced a mean bias of > 3% into the patients' results.

Kroll and Chesler[37] investigated the impact of matrix modification on HDL-C methods. They measured HDL-C in serial dilutions of a fresh serum pool, two concentrations of Sigma HDL-C lyophilized control materials, and CAP lyophilized serum-based linearity materials. Eight routine laboratory methods were tested, four using dextran sulfate and four using phosphotungstate precipitating agents. Kroll and Chesler concluded that matrix modifications in the lyophilized materials affected the precipitation step and resulted in apparent non-linearity which was not observed with the fresh serum pool.

Frozen serum pools are commonly considered to be less prone to matrix modifications than the typical freeze-dried commercial serum-based materials. However, frozen pools can represent a wide range of preparation protocols and have been reported to exhibit method- and material-specific matrix biases. As mentioned previously, the most successful frozen serum materials are prepared with great care to avoid alteration of lipoproteins or other serum components.[22, 23]

As early as 1976, Warnick and Albers[38] identified a difference in apparent bias between two non-enzymatic methods for TC and TG in the Lipid Research Clinics program when assessed using fresh plasma specimens versus frozen serum pools. The frozen pools were prepared by the CDC using Cohn fraction and egg white supplementation for cholesterol and triglycerides respectively.

Waymack et al.[39] evaluated eight frozen human serum pools used in the CDC Lipid Standardization Program for performance in enzymatic methods for TC. Some of the pools were supplemented with human Cohn fraction serum lipid concentrates. Fresh, non-frozen individual patients' sera with Abell-Kendall value assignment were used to establish assay performance. Five of the eight frozen pools had a matrix bias that was not a function of the reagent used but of unique instrument assay parameters.

Myers et al.[40] reported that three CDC Cohn fraction cholesterol supplemented, frozen human serum pools showed significant matrix bias with two of 16 routine enzymatic methods for TC, and three commercial liquid stabilized human serum pools showed matrix bias with nine of the 16 methods. For this study, non-supplemented, fresh-frozen serum pools were used as the controls for no matrix effects.

Miller et al.[41] evaluated matrix bias in pooled serum materials. Two non-frozen pools were prepared from two sets of eight freshly collected, off-the-clot individual patients' sera and tested with four routine methods. These non-frozen serum pools had no matrix effects as assessed by routine enzymatic TC results which were the same as the mean of the individual sera making up the pools. However, with less carefully controlled preparation conditions, frozen serum pools did exhibit matrix bias. Four frozen serum pools were prepared from a different set of off-the-clot, non-supplemented human serum which was pooled in 2–3 liter bottles, frozen in bulk, thawed, remixed, aliquoted, and re-frozen. One to four of these frozen human serum pools showed significant matrix bias as compared to non-frozen individual donor sera for each of four routine methods.

Tetrault et al.[13] prepared three frozen human serum pools from off-the-clot serum which was frozen, thawed, pooled, aliquoted, and re-frozen. One of the pools was supplemented with an ultracentrifugally concentrated human serum LDL fraction from outdated blood bank plasma. Matrix bias was determined as the difference in apparent bias indicated by the mean of 16 fresh non-frozen patient sera versus the frozen pooled materials. All concentration values were assigned by the CDC reference methods for TC and HDL-C. One or more of the frozen human serum pools showed matrix bias for four of seven routine enzymatic methods for TC and for six of seven routine methods for HDL-C.

Holani et al.[42] used the CAP matrix effect evaluation protocol[24] to test five CAP processed freeze-dried serum pools and nine CDC supplemented frozen serum pools using three commercial enzymatic reagents for TG measurement. Twenty-four freshly collected individual sera were used as controls for no matrix bias. All specimens were assayed by the CDC chromotropic acid TG reference method and by three glycerol blank corrected commercial reagent systems adapted to a Cobas-BIO analyzer (Roche Instruments, Nutley, NJ). Results of two of the commercial reagents for both CAP and CDC PT materials were commutable with fresh sera. Results of the third reagent system were commutable with the CDC frozen pools but had a significant matrix bias for four out of five CAP freeze-dried materials.

MATRIX ISSUES IN APOLIPOPROTEIN MEASUREMENTS

Apolipoprotein assays present a different challenge to control for matrix interactions between different lots of reagents and calibrators and inter-instrument analytical variability. There are substantial method/material matrix interactions with apolipoprotein assays. However, there are no credentialed reference methods with well-established performance characteristics. Thus, the method of accuracy transfer or validation based on splitting fresh human sera is not possible. Standardization of apolipoprotein AI (apo AI) and apolipoprotein B (apo B) accuracy is being accomplished using commutable serum reference materials, with consensus target values assigned, which are approved by the World Health Organization (WHO) and distributed to analytical method manufacturers. Thus, the state of the art depends on the continued commutability of the reference materials and the ability of manufacturers to transfer that accuracy to the secondary calibration materials provided with the assay systems.

Smith et al.[43] reported an international investigation of four non-supplemented lyophilized human serum pools by eight method principles in 140 laboratories. They found that some lyophilized materials had equivalent mean values for apo AI among the method groups, but that all materials had significantly different apparent mean values for apo B assays.

Marcovina et al.[18] prepared three non-supplemented human serum pools for apo AI and six such pools for apo B. Half of the vials were stored frozen at −78° C and the other half were lyophilized. Each material was assayed by five method principles with a common frozen serum pool used to standardize calibration of each method. Apo AI values were the same for frozen and lyophilized pools. Apo B values for the lyophilized pools differed from those of the frozen materials by −26% to +4% depending on the assay method.

Marcovina et al.[44] reported results from an investigation of reference materials for calibration of apo AI and B which was conducted by the International Federation of Clinical Chemistry Committee on Apolipoprotein Standardization. The inter-method commutability of 15 candidate reference materials for apo AI and 11 materials for apo B were evaluated by 26 and 28 methods, respectively, in 28 laboratories in nine countries. Three non-supplemented, fresh-frozen human serum pools were used to standardize calibration among the laboratories. Ten fresh-frozen individual donor sera were used to confirm standardization with an inter-method coefficient of variance (CV) of 5% for apo AI and 6.3% for apo B. For the candidate materials, inter-method CVs for apo AI ranged from 4.4% to 80.6%, with four of 15 materials having an inter-method CV < 5%. For apo B, inter-method CVs ranged from 6.0% to 35.1%, with three of 11 materials ≤ 7%. Only three materials for each apolipoprotein had no turbidity and nearly normal lipoprotein patterns on electrophoresis. The most suitable candidate reference materials for apo AI were lyophilized and those for apo B were liquid stabilized.

Subsequent work by Albers et al.[45] utilized linearity and parallelism evaluation to identify one material for apo AI (inter-method CV = 3%) and one for apo B (inter-method CV = 6%) which were sufficiently commutable for use as calibration reference materials.

Marcovina et al.[46] reported value assignment and use of the apo AI reference material to standardize calibration of 30 routine methods involving 23 manufacturers. Assays of 50 fresh-frozen individual donor sera by each participant resulted in an inter-laboratory CV for each sample ranging from 2.1% to 5.6%. Similarly, the apo B reference material was value assigned and used to standardize calibration of 28 methods from 21 manufacturers[47]. Comparison of interlaboratory results for fresh-frozen sera gave CVs ranging from 3.1% to 6.7%, again demonstrating good commutability of the reference material. These two materials have been endorsed by the WHO as International Reference Materials for Apolipoprotein A-I and Apolipoprotein B. These materials are only available to manufacturers and select reference laboratories.

PRACTICAL IMPACT OF MATRIX LIMITATIONS ON CALIBRATION AND PROFICIENCY TESTING IN ROUTINE LABORATORY PRACTICE

Calibration

Calibration of lipid testing is generally provided by the analytical system manufacturer. TC and HDL-C methods are standardized by splitting unadulterated patients' sera with a laboratory of the Cholesterol Reference Method Laboratory Network (CRMLN) sponsored by the CDC. LDL-C and TG are similarly standardized utilizing a laboratory certified by the older CDC Lipid Standardization Program. The Reference Method Network is developing reference equivalent methods for LDL-C and TG. Apolipoproteins AI and B are standardized by reference to the WHO International Reference Materials. For all analytes, the manufacturer must transfer the accuracy base to a series of secondary calibration products for use in many individual laboratories to calibrate individual lots of reagents used with individual analyzers.

Accuracy transfer to individual laboratories is a substantial analytical challenge.[48, 49] Manufacturing of equipment, reagents, and calibration products is performed to tolerances defined to allow the total error of the final analytical system to meet medical requirements at an acceptable cost. Manufacturing tolerances result in some degree of variability among instruments, lots of reagents, and lots of calibrators. Some variables, such as shipping and storage conditions, operating environment conditions, equipment maintenance, and operator training are beyond the control of manufacturers yet can affect the accuracy of results and must be accommodated in the total analytical system design.

The calibration material provided by an analytical system manufacturer is formulated and value assigned to compensate for any unique matrix effects and to provide correct calibration for patients' specimens assayed by that specific method. Because of unpredictable matrix interactions, one cannot use calibration materials from one manufacturer with a reagent or instrument system from a different manufacturer. If one intends to mix sources of instrument, reagent, and calibrator materials, that specific combination must be validated for accuracy using one of the strategies mentioned previously. The validation can be performed by a material vendor or the individual laboratory.

Verification of Accuracy

The success of accuracy transfer to individual laboratories has been investigated. Kimberly et al.[50] found that approximately 20% of clinical laboratories splitting patients' sera with one of the CRMLN laboratories during 1991-92 failed to meet the NCEP ± 3% accuracy guideline for TC. The CAP included a fresh-frozen serum specimen in the 1994 Comprehensive Chemistry Survey which was assayed by 570 routine laboratories[33]. Eleven of 15 peer groups had statistically significant mean calibration bias for TC versus the CDC Abell-Kendall method, with two peer groups exceeding the NCEP accuracy guideline. However, 97.6% of individual laboratories had TC results within the ± 8.9% total error specification for an individual measurement, suggesting generally excellent precision for these methods. For HDL-C, eight of ten methods had significant mean calibration bias versus the CDC reference method, with two peer groups exceeding 10% bias and five exceeding 5% bias. For TG, after correcting for free glycerol, 15 of 16 methods had significant mean calibration bias versus the CDC reference method, with two peer groups exceeding 10% bias and nine exceeding 5% bias.

The complexity of accuracy transfer from manufacturers and the available data documenting that process suggests that calibration accuracy should be verified in individual laboratories to ensure that NCEP performance guidelines are satisfied. If necessary, laboratories may need to make calibration adjustments to bring an individual assay system into conformance with NCEP accuracy recommendations. Primary accuracy verification for lipid analytes will continue to be accomplished by splitting fresh, non-frozen individual patients' sera with a National Reference Laboratory for TC and HDL-C, and with a CDC standardized laboratory for LDL-C and TG. A network of laboratories for verification of apolipoprotein and Lp(a) assays is in the formative stage.

When properly validated, frozen serum reference materials can provide a resource for accuracy validation. Frozen serum pools validated for commutability by the NCCLS subcommittee developing a guideline for preparation of serum cholesterol reference material have recently become available.[22] Vials of these pools have been value assigned for TC and TG by NIST definitive methods and for TC, HDL-C, LDL-C, and TG by CDC reference methods. These frozen serum reference materials are distributed through NIST and the CAP.

Other serum-based reference materials have not been validated for commutability between a large number of methods at the present time. However, some materials with NRSCL assigned values can be used for accuracy verification in situations when an analytical method has been shown to be free of matrix bias for that specific material.

Monitoring Relative Accuracy Over Time

Accuracy verification using sera split with a certified reference laboratory is time consuming, expensive, and requires several weeks to obtain results. Documentation of this process is necessary to demonstrate that NCEP performance criteria are being met and to support method calibration adjustments if necessary to maintain compliance with NCEP analytical goals. To verify calibration between interactions with a certified laboratory, it is recommended that each laboratory obtain and value assign stable reference materials at the same time that absolute accuracy is established as discussed above. Figure 11-2 illustrates the relationship between analytical accuracy validation and value assignment of a reference material for monitoring relative accuracy on a continuing basis.

Once a method is documented to provide accurate results for patients' specimens, a target value can be assigned to a stable reference material. This target value assign-

Figure 11–2 ✧ Schematic of Calibration Adjustment based on Individual Patients' Sera and Matrix Compensated Value Assignment of a Reference Material for Subsequent Verification of Field (Routine) Method Accuracy

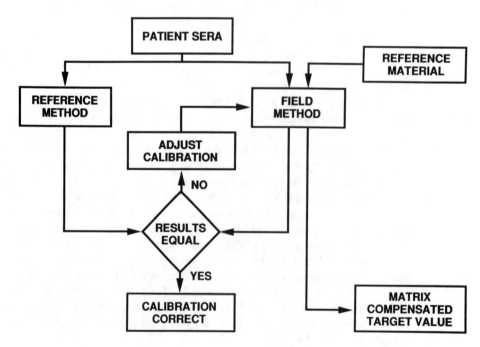

ment strategy compensates for any matrix interaction which may be present between the lots of reference materials and reagents in use. As long as the matrix relationship does not change, the reference material can be used to confirm that the method calibration has been maintained relative to the time when the absolute accuracy was validated. In many cases, a well-designed process-control (quality-control) system can support this function.

The key operational requirement for longitudinal reference materials is that they not have reactive characteristics that change with new lots of reagents or other components of the analytical system. The more commutable a reference material, the more useful it is for long-term method monitoring. As long as the reference material/reagent matrix relationship is constant, the reference material can be used to verify calibration accuracy after lot changes in manufacturer-provided calibration materials. If a matrix interaction is constant and predictable between reagent lots or other assay system variables, then that material can be used to validate accuracy following changes in lots of reagent or after a major instrument component is changed. Constancy of matrix interaction between lots of material and reagent is a difficult assumption to support because of the somewhat unpredictable nature of these analytical non-specificity components.

Some types of reference materials that can be useful for monitoring relative accuracy within an individual laboratory are listed in Table 11–2 in approximate order of matrix modification during preparation. Frozen aliquots of individual patient's sera or carefully prepared non-supplemented, fresh-frozen serum pools can be prepared in-house and can be value assigned by the routine laboratory or by a certified reference laboratory. These materials provide highly reliable reference specimens to validate accuracy and troubleshoot method problems.

As discussed previously, the CAP (325 Waukegan Road, Northfield, IL 60093-2750) and NIST (United States Department of Commerce, National Institute of Standards and Technology, Gaithersburg, MD 20899) have available two carefully prepared frozen serum pools with national reference method target values assigned. These materials have been documented to have excellent commutability with most routine methods for TC[22] and can be used to validate accuracy for many methods. Other commercial sources for quality off-the-clot frozen serum pools are Pacific Biometrics Research Foundation (1100 Eastlake Avenue, Seattle, WA 98109) and Solomon Park Research Laboratories (12815 N.E. 124th Street, Suite 1, Kirkland, WA 98034).

The CAP excess Chemistry Survey materials are freeze-dried pooled serum materials which have been assayed by thousands of laboratories and have statistically

Table 11–2 ❖ Materials Useful to Monitor Relative Accuracy
• Frozen (–70° C) aliquotes of a single donor serum.
• Non-supplemented frozen (–70° C) serum pools.
• Supplemented from (–70° C) serum pools.
• College of American Pathologists survey validated materials.
• NIST SRM 909b.
• Commercial lipid control materials.

reliable peer-group consensus mean values. The current CAP materials used for lipid analytes are prepared from off-the-clot human serum with low free glycerol and generally avoid supplementation except for a few higher concentration specimens.[23] The peer-group value assignment of the CAP materials circumvents the matrix issue but does not provide a direct verification of accuracy for an individual peer group.

NIST SRM 909b is a two-concentration set of supplemented, freeze-dried pooled serum materials that have definitive and reference method values assigned for lipid parameters. The SRM 909b processed serum-based materials do exhibit matrix bias with various methods and must be used in conjunction with appropriate accuracy validation based on fresh sera.

Least robust are various commercially available lipid control materials. These materials are intended for process monitoring and can be very stable formulations. They frequently have significant matrix interactions with many routine methods and must be used in conjunction with appropriate accuracy validation based on fresh sera. When target values are provided, they are commonly based on minimal statistical designs and do not include accuracy traceability to the NRSCL. Consequently, value assigned quality control materials should not be used for accuracy verification.

In-house value assignment of reference materials must be done during a period when two analytical conditions are satisfied. First, the analytical system is stable as evidenced from daily process quality control. Second, the analytical calibration is verified by a split patient correlation with a certified reference laboratory or by assay of NRSCL value assigned reference materials which have been documented to be commutable with the method and reagents in use. The in-house reference materials selected must be assayed a sufficient number of times to have a statistically useful confidence interval (CI) for the mean value, and over an adequate time period to represent typical analytical imprecision for the method. Multiple analytical runs on multiple days must be used, ideally with more than one lot of reagents and several calibration events.

As an example, Table 11-3 shows the 95% CI for the mean of various numbers of replicates (N) for a mean TC of 200 mg/dL (5.17 mmol/L) with method CVs of 2.5 and 1.5%. The CI indicates the concentration range within which the mean is likely to be found with 95% probability. For example, with 5 replicates and a method CV of 2.5%, the mean of 200 mg/dL (5.17 mmol/L) has a 0.95 probability of being in the interval 194–206 mg/dL (5.02–5.32 mmol/L). This example makes clear that adequate replication is necessary when assigning a target value to a reference material. A corollary conclusion is that a more reliable calibration of an analytical system will be achieved when the calibration materials are assayed in replicate.

Proficiency Testing

PT materials in common use exhibit sufficiently widespread matrix interactions that PT results cannot be used to evaluate a laboratory's ability to produce accurate lipid results for patients' specimens. Ross et al.[30] reported that 70% of the enzymatic methods in use for TC exhibited non-specific matrix interaction with one or more materials used in the 1989 CAP Survey program. The CAP included a fresh-frozen serum specimen and reference method value assignment in the 1994 Survey program to re-evaluate the state of the art. For TC, ten of 15 method peer groups exhibited significant matrix

Table 11–3 ✧ 95% Confidence Intervals (CI) for Various Numbers of Replicates (N)[a]		
	For 200 mg/dL (5.17 mmol/L)	
N	*CV = 2.5%*	*CV = 1.5%*
2	± 45 mg/dL (1.17 mmol/L)	± 27 mg/dL (0.70 mmol/L)
3	± 12 mg/dL (0.31 mmol/L)	± 7.5 mg/dL (0.19 mmol/L)
5	± 6.2 mg/dL (0.16 mmol/L)	± 3.7 mg/dL (0.10 mmol/L)
10	± 3.6 mg/dL (0.09 mmol/L)	± 2.1 mg/dL (0.05 mmol/L)
20	± 2.3 mg/dL (0.06 mmol/L)	± 1.4 mg/dL (0.04 mmol/L)

[a]Calculated as: $CI = \pm (t_{N-1, (1-a)/2}) \cdot (S^2/N)^{1/2}$ where t is the Student's t value for $N-1$ degrees of freedom and $(1-a)/2$ significance level, and s is the standard deviation for the assay.

bias with at least three of four PT materials.[33] All methods showed significant matrix bias with at least one of the four materials.

All providers of large PT programs in the United States are currently evaluating lipid assays by comparison of results to the peer-group mean. Peer-group evaluation compares an individual laboratory's result to the mean of all laboratories using the same method. Peer group evaluation judges a laboratory's ability to use a method as intended by the manufacturer and provides information on the inter-method precision of an analytical system.

Variability within a peer group can be caused by an individual laboratory's skill at applying the method and by calibration variability in the manufacturer's accuracy transfer process. Peer-group evaluation is minimally affected by the presence of matrix interactions since the method/material-specific interactions are a property of the assay system and should be the same for all participants. However, there can be variable matrix bias within a homogeneous peer group if reagent lots have different matrix interactions with a PT material. Some of the newer compact-analyzer methods that use dry-format reagents and membrane and filtration technology may be particularly sensitive to lot-specific matrix interactions. Variable matrix bias can also be present within a peer group composed of hybrid analytical systems which, for example, use reagents or calibration materials from different vendors.

A peer group evaluation protocol allows individual laboratories to ascertain whether they are applying a particular methodology in the same manner as other laboratories. Peer group evaluation does not provide information on the accuracy of patients' specimens, and thus does not allow validation of NCEP accuracy guidelines. Peer group evaluation does not allow comparison of results or performance characteristics among methods. Peer-group evaluation is not suitable for small method groups because a statistically valid group mean cannot be determined. Small peer groups cannot be evaluated against some other target value because matrix bias is likely to invalidate the comparison.

Laboratories that find it necessary to adjust the manufacturer's calibration settings to meet NCEP guidelines will need to report PT results in an appropriate way to permit useful evaluation. The method/material matrix interaction is a function of the methodology and is unaffected by calibration adjustments. However, the calibration offset will invalidate comparison of PT results to the peer group mean.

One should not report calibration-adjusted PT results with a method designation of "Other." PT providers may evaluate "Other" method groups against a reference-method-assigned target value, the all-method mean, or some other target value derived from the participants' results. In these cases, if there are any matrix-induced biases with the PT materials, reliable evaluation of the laboratory's performance will be impossible.

The most useful strategy is to report PT results after removing adjustment factors to revert to the manufacturer's intended calibration settings. In this way, PT results can be compared to an appropriate peer-group target value to evaluate the laboratory's ability to correctly use the analytical system. A calibration offset does not change matrix interaction. Thus, removing mathematical calibration adjustments prior to assaying the PT specimens or mathematically "back-calculating" the PT results to reflect the manufacturer's calibration settings does not alter the method's operational condition. Re-calibrating only for PT is incorrect because the method would not reflect the usual operating conditions for patient's specimens.

A critical point is the regulatory implication of adjusting manufacturer provided calibration to meet a laboratory's quality goals, and then removing the adjustment factors to report PT results. The pertinent CLIA regulations state:

> The laboratory must examine or test, as applicable, the proficiency testing samples it receives from the proficiency testing program in the same manner as it tests patient specimens.[51]

> Pertinent "reference" . . . ranges . . . must be available to the authorized person who ordered the tests or the individual responsible for utilizing the test results.[52]

> In addition, information that may affect the test results, such as test interferences, must be provided. . . .[53]

The CLIA regulations require use of calibration settings appropriate for the type of specimen being tested. For example, clinical specimens with unique fluid matrix properties, such as pleural fluid or spinal fluid, are frequently assayed using the same methods as serum, but with calibration settings adjusted for the matrix to obtain results that can be properly interpreted. The requirement to test PT samples in the same manner as patient specimens means that any special requirements of the PT specimen must be properly accommodated in the testing process. When analytical interferences, such as matrix interactions, are present, a laboratory is expected to assay the specimens as appropriate and provide results which can be properly interpreted according to their intended clinical use. In the case of PT specimens, the intended clinical use is to evaluate the laboratory's ability to apply a method correctly in the field setting. Since matrix-related interferences have a high probability of occurring in many method/-material combinations, the correct assay technique is to report the results according to the manufacturer's calibration settings to permit evaluation with the appropriate peer group.

An incorrect interpretation of the CLIA regulations would use the same calibration settings for PT samples as are used for patient testing. Note that this is the correct strategy when the manufacturer's calibration is not adjusted. However, if this interpretation were followed, the calibration adjustment which may be necessary to produce accurate results for patients' specimens would lead to incorrect inferences from the PT results. In fact, the PT results would be uninterpretable, since an analytical interference may be present and an invalid target value would be used for evaluation.

The specialty program offered by Pacific Biometrics Research Foundation offers an option for PT of lipid methods. This program uses freshly collected, non-supplemented, non-frozen pooled human serum specimens that are likely to have minimal method/material matrix interactions. Target values are assigned by certified reference methods. This approach offers the possibility for reliable evaluation of accuracy. Detailed evaluation of the effectiveness of this PT program awaits publication. A similar program is available in Canada through the Canadian Reference Foundation (307-2083 Alma Street, Vancouver, BC V6R 4N6).

SUMMARY AND FUTURE DIRECTIONS IN CONTROLLING MATRIX LIMITATIONS

Matrix modifications are inherent in the current state of the art for producing large quantities of stable serum-based reference materials. Recent efforts have successfully produced moderate quantities of highly commutable frozen serum pools. The generally satisfactory strategy is to use freshly collected, off-the-clot serum with no or minimal supplementation to achieve desired analyte concentrations. Future efforts should continue to develop and validate commutable materials, perhaps utilizing the tools of molecular biology to make robust molecules for reference materials.

Standardization and calibration can be successfully performed with the current materials and analytical strategies. Authentic clinical specimens split between routine and certified reference methods continues to be the primary mechanism to both establish and verify accuracy. Although expensive, this strategy has worked successfully at the manufacturer level to achieve practical standardization of TC, and is being extended to HDL-C, LDL-C, and TG. A second protocol adopted for apolipoproteins AI and B utilizes commutable reference materials with consensus target values. These materials are endorsed by the WHO and are used by manufacturers to calibrate commercial assay methods. Highly commutable frozen serum pool materials with definitive and reference method target values assigned are now available from NIST and the CAP. These materials will be invaluable to both manufacturers and clinical laboratories for standardizing and validating accuracy.

Accuracy transfer from manufacturers to individual laboratory instrument systems utilizes a variety of techniques and remains an important analytical challenge. The calibration materials provided by individual manufacturers for use with particular assay systems should not be used for calibration or accuracy validation of different systems. The likely presence of unpredictable matrix interactions with these materials precludes their use except as specifically documented. Good laboratory practice requires standardized, accurate results to meet national recommendations for medical diagnosis and therapeutic intervention for lipid disorders. Current regulations require that accuracy be independently verified at each laboratory testing location using a PT program. Consequently, all analytical methods should be designed to recover analyte from the usual patient specimens as well as from currently available reference materials. New measurement technology must address the PT requirement as an integral part of the assay system. Robust assay characteristics must be uniformly manufactured into subsequent lots of reagents, calibrators, and other analytical components of the measurement system.

Current large PT programs use serum-based materials which frequently have matrix interactions with routine methods, which compromise their ability to mimic the analytical performance of authentic clinical specimens. This matrix bias interferes with the ability to evaluate accuracy of a routine method versus a reference method. The current practice of evaluating PT results by conformance to a method peer group mean value only establishes that an individual laboratory utilizes a measurement system the same as other users of that system. Peer group evaluation does not evaluate the accuracy of a laboratory for analysis of patients' specimens. Consequently, laboratories must also perform a patient specimen comparison with a certified reference laboratory or utilize a documented commutable reference material with NRSCL target values to validate accuracy and conformance with NCEP guidelines.

It would be possible to evaluate accuracy in the presence of matrix bias if the method/material-specific matrix bias could be measured and were constant and predictable among all laboratories using a particular method. Longitudinal evaluation would be possible if subsequent lots of materials and method components maintained predictable method/material matrix interactions. The CAP tested this concept for evaluation of TC in the 1989 Survey Program and further developed the protocol and extended its application to HDL-C and TG plus other analytes in the 1994 Program.[30, 33] This evaluation strategy is very promising to permit PT to be used to assess a laboratory's accuracy for the clinically relevant patients' specimens. ✧

REFERENCES

1. Fasce CF, Rej R, Copeland WH, Vanderlinde RE. A discussion of enzyme reference materials: applications and specifications. Clin Chem 1973;19:5–9.
2. Miller WG, Kaufman H. College of American Pathologists Conference XXIII. Introduction: matrix effects and accuracy assessment in clinical chemistry. Arch Pathol Lab Med 1993;117:343–4.
3. National Committee for Clinical Laboratory Standards. Nomenclature and definitions for use in NRSCL and other NCCLS documents: proposed guideline, 2d ed. (NCCLS Document No. NRSCL8-P2). NCCLS, 940 West Valley Rd., Suite 1400 Wayne, PA 19087, 1993.
4. National Committee for Clinical Laboratory Standards. Evaluation of matrix effects: proposed guideline. (NCCLS Document No. EP14-P). NCCLS, 940 West Valley Rd., Suite 1400 Wayne, PA 19087, 1997.
5. ASTM Committee on Terminology. Compilation of ASTM standard definitions. Philadelphia, PA: American Society for Testing and Materials, 1990.
6. Rej R. Accurate enzyme activity measurements: two decades of development in the commutability of enzyme quality control materials. Arch Pathol Lab Med 1993;117:352–64.
7. Posner A. Problems in formulating method insensitive proficiency testing materials. Arch Pathol Lab Med 1993;117:422–4.
8. Kuchmak M, Hazlehurst JS, Olansky AS, Taylor L. Reference sera with graded levels of high density lipoprotein TC. Clin Chim Acta 1984;144:237–43.
9. Williams JH, Taylor L, Kuchmak M, Witter RF. Preparation of hypercholesterolemic and/or hypertriglyceridemic sera for lipid determinations. Clin Chim Acta 1970;28:247–53.

10. Kuchmak M, Taylor L, Williams JH. Preparation of reference sera with desired levels of TC and TG. Clin Chim Acta 1981;114:127–35.

11. Kuchmak M, Taylor L, Olansky AS. Low lipid level reference sera with human serum matrix. Clin Chim Acta 1981;116:125–30.

12. Cohn EJ, Strong LE, Hughes WL Jr, et al. Preparation and properties of serum and plasma proteins IV: a system for the separation into fractions of the protein and lipo-protein components of biological tissues and fluids. J Am Chem Soc 1946;68:459–75.

13. Tetrault GA, Miller WG, Chinchilli VM, et al. Regional interlaboratory standardization of determination of cholesterol, high-density lipoprotein cholesterol, and triglycerides. Clin Chem 1990;36:145–9.

14. Van Brunt N, Egensperger H, Greenberg N, Halstead R, Cassano T, Doptis P. Serum based quality control fluids and calibrators: is there an advantage of lyophilization over vacuum drying? [Abstract]. Clin Chem 1989;35:1101.

15. Baadenhuijsen H, Demacker PNM, Hessels M, Boerma GJM, Penders TJ, Weykamp C, Willems HL. Testing the accuracy of total cholesterol assays in an external quality-control program. Effect of adding sucrose to lyophilized control sera compared with use of fresh or frozen sera. Clin Chem 1995;41:724–30.

16. Rej R, Jenny RW, Bretaudiere JP. Quality control in clinical chemistry: characterization of reference materials. Talanta 1984;31:851–62.

17. Kroll MH, Chesler R, Elin RJ. Effect of lyophilization of results of five enzymatic methods for cholesterol. Clin Chem 1989;35:1523–6.

18. Marcovina SM, Adolphson JL, Parlavecchia M, Albers JJ. Effects of lyophilization of serum on the measurement of apolipoproteins A-1 and B. Clin Chem 1990;36:366–9.

19. Kroll MH, Chesler R. Effect of serum lyophilization on the rate constants of enzymatic methods for measuring cholesterol. Clin Chem 1990;36:534–7.

20. Noel SP, Dupras R, Filion AM. The activity of cholesterol ester hydrolase in the enzymatic determination of cholesterol: comparison of five enzymes obtained commercially. Analytical Biochemistry 1983;129:464–71.

21. Wiebe DA, Bernert JT. Influence of incomplete cholesteryl ester hydrolysis on enzymic measurements of cholesterol. Clin Chem 1984;30:352–6.

22. National Committee for Clinical Laboratory Standards. Preparation of serum cholesterol reference material: proposed guideline. (NCCLS Document No. C37-P). NCCLS, 940 West Valley Rd., Suite 1400 Wayne, PA 19087. Manuscript in preparation.

23. Myers GL, Ross JW, Smith SJ, Morris CH, Triplett RB, Groff M. Evaluating lyophilized human serum preparations for suitability as proficiency testing materials for high-density lipoprotein cholesterol measurement. Arch Pathol Lab Med 1995;119:686–94.

24. Eckfeldt JH, Copeland KR. Accuracy verification and identification of matrix effects: The College of American Pathologists' protocol. Arch Pathol Lab Med 1993;117:381–6.

25. Greenacre M. Correspondence analysis in medical research. Stat Meth Med Res 1992; 1:97–117.

26. Koch DD, Hassemer DJ, Wiebe DA, Laessig RH. Testing cholesterol accuracy: performance of several common laboratory instruments. JAMA 1988;260:2552–7.

27. Cooper GR, Smith SJ, Duncan IW, Mather A, Fellows W D, Foley T, Frantz ID, Gill JB, Grooms TA, Hynie I. Interlaboratory testing of the transferability of a candidate reference method for total cholesterol in serum. Clin Chem 1986;32:921–9.

28. Miller WG, Kaufman H, McLendon WW. College of American Pathologists Conference XXIII: matrix effects and accuracy assessment in clinical chemistry. Arch Pathol Lab Med 1993;117(4):343–436.

29. Naito HK, Yun-Sik K, Hartfiel JL, et al. Matrix effects on proficiency testing materials: impact on accuracy of cholesterol measurement in laboratories in the nation's largest hospital system. Arch Pathol Lab Med 1993;117:345–51.

30. Ross JW, Myers GL, Gilmore BF, Cooper GR, Naito HR, Eckfeldt J. Matrix effects and the accuracy of cholesterol analysis. Arch Pathol Lab Med 1993;117:393–400.

31. Cohen A, Hertz HS, Mendel J, et al. Total serum cholesterol by isotope dilution/mass spectrometry: a candidate definitive method. Clin Chem 1980;26:854-60.

32. Ellerby P, Myers GL, Cooper GR, et al. A comparison of results for cholesterol in human serum obtained by the reference method and by the definitive method of the National Reference System for Cholesterol. Clin Chem 1990;36:370-5.

33. Ross JW, Chair, Chemistry Resource Committee, College of American Pathologists. Personal communication.

34. Ferrero CA, Carobene A, Ceriotti F, Modenese A, Arcelloni C. Behavior of frozen serum pools and lyophilized sera in an external quality-assessment scheme. Clin Chem 1995; 41:575-80.

35. Lasky FD, Powers DM, Hassemer DJ, Wiebe DA. Quality of fluids used in external quality control programs affects the reliable assessment of accuracy of routine methods, as documented by cholesterol. Quality Control in the Clinical Laboratory '91. Proceedings of the 7th International Symposium on Quality Control, Tokyo, June 15-16, 1991;199-208.

36. Franzini C, Luraschi P. Commutability of control materials in cholesterol measurement. Scand J Clin Lab Invest 1993;53:51-55.

37. Kroll MH, Chesler R. Nonlinearity of high-density lipoprotein cholesterol determinations is matrix dependent. Clin Chem 1994;40:389-94.

38. Warnick GR, Albers JJ. Physiological and analytical variation in cholesterol and triglycerides. Lipids 1976;203-8.

39. Waymack PP, Miller WG, Myers GL. Assay instrument dependent matrix effects in standardization of cholesterol measurements. Clin Chem 1993;39:2058-62.

40. Myers GL, Schap D, Smith SJ, et al. College of American Pathologists–Centers for disease control collaborative study for evaluating reference materials for total serum cholesterol measurements. Arch Pathol Lab Med 1990;114:1199-1205.

41. Miller WG, Brown B, Dalby T. Cholesterol matrix effects in fresh non-frozen and frozen serum pools. [Abstract]. Clin Chem 1991;37:920.

42. Holani KK, Miller WG, Waymack PP. Robustness of three triglyceride reagents for matrix effects of proficiency testing materials. [Abstract]. Clin Chem 1993;39:1126.

43. Smith SJ, Henderson LO, Hannon WH, Cooper GR. Effects of analytical method and lyophilized sera on measurements of apolipoproteins A-1 and B: an international survey. Clin Chem 1990;36:290-6.

44. Marcovina SM, Albers JJ, Dati F, Ledue TB, Ritchie RF. International Federation of Clinical Chemistry standardization project for measurements of apolipoproteins A-1 and B. Clin Chem 1991;37:1676-82.

45. Albers JJ, Marcovina SM, Kennedy H. International Federation of Clinical Chemistry standardization project for measurements of apolipoproteins A-1 and B. II. Evaluation and selection of candidate reference materials. Clin Chem 1992;38:658-62.

46. Marcovina SM, Albers JJ, Henderson LO, Hannon WH. International Federation of Clinical Chemistry standardization project for measurements of apolipoproteins A-1 and B. III. Comparability of apolipoprotein A-1 values by use of international reference material. Clin Chem 1993;39:773-81.

47. Marcovina SM, Albers JJ, Kennedy H, Mei JV, Henderson LO, Hannon WH. International Federation of Clinical Chemistry standardization project for measurements of apolipoproteins A-1 and B. IV. Comparability of apolipoprotein B values by use of international reference material. Clin Chem 1994;40:586-92.

48. Lasky FD. Achieving accuracy for routine clinical chemistry methods by using patient specimen correlations to assign calibrator values: a means of managing matrix effects. Arch Pathol Lab Med 1993;117:412-19.

49. Gochman N, Hall S. Manufacturer's approach to transferring accuracy to multiple field installations. Arch Pathol Lab Med 1993;117:420-1.

50. Kimberly MM, Smith JS, Myers GL. Evaluation of performance criteria for clinical laboratories in the Cholesterol Reference Method Laboratory Network (CRMLN). [Abstract]. Clin Chem 1993;39:1123.

51. Federal Register, Vol. 57, No. 40 (Feb. 28, 1992), p. 7146, section 493.801, part b. Washington DC: U.S. Government Printing Office.

52. Federal Register, Vol. 57, No. 40 (Feb. 28, 1992), p. 7162, section 493.1109, part d. Washington DC: U.S. Government Printing Office.

53. Federal Register, Vol. 57, No. 40 (Feb. 28, 1992), p. 7162, section 493.1109, part g. Washington DC: U.S. Government Printing Office.

Standardization of Lipid and Lipoprotein Measurements

Gary L. Myers, Gerald R. Cooper, L. Omar Henderson, David J. Hassemer, and Mary M. Kimberly

12

BACKGROUND

❖   The National Cholesterol Education Program (NCEP) mounted a concerted national effort to identify and treat every American adult who has high blood cholesterol and therefore has increased risk of coronary heart disease (CHD). The association between increased total cholesterol (TC), due to increased concentrations of low-density lipoprotein cholesterol (LDL-C), and the risk of premature CHD has been well documented.[1, 2] In addition, high-density lipoprotein cholesterol (HDL-C) concentrations are known to be negatively associated with CHD risk.[3, 4] The association of triglycerides (TG) with the risk of CHD continues to be somewhat controversial; TG are generally considered to be less predictive of CHD risk than TC.[4-7] The importance of TG rests in their effect on the estimation of LDL-C by the Friedewald equation.[8] Data from many epidemiological and clinical studies suggest that apolipoprotein A-I (apo A-I) and apo B-100 (apo B) may have promise as predictors of CHD risk and may eventually serve as additional markers of CHD risk.[9, 10] Epidemiologic studies have also established a link between high concentration of Lp(a) and an increased risk of early coronary heart disease and stroke.[11-13]

In its first report, the Adult Treatment Panel (ATP) of the NCEP established uniform decision points for identifying individuals who have increased risk of CHD.[2] The ATP's guidelines outlined a systematic approach to treatment of increased blood cholesterol which based initial case findings on TC concentrations and cholesterol-lowering therapy on LDL-C as the primary decision point.

In 1993, the second report issued by the Adult Treatment Panel (ATP II) reaffirmed that lowering TC and LDL-C concentrations reduces the risk of CHD;[14] (see Chapter 2 for additional information). However, ATP II contains some new issues that distinguish it from ATP I. For the clinical laboratory, the most significant difference is the increased emphasis on HDL-C as an independent risk factor for CHD. Specifically, ATP II recommends the addition of HDL-C to initial TC testing, so that whenever serum TC is measured for assessing CHD risk, HDL-C should also be measured.

All this attention to TC and the lipoproteins has focused unprecedented national attention on clinical laboratories and the need to provide reliable measurements of TC, TG, HDL-C, and LDL-C. Given the central role of cholesterol measurement in the assessment and management of CHD risk, the NCEP established the Laboratory Standardization Panel on Blood Cholesterol Measurement to assess the reliability of cholesterol measurement in clinical laboratories and to recommend means to improve the precision and accuracy of cholesterol testing. In 1988, the Laboratory Standardization Panel[15] recommended that cholesterol measurements be standardized so that values are traceable to the Centers for Disease Control and Prevention (CDC) cholesterol reference method, which is a modification of the Abell-Kendall method,[16, 17] or to the National Institute of Standards and Technology (NIST) definitive method for cholesterol, which is isotope dilution–mass spectrometry.[18] In 1995 a second laboratory panel, the NCEP Lipoprotein Measurement Working Group, published similar guidelines for obtaining reliable TG,[19] HDL-C,[20] and LDL-C[21] measurements.

It is not possible or practical to require that all laboratories use the same methods, calibrators, and controls. The key point to emphasize here is that the basis of standardization should be *traceability*: all results should be tied to a defined common accuracy base. Standardization requires that a reproducible analytical base be established to serve as a common denominator that permits laboratories to compare results and monitor analytical performance to ensure continuing accurate and precise results. The major components of this benchmark accuracy base comprise a hierarchy of methods and materials and include a definitive method, primary reference materials, a reference method, and secondary reference materials.

THE ACCURACY BASE

For each lipid, lipoprotein, and apolipoprotein, an analytical method must be widely accepted as the basis for universal reference. While it is generally accepted that a definitive method establishes the true value for an analyte, definitive techniques are not widely available to fulfill all of the requirements necessary to provide a point of reference for effective laboratory standardization. As a result, a definitive method is primarily used to validate a more widely available reference method, which in turn is designed for broader use and application.

If reference methods are to serve as the reference point for laboratory standardization, the problem becomes how to interface the accuracy base with the laboratory community. The base must be transferable on a broad scale. The most rapid and economical means of broadening the transfer of this accuracy base and of multiplying the impact of laborious reference-method analyses has traditionally been through the use of high-quality secondary reference materials. However, this approach to standardization by assigning target values to reference materials by definitive and/or reference methods has been complicated by fluid matrix effects in some analytical systems. This phenomenon is discussed later in this chapter and is presented in greater detail in Chapter 11.

Table 12–1 summarizes the components that make up reference systems for the various lipids, lipoproteins and apolipoproteins.

Cholesterol

The standard for accuracy in blood cholesterol measurement is the National Reference System for Cholesterol (NRS/CHOL) established by the NCCLS.[22] The NRS/CHOL is

Table 12–1 ✧ Lipid and Lipoprotein Reference Systems*

	Definitive Method	1° Reference Material	Reference Method	2° Reference Material
Cholesterol (NRS/CHOL)	ID-MS (NIST)	NIST SRM 911b Pure cholesterol	Abell-Kendall (CDC)	CDC Frozen Pools NIST SRM 909 NIST SRM1951a CAP RM 026
HDL-C	Not Available	Not Available	UC/Heparin-Mn^{2+}-Abell-Kendall (CDC). Recommended by NCEP.	CDC Frozen Pools NIST SRM 1951a CAP RM 026
Triglyceride	ID-MS (NIST)	NIST SRM 1595 tripalmitin	Methylene chloride-silicic acid-chromo-tropic acid (CDC). Recommended by NCEP.	CDC Frozen Pools NIST SRM 1951a CAP RM 026
LDL-C	Not Available	Not Available	Beta-quantification (CDC). Recommended by NCEP.	CDC Frozen Pools NIST SRM 1951a CAP RM 026
Apo A-I	HPLC-MS (CDC) (primary standard only) (Candidate)	BCR-CRM 393 Purified APO AI	Not Available	WHO Reference Reagent SP1-01 (for manufacturers). Labelled by CDC-RIA comparison method.
Apo B	Not Available	1.030–1.050 d UC purified LDL	Not Available	WHO Reference Reagent SP3-07 (for manufacturers). Labelled by NWLRL-immuno-nephelometry comparison method.

*CDC = Centers for Disease Control, NCEP = National Cholesterol Education Program, WHO = World Health Organization, NWLRL = Northwest Lipid Research Laboratories, CAP = College of American Pathologists

a unique voluntary consensus standard endorsed by professional, industrial, and government organizations. It is made up of the NIST definitive method, the CDC reference method, and a certified pure cholesterol standard, NIST SRM 911b. Both the definitive and reference methods are calibrated using the NIST SRM 911b pure cholesterol material. The two methods are monitored on an ongoing basis, and comparisons have demonstrated a small but persistent positive bias in the reference method of +1.6% compared to the definitive method.[23] The results of further investigations suggest that more than half of the difference in cholesterol values determined by the two methods is from small contributions from cholesterol precursor sterols and phytosterols, which are measured by the reference method.[24] Since the observed bias is consistent and quite small, the reference method provides a practical basis for standardization of routine methods used in the clinical environment. The definitive method would be impractical for use in this manner.

HDL-C

The accuracy base for HDL-C is not as well defined and complete as that for TC. A significant problem is that the lipoproteins, as a heterogeneous mixture of lipids and proteins, are not rigidly defined. As a result, significant overlap can exist in the physical properties of the major lipoprotein classes. Therefore, developing a reference system for HDL-C will require that it be precisely defined. The current operational definition of HDL-C is based on physical separation, such as ultracentrifugation or chemical precipitation.

A definitive method for HDL-C does not exist. The reference point for HDL-C measurement, as recommended by the NCEP Lipoprotein Measurement Working Group,[20] is the CDC reference method, a multi-step procedure involving ultracentrifugation, precipitation, and cholesterol analysis.[25] The method combines removal of very-low-density lipoprotein (VLDL) by a beta-quantification ultracentrifugation procedure, isolation of HDL-C by precipitation of LDL-C from the beta-quantification bottom fraction ($d = 1.006$ Kg/L) by 46 mmol/L heparin–manganese (Mn^{+2}), and cholesterol analysis of the HDL-C supernate by the NRS/CHOL cholesterol reference method. The major problems with the HDL-C reference method are that it is technically demanding, requires a large sample volume (5 mL), has low throughput, and needs an expensive ultracentrifuge, which may preclude its widespread use for routine standardization of HDL-C measurements. However, since this HDL-C method has served as the reference method for the epidemiologic and clinical investigations by the CDC and National Heart, Lung and Blood Institute (NHLBI), from which CHD risk estimations and population distributions have been derived, there is considerable justification for continuing this procedure as a national reference method.

LDL-Cholesterol

Like HDL-C, the process of establishing an accuracy target for LDL-C is complicated due to its heterogeneity and the difficulty of precisely defining the fraction of interest. The CDC has adopted as a reference procedure for LDL-C a variation of the multi-step beta-quantification procedure used by the Lipid Research Clinics,[25] which combines separation by ultracentrifugation and chemical precipitation. In the CDC procedure, heparin-manganese precipitation is performed on the $d > 1.006$ Kg/L serum fraction rather than on whole plasma. The CDC reference value for LDL-C is calculated as the difference in cholesterol between the measured HDL-C and the cholesterol recovered in the $d > 1.006$ Kg/L fraction obtained by ultracentrifugation.

TG

The reference system for triglyceride now has the two main components necessary for establishing a defined accuracy base, i.e., a definitive and a reference method. NIST has developed a definitive method for TG utilizing isotope dilution-mass spectrometry (ID-MS).[26] The definitive method is actually two ID-MS methods: one for total glycerides (defined as the sum of triglycerides, diglycerides, monoglycerides, and free glycerol) and another for triglycerides only.[26] Total glycerides are measured because this represents the analytical species that the majority of clinical laboratories measure when testing for triglycerides. In both assays a known amount of [$^{13}C_3$] tripalmitin is added to the serum sample, which is then processed and derivatized, and the abundance ratios of selected ions are determined.[26]

A reference method for TG established at CDC in 1963, based on the method of Carlson[27, 28] and the techniques of Van Handel and Zilversmit[29] and Lofland,[30] has been used as the CDC's accuracy base for standardization programs. The method is complicated, requiring extraction with silicic acid and chloroform for removal of free glycerol and other interferences, filtration to remove the silicic acid particles, hydrolysis with alcoholic potassium hydroxide, and color development by metaperiodate-arsenite-chromotropic acid reagent. The extraction procedure removes phospholipids and free glycerol, but retains a minimal amount of some monoglycerides and diglycerides. In 1993 the CDC reference method was modified to replace chloroform with methylene chloride in order to eliminate the use of chloroform in the extraction step and to eliminate the need for filtration to remove the silicic acid particles. CDC is collaborating with members of the Cholesterol Reference Method Laboratory Network to further improve the TG method by combining the hydrolysis and extraction steps of the CDC method with color development by enzymatic endpoint procedure.

The CDC uses a triolein/tripalmitin (2:1 ratio) standard to reflect the average unsaturated/saturated TG composition in human serum. A tripalmitin standard (99.5% pure) is available from NIST, but because it is insoluble in aqueous medium, it is unsuitable for enzymatic methods.

Since the definitive method and reference method for TG do not measure exactly the same analytical species, a straightforward direct comparison of the two methods is not possible. To compare the two methods one must compare a measured value from one method with an estimated result from the other. It is most appropriate to compare the NIST measured result for total glycerides to a CDC estimated result for total glycerides. The CDC estimate for total glycerides is obtained by adding the CDC reference method result, which is a measure of triglycerides plus a small amount of unremoved mono- and diglycerides, together with the CDC result for free glycerol. In order to establish the target glycerol content of serum lipid reference materials, CDC developed an isotope dilution–gas chromatography–mass spectrometry method for the analysis of serum free glycerol.[31] In a preliminary evaluation, the NIST definitive method and the CDC reference method were compared using both frozen and lyophilized serum pools. There was an average bias of +1.1% between the two methods. More extensive comparisons are planned.

Lp(a)

A lack of an adequate accuracy base has inhibited standardization of Lp(a) assays and contributed to poor performance by laboratories.[32, 33] Significant inter-laboratory variation was observed with three different commercial methods for Lp(a), with coefficients of variation ranging from 21% for an ELISA kit to 30% for a radioimmunoassay kit. This large variation is due to the varied composition and specificity of antibodies and calibrators used to measure Lp(a) and the lack of common standards and poor assay precision. Large inter-assay variation in Lp(a) measurements may confound results in clinical studies attempting to show an association of Lp(a) with the risk of heart disease because of an inability to correctly classify subjects on the basis of their Lp(a) results.

To provide useful Lp(a) measurements, a major effort is needed to develop and validate an accuracy base for standardizing Lp(a) assays. Towards this goal, the International Federation for Clinical Chemistry (IFCC) has formed a Working Group for the Standardization of Lp(a) Assays. The IFCC Working Group has initiated a project to select a suitable Lp(a) secondary reference material to normalize and improve comparability of Lp(a) values between different measurement systems. Phase I of the project is underway and consists of identifying and testing suitable candidate Lp(a) secondary materials for imprecision, linearity, parallelism and their ability to provide between assay harmonization of Lp(a) measurements.

Apo A-I and B

Ideally, gravimetrically weighed pure apolipoproteins should be used as primary standards in apolipoprotein analysis. However, purified apolipoprotein may not be suitable for some immunological techniques, as the physical and chemical properties of purified apo B do not lend themselves to immunochemical analysis. Purified apo A-I can be used as a primary standard in some immunochemical techniques, and an ultracentrifugally prepared LDL fraction ($d = 1.030$–1.050 Kg/L) that excludes intermediate-density lipoprotein or lipoprotein(a) is currently the best choice as a surrogate primary standard for apo B. A purified apo AI has been developed by the European Bureau of Reference for use as a primary standard.[34] Reference methods for the immunochemical analysis of apo AI and B have not been universally accepted in the scientific community. Also, determination of the protein content of LDL presents significant problems[35] which are still under investigation.

The preferred approach to establishing an accuracy base is to use an accepted and well-documented reference method, or definitive method with primary standards, to set apolipoprotein mass units on a secondary reference material (SRM) in a suitable matrix base. These SRMs can then be used to set apolipoprotein mass units on calibration materials used by manufacturers of apolipoprotein measurement kits. This process is not possible at present because there is no universally accepted reference method for analysis of apo A-I or B.[36]

Reference and definitive methods for proteins depend on highly accurate protein determinations of primary standards. CDC has investigated and established an enzymatic digestion, liquid chromatography, isotope dilution–mass spectrometry method to assign mass values to an apo AI primary standard for use as a model for apolipoprotein primary standards.[37]

The IFCC Committee on Apolipoproteins, together with manufacturers of apolipoprotein diagnostic kits, began a collaborative program in 1988 to produce and evaluate SRMs for standardizing apolipoprotein measurements. In early 1989, more than 20 manufacturers and several reference laboratories evaluated 26 candidate SRMs and measured 10 frozen sera with assigned values for apo A-I and B. A lyophilized serum for apo A-I and a liquid stabilized serum for apo B were selected as reference materials on the basis of homogeneity, stability, reproducibility, and linearity upon dilution. The World Health Organization (WHO) has accepted these two serum matrix-based materials as reference reagents: SP1-01, a lyophilized material for apo A-I, and SP3-07, a stabilized liquid preparation for apo B. Mass units have been assigned using standardized immunoassay techniques and purified apo A-I and LDL (d = 1.030–1.050 Kg/L) as primary calibrators.[38, 39]

NATIONAL PERFORMANCE CRITERIA

The role of TC, HDL-C, LDL-C, and TG in the assessment of CHD risk has accentuated the need for more precise and accurate laboratory measurements.[14, 40] In order to properly assess the quality of analytical performance in individual laboratories, meaningful criteria to evaluate the reproducibility of measurements and the deviation from a target value are needed. CDC was the first organization to establish specific performance criteria for TC, TG, and HDL-C analysis, which were designed to improve the performance of specialized lipid laboratories participating in the CDC-NHLBI Lipid Standardization Program.[41]

In 1988, the NCEP Laboratory Standardization Panel recommended goals for both bias and precision of TC measurement.[15] Specifically, the panel recommended that, as a national goal, clinical laboratories should achieve a bias of ± 3% of the CDC reference method and an overall precision consistent with a coefficient of variation (CV) of 3% or less.[15] For a single analysis, the allowable total error (imprecision plus bias) would be ± 8.9% using L = 0.05 in a two-tailed test.[42] This was one of the most important recommendations from the Laboratory Standardization Panel in that it established for the first time specific national performance criteria by which clinical laboratories can judge the reliability of cholesterol assays.

Similarly in 1995, the NCEP Working Group on Lipoprotein Measurement issued national performance criteria for TG,[19] HDL-C,[20] and LDL-C.[21] The NCEP performance goals for HDL-C, LDL-C, and TG were presented in terms of allowable total error; in other words, method bias and method precision must satisfy the goals for total error.

Presented in Table 12-2 are the performance criteria for specialized lipid laboratories participating in the CDC-NHLBI Lipid Standardization Program, and the NCEP performance goals for clinical laboratories. In addition, under the Clinical Laboratory Improvement Amendments (CLIA) of 1988, the federal government has established national proficiency testing criteria for a large number of clinical analytes. The CLIA '88 evaluation criteria (total error) for TC, TG, and HDL-C are also presented in Table 12-2. Nationally accepted performance criteria for measurement of apolipoproteins by routine laboratories have not been established to date.

STANDARDIZATION ISSUES

When attempting to standardize laboratory measurements, one must consider factors that contribute to inaccuracy in the measurement process and affect the reliability of test results. Traditionally, major emphasis has been on analytical factors, i.e., factors that compromise accuracy during measurement. However, as efforts to control analytical imprecision and inaccuracy progress, concern has increased significantly about the effect on test results of preanalytical sources of variation, i.e., factors that operate before, during, and after blood collection and storage.[43] It is important, therefore, to carefully consider both preanalytical sources of variation and laboratory sources of error.

Table 12–2 ✧ National Performance Criteria for Lipid and Lipoprotein Measurement [a]

Analyte	CDC Standardization Criteria			NCEP Performance Criteria[b]			CLIA Evaluation Criteria[c]
	Concentration Range	Bias	Imprecision	Bias	Imprecision	Total Error	Total Error
Low TC	< 50 mg/dL (1.29 mmol/L) 50-99.9 mg/dL (1.29-2.58 mmol/L)	≤ 0.04 RV[d] ≤ 0.03 RV	SD[e] ≤ 0.04 RV SD ≤ 0.03 RV				
TC	100–149 mg/dL (2.59-3.85 mmol/L) ≥ 150 mg/dL (3.88 mmol/L	≤ 0.03 RV ≤ 0.03 RV	SD ≤ 4.0 mg/dL (0.10 mmol/L) CV[f] ≤ 3.0%	≤ 3% RV	CV ≤ 3%	≤ 9%	± 10%
TG (mmol/L)	0.00-0.99 1.00-1.99 2.00-2.49 ≥ 2.50	≤ 0.10 ≤ 0.11 ≤ 0.12 0.05 RV	SD ≤ 0.08 SD ≤ 0.09 SD ≤ 0.11 CV ≤ 5.0%	≤ 5% RV	CV ≤ 5%	≤ 15%	± 25%
HDL-C	< 40 mg/dL (1.03 mmol/L) ≥ 40 mg/dL (1.03 mmol/L)	≤ 0.08 RV ≤ 0.08 RV	SD ≤ 2.0 mg/dL (0.052 mmol/L) SD ≤ 0.06 RV	≤ 10% RV 1998: ≤ 5% RV	SD ≤ 2.5 at < 42 mg/dL. CV ≤ 6% at ≥ 42 mg/dL 1998: SD ≤ 1.7 at < 42 mg/dL (1.09 mmol/L) CV ≤ 4% at ≥ 42 mg/dL. (1.09 mmol/L)	≤ 23% 1998: ≤ 13%	± 30%
LDL-C				≤ 4% RV	CV ≤ 4%	≤ 12%	

[a]TC = Total Cholesterol, TG = Triglyceride, HDL-C = High-Density Lipoprotein Cholesterol, LDL-C = Low-Density Lipoprotein Cholesterol.
To convert TG values from mmol/L to mg/dL, divide by 0.0113.
[b]Performance criteria for TC recommended by the NCEP Laboratory Standardization Panel in: Clin Chem 1988;34:193-201. Performance criteria for TG recommended by the NCEP Lipoprotein Working Group in: Clin Chem 1995:41:1321-1426. Performance criteria for HDL-C recommended by the NCEP Lipoprotein Working Group in: Clin Chem 1995:41:1427-33. Performance criteria for LDL-C recommended by the NCEP Lipoprotein Working Group in: Clin Chem 1995:41:1414-20.
[c]Federal Register, February 28, 1992.
[d]RV = reference value assigned by CDC reference methods.
[e]SD = standard deviation.
[f]CV = coefficient of variation.

Preanalytical Consideration

Physicians need to understand and control, as much as possible, factors that can transiently alter a patient's usual lipid and lipoprotein concentrations.[44] Preanalytical factors include behavioral factors, the clinical state of the patient, patient preparation, and the collection, handling, storage, and shipment of patient samples.[43] Preanalytical factors are covered in detail in Chapter 4; hence, only a brief overview is given here.

Considerable variation in intra-individual biological variation has been reported in the literature. In order to obtain the best estimates of the average intra-individual biological variability (expressed as CV_b) in the concentrations in serum of TC, TG, HDL-C, and LDL-C, results from 30 studies published from 1970 to 1992 were evaluated by meta-analysis.[45]

A method based on relative range was developed to estimate the effect of biological variation on the total variation of the mean serum TC result.[44] This method can serve as a guide for determining the number of specimens required from an individual to minimize the effect of biological variation on the individual's TC result.[44] Using the meta-analysis results for CV_b and the NCEP performance goals, this method has been extended to estimate relative range goals for TG, HDL-C, and LDL-C.[46] The in-depth discussion of preanalytical variation presented in Chapter 4 includes detailed recommendations issued in 1990 by the NCEP Laboratory Standardization Panel.[42] The NCEP report does not cover apolipoproteins specifically, and although no thorough temporal studies on variation in apo AI or apo B have been conducted, similar precautions should be taken to minimize preanalytical variation in apolipoprotein measurements.[47]

Matrix Effects of Reference Materials

The traditional approach for standardization has been to use reference materials and calibrators that have been value-assigned by the reference or definitive methods. This approach is based on the assumption that reference materials mimic fresh patient specimens when assayed. However, recent studies have indicated that significant discrepancies in the measurement of cholesterol exist when some analytical systems are compared to the reference method using lyophilized and frozen processed serum materials.[48-56] The processed materials may undergo changes that affect their assay characteristics. The use of unprocessed fresh-frozen serum may alleviate the problems associated with matrix interactions, but even freezing appears to affect some analytical methods.[57] Matrix effects complicate standardization because different methods may produce different results for the same reference material and may yield erroneous conclusions about the performance of an analytical system. In addition to the matrix interactions affecting the cholesterol analysis, any changes in the specimen that affect the separation step may also give rise to matrix effects in the measurement of lipoproteins, including HDL-C. Efforts have been made to improve performance of materials for assessing HDL-C measurement.[58] Matrix effects in the measurement of TG have also been reported.[59]

Few guidelines exist which provide formulation specifications for preparing commutable lipid and lipoprotein reference materials. Published guidelines were developed before the widespread use of enzymatic assays and thus do not specifically address the problems of modern cholesterol methods.[60-63] An NCCLS Subcommittee on Cholesterol Reference Material Specifications has developed written guidelines for preparing frozen human serum pools which are commutable across different cholesterol test systems permitting proper calibration, accuracy assessment, and traceability of field methods to the NRS/CHOL. The guideline provides specifications for collecting and processing raw materials to manufacture frozen serum pools and for quality assurance of the final product. In preparing serum pools, it is generally assumed that pooling of individual donor units does not contribute significantly to matrix effects in the final product. To evaluate the scientific basis of the guideline and also evaluate the pooling effect, NCCLS had two cholesterol pools prepared according to the written specifications. Two frozen serum pools using a large number of selected individual donor units of "off-the-clot" serum were prepared and characterized. The performance of the pools was assessed in terms of the degree of commutability (true response versus predicted response) relative to the individual sera which comprise the pools. The experiment was statistically designed to detect a 2% matrix bias between the predicted and true response for each instrument system evaluated. All of the instrument systems evaluated had biases less than 2%, with most systems having biases less than 1.5%. Complete results from this study are being prepared for publication.

Until commutable materials free of matrix effects are routinely available, an interim approach that involves implementation of the NCEP Laboratory Standardization Panel's recommendations is to directly compare an analytical system with the cholesterol reference method through the use of split fresh patient specimens. Establishing traceability by comparing split fresh patient specimens is valid for both manufacturers of diagnostic systems and for clinical laboratories seeking to verify the performance of a cholesterol method. Since the same type of matrix limitations exist for lipoproteins and TG, the cholesterol experience is a good model for overall standardization.

Using purified apo A-I is usually acceptable, but apo B will not work well as a primary standard in all immunological methods of analysis. Freshly collected serum is the specimen of choice, but practical considerations of distribution and stability of the diagnostic products preclude using fresh materials. Lyophilized serum-based reference materials with assigned concentrations of apo A-I seem to work well in most immunological methods.[64] However, when certain methods, including radial immunodiffusion and immunoturbidimetry, are used, systematic differences in apo B measurements occur.[39, 65] Fresh-frozen serum seems to perform well in most immunological methods, if the protein epitope bound by the antibody is not sensitive to freeze/thaw cycles. Stabilized liquid preparations of whole serum appear to work satisfactorily for apo B analysis in most immunological techniques.[39, 65]

There are inherent problems in maintaining stability of large quantities of frozen or stabilized liquid apolipoprotein reference materials.[65] For a given method, reagent system, or combination of instrument system and reagents, the primary responsibility for establishing and maintaining an accuracy base rests with the manufacturer, which should calibrate each lot of secondary calibrators to the appropriate WHO-IFCC Reference Reagents (SP1-01 for apo A-I and SP3-07 for apo B).

TG Measurement and Free Glycerol

The TG measurement poses a unique matrix-effect type of problem resulting from the contribution of free glycerol. The question of blanking TG analyses for free glycerol has been debated.[66–68] A major justification for accurate TG measurements is its inclusion in the Friedewald equation used to estimate LDL-C.[8] Thus, not correcting for free glycerol may result in erroneous estimation of LDL-C. In a study of patients at a university hospital, the need for free glycerol blanking was evaluated, and, except in those situations in which abnormally increased glycerol is expected, no significant consequences resulted for the average individual when a glycerol blank was not used.[67] Serum glycerol blanking does, however, become extremely important when attempting to standardize TG measurements. Glycerol content in commercially prepared materials, such as survey samples, controls, and calibrators, can be quite variable, depending on the matrix of the source material and the fortification to increase lipid concentrations.[58, 59] This may make the standardization of TG measurements across the nation's clinical laboratories very difficult and the assessment of the accuracy of results impossible. It therefore becomes very important that laboratories evaluate each lot of materials for free glycerol.

Comparison of glycerol concentrations for several reference serum pools determined by using different enzymatic kits sometimes produced substantially different results.[31] Thus, potential matrix effects with different enzymatic free glycerol assays must also be considered. However, all the evaluated methods provided similar results when pure aqueous standards were tested and when standard addition studies were conducted.[31]

In addition to the issue of free glycerol blanking, enzymatic methods to determine TG may also be affected by the turbidity of the specimen.[69] In a recent study, effects of specimen turbidity and glycerol blanking on nine enzymatic TG methods were compared.[70] The results showed variability among the methods ranging from 6.2% to –15.6%.[70] It was found that methods using a bichromatic blank better minimized the interference from turbidity than did a reagent or serum blank, and therefore a bichromatic glycerol-blanked method was recommended to obtain a more accurate TG result for turbid specimens.[70]

Standardization of LDL-C

Although the primary decision factor for patient follow-up and treatment is now based on LDL-C, a routine direct assay for LDL-C measurement has not been available until just recently.[71] As a result, most laboratories have been determining LDL-C by an indirect estimation reported by Friedewald in 1972.[8] LDL-C is estimated from the formula:

$$LDL\text{-}C = TC - HDL\text{-}C - TG/5 \quad \text{(in mg/dL)}$$

Because TC, HDL-C, and TG are directly measured values, the calculated LDL-C is subject to independent errors in each of the three measurements. Since considerable emphasis has been placed on standardizing TC, HDL-C, and TG measurements, it generally has been assumed that LDL-C values are standardized when TC, HDL-C, and TG values are standardized. However, as the NCEP guidelines for measurement performance were developed, it became clear that even if TC, HDL-C, and TG measurements were all within the limits of acceptable performance, it did not guarantee that LDL-C measurements were within performance limits. Thus, it seems that the direct LDL-C method would have considerable advantage over the calculation method for

LDL-C since it is necessary to only insure the accuracy of one measurement rather than three. Various studies have now shown that the direct LDL-C measurements have a high correlation with the ultracentrifugation reference method.[72]

However, assessing the accuracy of the direct LDL-C method or standardizing it using the conventional approach is not possible because of its documented un-reliability with frozen specimens.[72, 73] This also excludes its use in virtually all current interventional and epidemiologic studies of cardiovascular disease. Once again, as a result of matrix effects between method and materials, the only reliable approach to assessing performance and establishing traceability is by fresh sample split comparisons with the reference method. The Cholesterol Reference Method Laboratory Network is investigating ways to provide access to the beta-quantification method for this purpose.

RESOURCES AVAILABLE FOR STANDARDIZATION

The NCEP's Laboratory Standardization Panel stated that to ensure reliable cholesterol results, the measurement of cholesterol in all clinical laboratories must be traceable to a national accuracy base such as the NRS/CHOL.[11] Achieving traceability to the NRS/CHOL or the accuracy bases for TG, the lipoproteins, and the apolipoproteins will require a unified national effort involving manufacturers, government agencies, and the clinical professions. The programs and resources available to assist clinical laboratories in standardizing the measurement of lipids and lipoproteins are summarized below.

CDC-NHLBI Lipid Standardization Program

Since 1957, the CDC in collaboration with the NHLBI has been developing, evaluating, and offering the resources needed to standardize the analytical measurement of TC, HDL-C, and TG. These standardization resources were developed because many investigators interested in the relationship between serum lipid concentrations and cardiovascular disease were concerned about the reliability of lipid analyses within laboratories and the comparability of results among laboratories. Through standardization programs, the CDC has offered these resources nationally and internationally to:[41]

1. epidemiologic laboratories, to ensure comparability of population studies and clinical trials

2. lipid methodology research laboratories, to help in the development of accurate methods

3. reference laboratories, to provide targets for proficiency testing programs

4. reference laboratories of manufacturers of diagnostic products, through which standardization assistance can be provided to all clinical laboratories.

CDC annually standardizes laboratories that support over 100 studies funded by the National Institutes of Health that investigate CHD and other related factors, including diabetes, nutrition, genetics, and health issues of women and minorities.

The CDC-NHLBI Lipid Standardization Program has three major phases. Part I is the preliminary evaluation phase, in which CDC reference materials and fresh patient specimens are analyzed concurrently. During this phase, a split-sample comparison with a laboratory participating in the Cholesterol Reference Method Laboratory Network is made to verify comparable performance of CDC materials versus patient samples when the participant's method is used. If analytical criteria are met by the participant and significant matrix effects on CDC pools are not seen, performance is assumed to be sufficient to ensure the quality of the relationship determined in the participant's laboratory between CDC's reference values and the participant's values. Part II is the principal phase in standardization and confirms the level of accuracy and precision found in Part I as well as the laboratory's ability to achieve and maintain acceptable performance. To ensure representative performance on the part of the analyst, the CDC samples are provided as unknowns to the participant. Part III monitors the ability of a participant laboratory to maintain acceptable performance for 12 months or longer. In this phase, CDC reference materials are distributed at quarterly intervals.

Criteria for acceptable performance in the CDC program were discussed earlier and summarized in Table 12–2. CDC standardization performance evaluations of individual laboratory results are based on fixed limits combined with target values established by the CDC reference methods. In this way, standardization permits evaluation of all components of method error.

Recently CDC has taken steps to provide standardization service for laboratories that determine LDL-C by beta-quantification. CDC has evaluated the applicability of frozen reference serum for standardizing LDL-C measurements.[74] Fresh serum was collected from 24 donors and analyzed for LDL-C by the beta-quantification method (LDL-C = bottom fraction – HDL-C). Aliquots were stored frozen at –60° C and re-analyzed at intervals for at least one year. The mean percentage of change in LDL-C upon freezing was –1.6%. In 19 of 24 samples the change was less than 2% and showed increasing negative change with increasing VLDL-C. Results from this study show that beta-quantification methods and other methods which are not sensitive to sample freezing can be standardized using frozen reference serum selected for reduced VLDL-C concentration.

Following the stability studies using frozen serum, a round robin analysis of four frozen reference sera value-assigned by the CDC beta-quantification method was carried out by 28 laboratories in the CDC-NHLBI Lipid Standardization Program.[75] The participants analyzed the samples in a single run and reported duplicate results for bottom fraction and HDL-C. Using results from 28 laboratories, the mean absolute bias for all samples was 5.3%±6.1. In general, the bias in the LDL-C result was directly related to the bias in the bottom fraction result. This brief study indicates that standardization of beta-quantification will require standardization of the bottom fractions.

For more information, contact the Special Activities Branch, Division of Environmental Health Laboratory Sciences, Centers for Disease Control and Prevention, 4770 Buford Highway, NE (F25), Atlanta, GA 30341-3724, Telephone 770-488-4126, Fax 770-488-4192.

THE CHOLESTEROL REFERENCE METHOD LABORATORY NETWORK

The NCEP's medical decision points for identifying individuals who have increased risk of CHD were derived from population studies and clinical trials that were standardized by CDC. To implement a national intervention and prevention strategy based on these uniform decision points requires that all cholesterol, HDL-C, LDL-C, and TG measurements be traceable to the CDC reference methods. The problems associated with matrix effects on the accuracy of cholesterol and HDL-C[76] measurement were briefly discussed in this chapter and are discussed in more detail in Chapter 11.

Matrix effects preclude the universal use of reference materials for establishing a chain of traceability from the field methods to the reference methods. Therefore, the recommended approach to assess how well a laboratory method correlates with the accuracy base is to directly compare diagnostic methods to the reference methods using fresh patient specimens.[15] Unfortunately, the sheer number of laboratories in the United States makes standardization using fresh patient comparisons a nearly impossible task. In contrast, the number of manufacturers that provide the diagnostic methods for measuring cholesterol, HDL-C, TG, and LDL-C is relatively small. Working with manufacturers of diagnostic methods to assist them in calibration is the most efficient way to establish traceability and to improve the measurement of these analytes in clinical laboratories. Therefore, CDC focused its efforts toward the manufacturers and developed the Cholesterol Reference Method Laboratory Network. The Cholesterol Reference Method Laboratory Network was established to assist manufacturers in correctly calibrating their measurement systems and establishing traceability to the NRS/CHOL. It was the first network of its kind to use fresh sample comparisons as the basis of accuracy transfer, and therefore serves as a model for other analytical systems that require fresh sample comparisons to establish traceability to an accuracy base.[77]

The Network consists of six U.S. Network laboratories (listed in Table 12–3) and six international laboratories (listed in Table 12–4). The Network laboratories perform the Abell-Kendall cholesterol reference method exactly as it is performed at CDC and are standardized to CDC through participation in the CDC-NHLBI Lipid Standardization Program. The international laboratories participating in the Network serve primarily as reference centers for their individual country and offer varying types of programs depending on the needs of the individual country. The international laboratories are also capable of providing certification services to manufacturers and clinical laboratories.

Since a reference system equivalent to the NRS/CHOL does not exist for HDL-C, the NCEP Lipoprotein Measurement Working Group has recommended the method used at CDC as the accepted accuracy base for HDL-C.[20] Although the method can be transferred, it is too labor-intensive and expensive to utilize in the Network for providing reference analyses for fresh sample comparisons. For practical reasons, at this time the Network laboratories have chosen to utilize a "designated comparison method" (titled based on NCCLS nomenclature)[78] for establishing traceability to the CDC reference method for HDL-C. The designated comparison method employs direct precipitation of the apo-B-containing lipoproteins with dextran sulfate of 50 kDa with magnesium, followed by determination using the Abell-Kendall reference method for cholesterol.[79, 80] Only samples with TG concentrations < 200 mg/dL (1.26 mmol/L) can be used in this protocol.

The performance of both methods is monitored monthly in each Network laboratory. These monthly surveys involve either the analysis of CDC serum reference pools or fresh-frozen, single-donor samples. For cholesterol, the Network laboratories must maintain a CV of less than 2% and a bias to CDC of less than 1%. Over the

---

Table 12–3 ◆ U.S. Laboratories Participating in the Cholesterol Reference Method Laboratory Network

---

State Laboratory of Hygiene
University of Wisconsin
Center for Health Sciences
465 Henry Mall
Madison, WI 53706
David Hassemer, M.S.
hassemer@clia.slh.wisc.edu
Phone 608-833-1770 (Ext. 102)
Fax 608-833-2803

Washington University School of Medicine
Core Laboratory for Clinical Studies
Box 8046
660 S. Euclid Avenue
St. Louis, MO 63110
Thomas G. Cole, Ph.D.
thom@imgate.wustl.edu
Phone 314-362-3516
Fax 314-362-4782

Northwest Lipid Research Laboratories
Core Laboratory
2121 N. 35th Street
Seattle, WA 98103
Santica Marcovina, Ph.D.
smm@u.washington.edu
Phone 206-685-3331
Fax 206-685-3279

**Jean Mayer USDA Human Nutrition
Research Center on Aging at
Tufts University**
711 Washington Street, Room 501
Boston, MA 02111
Judith R. McNamara, M.T. (ASCP)
mcnamara_li@hnrc.tufts.edu
Phone 617-556-3104
Fax 617-556-3103

Wadsworth Center for Laboratories and Research
New York State Department of Health
Empire State Plaza
Albany, NY 12201
Robert Rej, Ph.D.
bobrej@wadsworth.org
Phone 518-473-0117
Fax 518-473-2900

Pacific Biometrics Research Foundation
1100 Eastlake Avenue East
Seattle, WA 98109
Elizabeth Teng Leary, Ph.D.
102722.1040@compuserve.com
Phone 206-233-9151 Ext. 208
Fax 206-233-0198

---

period of one year, the within-lab CV ranged from 0.5% to 1.1%, with an average of 0.8%.[81] During the same period, the average bias of Network laboratories ranged from –0.8% to 0.4%, with an overall average of –0.3%.[81]

For HDL-C, the Network laboratories must maintain a bias versus the CDC reference method of ±5% and a CV of ≤ 3% at concentrations > 42 mg/dL (1.09 mmol/L); and a bias versus the CDC reference method of ± 2 mg/dL (0.05 mmol/L) and a standard deviation (SD) of ≤ 1.7 mg/dL (0.04 mmol/L) at concentrations ≤ 42 mg/dL (1.09 mmol/L). Over the period of one year, the within-laboratory CV ranged from 0 to 2.8%, with an average of 0.9% at concentrations > 42 mg/dL (1.09 mmol/L), and the within-laboratory SD ranged from 0 to 2.3 mg/dL (0.059 mmol/L) with an average of 0.4 mg/dL (0.01 mmol/L) at concentrations < 42 mg/dL (1.09 mmol/L). During the same period of time, the average bias versus the CDC reference method ranged from –4.7 to 3.6 %, with and overall average of ± 0.4 % at concentrations > 42 mg/dL (1.09 mmol/L), and the average bias versus the CDC reference method ranged from –3.1 to 6.1 mg/dL (–0.8 to 0.16 mmol/L) with an overall bias of –0.1 mg/dL (–0.003 mmol/L) at concentrations < 42 mg/dL (1.09 mmol/L).

Table 12–4 ❖ International Laboratories Participating in the Cholesterol Reference Method Laboratory Network

Rotterdam University Hospital
"Dijkzigt"
Department of Clinical Chemistry
Lipid Reference Laboratory
3015 GD Rotterdam
The Netherlands
Christa M. Boersma-Cobbaert, Ph.D.
boersma@ckcl.azr.nl
Phone 31-10-4633493
Fax 31-10-4367894

Canadian Reference Laboratory (1996) Ltd.
307-2083 Alma Street
Vancouver
British Columbia V6R 4N6
Canada
David W. Seccombe, M.D., Ph.D.
73361.1047@compuserve.com
seccombe@unixg.ubc.ca
Phone 604-222-1879
Fax 604-222-0134

Osaka Medical Center for Cancer and Cardiovascular Diseases
Department of Epidemiology and
Mass Examination for CVD
3 Nakamichi 1-chome
Higashinari-ku
Osaka 537 Japan
Masakazu Nakamura, Ph.D.
xnakamur@iph.pref.osaka.jp
Minoru Iida, M.D.
Phone 81-6-972-1181 Ext. 2211
Fax 81-6-972-7749

H.S. Raffaele
Laboratorio Analisi Cliniche
Via Olgettina 60
20132 Milano
Italy
Ferruccio Ceriotti, M.D.
ceriotf@rsisi.hsr.it
Phone 39-2-2643-2315 (or 2313)
Fax 39-2-2643-2640

Undergoing Standardization:

Institute of Biochemistry
Department of Pathological Biochemistry
Glasgow Royal Infirmary
4th Floor Alexandra Parade
Glasgow G31 2ER
Great Britain
Chris J. Packard, Ph.D.
Phone 44-141-552-3535
Fax 44-141-553-2558

Instituto Nacional de Saúde Dr. Ricardo Jorge
Av. Padre Cruz
1699 Lisboa
Portugal
Maria do Carmo Martins, Ph.D.
INSRJ@mail.telepac.pt (note attn: Dr. Martins)
Phone 351-1-757-7070
Fax 351-1-759-0441

The strategy for transferring the accuracy base for cholesterol and HDL-C to manufacturers and clinical laboratories via the Cholesterol Reference Method Laboratory Network is shown in Figure 11–1.

Certification of Instrument Systems, Reagents, and Reference Materials

Manufacturers of instruments and reference materials are key to achieving standardization of cholesterol and HDL-C measurements in clinical laboratories. Manufacturers should perform comparison analyses with the accuracy base using fresh patient specimens in order to document the performance of their own complete instrument systems,

Figure 12–1 ❖ Strategy for Transferring the Cholesterol Accuracy Base to Manufacturers and Clinical Laboratories*

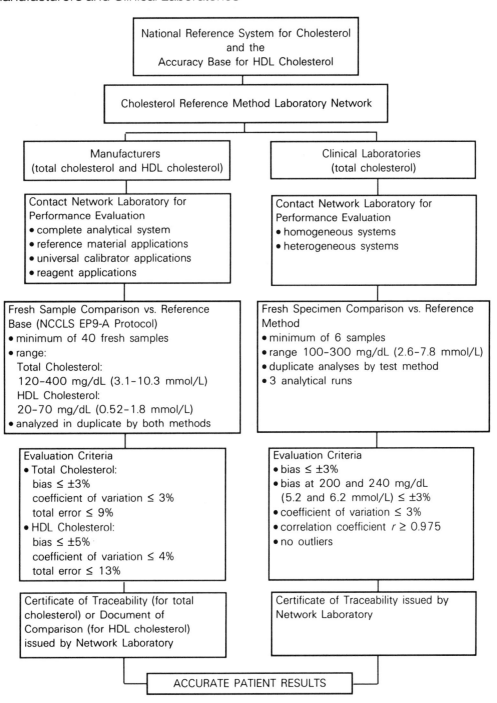

reagent applications on other instrument systems, reference materials, and calibrators. To document performance and traceability to the accuracy bases, the Network has adopted a methods evaluation protocol developed by NCCLS entitled "Method Comparison and Bias Estimation Using Patient Samples."[82] The comparison protocol requires analyzing a minimum of 40 patient specimens throughout the range of interest, in duplicate by each method. For cholesterol, once evaluation of the test method has been completed and certification criteria have been met, a dated Certificate of Traceability is issued to the manufacturer stating that the analytical system, reference material, or reagent application was traceable to the NRS/CHOL under the conditions tested. This Certificate of Traceability records the bias, CV, and total error for the analytical system.

The program for HDL-C is different in one respect from the certification program for total cholesterol. It has been shown through mathematical simulations that the most influential factor in the ability to determine the performance of an analytical system by comparison with a reference laboratory is the bias the reference laboratory has to the true accuracy base.[83] While the bias of the Network laboratories to CDC for HDL- C using the designated comparison method is considered excellent, it is not yet at the level needed to judge product performance as being acceptable or unacceptable by NCEP criteria. Instead, for HDL-C a dated Document of Comparison is issued to the manufacturer stating that the analytical system, reference material, or reagent application has been evaluated in comparison to the accuracy base. This Document of Comparison records the bias, CV, and total error for the analytical system.

Manufacturers are encouraged to reevaluate their systems whenever a new reagent or calibrator lot is prepared or at a minimum of every two years. The Network maintains two lists on the World Wide Web. The first is a list of analytical systems, reagents, and calibrators that have met the NCEP criteria for total cholesterol during the last two years. The second is a list of all analytical systems, reagents, and calibrators that have undergone evaluation for HDLC during the last two years. This list is published on the World Wide Web site of the American Association for Clinical Chemistry at http:\www.aacc.org\standards\index.html.

For more information about how to participate in the manufacturer programs, contact any one of the Network laboratories listed in Tables 12–3 and 12–4 or contact the Special Activities Branch, Centers for Disease Control and Prevention, 4770 Buford Highway NE, Atlanta, GA 30341-3724, Telephone 770-488-4126.

Certification of Clinical Laboratories

The Network also has a cholesterol certification program for clinical laboratories. Clinical laboratories will use either of two types of analytical systems, homogeneous or heterogeneous. In a homogeneous analytical system, the instrument, reagent, and calibrator are supplied by a single manufacturer, whereas in a heterogeneous system, each may come from different sources. For laboratories using a homogeneous system, documentation of performance and traceability to the reference method can be obtained from the manufacturer. However, the manufacturer's demonstration of traceability to the NRS/CHOL in itself does not guarantee accuracy in the hands of every eventual user. For this reason, it is recommended that laboratories using certified systems verify their system's performance by performing a direct comparison with a Network laboratory using fresh patient specimens. Laboratories using heterogeneous analytical systems must assume primary responsibility for documenting performance and establishing traceability to the NRS/CHOL. In many cases, the test system used by a laboratory will be unique to that laboratory, thus requiring individual documentation of accuracy.

For practical reasons, certification of a laboratory's traceability to the NRS/CHOL is not as extensive as that required for a manufacturer. However, laboratory certification is still based on a direct comparison with the reference method using fresh patient specimens. The current protocol requires that the laboratory analyze at least six patient specimens in duplicate in each of three runs. The TC values should cover a range that includes the NCEP recommended cholesterol decision points of 200 and 240 mg/dL (5.18 and 6.22 mmol/L).[2] Acceptable performance, indicating traceability to the NRS/CHOL, is documented by a certificate which is valid for 6 months from the date of comparison.[84]

CDC has implemented a Voice Information System to provide information about the clinical laboratory certification program. This system provides a general explanation of the Network and information about how clinical laboratories can verify accuracy in cholesterol testing. It also offers physicians a regional listing of labs that have met the national performance goals to which they can send their patients' samples. Listed are clinical laboratories that have successfully participated in the certification program within the last 12 months and the dates they received a Certificate of Traceability.

For more information about how to participate in the clinical laboratory cholesterol certification program, contact any one of the Network laboratories listed in Tables 12–3 and 12–4 or telephone the CDC Voice Information System at 404-332-2592. The Network currently has no specific HDL-C evaluation program for clinical laboratories.

TG

For reasons similar to those for the HDL-C method, it is impractical to use the CDC's TG reference method to provide TG reference services in the Network. The CDC and the Canadian Reference Laboratory, the Washington University School of Medicine, the Wadsworth Center for Laboratories & Research, and H. S. Raffaele are collaborating to modify the reference method by combining the extraction and hydrolysis steps of the current CDC reference method with an enzymatic endpoint method for determining TG. If successful, this method will have the advantages of ease in transfer and operation.

Apolipoprotein Standardization Programs

In 1981 the CDC formed an apolipoprotein working group to standardize apolipoprotein measurements. In 1983 a large pool of lyophilized human serum (CDC-1883) was prepared and used in several international surveys to determine the sources of variability in apolipoprotein measurements as well as the utility of this lyophilized material as a reference material for apolipoprotein measurement.[85–87] In 1985 a group of expert laboratories measured CDC-1883 serum using their own analytical techniques and calibrators. Preliminary-consensus mass units for apo A-I and B were assigned to CDC-1883. The accelerated thermal stability and temporal stability over 5 years have shown that this material is suitable as a stable point of reference for apo AI and B measurement. However, CDC-1883 demonstrates a matrix bias when used in certain immunological techniques to measure apo B. CDC-1883 has a labeled value of 124 mg/dL for apo A-I and is traceable to the WHO-IFCC Reference Reagent for apo A-I (SP1-01).

WHO and IFCC appointed CDC to be the repository for the WHO-IFCC International Reference Reagents for apo A-I (SP1-01) and apo B (SP3-07). WHO and IFCC appointed Dr. S. Marcovina, former Chair, IFCC Apolipoprotein Working Group, to conduct the standardization and distribution program for manufacturers using an IFCC calibration protocol. This protocol covers dose-response linearity and parallelism, intercept equality of the reference materials, as well as confirmation procedures using fresh serum. WHO-IFCC International Reference Reagents are available to manufacturers of reagents and/or instrumentation for apo AI and apo B measurements, to assign target values to calibrator and quality control materials, and to evaluate new reagents and instrument performance. Additionally, the reference preparations are available to international reference laboratories that are responsible for monitoring apo AI and apo B standardization within their countries. For clinical laboratories, the Northwest Lipid Research Laboratories offer three frozen serum pools with assigned values for apo A-I and B (traceable to the WHO-IFCC Reference Reagents) for calibration or confirmation of accuracy of their calibrators.

For more information, contact Dr. S. Marcovina, Northwest Lipid Research Laboratories, University of Washington, 2121 N. 35th Street, Seattle, WA 98103, Telephone (206) 685-3331.

The Subcommittee on Apolipoproteins of the NCCLS has prepared a proposed guideline for apolipoprotein assays (I/LA 15-P). For information contact: NCCLS, Wayne, PA 19087-1898, Telephone 610-688-0100, Fax 610-688-0700.

NATIONAL PROFICIENCY SURVEYS

The Clinical Laboratory Improvement Amendments (CLIA) passed by Congress in 1988 established standards designed to improve the quality of clinical laboratory testing in U.S. laboratories that conduct testing on human specimens for health assessment or for the diagnosis, prevention, or treatment of disease. CLIA '88 mandates proficiency testing as a means to externally evaluate the quality of a laboratory's performance. Each participating laboratory is challenged in three testing events annually. In each testing event, five unknown samples for each analyte or test are provided. Those proficiency testing programs that have been approved in 1997 by the Health Care Financing Administration are listed in Table 12-5.

All of the programs offer surveys that include TC, TG, and HDL-C. However, only Pacific Biometrics Research Foundation, Solomon Park Research Laboratories, and the New York State Health Department offer programs that use fresh or frozen human serum pools, thus eliminating matrix effects inherent in processed materials. This permits assessment of testing accuracy by comparison of survey results to a reference or definitive method target value. Since all of the other programs use processed materials (lyophilized or stabilized liquid), assessing accuracy for most systems is not possible due to matrix effects. For this reason participant performance must be evaluated using peer grouping.

Table 12–5 ✧ CLIA-Approved Proficiency Testing Programs

Program	Telephone	Sample Type
American Association of Bioanalysts	800-234-5315	Liquid
American Academy of Family Physicians	800-274-7911	Liquid
American Academy of Pediatrics	800-433-9016	Liquid
Accutest	800-356-6788	Liquid
American Proficiency Institute	800-333-0958	Liquid
American Society of Internal Medicine	800-338-2746	Liquid
College of American Pathologists (Surveys)	800-323-4040	Lyophilized
College of American Pathologists (EXCEL)	800-323-4040	Liquid
Idaho Bureau of Labs	208-334-2235, Ext. 246	Liquid
New Jersey Department of Health	609-530-6172	Lyophilized
New York State Department of Health	518-474-8739	Frozen Serum
Pacific Biometrics Research Foundation	206-233-9151	Fresh Serum
Puerto Rico Department of Health	809-764-7735	Lyophilized
Solomon Park Research Institute	800-769-7774	Fresh Serum
Wisconsin State Laboratory of Hygiene	800-462-5261	Liquid

OTHER NON-CLIA PROGRAMS

The University of Washington's Reference Lipoprotein Analysis Basic Survey

The Northwest Lipid Research Laboratories at the University of Washington, Seattle, conducts a quarterly survey called the Reference Lipoprotein Analysis Basic Survey (ReLABS). The goals of the program are to achieve and maintain the NCEP performance guidelines for cholesterol analysis and to standardize HDL-C, TG, LDL-C, and apo A-I and B measurements using fresh patient specimens. Participating manufacturers and clinical laboratories receive quarterly statistical reports and troubleshooting assistance. In addition, traceability of cholesterol testing to the National Reference System for Cholesterol is assessed every 6 months. A Certificate of Traceability is issued to laboratories that meet the established criteria for bias and precision in cholesterol testing.

Traceability testing for HDL-C and TG analysis will be added to the program when these services are provided by the Cholesterol Reference Method Laboratory Network.

For more information, contact Northwest Lipid Research Laboratories, University of Washington, 2121 N. 35th Street, Seattle WA 98103, Telephone 206-685-3317.

The Canadian Reference Laboratory's External Quality Assurance (EQA) Programs

The Canadian Reference Laboratory (CRL) supports the standardization of lipid testing in Canada. The CRL provides a number of external quality assurance (EQA) programs, all of which use fresh human serum as the quality control material. With the LIPID EQA program, laboratories receive three frozen samples of human serum drawn from normolipidemic and dyslipidemic subjects. Target values are assigned using CRL's reference methods standardized and credentialed by CDC. Preliminary reports are distributed by fax to participating laboratories within seven days of submitting their results. More complete reports follow by mail one week later. CRL offers a full range of EQA programs for clinical laboratories.

For more information, contact The Canadian Reference Laboratory (1996) Ltd., 307-2083 Alma Street, Vancouver, British Columbia V6R 4N6, Canada, Telephone 604-222-1355, Fax 604-222-1373, Web site, http://www.eqa.com.

SOURCES OF STANDARDS AND REFERENCE MATERIALS

Although matrix effects complicate the standardization of lipid and lipoprotein measurements, reference materials still play a significant role in assessing the performance of test systems.[88] The matrix sensitivity of either a homogeneous or heterogeneous analytical system to a specific reference material should be established by concurrent analysis with fresh patient specimens. If an evaluated instrument system has been shown to be matrix insensitive or if a consistent matrix discrepancy can be documented for a particular material, then that material could be used with reasonable confidence to assess performance of the system. The College of American Pathologists has developed a reliable protocol for verifying accuracy and demonstrating the presence of matrix interference in reference materials.[89]

The responsibility for assigning appropriate target values that are traceable to the recommended lipid, lipoprotein, and apolipoprotein accuracy base rests with the manufacturer. Reference materials provided by a manufacturer for a specific instrument system are suitable for that instrument system only and should not be assumed appropriate for other measurement systems unless specifically evaluated. Universal reference materials should be evaluated for each intended system application. Sources of primary standards are listed in Table 12-6 and available secondary reference materials are listed in Table 12-7. These lists are certainly not comprehensive, and more extensive information can be obtained from specific measurement system manufacturers or found in most clinical chemistry reagent catalogs. ✧

Note: Use of trade names in this chapter is for identification only and does not constitute endorsement by the Public Health Service or the U.S. Department of Health and Human Services.

Table 12–6 ✧ Primary Standards

Organization	Telephone	Standard
PUBLIC SOURCE		+
Natl. Institute for Standards & Technology	301-975-6776	Cholesterol (99.8%): SRM 911b Tripalmitin (99.5%): SRM 1595
COMMERCIAL SOURCES		
Aldrich Chemical Co.	800-558-9160	Cholesterol (99+%) Glycerol (99.5%) Tripalmitin (99%)
Alfa Aesar (Morton Thiokol Inc.)	800-343-0660	Glycerol (99.5+%)
American Biorganics, Inc.	716-283-1434	Cholesterol (99%)
Boehringer Mannheim Biochemicals	800-262-1640	Cholesterol (Precical) Glycerol (99.5%)
Calbiochem Biochemicals	800-854-3417	Cholesterol (95%)
Eastman Kodak Co. (Distributed by Fisher Scientific)	800-766-7000	Cholesterol (95%) Glycerol (99.5%) Tripalmitin (99%)
Gallard-Schlesinger	516-333-5600	Glycerol (99+%)
ICN Biomedicals, Inc.	714-545-0113	Cholesterol (99+%) Glycerol (99.5%) Triolein (95+%)
Malinckrodt/Baker	800-582-2537	Cholesterol "Baker" Glycerol (99.5%)
Sigma Chemical Co.	800-325-3010	Cholesterol (> 99%) Glycerol (99%) Triolein (99%) Tripalmitin (99%)

Table 12–7 ✧ Secondary Reference Materials

Organization	Telephone	Reference Material(s)
National Institute for Standards and Technology	301-975-6776	Cholesterol SRM 909c SRM 1951a: Lipid in frozen human serum Assigned values for TC and TG by NIST definitive methods and CDC reference methods. Assigned values for HDL-C and LDL-C assigned by CDC reference methods.
Centers for Disease Control and Prevention	770-488-4126	Frozen serum pools prepared from human based material. Target values assigned by the CDC reference methods for cholesterol, TG, and HDL-C. Available, on a limited basis, through the CDC-NHLBI Lipid Standardization Program.
College of American Pathologists	800-323-4040	Reference Material for lipids in frozen human serum: RM026 Assigned values for TC and TG by NIST definitive methods and CDC reference methods. Assigned values for HDL-C and LDL-C assigned by CDC reference methods.
Northwest Lipid Research Laboratories, University of Washington	206-685-3317	WHO-IFCC Reference Reagent SP1-01 for apo A-I WHO-IFCC Reference Reagent SP3-07 for apo B

REFERENCES

1. Lipid Research Clinics Program. The Lipid Research Clinics Primary Prevention Trial results. I: Reduction in incidence of coronary heart disease. II: The relationship of reduction in incidence of coronary heart disease to cholesterol lowering. JAMA 1984; 251:351-75.

2. The Expert Panel. Report of the National Cholesterol Education Program Expert Panel on detection, evaluation, and treatment of high blood cholesterol in adults. Arch Intern Med 1988;148:36-9.

3. Gordon DJ, Rifkind BM. High density lipoprotein: the clinical implications of recent studies. New England J Med 1989;148:1311-16.

4. NIH Consensus Conference. Triglyceride, high-density lipoprotein, and coronary heart disease. JAMA 1993;269:505-10.

5. Consensus Development Conference. Treatment of hypertriglyceridemia. JAMA 1984; 251:1196-1200.

6. Stein EA, Steiner PM. Triglyceride measurement and its relationship to heart disease. Clin Lab Med 1989;9(1):169-85.

7. Austin MA. Plasma triglyceride and coronary heart disease. Arterioscler Thromb 1991; 11:2-15.

8. Friedewald WT, Levy RI, Fredrickson DS. Estimation of the concentration of low-density lipoprotein cholesterol in plasma, without use of the preparative ultracentrifuge. Clin Chem 1972;18:499-502.

9. Albers JJ, Brunzell JD, Knopp RH. Apoprotein measurements and their clinical application. Clin Lab Med 1989;9:137-52.

10. LaMarche B, Moorjani S, Lupien PJ, et al. Apolipoprotein A-I and B levels and the risk of ischemic heart disease during a five-year follow-up of men in the Quebec Cardiovascular Study. Circulation 1996;94:273-8.

11. Kostner GM, Avogaro P, Cazzolato G, et al. Lipoprotein Lp(a) and the risk for myocardial infarction. Atherosclerosis 1981;38:51-61.

12. Schaefer EJ, Lamon-Fava S, Jenner JL, et al. Lipoprotein(a) levels and risk of coronary heart disease in men. JAMA 1994;271:999-1003.

13. Bostom AG, Cupples LA, Jenner JL, et al. Elevated plasma lipoprotein(a) and coronary heart disease in men aged 55 years and younger. JAMA 1996;276:544-548.

14. The Expert Panel. Summary of the Second Report of the National Cholesterol Education Program (NCEP) Expert Panel on Detection, Evaluation, and Treatment of High Blood Cholesterol in Adults (Adult Treatment Panel II). JAMA 1993;269:3015-23.

15. Current status of blood cholesterol measurement in clinical laboratories in the United States: A report from the laboratory standardization panel of the National Cholesterol Education Program. Clin Chem 1988;34:193-201.

16. Duncan IW, Mather A, Cooper GR. The procedure for the proposed cholesterol reference method. Atlanta, Ga: Centers for Disease Control, 1988.

17. Cooper GR, Smith SJ, Duncan IW, et al. Interlaboratory testing of the transferability of a candidate reference method for total cholesterol in serum. Clin Chem 1986;32: 921-9.

18. Cohen A, Hertz HS, Mendel J, et al. Total serum cholesterol by isotope dilution-mass spectrometry: a candidate definitive method. Clin Chem 1980;26:854-60.

19. Stein EA, Myers GL. National Cholesterol Education Program Recommendations for triglyceride measurement: Executive summary. Clin Chem 1995;41:1321-426.

20. Warnick GR, Wood PD. National Cholesterol Education Program Recommendations for measurement of high-density lipoprotein cholesterol: Executive summary. Clin Chem 1995;41:1427-33.

21. Bachorik, PS, Ross JW. National Cholesterol Education Program Recommendations for low-density lipoprotein cholesterol: Executive summary. Clin Chem 1995;41: 1414-20.

22. Vanderlinde RE, Bowers GN, Jr, Schaffer R, Edwards GC. The National Reference System for Cholesterol. Clin Lab Med 1989;9:89-104.

23. Ellerbe P, Myers GL, Cooper GR, et al. A comparison of results for cholesterol in human serum obtained by the reference and by the definitive method of the National Reference System for Cholesterol. Clin Chem 1990;36:370-5.

24. Bernert JT, Jr, Akins JR, Cooper GR, et al. Factors influencing the accuracy of the National Reference System total cholesterol reference method. Clin Chem 1991;37: 2053-61.

25. Hainline A, Jr, Karon J, Lippel K (eds.). Manual of laboratory operations: Lipid and lipoprotein analysis (2nd ed). [HEW Pub. No. (NIH) 75-628 (rev.), U.S. Government Printing Office Publication No. 1982-361-132:678.] Bethesda, MD: National Heart, Lung and Blood Institute, Lipid Research Clinics Program.

26. Ellerbe P, Sniegoski LT, Welch MJ. Isotope dilution mass spectrometry as a candidate definitive method for determining total glycerides and triglycerides in serum. Clin Chem 1995;41:397-404.

27. Carlson LA, Wadstrom LB. Determination of glycerides in blood serum. Clin Chim Acta 1959;4:197-205.

28. Carlson LA. Determination of serum triglycerides. J Ather Res 1963;3:334-6.

29. Van Handel E, Zilversmit DB. Micromethod for the direct determination of triglycerides in serum. J Lab Clin Med 1957;50:152-7.

30. Lofland HB, Jr. A semiautomated procedure for the determination of triglycerides in serum. Anal Biochem 1964;9:393-400.

31. Bernert JT, Jr, Bell CJ, McGuffey JE. Determination of free glycerol in human serum reference materials by isotope-dilution gas chromatography-mass spectrometry. J Chromatography 1992;578:1-7.

32. Labeur C, Rosseneu M, Henderson O. International Lp(a) Standardization. Chem Phys Lipids 1994;67/68:265-70.

33. Balbo-Enzi G, Baiocchi MR, Crepaldi G. Comparison of lipoprotein(a) assay methods in serum and in a plasminogen-free fraction. Clin Chim Acta 1993:218:83-95.

34. Shepherd J, Rosseneu M, Vercaemst R, Colinet E, Profilis C. Purification and certification of human apolipoprotein A-I and A-II reference materials (CRM 393 and 394). Community Bureau of Reference, 1991. (BCR Information series No. CD-NA-13393-EN-C, ISBN 92-826-2402-1.) Luxembourg: Commission of the European Communities, 1991, 78 pp.

35. Henderson LO, Powell MK, Smith SJ, et al. Impact of protein measurements on standardization of assays of apolipoprotein AI and B. Clin Chem 1990;36:1911-7.

36. Albers JJ, Marcovina SM. Standardization of apolipoprotein B and AI measurements. Clin Chem 1989;35:1357-61.

37. Barr JR, Maggio VL, Patterson DG, et al. Isotope dilution-mass spectrometric quantification of specific proteins: model application with apolipoprotein A-I. Clin Chem 1996; 42;1676-82.

38. Marcovina SM, Albers JJ, Henderson LO, Hannon WH. International Federation of Clinical Chemistry standardization project for measurement of apolipoproteins. III: Comparability of apo A-I values by the use of common reference material. Clin Chem 1993;39:773-81.

39. Marcovina SM, Albers JJ, Kennedy H, et al. International Federation of Clinical Chemistry standardization project for measurement of apolipoproteins AI and B. IV: Comparability of apo B values using international reference materials. Clin Chem 1994;40:586-92.

40. Naito HK. The need for accurate total cholesterol measurement. Clin Lab Med 1989;9: 37-60.

41. Myers GL, Cooper GR, Winn CL, Smith SJ. The Center for Disease Control, National Heart, Lung and Blood Institute Lipid Standardization Program: an approach to accurate and precise lipid measurements. Clin Lab Med 1989;9:105-35.

42. Recommendations for improving cholesterol measurement: A report from the Laboratory Standardization Panel of the National Cholesterol Education Program. (NIH Publication No: 90-2964). Bethesda, MD: National Institutes of Health, February 1990.

43. Cooper GR, Myers GL, Smith SJ, Sampson EJ. Standardization of lipid, lipoprotein, and apolipoprotein measurements. Clin Chem 1988;34:B95-105.

44. Cooper GR, Myers GL, Smith SJ, Schlant RC. Blood lipid measurements: variations and practical utility. JAMA 1992;267:1652-60.

45. Smith SJ, Cooper GR, Myers GL, Sampson EJ. Biological variability in the concentration of serum lipids: sources of variation among results from published studies and composite predicted values. Clin Chem 1993;39:1012-22.

46. Cooper GR, Smith SJ, Myers GL, et al. Estimating and minimizing effects of biologic sources of variation by relative range when measuring the mean of serum lipids and lipoproteins. Clin Chem 1994;40:227-32.

47. Cooper GR, Hannon WH, Henderson LO, Smith SJ. Apolipoprotein measurements: Pre-analytical issues and standardization. Proceedings of the Fourth Asian-Pacific Congress of Clinical Biochemistry. Hong Kong: Gardiner-Caldwell Communications, 1990: 392-7.

48. Greenberg N, Li ZM, Bower GN. National Reference System for Cholesterol (NRS-CHOL): problems with transfer of accuracy with matrix materials. Clin Chem 1988;34:1230-1.

49. Kroll MH, Chesler R, Elin RJ. Effect of the lyophilization on results of five enzymatic methods for cholesterol. Clin Chem 1989;35:1523-6.

50. Kroll MH, Chesler R. The effect of surfactant on the enzymatic determination of cholesterol with lyophilized materials. [Abstract]. Clin Chem 1990;36:960.

51. Lasky FD, Powers DM, Hassemer DJ, Wiebe DA. Quality of fluids used in external QC programs affects the reliable assessment of accuracy of routine methods, as documented by cholesterol. In: Kawai T, Ohba Y, Kanno T, Kawano K, Ueda K, Tatsumi E, eds. Quality control in the clinical laboratory '91. Princeton, NJ: Excerpta Medica 1992: 199-208. '

52. Koch DD, Hassemer DJ, Wiebe DA, et al. Testing cholesterol accuracy performance of several common laboratory instruments. JAMA 1988;260:2252-7.

53. Myers GL, Schap FD, Smith SJ, et al. CAP-CDC collaborative study for evaluating reference materials for total serum cholesterol measurements. Arch Pathol Lab Med 1990;114:1199-205.

54. Naito HK, Kwak YS, Hartfiel JL, et al. Matrix effects on proficiency testing materials: impact on accuracy of cholesterol measurement in laboratories in the nation's largest hospital system. Arch Pathol Lab Med 1993;117:345-51.

55. Ross JW, Myers GL, Gilmore BF, et al. Matrix effects and the accuracy of cholesterol analysis. Arch Pathol Lab Med 1993;117:393-400.

56. Waymack PP, Miller WG, Myers GL. Assay instrument-dependent matrix effects in standardization of cholesterol measurements. Clin Chem 1993;39:2058-62.

57. Miller WG, Levine J, Santulli M, et al. Effect of freezings on cholesterol in individual sera. [Abstract]. Clin Chem 1990;36:965.

58. Myers GL, Ross JW, Smith SJ, et al. Evaluating lyophilized human serum preparations for suitability as proficiency testing materials for HDL cholesterol measurement. Arch Pathol Lab Med 1995;119:686-94.

59. Holani KK, Miller WG, Waymack PP. Robustness of three triglyceride reagents for matrix effects of proficiency testing materials. Clin Chem 1993;39:1126.

60. Williams JH, Taylor L, Kuchmak M, Witter RF. Preparation of hypercholesterolemic and/or hypertriglyceridemic sera for lipid determinations. Clin Chim Acta 1970;28: 247-53.

61. Proksch GJ, Bonderman, DP. Use of a cholesterol-rich bovine lipoprotein to enhance cholesterol concentrations in the preparation of serum control materials. Clin Chem 1976;22:1302-5.

62. Kuchmak M, Taylor L, Williams JH. Preparation of reference sera with desired levels of cholesterol and triglyceride. Clin Chim Acta 1981;114:127-35.

63. Kuckmak M, Taylor L, Olansky AS. Low lipid level reference sera with human serum matrix. Clin Chim Acta 1981;116:125-30.

64. Smith SJ, Henderson LO, Hannon WH, et al. Effects of analytical method and lyophilized sera on measurements of apolipoproteins AI and B: an international survey. Clin Chem 1990;36:290-6.

65. Mei JV, Powell MK, Henderson LO, et al. Method-dependent variation in the stability of apolipoprotein B in a stabilized liquid reference material. Clin Chem 1994;40:716-22.

66. Rautela GS, Stater S, Arvon DA. Assessment of the need for triglyceride blank measurements. Clin Chem 1973;19:1193-5.

67. Jessen R, Cass C, Eckfeldt J. Do enzymatic analyses of serum triglycerides really need blanking for free glycerol? Clin Chem 1990;36:1372-5.

68. Cole T. Glycerol blanking in triglyceride assays: is it necessary? Clin Chem 1990;36:1267-8.

69. Klotzsch SG, McNamara JR. Triglyceride measurements: a review of methods and interferences. [Review]. Clin Chem 1990;36:1605-13.

70. Sampson M, Ruddel M, Elin RJ. Effects of specimen turbidity and glycerol concentration on nine enzymatic methods for triglyceride determination. Clin Chem 1994;40:221-6.

71. Leary ET, Tjersland G, Warnick GR. Evaluation of the Genzyme immunoseparation reagent for direct quantitation of LDL cholesterol. [Abstract]. Clin Chem 1993;39:1124.

72. McNamara JR, Cole TG, Contois JH, et al. Immunoseparation method for measuring low-density lipoprotein cholesterol directly from serum evaluated. Clin Chem 1995;41:232-40.

73. Jialal I, Hirany SV, Devaraj S, Sherwood, TA. Comparison of an immunoprecipitation method for direct measurement of LDL-Cholesterol with beta-quantification (ultracentrifugation). Amer J Clin Pathol 1995;104:76-81.

74. Waymack P, Chen W, Ethridge SF, Myers GL. Stability to freezing of low-density lipoprotein (LDL) cholesterol in serum [Abstract]. Clin Chem 1996;42:S291.

75. Waymack PW, Ethridge SF, Chen W, Myers, GL. Beta-quantification round robin for low-density lipoprotein cholesterol using frozen reference serum. Presented at the Frontiers in Lipid and Lipoprotein Research Conference. October 5, 1996, Dallas, Texas.

76. Kroll MH, Chesler R. Nonlinearity of high-density lipoprotein cholesterol determinations is matrix dependent. Clin Chem 1994;40:389-94.

77. Thienpont LM, Van Landuyt KG, Stockl D, De Leenheer AP. Four frequently used test systems for serum cholesterol evaluated by isotope dilution gas chromatography-mass spectrometry candidate reference method. Clin Chem 1996;42:531-5.

78. National Committee for Clinical Laboratory Standards. Development of designated comparison methods for analytes in the clinical laboratory: proposed guideline (2nd ed.). (NCCLS document NRSCL6-P2, ISBN 1-56238-227-6). Villanova, PA: NCCLS, 1993.

79. Kimberly MM, Waymack PP, Myers GL, Cole TG, Ferguson C, Gibson D, Leary ET, Warnick GR. Comparison of precipitation methods for determination of HDL cholesterol in the Cholesterol Reference Method Laboratory Network. [Abstract]. Clin Chem 1994;40:1105.

80. Kimberly MM, Waymack PP, Smith SJ. Evaluation of frozen vs. fresh samples by the designated comparison method for HDL Cholesterol in the Cholesterol Reference Method Laboratory Network. [Abstract]. Clin Chem 1995;41:S136.

81. Kimberly MM, Myers GL, Howard SM, Waymack PP. Performance of laboratories participating in the Cholesterol Reference Method Laboratory Network (CRMLN). [Abstract]. Clin Chem 1992;38:1061.

82. National Committee for Clinical Laboratory Standards. Method comparison and bias estimation using patient samples, approved guideline. (NCCLS document EP9-A, ISBN 1-56238-283-7). Wayne, PA: NCCLS, 1995.

83. Bennett ST, Eckfeldt JH, Belcher JD, Connelly DP. Certification of cholesterol measurements by the National Reference Method Laboratory Network with routine clinical specimens: effects of network laboratory bias and imprecision. Clin Chem 1992;38:651-7.

84. Centers for Disease Control. Clinical laboratory measurements traceable to the National Reference System for Cholesterol. Morbidity and Mortality Weekly Report. U.S. Department of Health and Human Services, Public Health Service. 1994;43:149-50.

85. Cooper GR, Smith SJ, Wiebe DA, et al. International survey of apolipoproteins AI and B measurements (1983-84). Clin Chem 1985;31:223-8.

86. Smith SJ, Henderson LO, Cooper GR, Hannon WH. An evaluation of the trends in analytical performance of international apolipoprotein AI and B assays. Clin Chem 1988;34:1644-6.

87. Smith SJ, Cooper GR, Henderson LO, Hannon WH. Apolipoprotein Standardization Collaborating Group: An international collaborative study on standardization of apolipoproteins AI and B. Part I: Evaluation of a lyophilized candidate reference and calibration material. Clin Chem 1987;33:2240-9.

88. Miller WG. How useful are reference materials? [Editorial]. Clin Chem 1996;42:1733-4.

89. Eckfeldt JH, Copeland KR. Accuracy verification and identification of matrix effects: the College of American Pathologists' protocol. Arch Pathol Lab Med 1993;117:381-6.

Measurement and Clinical Significance of High-Density Lipoprotein Cholesterol Subclasses

13

G. Russell Warnick

CLINICAL SIGNIFICANCE

❖ The inverse relationship between high-density lipoprotein cholesterol (HDL-C) values and risk of coronary heart disease (CHD) is well established in epidemiological studies.[1-7] A consensus panel sponsored by the National Institutes of Health (NIH) and the Adult Treatment Panel of the National Cholesterol Education Program (NCEP) confirmed the protective role of high-density lipoprotein (HDL) and recommended its measurement in making treatment decisions.[8-11] Chapter 7 provides detailed information about the clinical value of HDL-C and recommendations for its measurement.

In fact, the predictive association between HDL and CHD risk is much more complicated because HDL is actually a heterogeneous mixture of lipoprotein particles differing in size, density, and lipid and apolipoprotein composition as well as function. In 1954, DeLalla, Elliot, and Gofman,[12] pioneers in establishing the implications of the lipoproteins in CHD risk, first reported the heterogeneous nature of HDL based on observations using the analytical ultracentrifuge. DeLalla and colleagues observed two major subclasses, designated as HDL2 and HDL3, as well as a relatively minor subclass designated as HDL1. They also reported substantial gender differences, with females having significantly higher HDL2 values than males, but relatively similar HDL3 values. In 1966, these same researchers reported results from a prospective study indicating that subjects with CHD had lower HDL2 values but similar HDL3 values relative to subjects without CHD.[13]

These early reports on the association between CHD risk and HDL and its subclasses were largely ignored for many years but have been confirmed by more recent studies using a variety of measurement techniques and study designs with various populations.[14-22] For example, in a study employing coronary angiography, Miller and colleagues[14] demonstrated that the extent of atherosclerosis is associated with decreased HDL2-C rather than with HDL3-C values. Ballantyne et al.[15] reported that HDL2-C but not HDL3-C was reduced in survivors of myocardial infarction relative to control subjects. In a more recent retrospective study,[21] concentrations of the larger HDL2 particles were shown to be most strongly associated with extent and progression of CHD. However, results from a case-control design within the Physician's Health Study[22] indicated the strongest association between the smaller HDL3 particles and

CHD risk. The inference from these studies is that measurement of the HDL subclasses might improve the prediction of risk for CHD.

HDL is in fact more heterogeneous than implied by these studies, which examined major HDL subclasses obtained by ultracentrifugation or gradient electrophoresis. Isoelectric focusing, a high-resolution technique that achieves separations based on particle charge, reportedly resolved HDL3 into as many as 12 separate peaks[23] and HDL2 into at least 5,[24] suggesting that the common HDL2/HDL3 fractions are still heterogeneous. One of the newer gradient gel electrophoresis methods, resolving by particle size, obtains 10 bands in the HDL2 class and 4 in the HDL3 class.[25] These particles, when fractionated by density, charge, or size, contain varying combinations of apolipoproteins.[26, 27] The major distinction between particles involves those that contain apolipoprotein (apo) AI without apo AII and those that contain apo AI with apo AII. In addition, there are minor particles with only apo AII and combinations with other HDL proteins such as apo E. A particle within the HDL range containing only apo E was recently reported.[28]

These studies emphasize the considerable particle heterogeneity within the major HDL subclasses. Depending on the properties exploited in achieving separations, different subpopulations of HDL particles may be obtained, and particles of varying function may be included within the separated subclasses. Therefore, the apparent associations between CHD risk and the major HDL subclasses may vary by separation method. Nevertheless, quantitation of HDL subclasses does potentially improve assessment of CHD risk, although the choice of method and fraction is somewhat uncertain. The implications of HDL subclasses are perhaps in some respects analogous to those of total cholesterol (TC), whose value as a predictor of CHD risk can be improved by quantitating the major lipoproteins, the risk-positive low-density lipoprotein cholesterol (LDL-C), and the risk-negative HDL-C.

Measurement of HDL subclasses has been a useful research tool in studies of lipoprotein metabolism, pathophysiology, and association with CHD risk. One must recognize that the variety of methods used in published clinical applications may use the same nomenclature to refer to subclasses which in fact comprise different populations of particles. HDL is still generally separated into the two major subclasses, HDL2 and HDL3, with hydrated densities originally considered to be 1.063–1.125 Kg/L and 1.125–1.210 Kg/L, respectively.[12, 29] Inter-individual differences in HDL values are largely due to the larger and lighter HDL2; the smaller, more dense HDL3 fraction is relatively more consistent within and among individuals.[10]

The HDL2 and HDL3 fractions appear to be metabolically interrelated.[30] Patsch et al.[31] demonstrated that particles in the HDL3 range are converted into HDL2-like particles during lipolysis of very-low-density lipoprotein (VLDL) by hepatic lipoprotein lipase. Patsch and colleagues hypothesized that HDL3 assimilates surface components, cholesterol, and phospholipids derived from lipolysis of triglyceride-rich VLDL particles, and that it is thereby converted to the larger and lipid-enriched HDL2. The lipid enrichment of HDL3 may also result from transfers from cell membranes as the particles transit the circulation. A parallel process in the conversion of HDL3 to HDL2 is the action of lecithin:cholesterol acyltransferase (LCAT), which esterifies the free surface cholesterol, thereby moving it to the core. In the process of cholesterol removal, designated as reverse cholesterol transport, the esterified cholesterol can be transferred to low-density lipoprotein (LDL) for removal by the liver, or the HDL particles can be removed by specific receptor-mediated processes. These interconversions of HDL subclasses are considered reversible but are highly complex and have yet to be fully elucidated.

Factors that influence the plasma HDL-C concentration often have differential effects on the two major subclasses. For example, the increased HDL values in women are primarily due to increased HDL2.[32] High-estrogen oral contraceptives increase HDL2 values but have no discernible effect on HDL3.[32] Exercise increases the HDL2 and may also promote a slight decrease in the HDL3.[33, 34] Thus, female gender, estrogen use, and exercise are all associated with increased HDL2 and thereby with decreased risk of CHD. Alcohol intake is known to increase HDL values, and moderate intake is associated with a decreased risk of CHD.[35, 36] One might expect that this benefit is mediated by increasing the HDL2 fraction, but in fact Haskell et al.[37] found that, among moderate drinkers, HDL3 concentrations decreased with abstention from alcohol and increased upon resumption of drinking; there was no significant effect on the reputedly anti-atherogenic HDL2 fraction. Haffner et al.[38] also reported that HDL3, rather than HDL2, was increased by alcohol consumption and decreased by smoking. These latter studies emphasize the complexities of the HDL subclass associations with metabolic factors and CHD risk.

OVERVIEW OF METHODS

Methods for separation of HDL subclasses are summarized in Table 13-1 and discussed in the following sections.

Table 13–1 ✧ Methods for Separation of HDL Subclasses

Property	Method
Density	Analytical ultracentrifugation
	Sequential density ultracentrifugation
	Density gradient ultracentrifugation: Swinging bucket rotors Vertical rotors Zonal rotors
Size	Gradient gel electrophoresis
	Chromatographic procedures
Charge and Size	Chemical precipitation: Heparin-Mn^{2+} and 15 kDa dextran sulfate Dextran sulfate (50 kDa) and Mg^{2+} Polyethylene glycol Polyethylene glycol and 15 kDa dextran sulfate
Apolipoprotein composition	Immunoaffinity fractionation
	Enzyme-linked immunosorbent assay
	Differential electroimmunoassay

Ultracentrifugation Methods

The HDL subclasses were first identified by using analytical ultracentrifugation and observing their flotation rates through Schlieren patterns.[12] Since analytical ultracentrifugation is technically demanding and requires very expensive, specialized equipment, it is rarely used today, even in specialty laboratories. Although updated methods have been reported,[39] analytical ultracentrifugation is generally reserved for research and is not considered practical for use in large-scale studies.

Sequential Density Ultracentrifugation

Sequential density ultracentrifugation is more common and is considered by most to be the traditional standard for accuracy in HDL subclass quantitation.[12, 29] Total HDL can be isolated by flotation within the 1.063–1.21 Kg/L density interval after prior separation by flotation of VLDL and LDL at density 1.063 Kg/L. Specimens are adjusted to the indicated density by addition of a salt such as KBr and subjected to ultracentrifugation at forces upwards of 100,000 ×g, during which lighter particles float to the top and heavier particles sink to the bottom. The fractions are recovered by careful pipetting, often in conjunction with tube slicing to separate the top and bottom fractions. The bottom fraction is adjusted to the next sequential density to cause flotation of the heavier particles. An advantage of sequential flotation methods is the ability to recover fractions on a preparative scale for physical or chemical analysis. The range of densities conferred by the heterogeneity in lipid to protein proportions makes density separation appropriate. Considerable versatility is afforded by the variety of ultracentrifuges and rotors available today, accommodating large volumes and many samples in conventional floor models and convenient table-top models suitable for micro-scale fractionation.

Sequential density ultracentrifugation does have its disadvantages, however, including the fact that only one fraction is isolated in each centrifugation step, thus requiring a sequential centrifugation step for each fraction. The labile lipoproteins may be altered by the harsh conditions, high salt, and high gravity, with loss of loosely bound apolipoproteins or deterioration during the course of a multi-step ultracentrifugal procedure.[40] In addition, the recovered HDL is likely to be contaminated with apo-B-containing lipoproteins in the low end of the density range. For example, the density range of lipoprotein(a) [Lp(a)] overlaps that of HDL. Sequential density ultracentrifugation is tedious and very time consuming, and the specialized equipment and proficiency required may not be available in many laboratories.

A more convenient variation of sequential density ultracentrifugation for quantitation of the HDL2/HDL3 subclasses involves a single fractionation of serum, usually performed at density 1.125 Kg/L.[41, 42] Cholesterol recovered in the bottom fraction is taken as a measure of HDL3. Total HDL-C can be determined by a conventional precipitation method and the HDL2-C is calculated by difference (Total HDL-C – HDL3-C.) An alternative procedure involves density adjustment and centrifugation of the HDL supernate obtained by a precipitation method.[43–46] A more recent evaluation suggests that separation at a density of 1.100 Kg/L gives more specific fractionation in a single centrifugation.[47]

As indicated previously, the major HDL subclasses, HDL2 and HDL3, were originally separated at a density of 1.125 Kg/L.[12, 29] In 1972, Kostner and Alaupovic[48] recommended that the optimal density for separation of the two major subclasses was 1.100 Kg/L. In a landmark study reported by Anderson et al.[49] in 1977, sequential density separation was used in combination with density gradient ultracentrifugation to subdivide the HDL2 particles into two subclasses, HDL2b (d = 1.063–1.100 Kg/L) and HDL2a (d = 1.100–1.125 Kg/L). Using this method, the lightest subclass–HDL2–was clearly separated from HDL2a and HDL3, while the HDL2a subclass showed appreciable overlap with HDL3, suggesting that fractionation at a density of 1.125 Kg/L cross-contaminates the HDL2a and HDL3. These researchers decided to seek three major density subfractions because they had observed three major bands using an early version of gradient gel electrophoresis. This observation supports recent recommendations for a major fractionation at 1.100 Kg/L.[47, 48] There has been no general consensus on the choice of density, but there is considerable evidence that the lower density cutpoint is more specific.

Density Gradient Ultracentrifugation

Density gradient ultracentrifugation methods have been used to separate the major lipoprotein classes including HDL in a single spin,[50, 51] which for some purposes has an advantage over sequential methods. The major HDL subclasses, and even some of the minor subclasses, can also be separated under appropriate conditions. Density gradient fractionation methods have been described for fixed-angle, vertical, swinging-bucket, and zonal rotors. Separations may be made in continuous (smooth) gradients, or, more commonly, in discontinuous (stepwise) gradients. Bands can then be recovered based on rate of flotation (non-equilibrium) or after fractions reach their equilibrium densities. Fractions may be recovered by pipetting from the top of the tube or by puncturing the tube and collecting the effluent from the bottom in appropriate fractions. The isolated fractions are available for analysis and are usually quantified in terms of the cholesterol content and sometimes the amounts of other lipids and apolipoproteins or total protein. Since the density gradient methods give reasonably good resolution in a single centrifugation, they are less likely to alter the lipoproteins. Depending on the conditions of ultracentrifugation, the fractions may not be completely separated and may be contaminated with other plasma proteins. The number of specimens that can be processed at one time is determined by the capacity of the rotor, but is usually lower than with the sequential density techniques. Meticulous technique is required to achieve the reproducibility required for analytical purposes. Gradient ultracentrifugation is usually used in the research-oriented laboratories for small-scale studies.

Three density gradient procedures for isolating HDL subclasses are described here as examples of the technique. A representative approach for processing several specimens simultaneously employs a swinging-bucket rotor.[52-55] Specimens are adjusted to appropriate density and are often pre-stained with a lipophilic dye. They are then introduced into a stepwise gradient established with the tube in the vertical position. The tubes are placed into hinged buckets which allow the tubes to swing out to the horizontal during centrifugation, minimizing disruption of the gradient and affording good separation of the lipoproteins as they migrate along the length of the tube. Following centrifugation, typically for 20–30 h, the tubes return to the vertical and fractions and are recovered for analysis.

A variation of this approach using a vertical rotor has been refined by Segrest et al.[56-58] into a complete analytical system designated as the vertical autoprofiler (VAP). Specimens are similarly introduced into a gradient, but tubes are placed into cavities in the vertical rotor which hold the tubes upright and at right angles to the gravitational force at speed. Rather than the tubes swinging out, the gradient reorients so that separation occurs more rapidly along the shorter side-to-side distance. As the rotor slows, the gradient shifts back to the length of the tube. Fractions may be recovered by puncturing the bottom of the tube. In the VAP procedure, the effluent drawn from the bottom of the tube is continuously analyzed for cholesterol using a continuous-flow chemistry analyzer. The effluent can be split, with a portion going to a fraction collector or used for continuous, simultaneous analysis of other constituents. The cholesterol profile of the effluent is deconvoluted by computerized analysis with quantitation of major lipoproteins and minor subclasses including HDL2 and HDL3.

The vertical rotor method has the advantage of giving a complete lipoprotein profile in a single spin, yet it does suffer the general disadvantages of sequential density ultracentrifugation. An additional problem is that some lipoprotein material may adhere to the sides of the tube and not be recovered.

Another gradient method that has value for large-scale preparative isolations but has also been used as a standard for quantitation involves zonal ultracentrifugation.[59-63] For separation of HDL subclasses, a sample is introduced into a spinning single-cavity rotor containing a three-step gradient. After centrifugation for 24 h, fractions are recovered from the slowly spinning rotor for analysis. This large-scale method has better resolving power than other density gradient methods, with three fractions in the HDL2 range and five in the HDL3 range.[60] The major fractions are designated as HDL2, HDL3L, and HDL3D. Since this method accommodates only one specimen per run, it is generally reserved for detailed studies of compositional changes in metabolism and lipoprotein characterization. The highly specialized equipment and expertise required are available in only a few centers. (For more details of ultracentrifugation methods, see Chapter 29.)

Electrophoresis Methods

Electrophoretic methods using a homogeneous gel separate particles on the basis of their charge and size; mobility is enhanced by charge and inhibited by size. With a gradient gel, the separation is based on size: particles migrate until their size restricts further penetration into the gradient.[26] Gradient gel electrophoresis (GGE) in 4–30% gels has been used to study HDL particle size profiles in normal human plasma.[64-66] HDL can be detected directly from plasma using lipid staining after electrophoresis, or a protein stain can be used with the ≤ 1.21 Kg/L density fraction isolated by ultracentrifugation. Blanche et al.[64] observed five HDL subclasses, designated (HDL2a)gge, (HDL2b)gge, (HDL3a)gge, (HDL3b)gge, and (HDL3c)gge. The (HDL2b)gge particles correspond to the HDL2b component obtained by gradient ultracentrifugation with a mean hydrated density of 1.090 Kg/L. The (HDL3a)gge and (HDL3b)gge particles correspond to HDL3L, with a mean hydrated density of 1.140 Kg/L, and to HDL3D, with a mean hydrated density of 1.160 Kg/L, identified by rate zonal ultracentrifugation.[60] The (HDL2a)gge and (HDL3c)gge particles are minor particles which are observed less frequently in normal subjects. More recently, Li et al.[25] have reported 14 peaks obtained with a modified GGE method in 4–30% gels: 7 peaks corresponding to the HDL2b range, 3 peaks corresponding to HDL2a, and 4 peaks corresponding to HDL3. Another approach[67] uses a discontinuous gradient to resolve HDL2 and HDL3.

Gradient gel electrophoresis has subsequently been useful in characterizing the HDL subclasses. Li et al.[25] reported apolipoprotein composition of the subclasses and comparisons with other separation methods. Williams and Kraus et al.[68] compared separations by GGE to those by a precipitation method. Subsequently, GGE has been used to characterize HDL subclasses in studies of genetics,[69-70] diabetes,[71] and diet.[72]

GGE is a relatively rapid and reproducible method for determining HDL subclasses which are in reasonably good agreement with those obtained by ultracentrifugation methods. However, because quantitation is based on staining, either by lipophilic dyes or protein stains, results may not agree with ultracentrifugal quantitations based on cholesterol content. The particles may be only partially resolved and are available in very limited quantities for characterization. Nevertheless, GGE will have considerable use in research studies.

Another electrophoretic method used to separate HDL subclasses is isotachophoresis. Nowicka et al.[73] obtained three major HDL subclasses with fast, intermediate, and slow mobility and determined the interactions of the particles with macrophages. The fast migrating particles, rich in apo AI, correspond to HDL3a and HDL3b, the intermediate to particles with size between HDL2a and HDL3b, and the slow, the predominant class, to HDL2b, HDL3a, and HDL3c.

Chromatographic and Other Methods

Various chromatographic methods also separate HDL subclasses based on particle size.[74, 75] A gel permeation column in high-performance liquid chromatography (HPLC) with quantitation of eluate fractions by enzymic cholesterol assay gave separations that corresponded reasonably well to those obtained by sequential density ultracentrifugation.[74] Resolution of two HDL2 and three HDL3 fractions, approximating those observed with GGE, was obtained with a Superose 6B column in fast protein liquid chromatography.[75] Newer gel permeation columns are reported to be more rugged (see Chapter 3). NMR spectroscopy quantitates 5 HDL subclasses from serum without the need for a separation step (see Chapter 28).

Precipitation Methods

The most common methods for routine separation of the total HDL class involve chemical precipitation of VLDL and LDL with quantitation of HDL as cholesterol remaining in the supernate (see Chapter 7). The precipitation techniques are convenient and are amenable to processing large numbers of specimens without the need for expensive or specialized equipment; hence, it is not surprising that precipitation methods were adapted for quantitation of the major HDL subclasses. Selective precipitation exploits differences in size and charge properties of the lipoproteins. Since the HDL subclasses demonstrate relatively smaller differences in these properties than the major lipoproteins, their separation by precipitation is more tenuous. Nevertheless, with careful standardization and attention to technique, the precipitation methods have advantages, especially for large population studies.

One early method[76] involved the addition of heparin-Mn^{2+} for removal of VLDL/LDL, followed by addition to the HDL supernate of 15 kDa dextran sulfate to precipitate HDL2. Cholesterol was assayed in the supernates and HDL2 calculated by subtracting HDL3-C from total HDL-C. The optimum dextran sulfate concentration was determined in comparisons with ultracentrifugation at a density of 1.125 Kg/L. In pooled sera, the amount of dextran sulfate required to achieve separation by precipitation equivalent to the ultracentrifugal fractionation varied over a twofold range. At the concentration of dextran sulfate considered to be optimal for patient specimens, precipitation results correlated reasonably well with ultracentrifugation. The authors concluded that the precipitation method is best suited for large-scale trials, and recommended optimizing concentrations for the conditions of a particular study.

Subsequent evaluations of the method have confirmed that this method does give convenient and reasonably accurate quantitation of the HDL2/HDL3 subclasses, but that it is neither highly specific nor rugged.[77-81] Most researchers have endorsed the recommendation that the method be used for large-scale trials and not for routine evaluation of patients. One report cited interference from blood clotting proteins and the need for substantially different dextran sulfate concentrations for serum than for EDTA plasma.[82] A particular disadvantage of this method is that the manganese cation interferes with the common enzymic cholesterol assays; for this reason, the use of heparin and manganese for precipitation has diminished with increased use of the enzymic assays in both routine and research laboratories.

A similar precipitation procedure[83, 84] uses dextran sulfate (50 kDa) and Mg2+ to separate total HDL first and then HDL3 in sequence. The first version precipitated HDL2 from the HDL supernate, whereas a subsequent modification,[85] considered more convenient and equally accurate, precipitated VLDL, LDL, and HDL2 together from a second plasma aliquot. Evaluators of the first version observed results in good agreement with zonal ultracentrifugation[62] and concluded that the convenient precipitation method is well suited for population studies. Since this method uses the dextran sulfate reagent, which is compatible with enzymic cholesterol assays and is increasingly common for routine HDL separations, the dextran sulfate technique is described in more detail later in this chapter.

HDL subclasses have also been separated in a dual precipitation procedure using polyethylene glycol (PEG) 6,000 to remove VLDL and LDL from serum, followed by addition of 15 kDa dextran sulfate to precipitate HDL2 from the first supernate.[86] One evaluator observed agreement with ultracentrifugation,[87] although a subsequent evaluator urged caution in using the method for routine characterization of patients.[88] Another method used PEG for both steps, the first precipitating VLDL and LDL and the second precipitating VLDL, LDL, and HDL2 from a second aliquot of serum.[89-91] A comparison between these two types of PEG methods revealed substantial disagreement.[92] Use of PEG for HDL separations is common in Europe and Australia but not in the United

States. As a precipitant, PEG is much less effective than the polyanions (heparin and dextran sulfate), and the hundredfold higher concentrations required result in highly viscous solutions which are difficult to pipette reproducibly. The inexpensive, single constituent reagent is an advantage, but there are batch-to-batch differences that must be considered in formulating a consistent reagent solution.

Particle Assays

HDL particles can also be separated based on their particular apolipoprotein constituents.[26-27] The major classes contain either apo AI alone or apo AI and apo AII together. These classes of particles have been fractionated by immuno-affinity techniques using antibodies specific for the apolipoproteins.[26, 93] Antibodies to apo AII bind the latter particles, after which those particles with apo AI only can be bound by antibody to apo AI. The two types of particles have also been quantified by enzyme-linked immunosorbent assay (ELISA) in a sandwich format.[27] The antibody to apo AII coated on microtiter plates binds those particles that contain apo AII. A second enzyme-labeled antibody to apo AI quantitates the apo AI:AII species in terms of the apo AI content. Total apo AI is quantitated by a conventional ELISA and the apo-AI-only species is calculated by difference.

A differential electroimmunoassay has also been reported.[94] Specimens are electrophoresed through a gel containing a high concentration of antibody to apo AII and a normal concentration of antibody to apo AI. Particles with both apolipoproteins are precipitated in a small "rocket" near the origin, leaving those particles with apo AI only to migrate into the gel. The conventional rockets formed are then quantified compared to a standard. The apo AI:AII particles are calculated by difference. These techniques are described in greater detail in Chapter 24.

Convenient Precipitation Method for Large-Scale Studies

This method is a variation of the dextran sulfate method for quantitation of total HDL-C, as described in Chapter 7.[83-84] HDL-C is quantitated by measuring cholesterol in the first supernate after precipitation of VLDL and LDL. HDL3 is measured in a second supernate from a second aliquot of serum after precipitation of HDL2, LDL, and VLDL. HDL2 is calculated as the difference in cholesterol between the two supernates. Use of the method for characterization of CHD risk in patients in the routine laboratory is not recommended, but the procedure is considered suitable for research investigations.[62]

Solutions

The dextran sulfate is of 50,000 kDa (Dextralip 50 from Genzyme Corp., Boston, MA). Reagent-grade magnesium chloride and sodium azide are available from several sources.

TOTAL HDL REAGENT (DS1) PREPARATION

Weigh out 1.0 g dextran sulfate, 10.16 g $MgCl_26 \cdot H_2O$, and 50 mg NaN_3. Dissolve and mix well in deionized water. QS to 100 mL. It is not advisable to adjust pH, as fluctuations in ionic strength resulting from pH adjustment seem to contribute to more variability than the slight batch-to-batch differences in pH. The final working reagent contains 10 mg/mL dextran sulfate, 0.5 mol/L $MgCl_2$, and 0.05% NaN_3.

HDL3 REAGENT (DS2) PREPARATION

Weigh out 1.91 g dextran sulfate, 39.74 g $MgCl_2 \cdot 6H2O$, and 50 mg NaN_3. Dissolve and mix well in deionized water. QS to 100 mL. The final working reagent contains 19.1 mg/mL dextran sulfate, 1.95 mol/L $MgCl_2$, and 0.05% NaN_3.

Two or more quality control pools are included in the precipitation steps and in the cholesterol analysis together with patient specimens. Additional pool(s) with low cholesterol in the HDL/HDL3 range can be included in the analysis step only.

Precipitation Sequence

1. Allow specimens to equilibrate to room temperature and mix thoroughly before pipetting.

2. Pipette 0.5 mL specimen or control into appropriately labeled tubes. Pipette one aliquot for total HDL (DS1) and one for HDL3 (DS2) determination. Volumes can be adjusted provided reagent volumes are adjusted accordingly.

3. Add 50 μL of the appropriate reagent (DS1 or DS2) to each tube and vortex for 5 sec.

4. Allow tubes to stand at room temperature for 5–30 min.

5. Centrifuge for 5 min. at 12,000 ×g. Alternatively, centrifuge at 1500 ×g for 30 min. or some intermediate combination of g and minutes.

6. Visually examine each supernate for turbidity. If supernate is clear, transfer the supernate—carefully, so as not to disturb the pellet—to a storage vial or sample cup.
    Note: Incomplete sedimentation of apo-B-containing lipoproteins is indicated by the presence of cloudy or turbid supernates in hypertriglyceridemic specimens. Cloudy supernates may be cleared by ultrafiltration with a 0.22 μm filter or by repeating the precipitation procedure with the original specimen diluted 1:1 with saline. Alternatively, the dilution can be made subsequently on turbid supernates. Simply mix equal volumes of the turbid supernate with an equal volume of saline solution containing precipitation reagent at the same concentration as the original specimen.

7. Perform the cholesterol analysis on clear supernates.
    Note: The cholesterol assay should be optimized for good performance in the low HDL/HDL3 cholesterol concentration range. Analysis of the total HDL and HDL3 supernates consecutively for each specimen may decrease analytical variation and improve precision in the calculation of HDL2 (HDL2 = Total HDL – HDL3).

8. Correct cholesterol results in the supernates for reagent dilution by multiplying by the factor 1.1. If a turbid supernate was diluted with saline, further multiply the result by the dilution factor (e.g., × 2).

9. Calculate the HDL2 cholesterol value as: HDL2 = Total HDL – HDL3

Since the separation of HDL subclasses is relatively sensitive to reaction conditions and technique, the method should be validated for individual laboratory conditions. Comparison may be made to ultracentrifugation or to an experienced laboratory. Standardization of conditions and technique is essential to achieving reproducible results.

SUMMARY

HDL is highly heterogeneous, consisting of particles with a range of size, density, and composition and with a variety of different functions. While the HDL class in its entirety is clearly anti-atherogenic and predictive of CHD risk, subclasses of particles may be more or less protective. Quantitation of specific subclasses may be useful in research applications and provide a better indication of CHD risk, just as measurement of the major lipoproteins, HDL and LDL, better assesses overall risk than TC alone. Drawbacks are that the available separation methods are technically difficult and tedious (e.g., ultracentrifugation); require specialized equipment and skills (e.g., GGE and column chromatography); or are highly sensitive to reaction conditions (e.g., precipitation). Therefore, the measurement of the subclasses is still somewhat tenuous and their predictive value is uncertain. With further refinements in methods and validation in research investigations, measurement of certain HDL subspecies may eventually improve the prediction of CHD risk. ✧

Acknowledgments: *The author wishes to thank Carol Flynn, and Gayle Tjersland for their assistance in the preparation of this chapter, and Judy McNamara and Nader Rifai for their helpful comments on the manuscript.*

REFERENCES

1. Miller GJ, Miller NE. Plasma high density lipoprotein concentration and development of ischemic heart disease. Lancet 1975;i:16–9.
2. Rhoads GG, Gulbrandsen CL, Kagan A. Serum lipoproteins and coronary heart disease in a population study of Hawaii Japanese men. N Engl J Med 1976;294:293–8.
3. Gordon T, Castelli WP, Hjortland MC, et al. High density lipoprotein as a protective factor against coronary heart disease: The Framingham Study. Am J Med 1977;62; 707–14.
4. Kannel WB, Castell WP, Gordon T. Cholesterol in the prediction of atherosclerotic disease: new perspectives based on The Framingham Study. Ann Intern Med 1979;90: 85–91.
5. Miller NE, Thelle DS, Forde OH, et al. The Tromso Heart Study. High-density lipoprotein and coronary heart-disease: a prospective case-control study. Lancet 1977;1:965–8.
6. Abbott RD, Wilson PWF, Kannel WB, et al. High density lipoprotein cholesterol, total cholesterol screening, and myocardial infarction. The Framingham Study. Arteriosclerosis 1988;8:209–11.

7. Jacobs DR Jr., Mebane IL, Bangdiwala SI, et al. High density lipoprotein cholesterol as a predictor of cardiovascular disease mortality in men and women: the follow-up study of the Lipid Research Clinics prevalence study. Am J Epidemiology 1990;131: 32-47.

8. NIH Consensus Development Conference. Triglyceride, high density lipoprotein, and coronary heart disease. Consensus statement. Bethesda, MD: National Institutes of Health, Feb. 26-28, 1992.

9. National Cholesterol Education Program. Report of the Expert Panel on Detection, Evaluation, and Treatment of High Blood Cholesterol in Adults. Arch Intern Med 1988; 148:36-69.

10. The Expert Panel. Summary of the Second Report of the National Cholesterol Education Program (NCEP) Expert Panel on Detection, Evaluation and Treatment of High Blood Cholesterol in Adults (Adult Treatment Panel II). JAMA 1993;269(23);3015-23.

11. National Cholesterol Education Program. Second report of the Expert Panel on Detection, Evaluation, and Treatment of High Blood Cholesterol in Adults (NIH Publication No. 93-3095). Bethesda, MD: National Institutes of Health, 1993.

12. DeLalla OF, Elliot HA, Gofman JW. Ultracentrifugal studies of high density serum lipoproteins in clinically healthy adults. Am J Physiol 1954;179:333-7.

13. Gofman JW, Young W, Tandy R. Ischemic heart disease, atherosclerosis, and longevity. Circulation 1966;34:679-97.

14. Miller NE, Hammett F, Saltissi S, et al. Relation of angiographically defined coronary artery disease to plasma lipoprotein subfractions and apolipoproteins. Br Med J 1981; 282:1741-4.

15. Ballantyne FC, Clark RS, Simpson HS, et al. High density and low density lipoprotein subfractions in survivors of myocardial infarction and in control subjects. Metabolism 1982;31:433-9.

16. Nichols AV. Human serum lipoproteins and their interrelationships. Adv Biol Med Phys 1967;11:109-58.

17. Anderson DW, Nichols AV, Pan SS, Lindgren FT. High density lipoprotein distribution: resolution and determination of three major components in a normal population sample. Atherosclerosis 1978;29:161-79.

18. Glueck CJ, Fallat RW, Millett F et al. Familial hyperalphalipoproteinemia. Arch Intern Med 1975;135:1025-8.

19. Glueck CJ, Gartside P, Fallat RW, et al. Longevity syndromes: familial hypobeta and familial hyperalpha lipoproteinemia. J Lab Clin Med 1976;88:941-57.

20. Patsch W, Kuisk I, Glueck C, et al. Lipoproteins in familial hyperalphalipoproteinemia. Arteriosclerosis 1981;1:156-61.

21. Johanson J, Carlson LA, Landou C, et al. High density lipoproteins and coronary atherosclerosis: a strong inverse relation with the largest particles is confined to normotriglyceridemic patients. Arterioscler Thromb 1991;11:174-82.

22. Stampfer MJ, Sacks FM, Salvini S, et al. A prospective study of cholesterol, apolipoproteins, and the risk of myocardial infarction. N Engl J Med 1991;325:377-81.

23. Sundaram GS, Mackenzie SL, Sodhi HS. Preparative isoelectric focusing of human serum high-density lipoprotein (HDL3). Biochim Biophys Acta 1974;337:196-203.

24. Mackenzie SL, Sundaram GS, Sodhi HS. Heterogeneity of human serum high-density lipoprotein (HDL2). Clin Chim Acta 1973;43:223-9.

25. Li Z, McNamara JR, Ordovas JM, et al. Analysis of high density lipoproteins by a modified gradient gel electrophoresis method. J Lipid Res 1994;35:1698-1711.

26. Cheung MC, Albers JJ. Distribution of cholesterol and apolipoprotein A-I and A-II in human high density lipoprotein subfractions separated by CsCl equilibrium gradient centrifugation: evidence for HDL subpopulations with differing A-I/A-II molar ratios. J Lipid Res 1979;20:200-7.

27. Fruchart JC, Bard JM. Lipoprotein particle measurement: an alternative approach to classification of lipid disorders. Curr Opin Lipidol 1991;2:362-6.

28. Huang Y, von Eckardstein A, Wi S, et al. A plasma lipoprotein containing only apolipoprotein E and with γ mobility on electrophoresis releases cholesterol from cells. Proc Natl Acad Sci USA 1994;91:1834-8.

29. Havel RJ, Eder HA, Bragdon JH. The distribution and chemical composition of ultra-centrifugally separated lipoproteins in human serum. J Clin Invest 1955;34:1345.

30. Eisenberg S. Plasma lipoproteins. In: Albers JJ, Segrest JP, eds. Methods in enzymology, Vol. 129, Orlando, FL: Academic Press, 1986:347-66.

31. Patsch JR, Gotto AM, Olivercrona T, et al. Formation of high density lipoprotein 2-like particles during the lipolysis of very low density lipoprotein in vitro. Proc Nat Acad Sci 1978;75:4519-23.

32. Krauss RM. Regulation of high density lipoprotein levels. Med Clin North Amer 1982; 66:403-30.

33. Krauss RM, Wood PD, Giotas C, et al. Heparin-released plasma lipase activities and lipoprotein levels in distance runners. [Abstract]. Circulation 1979;59(Suppl 2):II-73.

34. Wood PD, Haskell WL, Blair SN, et al. Increased exercise level and plasma lipoprotein concentrations: a one-year, randomized, controlled study in sedentary middle-aged men. Metabolism 1983;32:31-9.

35. Klatsky AL, Friedman GD, Siegelaub AB. Alcohol consumption before myocardial infarction: results from the Kaiser-Permanente epidemiologic study of myocardial infarction. Ann Intern Med 1974;81:294-301.

36. Dyer AR, Stamler J, Paul O, et al. Alcohol consumption and 17-year mortality in the Chicago Western Electric Company study. Prev Med 1980;9:78-90.

37. Haskell WL, Camargo C, Williams PT, et al. The effect of cessation and resumption of moderate alcohol in take on serum high-density-lipoprotein subfractions. N Engl J Med 1984;310:805-10.

38. Haffner SM, Applebaum-Bowden D, Wahl PW, et al. Epidemiological correlates of high density lipoprotein subfractions, apolipoproteins A-I, A-II and D, and lecithin cholesterol acyltransferase: effects of smoking, alcohol and adiposity. Arteriosclerosis 1985;5:169-77.

39. Albers JJ, Warnick GR, Nichols AV. Laboratory measurement of HDL. In Miller NE, Miller GJ, eds. Clinical and metabolic aspects of high-density lipoproteins. New York: Elsevier Science Publishers B.V., 1984.

40. Kunitake ST, Kane JP. Factors affecting the integrity of high density lipoproteins in the ultracentrifuge. J Lipid Res 1982;23:936-40.

41. Kirstein P, Carlson K. Determination of the cholesterol content of high density lipoprotein subfractions HDL2 and HDL3, without contamination of Lp(a) in human plasma. Clin Chim Acta 1981;113:123-34.

42. Wallentin L, Fåhraes L. HDL3 and HDL2 determination by a combined ultracentrifugation and precipitation procedure. Clin Chim Acta 1981;116:199-208.

43. Eyre J, Hammett F, Miller NE. A micro-method for the rapid ultracentrifugal separation of human plasma high density lipoprotein subfractions, HDL2 and HDL3. Clin Chim Acta 1981;114:225-31.

44. März W, Groβ W. Ultracentrifugal determination of high-density lipoprotein subfractions HDL2 and HDL3 in a high capacity fixed angle rotor. Ärztl Lab 1988;34:265-70.

45. Rifai N, King ME. Further evidence for the heterogeneity of high density lipoprotein isolates: HDL2:HDL3 cholesterol ratios and the presence of apolipoprotein B. Annals of Clinical and Laboratory Science 1987;17:345-9.

46. Asayama K, Miyao A, Kato K. High-density lipoprotein (HDL), HDL2, and HDL3 cholesterol concentrations determined in serum of newborns, infants, children, adolescents, and adults by use of a micromethod for combined precipitation ultracentrifugation. Clin Chem 1990;36:29-131.

47. Demacker PN, van Sommeren-Zondag DF, Stalenhoef AF, et al. Ultracentrifugation in swinging-bucket and fixed-angle rotors evaluated for isolation and determination of high-density lipoprotein subfractions HDL2 and HDL3. Clin Chem 1983;29:656-63.

48. Kostner G, Alaupovic P. Studies of the composition and structure of plasma lipoproteins: separation and quantification of the lipoprotein families occurring in the high density lipoproteins of human plasma. Biochemistry 1972;11:3419-28.

49. Anderson DW, Nichols AV, Forte TM, et al. Particle distribution of human serum high density lipoproteins. Biochim Biophys Acta 1977;493:55-68.

50. Redgrave TG, Roberts DCK, West CE. Separation of plasma lipoproteins by density gradient ultracentrifugation. Anal Biochem 1975;65:42-49.

51. Foreman JR, Karlin JB, Edelstein C, et al. Fractionation of human serum lipoproteins by single-spin ultracentrifugation: quantification of apolipoproteins B and A-I and lipid components. J Lipid Res 1977;18:759-67.

52. Chapman MJ, Godstein S, Lagrange D, et al. A density gradient ultracentrifugal procedure for the isolation of the major lipoprotein classes from human serum. J Lipid Res 1981;22:339-58.

53. Terpstra AHM, Woodward CJH, Sanchea-Munz FJ. Improved techniques for the separation of serum lipoproteins by density gradient ultracentrifugation: visualization by prestaining and rapid separation of serum lipoproteins from small volumes of serum. Anal Biochem 1981;111:149-57.

54. Nilsson J, Mannickarottu V, Edelstein C, et al. An improved detection system applied to the study of serum lipoproteins after single-step density gradient ultracentrifugation. Anal Biochem 1981;110:342-8.

55. Groot PHE, Scheek LM, Havekes L, et al. A one-step separation of human serum high density lipoproteins 2 and 3 by rate-zonal density gradient ultracentrifugation in a swinging bucket rotor. J Lipid Res 1982;23:1342-53.

56. Chung BH, Segrest JP, Cone JT, et al. High resolution plasma lipoprotein cholesterol profiles by a rapid, high volume semi-automated method. J Lipid Res 1981;22:1003-14.

57. Cone JT, Segrest JP, Chung BH, et al. Computerized rapid high resolution quantitative analysis of plasma lipoproteins based upon single vertical spin centrifugation. J Lipid Res 1982;23:923-35.

58. Cheung MC, Segrest JP, Albers JJ, et al. Characterization of high density lipoprotein subspecies: structural studies by single vertical spin ultracentrifugation and immunoaffinity chromatography. J Lipid Res 1987;28:913-29.

59. Patsch JR, Sailer S, Kostner G, et al. Separation of the main lipoprotein density classes from human plasma by rate-zonal ultracentrifugation. J Lipid Res 1974;15:356-66.

60. Patsch W, Schonfeld G, Gotto AM (Jr.), et al. Characterization of human high density lipoproteins by zonal ultracentrifugation. J Biol Chem 1980;255:3178-85.

61. Schmitz G, Assmann G. Isolation of human serum HDL1 by zonal ultracentrifugation. J Lipid Res 1982;23:903-10.

62. Patsch W, Brown SA, Morrisett JD, et al. A dual-precipitation method evaluated for measurement of cholesterol in high-density lipoprotein subfractions HDL2 and HDL3 in human plasma. Clin Chem 1989;35:265-70.

63. Patsch JR, Patsch W. Zonal ultracentrifugation. In: Albers JJ, Segrest JP, eds. Methods in enzymology, Vol. 129. Orlando, FL: Academic Press, 1986:3-26.

64. Blanche PJ, Gong EL, Forte TM, et al. Characterization of human high-density lipoproteins by gradient gel electrophoresis. Biochimica et Biophysica Acta 1981;665:408-19.

65. Nichols AV, Blanche PJ, Gong EL. Gradient gel electrophoresis of human plasma high density lipoproteins. In: L Lewis, Opplt JJ, eds. CRC handbook of electrophoresis, Vol. III. Boca Raton, FL: CRC Press, 1980:29-47.

66. Verdery RB, Benham DF, Baldwin HL, et al. Measurement of normative HDL subfraction cholesterol levels by Gaussian summation analysis of gradient gels. J Lipid Res 1989;30:1085-95.

67. Atger V, Malon D, Bertire MC, et al. Cholesterol distribution between high-density-lipoprotein subfractions HDL2 and HDL3 determined in serum by discontinuous gradient gel electrophoresis. Clin Chem 1991;37:1149-52.

68. Williams P, Krauss R, Vranizan K, et al. Associations of lipoproteins and apolipoproteins with gradient gel electrophoresis estimates of high density lipoprotein subfractions in men and women. Arterioscler Thromb 1992;12:332-40.

69. Williams P, Vranizan K, Austin M, et al. Familial correlations of HDL subclasses based on gradient gel electrophoresis. Arterioscler Thromb 1992;12:1467-74.

70. Krauss R, Williams P, Blanche P, et al. Lipoprotein subclasses in genetic studies: the Berkeley data set. Genet Epidemiol 1993;10:523-8.

71. Williams P, Haskell W, Vranizan K, et al The associations of high-density lipoprotein subclasses with insulin and glucose levels, physical activity, resting heart rate, and regional adiposity in men with coronary artery disease: The Stanford Coronary Risk Intervention Project Baseline Survey. Metabolism 1995;44:1234-40.

72. Williams P, Dreon D, Krauss, R. Effects of dietary fat on high-density-lipoprotein subclasses are influenced by both apolipoprotein E isoforms and low-density-lipoprotein subclass patterns 1-3. Am J Clin Nutr 1995:61:1234-40

73. Nowicka G, Brüning T, Böttcher A, et al. Macrophage interaction of HDL subclasses separated by free flow isotachophoresis. J Lipid Res 1990;31:1947-63.

74. Okazaki M, Itakura H, Shiraishi K, et al. Serum lipoprotein measurement: liquid chromatography and sequential flotation (ultracentrifugation) compared. Clin Chem 1983; 29:768-73.

75. Clifton PM, MacKinnon AM, Barter PJ. Separation and characterization of high-density lipoprotein subpopulations by gel permeation chromatography. J Chromatography 1987; 414:25-34.

76. Gidez LI, Miller GJ, Burstein M, et al. Separation and quantitation of subclasses of human plasma high density lipoproteins by a simple precipitation procedure. J Lipid Res 1982;23:1206-23.

77. Simpson HS, Ballantyne FC, Packard CJ. High-density lipoprotein subfractions as measured by differential polyanionic precipitation and rate zonal ultracentrifugation. Clin Chem 1982;28:2040-3.

78. Daerr WH, Windler EET, Rohwer HD, et al. Limitations of a new double-precipitation method for the determination of high density lipoprotein subfractions 2 and 3. Atherosclerosis 1983;49:211-13.

79. Martini S, Baggio G, Baroni L, et al. Evaluation of HDL2 and HDL3 cholesterol by a precipitation procedure in a normal population and in different hyperlipidemic phenotypes. Clin Chim Acta 1984;137:291-8.

80. Demacker PNM, Hak-Lemmers HLM, Hijmans AGM, et al. Evaluation of the dual-precipitation method for determination of cholesterol in high-density lipoprotein subfractions HDL2 and HDL3 in serum. Clin Chem 1986;32:819-25.

81. Cloey TA, Bachorik PS. Use of a dual-precipitation procedure for measuring high-density lipoprotein 3 (HDL3) in normolipidemic serum. Clin Chem 1989;35:1390-3.

82. Demacker PNM, Hak-Lemmers HLM, van Heijst PJ. Interference of blood clotting factors in the determination of HDL2- and HDL3-cholesterol by the dual precipitation method. Clin Chim Acta 1987;165:133-9.

83. Warnick GR, Benderson JM, Albers JJ. Quantitation of high-density-lipoprotein subclasses after separation by dextran sulfate and Mg2 precipitation. [Abstract]. Clin Chem 1982;28:1574.

84. Bachorik PS, Albers JJ. Precipitation methods for quantification of lipoproteins. In: Albers JJ, Segrest JP, eds. Methods in enzymology, Vol. 129. Orlando, FL: Academic Press, 1986:78-100.

85. Nguyen T, Warnick GR. Improved methods for separation of total HDL and subclasses. [Abstract]. Clin Chem 1989;35:1086.

86. Lundberg B, Högström S., Pietiläinen P, et al. Separation of plasma high-density lipoprotein subclasses by a combined precipitation method using polyethylene glycol 6000 and dextran sulfate. Scan J Clin Lab Invest 1984;44:305-9.

87. Dias VC, Parsons HG, Boyd ND, et al. Dual-precipitation method evaluated for determination of high-density lipoprotein (HDL), HDL2 and HDL3 cholesterol concentrations. Clin Chem 1988;34:2322-7.

88. Demacker PNM. Differential determination of HDL-subfractions in clinical laboratories. Clin Chem 1989;35:701-2.

89. Kostner GM, Molinari E, Pichler P. Evaluation of a new HDL2/HDL3 quantitation method based on precipitation with polyethylene glycol. Clin Chim Acta 1983;148:139-47.

90. Brugger P, Kostner GM, Kullich WC, et al. Plasma concentrations of high-density lipo-protein (HDL)-2 and HDL-3 in myocardial infarction survivors and in control subjects. Clin Cardiol 1986;9:273-6.

91. Widhalm K, Pakosta R. Precipitation with polyethylene glycol and density-gradient ul-tracentrifugation compared for determining high-density lipoprotein subclasses HDL2 and HDL3. Clin Chem 1991;37:238-40.

92. Leino A, Viikari J, Koskinen P, et al. Problems with PEG-based precipitation methods in the determination of HDL2- and HDL3- cholesterol. Scand J Clin Lab Invest 1987;47:705-8.

93. James RW, Proudfoot A, Pometta D. Immunoaffinity fractionation of high-density lipo-protein subclasses 2 and 3 using anti-apolipoprotein A-I and A-II immunosorbent gels. Biochim Biophys Acta 1989;1002:292-301.

94. Parra HJ, Mezdour H, Ghalim N, et al. Differential electroimmunoassay of human Lp A-I lipoprotein particles on ready-to-use plates. Clin Chem 1990;36:1431-5.

Measurement and Clinical Significance of Low-Density Lipoprotein Subclasses

John E. Hokanson, Melissa A. Austin, and John D. Brunzell

INTRODUCTION

❖   The important relationship between increased plasma low-density lipoprotein (LDL) cholesterol and increased risk of coronary heart disease (CHD) has been definitively established. In addition, there now is accumulating evidence that subclasses of LDL, characterized by variations in the size, flotation rate, density, and chemical composition of LDL particles, have important clinical significance as well. The heterogeneity of LDL particles has been recognized for many years,[1-4] and a number of techniques have been developed for detecting and characterizing the variation in LDL.[4] This chapter focuses on techniques now widely used in research laboratories for measuring LDL heterogeneity: non-denaturing gradient gel electrophoresis (GGE), non-equilibrium density gradient ultracentrifugation (DGUC), and equilibrium DGUC. The rapid progress made in understanding the role of LDL subclasses in relation to risk of CHD has important clinical implications.

BLOOD COLLECTION AND STORAGE

Appropriate collection and handling of samples are important for maintaining the physical integrity of LDL. Blood should be drawn after a 12-h fast, collected in 0.1% EDTA inverted gently to avoiding hemolysis, and centrifuged immediately at 1000 g for 15–20 minutes at 4° C. In some cases when chylomicrons are present, plasma should be centrifuged for 30 min at 20,000 rpm and the chylomicrons aspirated off the top. Plasma samples may be stored at 4° C for no more than one week without alteration in the LDL subclass distribution. For long-term storage, samples should be stored at –70° C. Paired analyses of fresh plasma compared to aliquots stored at –70° C indicate the mean of the absolute value of the difference in LDL peak particle diameter was 0.9 ± 0.6%, with no detectable difference in LDL flotation rate. LDL size and flotation rate are stable for at least 29 months for samples store at –70° C.[5] Thus, fasting plasma samples collected in EDTA and stored at –70° C can be used for determining LDL subclass distribution.

LOW-DENSITY LIPOPROTEIN SIZE

Krauss and Burke[6] developed the gradient gel electrophoresis procedure using non-denaturing conditions to characterize LDL particle size distribution. Polyacrylamide gradients can be formed following the procedure developed by Rainwater et al.,[7] and modified for LDL.[8] Solutions of 2% and 14% polyacrylamide are pumped into a mixing chamber at a rate controlled by a dual-pump gradient controller and software (ISCO, Lincoln, NE). The linear gradient solution is then pumped into a level gel casting chamber holding 8 glass gel cassettes (GSC-8, Pharmacia, Piscataway, NJ) under a layer of ethanol/water 1:4 (vol/vol). Polymerization occurs within 3 h at a stable room temperature (20–22° C), and the gels are then placed in distilled H_2O for 5 min and stored at 4° C in sealed plastic bags containing electrophoresis buffer.

Electrophoresis is performed in a GE-4 electrophoresis system (Pharmacia, Piscataway, NJ) using tris(hydroxymethyl)aminomethane(0.09M)/boric acid (0.08M)/Na_2 EDTA (0.003M) electrophoresis buffer at pH 8.3 and maintained at 10° C. Gels are pre-electrophoresed for 30 min at 125 volts. Five µL of plasma or 5 µg of LDL, isolated by sequential ultracentrifugation,[9] is diluted 4:1 with a 50% sucrose/0.01% bromophenol blue tracking solution in electrophoresis buffer. Ten µL of sample is added to each well, with tracking solution added to unused wells. Two quality-control LDL samples are run on each gel. Standards of known diameter: ferritin (12.2 nm), thyroglobulin (17.0 nm), thyroglobulin dimer (23.6 nm; Pharmacia, Piscataway NJ), and uniform latex microspheres of carboxylated polystyrene (38.0 nm; Duke Scientific, Palo Alto, CA) are loaded onto each gel. A run-in time of three 15-min steps is performed at 20, 40, and 80 volts. Electrophoresis is then maintained for 24 h at 125 volts (3,000 volt hours).

Gel cassettes are removed from the electrophoresis tank, the glass plates carefully removed from the gel, and the gel placed into a staining solution. Plasma sample gels are stained for lipid in 0.04% Oil Red O in 60% ethanol at 55–60° C for 24 h and destained using 5% acetic acid. Isolated LDL gels are stained for protein in 1.0% Coomassie Brilliant Blue R250 (Sigma Chemical, St. Louis, MO) in 50% methanol and 10% acetic acid for at least 6 h and destained using a 20% methanol/9% acetic acid solution. Protein standards from plasma sample gels are stained by placing a strip of filter paper over the standard lane and carefully pipetting the Coomassie R250 protein stain onto the filter paper.

Densitometry of each lane using a QuickScan densitometer (Helena Laboratories, Beaumont, TX) provides a graphical representation of the size distribution of LDL. Densitometry of standard lanes is used to calculate a quadratic calibration curve relating migration distance of the standards in the gel to particle diameter. The major peak particle diameter of LDL (LDL-PPD) is estimated from this standard curve. Peak particle diameter (Å) is reproducible, with a coefficient of variation of 2.5% from 87 consecutive gels.[10]

In addition to the continuous LDL-PPD determination, a dichotomous classification of LDL heterogeneity can be used to identify LDL subclass patterns, or phenotypes, denoted A and B.[11, 12] (See Figure 14–1.) LDL subclass phenotype A is characterized by a predominance of large LDL particles and skewing of the densitometric scan to the right, while LDL subclass phenotype B is characterized by a predominance of

Figure 14–1 ❖ Examples of LDL Subclass Phenotypes A and B as Determined by GGE of LDL from Individual Study Subjects

Phenotype A is characterized by a predominance of large, buoyant LDL, while phenotype B is characterized by a predominance of small, dense LDL. The estimated diameter (Å) of the major LDL subclass is also shown for each scan.

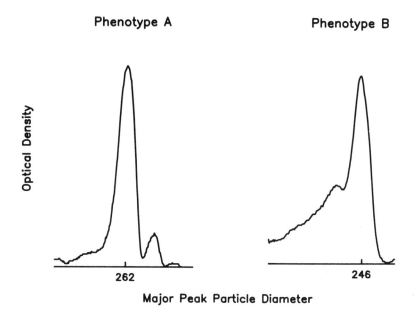

Major Peak Particle Diameter

small LDL particles and skewing of the curve to the left. In general, the peak particle diameter corresponding to the major LDL subclass has an estimated diameter greater than 255Å in subjects with phenotype A, while those with phenotype B have peak particle diameter less than or equal to 255Å. In studies to date, 85–90% of study subjects clearly have either LDL subclass phenotype A or B, while the remainder have an intermediate phenotype.[12] In rare conditions, a study subject may have so little plasma LDL that the LDL subclass phenotype cannot be determined by GGE.[13]

An alternative GGE procedure has been developed by McNamara et al. to describe LDL heterogeneity by defining seven size subfractions of LDL.[14] Plasma samples are electrophoresed under similar conditions as described above for 6 h at 240 volts (2,700 volt hours) and subsequently stained for lipid using Sudan Black B. Gels are destained using ethylene glycol/monoethyl ether. A pooled plasma sample containing three of the seven major bands of LDL is also run on each gel to identify the sample LDL subfractions. Densitometry is performed on each lane with a laser densitometer. The percent of total LDL is estimated for each LDL subfraction as the area under the peak for each subfraction divided by the total area for LDL. Each percentage is then weighted by multiplying it by the defined LDL subclass (1 through 7) to produce an overall LDL score.

Using these techniques, studies have demonstrated significant genetic influences on LDL size. Two large family studies using the phenotype A and B definitions have used complex segregation analysis to conclude that LDL subclass phenotype B is influenced by a single major gene.[15, 16] The first study was based on primarily healthy families, while the second study was based on families with familial combined hyperlipidemia (FCHL). In both studies, the proposed gene controlling phenotype B was estimated to have a common allele frequency, a dominant or additive mode of inheritance, and reduced penetrance in young males and pre-menopausal women.

Two large studies of twins, one of women and the other of men, have confirmed the presence of genetic influences on LDL heterogeneity by reporting heritability estimates ranging from 0.39 to 0.55 for LDL peak particle diameter and LDL score, respectively.[17, 18] These results indicate that one-third to one-half of the variance is attributable to genetic influences in women. In men, the "among components" estimate of heritability lacked sufficient statistical power to provide a statistically significant result. However, these studies also demonstrate the importance of non-genetic environmental and behavioral influences, and likely genetic-environmental interactions, on small, dense LDL.

LOW-DENSITY LIPOPROTEIN FLOTATION RATE

Several different methods of density gradient ultracentrifugation have been used to characterize LDL flotation rate. Lipoproteins were first characterized by flotation rate (Svedberg flotation unit) using the analytical ultracentrifuge.[1] Subsequently Chung et al. developed a procedure using a vertical rotor in a preparative ultracentrifuge.[19] Methods for characterizing LDL subclasses based on flotation rates are modifications of this method.

One of these methods is designed to optimize the resolution of apo-B-containing lipoproteins.[20] A discontinuous salt gradient is produced by layering 1 mL of plasma adjusted to a density of 1.08 Kg/L (total volume 5 mL) below 13 mL of a 1.006 Kg/L NaCl solution in a Sorvall TV-865B tube (DuPont, Wilmington, DE).* Samples are then centrifuged at 65,000 rpm for 90 min at 10° C. While maintaining temperature, centrifuge tubes are placed in a tube fractionator (ISCO, Lincoln, NE), pierced, and drained from the bottom using a P-1 peristaltic pump (Pharmacia, Piscataway NJ) at a flow rate of 1.0 mL/minute. Thirty-eight 0.47 mL fractions are collected. Cholesterol is measured in each fraction by enzymatic kit (Diagnostic Chemicals, Canada). LDL relative flotation (Rf) is calculated as the fraction number of the major peak of LDL divided by the total number of fractions. Recovery of cholesterol using this method is 92.5% ± 6.4% of total plasma cholesterol. The between-rotor coefficient of variation (CV) of the LDL Rf values is 3.5%. In addition, it is a highly reproducible method of determining the distribution of cholesterol in the entire lipoprotein spectrum in a single ultracentrifugation step.

---

*This gradient may also be formed in a VTi 65.1 (Beckman Instruments, Palo Alto, CA) using 4 mL of *d* = 1.08 Kg/L below 9.5 mL of *d* = 1.006 Kg/L and centrifuged for 70 min at 65,000 rpm.[21]

This technique has been used to investigate the involvement of hepatic lipase (HL) in determining the physical characteristics of LDL.[5] In a sample of 23 normolipidemic males and a sample of 21 male patients with coronary artery disease (CAD), subjects with low HL activity had relatively buoyant LDL, while those with high HL activity had relatively dense LDL. Based on linear regression analysis, HL activity explained more than half of the variance in LDL Rf in each of the groups. Recently, it has been shown that changes in HL are highly correlated with changes in LDL Rf.[22] In both male and female normal subjects, analysis of the chemical composition of LDL particles show that free cholesterol, cholesterol ester, and phospholipid are positively correlated with LDL Rf while LDL particle triglyceride shows no relationship to LDL Rf.[13] These results support the hypothesis that HL may be involved in determining physicochemical characteristics of LDL particles.

Similar to the results based on GGE, plasma triglyceride (TG) concentrations have been shown to be inversely associated with LDL Rf among normal subjects and among subjects with familial hypercholesterolemia, familial hypertriglyceridemia, and FCHL.[23] Further, when 13 patients with well-characterized FCHL and with LDL subclass phenotype B were treated with gemfibrozil for 3 months, dense LDL persisted despite a 55% decrease in TG values.[10] However, changes in LDL Rf were inversely correlated with changes in TG concentration, indicating an increase in buoyant LDL as well.

An alternative method for determining LDL Rf uses ultracentrifugation in a vertical rotor with a continuous flow auto-analyzer and mathematical curve deconvolution of 6 LDL subclasses.[24] A discontinuous salt gradient is formed by underlaying 70 μL of plasma adjusted to a density of 1.08 Kg/L to a final volume of 650 μL under 4.65 mL of a 1.041 Kg/L NaCl solution. Tubes are sealed and loaded into a VTi-80 rotor (Beckman Instruments, Palo Alto, CA) and centrifuged at 80,000 rpm for 1 hour at 20° C. The sample is pumped out of the bottom of the centrifuge tube into a continuous-flow cholesterol analyzer (VAP-II). Mathematical equations are used to deconvolute the cholesterol curve into six subclasses of LDL using exponential Gaussian distributions which provided the best least-squares fit to the overall data. The within-rotor CV of the cholesterol concentration of the major subclass of LDL is 1.9% to 8.3%; the between-rotor CV is 5.2%.

LOW-DENSITY LIPOPROTEIN DENSITY

Several methods exist for determining the density of LDL subclasses. These methods often require pre-isolation of LDL and long ultracentrifugation time. Important studies on the chemical composition of LDL subclasses have used these methods,[25-30] but they have limited use in a clinical setting. Two methods for determining LDL subclass density which do not require previous isolation of LDL are discussed here.

In the method developed by Marzetta et al.,[31] a discontinuous salt gradient is prepared by underlaying 3.7 mL of *d* = 1.006 Kg/L NaCl with 5.7 mL of *d* = 1.063 Kg/L KBr and 2.3 mL of plasma raised to a density of 1.21 Kg/L with solid KBr in a SW41 centrifuge tube (Beckman Instruments, Palo Alto, CA). Tubes are placed in the SW41 swinging bucket rotor (Beckman Instruments, Palo Alto, CA) and centrifuged for 24 h at 41,000 rpm at 15° C. After centrifugation, each centrifuge tube is placed in an tube fractionator (ISCO, Lincoln, NE) and drained from the top by pumping a dense solution of Fluorinert (1.85 Kg/L) (3M, St. Paul, MN) into the bottom of the centrifuge tube at a flow rate of 0.8 mL/min. The sample flows through a UV monitor and absorbance at 280 nm is recorded on a chart recorder. Thirty eight fractions are collected and cholesterol is measured using an enzymatic kit (Sigma Chemical, St. Louis, MO). The density of each fraction is determined by refractometry of fractions collected from a tube containing the same discontinuous salt gradient in the absence of plasma. The density of fractions in the LDL range (1.0203–1.0548) have a CV of 0.2% to 0.06%, respectively.

In an alternate method for determining the density distribution of LDL, plasma is prestained with a 15 gm/L solution of Coomassie Brilliant Blue R250 (Sigma Chemical, St. Louis, MO), and 3.4 mL of stained plasma is raised to a density of 1.10 Kg/L using solid KBr.[32] The sample is overlayered with 2.5 mL of d = 1.065 Kg/L and 2.5 mL of d = 1.020 Kg/L KBr solutions and 2.9 mL of d = 1.006 Kg/L NaCl solution, all at pH 4.5–5.0. Tubes are centrifuged in a SW41 rotor (Beckman Instruments, Palo Alto, CA) at 37,000 rpm for 19.5 h with 15 min acceleration and 45 min deceleration time. A photograph is taken of the centrifuge tube, and a densitometric scan of this photograph yields a density distribution profile of LDL. LDL subclass peaks are identified and the area under each curve is calculated, assuming Gaussian curves. Finally, the area under each LDL subclass peak is expressed as percentage of the total area. Recovery of LDL (1.019 < d < 1.063) cholesterol by this method was 86.4 ± 2.0% The within-run CV for the LDL cholesterol ranges from 3.0% to 7.8% and the between-run CV ranges from 1.8% to 2.3%.

In a study of 131 healthy individuals, this DGUC technique identified three sub-classes in most (88%) of the study subjects, while the remainder (12%) had two subclasses.[32] By defining a continuous LDL density variable using percentage of area and density midpoints for LDL$_1$, LDL$_2$, and LDL$_3$, LDL density was found to be associated with gender, serum TG, HDL cholesterol, and the ratio of LDL cholesterol to LDL apo B.

A subsequent report of genetic studies defined a different continuous variable, "K," based on the same procedures but using relative peak heights rather than areas.[33] Specifically, percentage peak heights designated as %h1, %h2, and %h3 are calculated for LDL$_1$, LDL$_2$, and LDL$_3$, respectively. Genetic studies of LDL density were performed by defining buoyant LDL as 0 < K < 1, and dense LDL as –1 < K < 0.. Among 159 family members, K was found to have an approximately normal distribution. Segregation analysis indicate genetic influences of the K parameter; however, the median value of K was lower for men than for women, decreased with age, and was lower for pre-menopausal women taking oral contraceptives than for those not taking oral contra-ceptives.[33, 34] These studies again indicate both genetic and non-genetic influences on LDL subclass distribution.

RELATIONSHIP AMONG METHODS OF DETERMINING LDL SUBCLASSES

There is a high degree of correlation between these different methods of determining LDL subclasses, despite the fact that the methods use different physical properties of LDL and have different analytical strategies for reporting LDL heterogeneity. As shown in Figure 14–2, LDL Rf and LDL-PPD have a correlation coefficient of 0.68 ($p < 0.01$), and this relationship has been replicated in other studies.[13] In addition, LDL-PPD is significantly correlated with LDL peak density ($r = 0.88$).[20] LDL-PPD is also highly correlated with LDL-VAPII major peak Rf ($r = 0.86$).[24] When subjects are classified as LDL subclass phenotype A or B, there are a significant differences in LDL Rf[13] and the overall distribution LDL. (See Figure 14–3.)

CLINICAL SIGNIFICANCE

There is now a growing body of evidence to support the role of small, dense LDL as a risk factor for coronary heart disease. Since the early 1980s, at least 9 case-control studies have demonstrated that a predominance of small, dense LDL particles is more common in cases than in controls.[11, 27, 29, 35-40] The cases in these studies were either MI survivors or patients with CAD documented by angiography. Importantly, even though a variety of laboratory techniques were used to characterize LDL subclasses, the results uniformly showed an association between small, dense LDL and risk of CHD. The relative risks (RRs) in these studies ranged from 3.0[11] to 6.9.[40]

Results from prospective studies examining small, dense LDL as a risk factor for coronary disease have recently been published. Using nested case-control analyses of prospective cohorts from the Stanford Five City Project,[41] the Physicians Health

Figure 14–2 ✧ Relationship between LDL Peak Particle Diameter Estimated by GGE and LDL Rf by Non-equilibrium DGUC

Results from 23 middle-aged males with normal lipid values.[22] The correlation coefficient is 0.68 ($p < .01$)

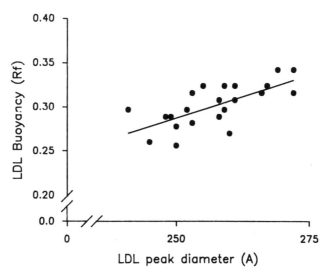

Figure 14–3 ✧ Mean Cholesterol Distribution by Non-equilibrium DGUC and Difference Plot Comparing Mean Values for Subjects with LDL Phenotype A and Phenotype B

Left view: Non-equilibrium DGUC of plasma from middle-aged males with normal lipid values.[22] Mean cholesterol values (mg/dL) are shown in each of 38 fractions in 9 males with LDL subclass phenotype A (solid symbols), and in 18 males with LDL subclass phenotype B (open symbols).

Right view: DGUC difference plot comparing mean values for subjects with LDL subclass phenotype B and those with phenotype A (B-A). Bars represent 95% confidence intervals of difference in means for each fraction. The plot shows that phenotype B subjects have more VLDL cholesterol, less buoyant LDL, more dense LDL, and less HDL cholesterol compared to phenotype A subjects.

To convert to mmol/L, multiply by 0.0259.

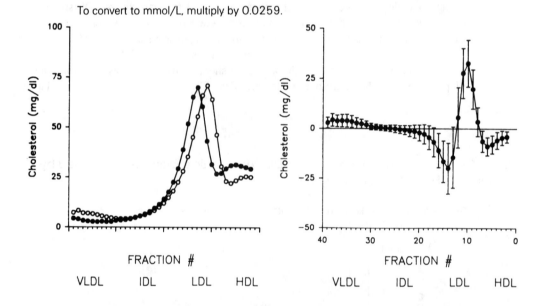

Study,[42] and the Quebec Cardiovascular Study,[43] important contributions to our understanding of LDL subclasses and coronary disease have been made.

The Stanford study was based on incident cases of CHD, both fatal and non-fatal, identified through community surveillance from 1979 to 1992. Controls were selected based on matching criteria for age, sex, ethnicity, treatment or control city, and time of surveillance. The laboratory analyses were performed on *non-fasting* baseline blood samples obtained from these study subjects. A total of 124 case-control pairs were identified, 90 men and 34 women pairs. The analysis was based on the case-control difference in LDL-PPD. For all subjects, a highly significant case-control mean difference was found (–5.1Å, $p < 0.001$), demonstrating that smaller LDL size predicted incident CHD in this population.[41] Importantly, multivariate analysis showed this difference in

LDL size was independent of TG, high-density lipoprotein cholesterol (HDL-C), smoking, systolic blood pressure, and body mass index (BMI).

The findings from the Physicians Health Study were based on a 7-year follow-up of 266 men with incident non-fatal MI or fatal CHD. Controls were matched for age, smoking, and time of randomization. Similar to the Stanford study, study participants were "not specifically instructed to provide fasting specimens." In this study, mean baseline LDL-PPD was smaller in cases compared to controls (256Å vs. 259Å, respectively; p 0.001).[42] The RR was 1.38 (95% CI 1.18 to 1.62) for an 8Å decrease in LDL-PPD. Baseline TG levels were also significantly different: 203 mg/dL (5.26 mmol/L) for cases vs. 155 mg/dL (4.01 mmol/L) for controls (p = 0.001). Thus, both LDL size and plasma TG were significant predictors of future CHD in this study. However, in contrast to the Stanford study, the association of LDL size with CHD was not independent of TG and HDL-C (RR = 1.09, p = 0.46).

The Quebec Cardiovascular Study followed 2,103 men initially free of ischemic heart disease (IHD) for five years. Of the 114 incident cases of IHD, 103 were matched with a control subject based on age, cigarette smoking, BMI, and alcohol intake. There was no difference in the mean baseline LDL-PPD between these cases and matched controls.[43] When LDL size was categorized as small (≤ 25.64 nm), intermediate (25.64 < LDL-PPD ≤ 26.05 nm) or large (> 26.05 nm), small LDL was significantly associated with IHD with an odds ratio of 3.6 (p < 0.01). In multivariate analysis, after controlling for plasma TG, apolipoprotein B, and HDL-C, the risk of IHD due to small LDL was attenuated to an odds ratio of 2.5 (p < 0.08). When men taking beta-blockers or diuretics were excluded from the multivariate analysis, the risk of IHD due to small LDL was 3.9 (p < 0.05). Thus, small LDL is associated with coronary disease in this study, and this relationship is modulated by lipids, apolipoproteins, and drugs.

Recent intervention studies have added new information regarding the clinical significance of small, dense LDL. In the Stanford Coronary Risk Intervention Project, 213 men with CAD who were undergoing angiography were randomized to usual care or to a coronary disease risk-reduction program.[44] The risk-reduction program included diet, exercise, and life style modifications, as well as lipid-lowering drugs if target lipid levels could not be met. Subjects were followed for four years with annual coronary angiography. LDL flotation rate was determined by analytical ultracentrifugation and subjects were classified as having either buoyant or dense LDL. Among subjects with buoyant LDL, there were no differences in annualized angiographic changes between the usual care and the risk-reduction groups. In contrast, among subjects with dense LDL, those on the risk-reduction program showed less progression of coronary disease based on minimum artery diameter (p < 0.007), and marginally favorable differences in mean artery diameter (p < 0.09) and stenosis (p < 0.08).[44] Thus, LDL buoyancy predicts subsequent response to an aggressive coronary risk reduction program.

Preliminary data from a recent study has suggests a mechanism for this difference in changes in coronary angiography. In the Familial Atherosclerosis Treatment Study, men undergoing coronary angiography were asked to participate in a study comparing the effect of intensive lipid-lowering therapy versus conventional therapy on coronary angiography.[45] Forty-four men who were randomized to treatment groups and followed for 2.5 years had LDL Rf measured on and off therapy.[46] Subjects with FCHL or elevated Lp(a), who had dense LDL at baseline, received the largest benefit of intensive therapy as determined by a decrease in coronary disease stenosis. Interesting, changes in LDL Rf were significantly associated with changes in stenosis, accounting for more than 45% of the variance. In addition, changes in LDL Rf were strongly correlated with changes in hepatic lipase ($r = 0.80$). These results indicate that decreases in HL mediate changes in LDL buoyancy, from dense to buoyant LDL, and are associated with an improvement in coronary stenosis.

Thus, although a variety of laboratory techniques were used in these studies to characterize LDL size, flotation rate, and density, the results uniformly demonstrate that small, dense LDL particles are more common among coronary disease cases than controls. Prospective studies have now indicated small, dense LDL predicts subsequent CAD. In addition, subjects with small, dense LDL appear to receive the largest benefit from lipid-lowering treatment by converting small, dense LDL to more buoyant LDL. The mechanism(s) explaining the associations between small, dense LDL and coronary disease may be multifactorial and remain to be elucidated.

Atherogenetic Mechanisms

These studies have led to numerous investigations of the possible biological mechanisms underlying the observed epidemiological associations. Although the metabolic processes involved remain to be definitively established, several explanations have been proposed. The relationship between small, dense LDL and coronary disease may be ascribed to:

1. the association of small, dense LDL with other atherogenic lipoproteins, including increased plasma TG and decreased HDL-C.[12]

2. the presence of the insulin resistance syndrome[47] or the visceral adiposity syndrome[48] in subjects with small, dense LDL.

3. increased oxidative susceptibility of small, dense LDL particles.[49, 50]

4. a lower affinity of small LDL for the LDL receptor due to alterations in apolipoprotein B conformation.[51]

5. increased inflow of dense LDL into the aortic intima.[52]

6. increased binding of dense LDL to arterial wall proteoglycans.[53]

Thus, the small, dense LDL phenotype may confer atherosclerosis susceptibility through multiple mechanisms that are not mutually exclusive, and in fact may be synergistic.[54]

LDL Subclasses and the Atherogenic Lipoprotein Phenotype

Many studies, including several of the studies noted above, have reported associations between small, dense LDL and other lipoprotein-related risk factors. Examples of four studies that have compared plasma concentrations of lipids and apolipoproteins among subjects with LDL subclass phenotypes A and B are presented in Table 14–1. Although the types of subjects examined in these studies were quite different, including normal subjects ($n = 72$),[13] members of primarily healthy families ($n = 301$),[15] members

Table 14-1 ✧ Mean Concentrations of Lipids and Apolipoprotein Risk Factors by LDL Subclass Phenotype

Risk Factor*	Adjusted Means (mg/dL)		Difference in Means
	PHENOTYPE A	PHENOTYPE B	
Triglyceride			
Normal subjects	51	102	+51**
Healthy families	69	141	+70**
FCHL families	94	184	+90**
Women twins	83	161	+78**
HDL-Cholesterol			
Normal subjects	64	48	-16**
Healthy families	46	37	-9**
FCHL families	48	41	-7**
Women twins	66	57	+-9**
LDL-Cholesterol			
Normal subjects	95	112	+17***
Healthy families	116	126	+10***
FCHL families	133	139	+6
Women twins	117	122	+5
Apolipoprotein B			
Normal subjects	77	100	+23**
Healthy families	76	98	+12**
FCHL families	117	138	+21**

*Sources: Normal subjects: Capell et al.[13] Healthy families: Austin et al.[15]
FCHL families: Austin et al.[16] Women twins: Selby et al.[47]
**p < .01
***p < .05
To convert cholesterol from mg/dL to mmol/L multiply by 0.0259.
To convert triglyceride from mg/dL to mmol/L multiply by 0.0113.

of families with FCHL (n = 173),[16] and a large sample of women twins (n = 682),[47] the magnitude of the lipid differences was remarkably similar. The largest difference is seen for plasma TG: Subjects with LDL subclass phenotype B have mean concentrations that are approximately 80 mg/dL (90 mmol/L) higher than those with phenotype A. In addition, LDL subclass phenotype B is simultaneously associated with significant decreases in HDL-C, with differences of 7–16 mg/dL (18–41 mmol/L). These close relationships between LDL size and both plasma TG and HDL-C have been confirmed in a cross-sectional study among Mexican-Americans,[55] and in a longitudinal study among subjects from the Framingham Offspring Study.[56] Interestingly, LDL subclass phenotypes do not show as strong a relationship with LDL cholesterol concentrations.

LDL subclass phenotypes are also consistently associated with variations in apolipoprotein concentrations and with lipoprotein mass values. As shown in Table 14–1, phenotype B subjects have significantly increased mean apolipoprotein B concentrations compared to subjects with phenotype A.[12, 13, 16] In addition, phenotype B is associated with increased VLDL mass, IDL mass, and decreased HDL₂ mass[12] (data not shown in table). As a result of these associations, phenotype B has been termed an "atherogenic lipoprotein phenotype."[12] This constellation of lipid, lipoprotein, and apolipoprotein abnormalities may represent a marker for an underlying pathogenic process leading to increased risk of CHD.

Oxidative Susceptibility of LDL Subclasses

Although the mechanisms underlying the association of small, dense LDL with risk of CHD are not yet established, several intriguing studies have reported that small, dense LDL particles are more susceptible to oxidation than large LDL particles, at least *in vitro*. In the first such study, three density subclasses of LDL were examined in 11 healthy volunteers.[49] Based on the method described by Esterbauer,[57] the two most dense LDL subclasses were less well protected against oxidative modification than the most buoyant subclass.[49] These results were confirmed in a subsequent study based on LDL from nine healthy males: oxidative susceptibility of LDL progressively increased with increasing density across five of six LDL subclasses.[58]

Similar findings have been reported in patients with combined hyperlipidemia (increased cholesterol and TG) and with hypertriglyceridemia.[59, 60] In comparing nine patients with combined hyperlipidemia who were under strict dietary control to five normal subjects, five LDL subclasses were isolated by DGUC. In both groups, the most dense of the LDL subclasses (d = 1.050–1.063 kg/L) had significantly reduced oxidative resistance compared to the other four density subclasses. LDL isolated from 12 hypertriglyceridemic subjects also has been shown to have enhanced susceptibility to oxidation compared to LDL from age- and sex-matched controls.[60] Interestingly, in this study 2 months of clofibrate treatment resulted in both a more buoyant LDL profile and reduced susceptibility of LDL to oxidation.

Finally, the oxidative susceptibility of LDL from subjects specifically characterized to have LDL subclass phenotypes A and B has recently been investigated.[50] Although the major peak of LDL from phenotype B subjects was more susceptible to oxidative modification than the major peak from phenotype A subjects, this difference was attributable to the predominance of small, dense LDL in the phenotype B subjects.

Taken together, the results of these studies suggest that small, dense LDL may contribute more to foam cell formation during atherogenesis than large, buoyant LDL, resulting in increased risk of CHD among individuals with small, dense LDL.

SUMMARY

A variety of methods are available for characterizing the distribution of LDL particles. Using the physical properties of LDL; size, flotation rate, and density, important advances in our understanding of the role of LDL subclasses in atherosclerosis have been made. Both genetic and environmental influences on LDL subclasses have been demonstrated in studies of families and twins. Epidemiological studies have demonstrated that small, dense LDL is associated with increased risk of CHD, and the presence of small, dense LDL precedes clinical events. Intervention studies have shown that small, dense LDL predicts the angiographic changes in response to lipid-lowering therapy, and that converting small, dense LDL to buoyant LDL is associated with coronary disease regression. These and other studies have shown that subjects with small, dense LDL are characterized by an atherogenic lipoprotein profile, including increased plasma TG and apolip-oprotein B and decreased HDL-C. The possibility that small, dense LDL may contribute to CHD because of its increased oxidative susceptibility raises the possibility that small, dense LDL may be directly involved in atherosclerosis. However, the mechanism to explain the association between small, dense LDL and coronary disease remains to be definitively established.

Acknowledgments: *This work was supported by NIH R-01 Grants HL46880 and HL49513 and NIH Program Project Grant HL-30086. Some of the studies were performed on the University of Washington Medical Center GCRC, NIH grant RR37. This work was performed during Dr. Austin's tenure as an Established Investigator of the American Heart Association. The authors wish to thank Chris Casazza and Cherry Tamblyn for their critical reading of the technical aspects of this manuscript.*

REFERENCES

1. Lindgren F, Jensen L, Wills R, Freeman N. Flotation rates, molecular weights and hydrated densities of the low density lipoproteins. Lipids 1969;4:337–44.
2. Adams G, Schumaker V. Polydispersity of human low-density lipoproteins. Ann NY Acad Sci 1969;164:130–46.
3. Hammond M, Fisher W. The characterization of a discrete series of low density lipoproteins in the disease, hyper-pre lipoproteinemia. J Biol Chem 1971;246:5454–65.
4. Krauss R, Blanche P. Detection and quantitation of LDL subfractions. Curr Opin Lipidol 1992;3:377–83.
5. Zambon A, Austin MA, Brown BG, Hokanson JE, Brunzell JD. Effect of hepatic lipase on LDL in normal men and those with coronary artery disease. Arterioscler Thromb 1993;13:147–53.
6. Krauss R, Burke D. Identification of multiple subclasses of plasma low density lipoproteins in normal humans. J Lipid Res 1982;23:97–104.
7. Rainwater D, Andres D, Ford A, Lowe W, Blanche P, Krauss R. Production of polyacrylamide gradient gels for the electrophoretic resolution of lipoproteins. J Lipid Res 1992;33:1876–81.
8. Austin MA, Mykkanen L, Kuusisto J, Edwards KL, Nelson C, Haffner SM, Pyorala K, Laakso M. Prospective study of small LDLs as a risk factor for non-insulin dependent diabetes mellitus in elderly men and women. Circulation 1995;92:1770–8.
9. Havel R, Eder H, Bragdon J. The distribution and chemical composition of ultracentrifugally separated lipoproteins in human serum. J Clin Invest 1955;34:1345–53.
10. Hokanson JE, Austin MA, Zambon A, Brunzell JD. Plasma triglyceride and LDL heterogeneity in familial combined hyperlipidemia. Arterioscler Thromb 1993;13:427–34.
11. Austin M, Breslow J, Hennekens C, Buring J, Willett W, Krauss RM. Low-density lipoprotein subclass patterns and risk of myocardial infarction. JAMA 1988;260:1917–21.
12. Austin M, King M-C, Vranizan K, Krauss RM. The atherogenic lipoprotein phenotype (ALP): a proposed genetic marker for coronary heart disease risk. Circulation 1990;82:495–506.
13. Capell WH, Zambon A, Austin MA, Brunzell JD, Hokanson JE. Compositional differences of LDL particles in normal subjects with LDL subclass phenotype A and LDL subclass phenotype B. Arterioscler Thromb Vasc Biol 1996;16:1040–6.
14. McNamara J, Campos H, Ordovas J, Peterson J, Wilson P, Schaefer E. Effect of gender, age, and lipid status on low density lipoprotein subfraction distribution: results of the Framingham Offspring Study. Arteriosclerosis 1987;7:483–90.

15. Austin M, King M-C, Vranizan K, Newman B, Krauss R. Inheritance of low density lipoprotein subclass patterns: results of complex segregation analysis. Am J Hum Genet 1988;43:838–46.

16. Austin MA, Brunzell JD, Fitch WL, Krauss RM. Inheritance of low density lipoprotein subclass patterns in familial combined hyperlipidemia. Arteriosclerosis 1990;10: 520–30.

17. Austin M, Newman B, Selby J, Edwards K, Mayer E, Krauss R. Genetics of low-density lipoprotein subclasses in women twins: concordance, heritability and commingling analysis. Arterioscler Thromb 1993;13:687–95.

18. Lamon-Fava S, Jimenez D, Christian J, et al. The NHLBI Twin Study: heritability of apolipoprotein A-I, B, and low density lipoprotein subclasses and concordance for lipoprotein(a). Atherosclerosis 1991;91:97–106.

19. Chung BH, Segrest JP, Cone JT, Pfau J, Geer JC, Duncan LA. High resolution plasma lipoprotein cholesterol profiles by a rapid, high volume semi-automated method. J Lipid Res 1981;22:1003–14.

20. Auwerx JH, Marzetta CA, Hokanson JE, Brunzell JD. Large buoyant LDL-like particles in hepatic lipase deficiency. Arteriosclerosis 1989;9:319–25.

21. Purnell JQ, Marcovina SM, Hokanson JE, Kennedy H, Cleary PA, Steffes MW, Brunzell JD. Levels of lipoprotein(a), apolipoprotein B, and lipoprotein cholesterol distribution in IDDM: results from follow-up in the Diabetes Control and Complications Trial. Diabetes 1995;44:1218–26.

22. Zambon A, Brown BG, Hokanson JE, Brunzell JB. Hepatic lipase changes predict coronary artery disease progression/regression in the familial atherosclerosis treatment study (FATS). Circulation 1996;94:I-539.

23. Failor RA, Hokanson JE, Brunzell JE, Low density lipoproteins in familial hyperlipidemias, In: Fidge N, Necitel P, eds, Atherosclerosis VII. Amsterdam: Elsevier Sciences, 1986: 156–63.

24. Kulkarni KR, Garber DW, Jones MK, Segrest JP. Identification and cholesterol quantification of low density lipoprotein subclasses in young adults by VAP-II methodology. J Lipid Res 1995;36:2291–302.

25. Shen MM, Krauss RM, Lindgren FT, Forte TM. Heterogeneity of serum low density lipoproteins in normal human subjects. J Lipid Res 1981;22:236–44.

26. Teng B, Thompson GR, Sniderman AD, Forte TM, Krauss RM, Kwiterovich PO, Jr. Composition and distribution of low density lipoprotein fractions in hyperapobetalipoproteinemia, normolipidemia, and familial hypercholesterolemia. Proc Natl Acad Sci USA 1983;80:6662–6.

27. Crouse J, Parks J, Schey H, Kahl FR. Studies of low density lipoprotein molecular weight in human beings with coronary artery disease. J Lipid Res 1985;26:566–74.

28. Chapman M, Laplaud P, Luc G,et al. Further resolution of the low density lipoprotein spectrum in normal human plasma: physicochemical characteristics of discrete subspecies separated by density gradient ultracentrifugation. J Lipid Res 1988;29:442–58.

29. Coresh J, Kwiterovich PJ, Smith H, Bachorik P. Association of plasma triglyceride and LDL particle diameter, density and chemical composition with premature coronary artery disease in men and women. J Lipid Res 1993;34:1687–97.

30. Hokanson JE, Krauss RM, Albers JJ, Austin MA, Brunzell JD. LDL physical and chemical properties in familial combined hyperlipidemia. Arterioscler Thromb Vasc Biol 1995; 15:452–9.

31. Marzetta CA, Foster DM, Brunzell JD. Relationships between LDL density and kinetic heterogeneity in subjects with normolipidemia and familial combined hyperlipidemia using density gradient ultracentrifugation. J Lipid Res 1989;30:1307–17.

32. Swinkels D, Hak-Lemmers H, Demacker P. Single spin density gradient ultracentrifugation method for the detection and isolation of light and heavy low density lipoprotein subfractions. J Lipid Res 1987;28:1233–9.

33. de Graaf J, Swinkels D, de Haan A, Demacker P, Stalenhoef A. Both inherited susceptibility and environmental exposure determine low density lipoprotein subfraction pattern distribution in healthy, Dutch families. Am J Hum Genet 1992;51:1295–1310.

34. Bredie SJ, Kiemeney LA, de Haan AF, Demacker PN, Stalenhoef AF. Inherited suscep-tibility determines the distribution of dense low-density lipoprotein subfraction profiles in familial combined hyperlipidemia. Am J Hum Genet 1996;58:812-22.
35. Fisher WR. Heterogeneity of plasma low density lipoproteins manifestations of the physiologic phenomenon in man. Metabolism 1983;32:283-91.
36. Griffin B, Caslake M, Yip B, Tait G, Packard C, Shepherd J. Rapid isolation of low density lipoprotein (LDL) subfractions from plasma by density gradient ultracentrifuga-tion. Atherosclerosis 1990;83:59-67.
37. Tornvall P, Karpe F, Carlson L, Hamsten A. Relationship of low density lipoprotein subfractions to angiographically defined coronary artery disease in young survivors of myocardial infarction. Atherosclerosis 1991;90:67-80.
38. Campos H, Genest JJ, Blijlevens E, et al. Low density lipoprotein particle size and coronary artery disease. Arterioscler Thromb 1992;12:187-95.
39. Jaakkola O, Solakivi T, Tertov V, Orekhov A, Miettinen T, Nikkari T. Characteristics of low-density lipoprotein subfractions from patients with coronary artery disease. Coronary Artery Disease 1993;4:379-85.
40. Griffin BA, Freeman DJ, Tait GW, Thomson J, Caslake MJ, Packard CJ, Shepherd J. Role of plasma triglyceride in the regulation of plasma low density lipoprotein (LDL) subfractions: relative contribution of small, dense LDL to coronary heart disease risk. Atherosclerosis 1994;106:241-53.
41. Gardner CD, Fortmann SP, Krauss RM. Association of small low-density lipoprotein particles with the incidence of coronary artery disease in men and women [comments]. JAMA 1996;276:875-81.
42. Stampfer MJ, Krauss RM, Ma J, Blanche PJ, Holl LG, Sacks FM, Hennekens CH. A prospective study of triglyceride level, low-density lipoprotein particle diameter, and risk of myocardial infarction. JAMA 1996;276:882-8.
43. Lamarche B, Tchernof A, Moorjani S, Camtin B, Dagenais G, Lupien P, Despres J-P. Small, dense low-density lipoprotein particles as a predictor of risk of ischemic heart disease in men: prospective results from the Quebec Cardiovascular Study. Circulation 1997;95:69-75.
44. Miller BD, Alderman EL, Haskell WL, Fair JM, Krauss RM. Predominance of dense low-density lipoprotein particles predicts angiographic benefit of therapy in the Stanford Coronary Risk Intervention Project. Circulation 1996;94:2146-53.
45. Brown G, Albers JJ, Fisher LD, Schaefer SM, Lin JT, Kaplan C, Zhao XQ, Bisson BD, Fitzpatrick VF, Dodge HT. Regression of coronary artery disease as a result of intensive lipid-lowering therapy in men with high levels of apolipoprotein B. N Engl J Med 1990;323:1289-98.
46. Zambon A, Brown BG, Hokanson JE, Brunzell JD. Familial diagnosis of dyslipidemia affects coronary disease regression in the in the familial atherosclerosis treatment study (FATS). J Invest Med 1997;45:A105.
47. Selby J, Austin M, Newman B, Mayer E, Krauss RM. LDL subclass phenotypes and the insulin resistance syndrome in women. Circulation 1993;88:381-7.
48. Fujimoto W, Abbate S, Kahn S, Hokanson JE, Brunzell JD. The visceral adiposity syn-drome in Japanese-American men. Obesity Research 1994;2:364-71.
49. de Graaf J, Hak-Lemmers H, Hectors M, Demacker P, Hendriks J, Stalenhof AFH. Enhanced susceptibility to in vitro oxidation of the dense low density lipoprotein sub-fraction in healthy subjects. Arterioscler Thromb 1991;11:298-306.
50. Chait A, Brazg R, Tribble D, Krauss R. Susceptibility of small, dense, low-density lipo-proteins to oxidative modification in subjects with the atherogenic lipoprotein pheno-type, pattern B. Am J Med 1993;94:350-6.
51. Galeano NF, Milne R, Marcel YL, Walsh MT, Levy E, Ngu'yen TD, Gleeson A, Arad Y, Witte L, al Haideri M, et al. Apoprotein B structure and receptor recognition of tri-glyceride-rich low density lipoprotein (LDL) is modified in small LDL but not in triglyc-eride-rich LDL of normal size. J Biol Chem 1994;269:511-9.

52. Bjornheden T, Babyi A, Bondjers G, Wiklund O. Accumulation of lipoprotein fractions and subfractions in the arterial wall, determined in an in vitro perfusion system. Atherosclerosis 1996;123:43-56.

53. Anber V, Griffin BA, McConnell M, Packard CJ, Shepherd J. Influence of plasma lipid and LDL-subfraction profile on the interaction between low density lipoprotein with human arterial wall proteoglycans. Atherosclerosis 1996;124:261-71.

54. Austin MA, Krauss RM. LDL density and atherosclerosis [letter; comment]. JAMA 1995; 273:115.

55. Haffner S, Mykkanen L, Valdez R, Paidi M, Stern M, Howard B. LDL size and subclass pattern in a biethnic population. Arterioscler Thromb 1993;13:1623-30.

56. McNamara J, Jenner J, Li Z, Wilson P, Schaefer E. Change in LDL particle size is associated with change in plasma triglyceride concentration. Arterioscler Thromb 1992; 12:1284-90.

57. Esterbauer H, Striegl G, Puhl H, Rotheneder M. Continuous monitoring of in vitro oxidation of human low density lipoprotein. Free Rad Res Commun 1989;6:67-75.

58. Tribble D, Holl L, Wood P, Krauss RM. Variations in oxidative susceptibility among six low density lipoprotein subfractions of differing density and particle size. Atherosclerosis 1992;93:189-99.

59. Dejager S, Bruckert E, Chapman J. Dense low density lipoprotein subspecies with diminished oxidative resistance predominate in combined hyperlipidemia. J Lipid Res 1993;34:295-308.

60. de Graaf J, Hendriks J, Demacker P, Stalenhoef A. Identification of multiple dense LDL subfractions with enhanced susceptibility to in vitro oxidation among hypertriglyceridemic subjects: normalization after clofibrate treatment. Arterioscler Thromb 1993;13: 712-19.

Lipoprotein(a): Structure, Measurement, and Clinical Significance

15

Santica M. Marcovina and Marlys L. Koschinsky

INTRODUCTION

❖ In 1963, Kåre Berg observed that rabbits immunized with human low-density lipoproteins (LDL) produced an antiserum which reacted with an antigenic component that appeared to be present within the LDL fraction of some but not all of the individuals tested.[1] Berg called this newly discovered antigen lipoprotein(a) [Lp(a)], and he found that the presence of this antigen was genetically determined by an autosomal dominant mode of inheritance.[2] Subsequent studies provided evidence that Lp(a) is a specific family of lipoprotein particles whose protein moiety is comprised of at least two major proteins, a single copy of apo B-100 linked to a single copy of a protein of variable mass which has not been found in any other lipoprotein. This protein, which is responsible for the peculiar characteristics of Lp(a), is called apolipoprotein(a) [apo(a)].

Over the past several decades, numerous studies have established that increased Lp(a) concentrations are associated with increased risk of cardiovascular and cerebral vascular disease. Although the mechanism of Lp(a) atherogenicity or thrombogenicity has yet to be clarified, numerous structural, genetic, and metabolic studies have provided some intriguing possibilities to explain its association with atherosclerosis.

STRUCTURE OF LIPOPROTEIN(a)

Lp(a) is formed by the assembly of a lipoprotein which is structurally very similar to LDL in protein and lipid composition with a carbohydrate-rich, highly hydrophilic protein named apo(a). One molecule of apo B-100 in Lp(a) is covalently linked to apo(a) by a single disulfide bridge, although non-covalent interactions are required for the initial association of the two proteins.[3-5] Lp(a) has peculiar characteristics and, unlike the other human plasma lipoproteins, it cannot be classified on the basis of its physical-chemical properties as defined by the classical lipoprotein separation methods such as density gradient ultracentrifugation and electrophoretic separation. In fact, in electrophoresis Lp(a) has a pre-beta mobility similar to very-low-density lipoproteins (VLDL),[6] and in ultracentrifugation its density spans both the LDL and high-density lipoprotein (HDL) range, with most of the Lp(a) found within the 1.050–1.100 kg/L density range.[7] However, Lp(a) can be detected in small amounts in all density intervals in the range of 1.000–1.210 kg/L,[8, 9] and the concentration of Lp(a) appears to significantly increase in the triglyceride-rich < 1.006 kg/L density fraction after a fatty meal.[10, 11] In studies performed on Lp(a) from different individuals, Fless et al.[8] not only confirmed the broad inter-individual heterogeneity of Lp(a) particles, but also found that Lp(a) exhibits intra-individual density heterogeneity due to differences in the protein to lipid ratio in Lp(a) particles.

Considering that apo(a)-free Lp(a) obtained by reduction of the disulfide bond between apo(a) and apo B-100 has physical-chemical properties similar if not identical to LDL, it is evident that the peculiar characteristics and the size and density heterogeneity of Lp(a) are almost entirely accounted for by the presence of its distinct protein component, apo(a). Apo(a) is a carbohydrate-rich protein which exhibits both intra- and inter-individual variations in size. The mean carbohydrate content has been estimated to be 28% by weight with a molar ratio of 3:7:5:4:7 for mannose, galactose, galactosamine, glucosamine, and sialic acid, respectively.[12] Although differences in apo(a) size are primarily related to differences in the length of the polypeptide chain,[13, 14] a contribution of carbohydrate heterogeneity to the size heterogeneity cannot be excluded. The analysis of the apo(a) cDNA isolated from human liver libraries led to the discovery that apo(a) has a high degree of homology with the serine protease zymogen plasminogen.[15] Plasminogen contains a protease domain and one copy each of five domains called kringles, designated as kringle 1 through kringle 5. A kringle is a highly conserved, tri-loop polypeptide structure stabilized by three disulfide bridges also found in other proteins involved in hemostasis and fibrinolysis.[16, 17] The tri-loop structure is similar in shape to the danish pastry called a kringle, from which its name derives.

The basic structure of apo(a) is graphically represented in Figure 15-1. Apo(a) contains a kringle domain and a carboxyl-terminal protease domain with 85% amino acid identity with the plasminogen protease domain. Despite the high degree of sequence conservation between the apo(a) and plasminogen protease domain, there is no proteolytic activity associated with apo(a) due to critical amino acid substitutions within this domain.[18] The kringle domain is composed of 11 distinct kringle types, ten of which are similar but not identical to each other and to plasminogen kringle 4, and one which shares over 85% amino acid identity with plasminogen kringle 5. The ten kringles are identified as kringle 4 (K4) type 1 through type 10, and their sequence identity with plasminogen K4 ranges between 78% and 88%.[15, 19, 20] Apo(a) K4 type 1 and types 3 through 10 appear to have only one copy present per apo(a) molecule, while K4 type 2 is present in multiple repeats varying in number from as few as 3 to as many as 40.[21, 22] The number of K4 type 2 repeats is therefore responsible for the size heterogeneity of apo(a) and ultimately of Lp(a) and for the different apo(a) isoforms.

Based on the cloned sequence,[15] the molecular mass of apo(a) protein varies from 187 kD for an apo(a) which contains 12 K4 domains, to 662 kD for an apo(a) which contains 50 K4 domains. Therefore, the weight ratio of apo(a) to apo B varies significantly in Lp(a) particles. For example, Lp(a) particles with 20 apo(a) K4 domains have about 64% of their protein mass as apo B and 36% as apo(a). In contrast, large Lp(a) particles containing 40 apo(a) K4 domains contain approximately an equal proportion of apo(a) and apo B protein (see Figure 15-2).

Figure 15–1 ✧ Schematic Representation of the Structure of Apo(a)

The bottom diagram shows the organization of apo(a). Apo(a) contains 10 distinct kringle 4 (K4) sequences (designated T1–T10), which are highly similar to the plasminogen K4 sequence. The K4 sequences in apo(a) are followed by domains which share extensive sequence similarity with the kringle 5 and the protease domain of plasminogen. K4 type 2 is present in a variable number of identical copies in apo(a), which forms the basis of apo(a) isoform size hetero-geneity; K4 type 1 and types 3–10 are present in single copy in each isoform. In the inset is an enlargment of K4 type 2 with the amino acid sequence, the three internal disulfide bonds, and the putative glycosylation sites indicated.

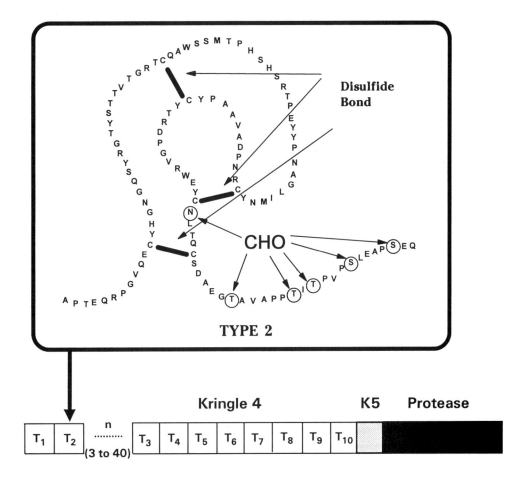

Figure 15–2 ✧ Schematic Representation of the Relative Proportion of Apo(a) and Apo B-100 in Lp(a) of Different Sizes

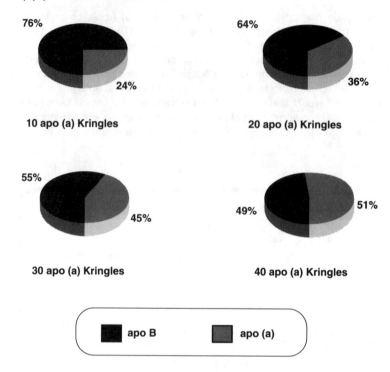

The apo(a) gene can be considered one of the most polymorphic transcribed genes in the human genome. The apo(a) gene can be divided into four main regions: the sequence coding for the signal peptide, the plasminogen-like K4 domain coding sequence containing several tandem repeats of a 5.5 Kb sequence encoding a cysteine-rich motif, the plasminogen-like K5 domain coding sequence, and the plasminogen-like protease domain coding sequence.[15] The apo(a) gene resides on chromosomes 6q 26–27 in close proximity to the plasminogen gene.[23] The closeness of the two genes and their remarkable sequence homology suggest a common origin, either from duplication of the plasminogen gene or from a common ancestral precursor.

GENETIC DETERMINANTS OF LIPOPROTEIN(a) LEVELS

Early family studies using diffusion in agarose gel indicated the presence of Lp(a) segregated in a Mendelian autosomal-dominant fashion determined by two alleles, Lp(a⁺) and Lp(a⁰) or null allele.[2] At that time, Lp(a) was found in only 30–40% of the subjects studied in different populations.[2] Numerous studies in which quantitative immunochemical methods have been used to measure Lp(a) have firmly established that Lp(a) concentrations, which range from < 0.1 mg/dL to > 100 mg/dL, are strongly influenced by genetic factors.[24-26]

Discovery of genetic size polymorphism of apo(a) by Utermann and colleagues provided new insights into the genetic control of Lp(a). Apo(a) isoforms were determined by the mobility of apo(a) in sodium dodecylsulphate polyacrylamide gel electrophoresis (SDS-PAGE) under reducing conditions. Six different apo(a) isoforms were identified: F, B, S1, S2, S3, and S4.[27] The apo(a) isoforms are specified by alleles at a single apo(a) locus. In addition, a null allele has been postulated to account for the segregation of apo(a) isoforms in families and in individuals with no detectable apo(a).[28] These studies indicated that apo(a) isoforms are specified at a single locus by multiple autosomal alleles co-dominantly expressed. Additionally, it was shown that the size of the apo(a) isoforms were, in general, inversely correlated with the Lp(a) plasma concentrations.

Gaubatz, et al.[29] resolved 11 different apo(a) isoforms using PAGE combined with a sensitive detection system. Kamboh et al.,[30] using an improved separation technique, were able to distinguish as many as 23 apo(a) isoforms by SDS agarose gel electrophoresis followed by immunoblotting. Marcovina et al.[31] developed a modification of the procedure of Kamboh et al. using agarose gel electrophoresis followed by immunoblotting with ^{125}I-labelled monoclonal antibody and autoradiography. This approach allowed the identification of 34 apo(a) isoforms in a biracial population and is entirely consistent with the observations of Lackner et al.,[21] in which a total of 34 apo(a) alleles could be distinguished.

By using pulsed-field gel electrophoresis and genomic blotting,[32] it was determined that 94% of Caucasians are heterozygous at the apo(a) locus.[33] Examination of Lp(a) concentrations and apo(a) genotypes in 48 nuclear Caucasian families indicates that the apo(a) gene accounts for greater than 90% of the variation in plasma Lp(a) concentrations.[33] The number of K4 repeats in the apo(a) gene accounted for about 70% of the Lp(a) variation, and the other factors at the apo(a) locus accounted for about 20% of the inter-individual variation in plasma Lp(a) concentrations.

A recently identified repeat polymorphism of the pentanucleotide sequence TTTTA present at −1371 upstream of the translational start site in the apo(a) gene may account for 10–14% of the inter-individual variations in Lp(a) levels in Caucasians.[34] It has been shown that the number of pentanucleotide repeats (PNR), 6–11, correlate inversely with plasma Lp(a) levels in Whites; this correlation was not observed in Black African subjects. Whether or not the effect of the PNR polymorphism is dependent on the number of K4 repeats in apo(a) remains unclear at present, and the direct role of this sequence in determining Lp(a) levels remains to be addressed.

There have been several reports of the effects of other genes on plasma Lp(a) levels. Although mutations in the LDL receptor gene have been reported to result in elevated Lp(a) levels,[35] this is contradicted by a number of other studies which suggest no role for this receptor in Lp(a) catabolism. Similarly, although an association between apo E isoform type and plasma Lp(a) levels has been suggested, the results of independent studies addressing this relationship are conflicting. The role of apo B-100 in determining plasma Lp(a) levels was initially suggested by studies in which patients heterozygous for genetic defects in apo B-100 synthesis had lower Lp(a) levels than their unaffected relatives.[36] However, it has recently been reported that low LDL levels present in patients with hypobetalipoproteinemia had no effect on corresponding Lp(a) levels.[37]

MEASUREMENT OF LIPOPROTEIN(a)

The high size heterogeneity of apo(a), the distinct protein component of Lp(a), its association with apo B-100 to form a single macromolecular complex, and the amino acid sequence homology with plasminogen constitute major challenges to the development of suitable immunoassays for the quantitative determination of Lp(a) in human plasma. To obtain purified apo(a), reducing agents are used to dissociate apo(a) from apo B. However, it has been demonstrated that the use of reducing agents results in a marked decrease of apo(a) immunoreactivity, probably due to the cleavage of the intrachain disulfide bonds of the kringle domains.[38] The fact that the structure of isolated apo(a) is immunochemically different from apo(a) in Lp(a) has been further demonstrated by the observation that monoclonal antibodies raised against purified apo(a) have limited reactivity with native Lp(a).[39] Therefore, antibodies against apo(a) are generated by immunizing animals with intact Lp(a). If the generated antibodies are polyclonal, they need to be absorbed against apo B. Additionally, their immunoreactivity should also be tested against plasminogen in the assay format in which the antibodies are intended to be used, and, if cross-reactivity is detected, the antibodies should be absorbed against plasminogen. Similarly, when monoclonal antibodies against apo(a) are produced, they should be selected to react to epitopes present only in apo(a), so as to prevent cross-reactivity with plasminogen.

A major problem in the generation of antibodies for measuring apo(a) derives from the size heterogeneity of apo(a), which is due to the variable number of K4 type 2 repeats present in the various apo(a) polymorphs.[21, 22] In fact, repeated antigenic determinants are present in variable numbers in different apo(a) particles, and therefore the immunoreactivity of the antibodies directed to these repeated epitopes will vary depending on the size of apo(a). As a consequence, it is expected that immunoassays using polyclonal antibodies or monoclonal antibodies directed to epitopes present in K4 type 2 will tend to underestimate apo(a) concentration in subjects with apo(a) of a smaller size than the apo(a) present in the assay calibrator, and to overestimate the apo(a) concentration of the larger apo(a) particles.

The problem of variable immunoreactivity of the antibodies can be solved by selecting monoclonal antibodies directed to apo(a) antigenic determinants not expressed in K4 type 2. However, the use of monoclonal antibodies will limit the choice of the assay format mainly to enzyme-linked immunosorbent assay (ELISA). Oxidative modification of Lp(a) may produce significant changes in Lp(a) conformation,[40] and the same may occur with carbohydrate removal. The immunoreactivity of some of the monoclonal antibodies produced in our laboratory was differentially affected by carbohydrate removal and Lp(a) oxidation. The removal of sialic acid, for example, resulted in total loss of immunoreactivity for one monoclonal antibody, while the immunoreactivity of other antibodies was significantly higher (unpublished observations). Therefore, to avoid technical artifacts and lack of comparability of values, the monoclonal antibodies to be used in Lp(a) immunoassays should be selected after a careful characterization of their epitope specificity and immunochemical properties.

Specific recommendations for selecting and characterizing monoclonal antibodies for measuring apo AI and B are contained in a document of the International Federation of Clinical Chemistry.[41] Most of the recommendations made in this document are also applicable to monoclonal antibodies to apo(a).

A second approach to solve the effect of the size heterogeneity of apo(a) on the antibody immunoreactivity has been proposed by several investigators.[42-46] This approach involves the use of a sandwich-type ELISA in which the Lp(a) particles in plasma are captured by monoclonal or polyclonal antibodies against apo(a), and then Lp(a) concentration is measured by enzyme-conjugated monoclonal or polyclonal antibodies against the apo B component of Lp(a). It should be noted that even though the immunoreactivity of apo B in Lp(a) has been found to be only modestly lower than that in LDL,[47] studies performed with monoclonal antibodies clearly indicate that the epitope expression of apo B in Lp(a) is different from that in LDL.[48, 49] Therefore, the anti-apo B antibodies to be used in Lp(a) assays, particularly monoclonal antibodies generated against LDL–apo B, should be carefully characterized.

Conceptually, it is true that Lp(a) assays using anti-apo B antibodies or anti-apo(a) monoclonal antibodies directed to epitopes present in apo(a) domains other than K4 type 2 are not affected by variation in Lp(a) size. However, the results of Lp(a) concentration in different samples will depend on the isoforms in the assay calibrator. In the immunoassays, the concentration of an analyte is obtained by comparing the immunoreactivity of the samples with that of the calibrator, which contains a known concentration of the analyte. Therefore, the composition of the assay calibrator should be very similar to that of the samples being analyzed. Considering the high heterogeneity of apo(a) size, this requirement is impossible to attain; therefore, the composition of the calibrator in the immunoassays is an arbitrary choice that will influence the values obtained in the samples.

Following the approach of Albers et al.,[50] historically the values assigned to Lp(a) assay calibrators, and consequently Lp(a) concentrations in the measured samples, have been expressed in terms of total lipoprotein mass. However, obtaining an accurate determination of Lp(a) particle mass is difficult in that it requires the summation of the independent determination of Lp(a) protein, lipid, and carbohydrate components.

Because Lp(a) is a heterogeneous complex of two proteins, the total protein mass is determined in the primary standard, usually by the Lowry method. However, considering the size heterogeneity of apo(a), the ratio of apo(a) to apo B in Lp(a) particles is highly variable, as illustrated in Figure 15–2. Therefore, it is evident that, independent of whether the values are expressed in terms of lipoprotein or protein mass, the ratio of apo(a) to apo B in the calibrator will affect the results for the samples. This concept is illustrated by the following example:

Lp(a) analyses are performed by the same ELISA, with an anti-apo-B antibody enzyme-conjugate used for detection, calibration with two different Lp(a) preparations, and total protein mass determined by the Lowry method. The first preparation is an Lp(a) in which apo B is 70% of the total protein mass, and the second preparation is an Lp(a) in which apo B is 50% of the total protein mass. Considering the higher proportion of apo B in the first preparation, it is evident that the anti-apo-B antibodies will have a higher reactivity than with the second preparation. As a consequence, the same samples will have lower Lp(a) values in the assay calibrated with the first standard than those obtained by the assay calibrated with the second standard. Therefore, it is misleading to state that Lp(a) concentration may be accurately quantified regardless of the apo(a) isoforms with values expressed in terms of Lp(a) mass.[45]

The only potentially accurate measurements, independent of apo(a) size polymorphism, are those obtained by methods using monoclonal antibodies specific to epitopes that are not present in K4 type 2, or antibodies to apo B using calibrators with value assigned in terms of nmol/L.

To quantify the influence of apo(a) size polymorphism on the accuracy of Lp(a) values, we produced, selected, and extensively characterized several monoclonal antibodies for their immunochemical properties and apo(a) domain specificity.[51] We developed and optimized three sandwich ELISA systems using monoclonal antibodies (MAb) or polyclonal antibodies (PAb) with different specificities as detection antibodies: Mab a-5, specific for apo(a) K4 types 1 and 2, MAb a-40, specific for apo(a) K4 type 9, and a PAb specific for apo B-100. The measurements were performed on microtiter plates coated with MAb a-6, specific to K4 type 2, to capture the Lp(a) particles. The assays were calibrated with the same serum containing apo(a) with 21 K4 domains and with an Lp(a) value assigned in nmol/L. Using all three ELISAs, we measured Lp(a) in a group of 723 subjects selected to have a single apo(a) isoform, as determined by a high-resolution phenotyping system.[31] Essentially identical results were obtained by the two methods that measured Lp(a) by use of either a polyclonal antibody against apo B or the monoclonal antibody against K4 type 9, which is present only once per apo(a) particle. In contrast, the ELISA using MAb a-5, specific for apo(a) kringle 4 type 2 repeats, overestimated Lp(a) concentration in samples containing apo(a) with more than 21 kringle 4 repeats and underestimated Lp(a) samples containing apo(a) with fewer than 21 kringle 4 repeats. The results of this study clearly demonstrate that antibody specificity and apo(a) size heterogeneity can significantly affect Lp(a) measurements.

Despite all of the above-mentioned problems, numerous immunochemical methods for the measurement of Lp(a) in a wide variety of formats, some of which are commercially available, have been reported.[52, 53] Albers et al. were the first to report the development of a radial immunodiffusion (RID) and subsequently of a radioimmunoassay (RIA) for the measurement of Lp(a).[50, 54] Other assay formats include electroimmunodiffusion,[55, 56] ELISA,[42–45, 57–59] latex immunoassay,[60] immunonephelometric assay,[61] immunoturbidimetric assay,[62] and fluorescence assay.[46]

We have compared Lp(a) values obtained by two direct binding ELISA methods developed in our laboratory and seven commercially available methods, all calibrated with the same fresh-frozen serum with an intermediate size apo(a) isoform.[63] Despite the significant differences in antibody source and in assay format, a common calibrator was able to decrease the differences in Lp(a) values obtained by the different methods. The results of two international surveys of Lp(a) measurements indicated that the lack of a common primary standard and poor assay precision were the main factors responsible for the high inter-laboratory variation observed in the surveys.[64] A potential approach to bypass the problems of the immunochemical determination of Lp(a) could be to quantify Lp(a) by its cholesterol content. To this end, two methods were recently reported. In one method, cholesterol is enzymatically measured by a continuous flow analyzer in lipoprotein classes separated by single-spin vertical rotor ultracentrifugation.[65] The second reported method is based on the use of lectin affinity to separate Lp(a) from other lipoproteins with measurement of Lp(a) cholesterol by enzymatic assay.[66] Both of these methods have the potential for use in screening subjects with high Lp(a) concentrations. However, further studies are required to compare the clinical significance of Lp(a) cholesterol with that of Lp(a) mass or Lp(a) particle number.

At the present time, there is no standardization for measurements of Lp(a). We have summarized[52] the problems that must be addressed in order to standardize Lp(a) measurement:

1. careful selection and characterization of the antibodies, optimization of the assay format, and demonstration that apo(a) size heterogeneity does not affect the accuracy of the results.

2. selection of the apo(a) polymorph in the primary standard, reference material, and assay calibrators.

3. development of a common, validated method for isolation of Lp(a) to be used as primary standard.

4. development of suitable reference material.

5. expression of apo(a) values.

6. development of a reference method.

The International Federation of Clinical Chemistry (IFCC) has formed a Working Group on Lp(a) with the aim to produce, select, and characterize a suitable reference preparation for Lp(a). Work is in progress to assign an accuracy-based target value to two preparations. Extensive work will then be required to document to what extent a common reference material is able to decrease the large among-method variability of Lp(a) values. However, it must be noted that the availability of a common reference preparation can only reduce the variability due to the calibration component of the different assays. Manufacturers of Lp(a) test kits should include standardization as one of their primary design goals by making available to clinical chemistry laboratories Lp(a) assays documented to be unaffected by apo(a) size polymorphism. Provision of an IFCC reference material for such assays would be an important contribution to the comparability of Lp(a) values.

POPULATION STUDIES

As we have discussed, Lp(a) concentrations are almost entirely genetically determined, and variation at the apo(a) locus contributes to this heritability.[33, 67] Numerous studies[68–75] also reported that Lp(a) values vary greatly between ethnic groups, and that this variability cannot be entirely explained by differences in apo(a) isoform size. The frequency distribution of Lp(a) in Whites is highly skewed toward the low concentrations. In contrast, in the Black population the distribution is almost Gaussian, and the median Lp(a) value in Blacks is nearly three times as high as in Whites.[75] In both Black and White infants, Lp(a) concentrations are lower at birth and rise to adult concentrations by age 2 years.[76] A more recent study performed in a consecutive series of 1032 babies reported longitudinal changes in Lp(a) concentrations during the first year of life.[77] Lp(a) concentrations measured during the first postnatal week predicted the concentrations at 8.5 months, at which time Lp(a) concentrations were of the same order of magnitude as those of the parents.

After the initial rise in early childhood, Lp(a) concentrations were reported to be stable throughout adulthood, with no significant gender-related differences.[50, 69] However, results from four major population-based studies do not entirely confirm these findings.

In the CARDIA study,[75] Lp(a) concentrations were determined in a group of 4165 young adults comprising approximately the same number of Blacks and Whites and men and women. In this study, no gender-related difference in Lp(a) concentrations was found among Whites. Among Blacks, a small but statistically significant ($p < .05$) difference was found, with concentrations of Lp(a) higher in women than in men.

In the PROCAM study,[78] Lp(a) concentrations were measured in 1865 White males (age 20–64 years) and 819 females (age 20–59 years). The gender-related mean values were not significantly different. However, in men, Lp(a) concentrations remained constant with age, while Lp(a) concentrations in postmenopausal women were 2.1 mg/dL higher. The same observation was made in the ARIC study,[74] in which Lp(a) concentrations were determined in a large cohort of Black and White subjects. Premenopausal women from both races had lower Lp(a) concentrations than postmenopausal women. Additionally, it was found that both Black and White postmenopausal women on hormone replacement therapy had lower Lp(a) concentrations than women not on hormone therapy.[79]

Among 1284 White men and 1394 White women participating in the Framingham Offspring study,[80] no gender-related differences in Lp(a) values were found. Although Lp(a) concentrations were 8% higher in postmenopausal women than in premenopausal women, this difference was not statistically significant. Furthermore, there was no significant difference in Lp(a) concentration between postmenopausal women on estrogen therapy and those not taking estrogen. The findings of this study contradict previous reports[74, 78, 79] and are rather surprising in view of the fact that a decrease in Lp(a) concentrations in women on hormone replacement therapy has been reported in several additional studies.[81–84]

Data from all the population-based studies indicate that Lp(a) concentrations are race-related, with Blacks having the most striking difference compared to other races, both in terms of Lp(a) values and distribution. In this regard, it has recently been demonstrated that the Black American population has an increased frequency of intermediately-sized alleles, whereas Whites have a higher frequency of both small and large alleles;[85] the major determinant of increased Lp(a) levels in the Black population was found to be attributable to a four- to fivefold increase in the Lp(a) levels associated with intermediate apo(a) isoform sizes relative to Whites.[85] It is also likely that differences in Lp(a) concentration may be observed among ethnic groups within the same race. Therefore, population-based reference values, as well as the concentration at which Lp(a) is considered to be a risk factor, should be established for each ethnic group.

THROMBOTIC AND ATHEROGENIC ACTIVITIES OF LIPOPROTEIN(a)

Components of Lp(a) have similarities to both LDL and plasminogen, suggesting that Lp(a) may represent a bridge between the fields of atherosclerosis and thrombosis.[86] Recent studies have demonstrated that Lp(a) inhibits fibrinolysis by competing with plasminogen for binding to fibrin[87-90] and to cell surfaces.[88, 91, 92] The presence of both apo(a) and apo B has been documented in atheromatous plaques in arteries and vein grafts,[93-100] with Lp(a) co-localizing with fibrin.[99] Lp(a) has been shown to regulate the expression of plasminogen activator inhibitor-1 (PAI-1) in endothelial cells, which in turn inhibits the generation of plasmin by complexing and inactivating tissue-type plasminogen activator (tPA).[101] Another study reported that Lp(a) can inhibit the production and/or secretion of tPA from human endothelial cells,[102] which may also lead to impaired plasminogen activation and inhibition of fibrinolysis.

There have been conflicting reports on the effect of Lp(a) on the lysis of fibrin clots. Although studies have reported that apo(a)/Lp(a) interferes with the lysis of fibrin clots *in vitro*,[103] as well as the lysis of fibrin clots introduced into mice over-expressing apo(a) from a transgene[104] and the lysis of clots containing human recombinant apo(a) in a rabbit vein fibrinolysis model,[105] other studies have reported either no effect of Lp(a) on this process,[106] or a stimulatory effect on clot lysis.[107] These discrepancies may be attributable to differences in experimental methodologies and/or the source of Lp(a)/apo(a) used for these studies.

Harpel et al.[108, 109] have shown that sulfhydryl compounds such as homocysteine, known to be associated with atherosclerosis and thromboembolic disease, and glutathione increase the affinity of Lp(a) for fibrin. They further propose that following vascular injury, partial plasmin degradation of the thrombus formed at the vessel wall produces a substrate that binds Lp(a) with a higher affinity than intact fibrin.[87] Increased concentrations of homocysteine and glutathione leaking from red cells and platelets in the thrombus increase the affinity of Lp(a) for fibrin. During the repair process, the Lp(a)-fibrin complex is incorporated into the vessel intima, contributing to the formation of an atheromatous plaque. Lp(a) is also thought to promote the growth of plaques by inhibiting plasmin-dependent activation of transforming growth factor beta (TGF-β), thereby promoting proliferation of smooth muscle cells.[110-112] It has also been suggested that formation of an insoluble complex of Lp(a) with calcium in atherosclerotic lesions may contribute to plaque growth.[113]

Preliminary studies suggest that the formation of *in vitro* apo(a)-elastin complexes is potentiated by calcium (co-author's unpublished data). The incorporation of Lp(a)-derived cholesterol into plaque has also been documented.[114] Thus, Lp(a) is thought to contribute to the continuous growth of the lesion as well as the acute thrombotic event that occurs after a plaque ruptures by inhibiting the activation of plasminogen by tPA. It is still possible, however, that localization of apo(a) in plaque may represent a secondary phenomenon, and that Lp(a) is not causally related to lesion development. The latter hypothesis is supported by a recent study in which elevated Lp(a) levels were no longer atherogenic if LDL levels were substantially reduced, suggesting that Lp(a) may not be a primary causative agent in atherogenesis.[115] Scanu has suggested that the action of Lp(a) at the cell surface may be related to focal events rather than plasma concentrations of the lipoprotein;[116] this may also explain why Lp(a) levels are not generally correlated with fibrinolytic parameters such as α_2-antiplasmin/plasmin complexes[117] or fibrin degradation products such as D-dimer.[118]

Results from these and other studies have prompted investigators to examine the relationship of Lp(a) concentration in plasma and the success of thrombolytic therapy. Five studies have shown that baseline Lp(a) concentrations do not affect the outcome of thrombolytic therapy.[119-123] Reports of Lp(a) concentrations during thrombolytic therapy are contradictory. Qiu et al. reported no effect of streptokinase or single-chain form tPA therapy on plasma Lp(a) concentrations in unstable angina,[121] while Hegele et al., reported acute reduction of Lp(a) concentrations by double-chain form tPA.[124] Comparison of these studies is difficult because one study sampled Lp(a) concentrations 6 h after therapy while the other sampled after 12 h, and different forms of tPA were used. Di Lorenzo et al. reported acute lowering of Lp(a) concentrations by heparin in patients undergoing percutaneous transluminal coronary angioplasty (PTCA),[125] but Hegele et al. observed that heparin alone had no effect.[124] All of these studies were done with small numbers of patients and must be repeated with sample sizes adequate to represent the different isoforms of apo(a), some of which may have different effects on fibrinolysis *in vivo*; differences in *in vitro* fibrinolytic activity for different apo(a) isoforms were recently demonstrated.[126, 127]

CLINICAL SIGNIFICANCE OF LIPOPROTEIN(a)

Lp(a) Concentrations and Coronary Heart Disease

In the early 1970s, several studies reported the association between coronary heart disease (CHD) and a plasma lipoprotein that was detected by electrophoresis and named pre-beta-1 lipoprotein because of its mobility relative to LDL in gels.[128-130] Subsequent studies demonstrated that pre-beta-1 was Lp(a) and confirmed its association with CHD.[131-133] In 1977, Albers et al. were the first to report the association between high concentrations of Lp(a), determined by an immunochemical method, and CHD.[54] The distribution of Lp(a) was measured in 90 myocardial infarction (MI) survivors and in their healthy spouses, and was found to be shifted to higher concentrations in MI survivors than in the spouse controls. In another study of MI survivors performed in 1981, Kostner et al. found that the relative risk for MI in subjects with Lp(a) concentrations > 30 mg/dL, expressed in terms of total Lp(a) mass, were 1.75-fold higher than in subjects with Lp(a) concentrations < 30 mg/dL.[134]

More recently, Dahlen and coworkers studied 307 patients who underwent coronary angiography and reported that the coronary lesion score significantly correlated with Lp(a) values; multivariate analysis demonstrated that high Lp(a) concentrations were associated significantly and independently with CHD.[135] In a study aimed at evaluating Lp(a) in the context of other risk factors, Armstrong et al. found that Lp(a) was an even stronger predictor of CHD if other risk factors were also present.[136]

Interest in Lp(a) increased with the discovery that apo(a) has a high homology with plasminogen,[15] and numerous clinical studies subsequently reported the association of Lp(a) with CHD,[137-141] MI,[142-144] stenosis following coronary artery bypass graft surgery (CABG),[145, 146] restenosis after PTCA,[147-149] progression of CHD in familial hypercholesterolemia (FH),[150-153] and stroke.[154-161] One study reported no significant difference in Lp(a) concentrations between CABG patients and controls, although a trend toward higher Lp(a) concentrations with increasing severity of disease was reported.[162]

Two preliminary studies examined the utility of acute lowering of Lp(a) and LDL concentrations in patients by LDL-apheresis before and after PTCA for preventing restenosis.[163, 164] In one study, in patients with Lp(a) concentration of > 30 mg/dL, restenosis rates were lower in those patients in whom a reduction of 50% or more of the initial Lp(a) concentration was achieved.[163] In the second study, restenosis was observed in only one out of ten patients treated once every 2 weeks for 3–4 months; three patients pheresed for 2 years did not restenose.[164] Similarly, Walzl et al. reported that plasmapheretic reduction of lipids, including Lp(a), in patients shortly after a stroke contributed to improved neurological recovery.[165] These are the first studies to show an improvement in clinical outcome as a result of lowering Lp(a) concentrations.

Only a few studies have looked at the relationship of Lp(a) phenotype to CHD. Kark and co-workers reported a significantly higher prevalence of low-molecular-weight apo(a) isoforms in female, but not in male, MI survivors compared to controls.[143] Similarly, two studies reported a higher prevalence of low-molecular-weight isoforms in FH patients with CHD compared to those without disease.[150, 151] Guo et al. reported the interesting finding that in FH patients heterozygous for apo(a) isoform, the different isoforms resided on distinct lipoprotein particles.[151] A recent prospective study by Wild and coworkers suggests that Lp(a) levels are an independent risk factor for the development of CHD in men and suggest that the size of apo(a) may also play a role in this process.[166] Further studies with larger sample sizes are needed to better define the contribution of Lp(a) concentrations and apo(a) isoforms to risk of disease in men and women and in different ethnic groups.

Among numerous retrospective case-control studies, virtually all have shown a strong association between Lp(a) and CHD. In contrast, relatively few prospective studies of the significance of increased Lp(a) concentrations have been conducted, and the results are quite discordant. In fact, while six of these prospective studies concluded that Lp(a) concentration is a risk factor for MI or CHD in men, [141, 166–170] three other nested case-control studies reached opposite conclusions. In a subset of Helsinki Heart Study participants, Lp(a) levels did not differ between 138 male subjects with CHD and 130 control subjects in a group of men ranging from 40 to 55 years of age who were followed for 5 years.[171] In a large prospective study of 7424 Finnish men and women ranging from 40 to 64 years of age, no significant differences were found between Lp(a) levels in 134 male and 131 female case-control pairs.[172] In the Physician's Health Study, Ridker and co-workers found no evidence of association between Lp(a) and risk of future MI during a mean 5-year follow-up period.[173] Two provocative editorials have critically evaluated the possible explanations for these discordant findings and underlined the limitations of the present studies.[174, 175]

The role of elevated Lp(a) concentrations as a risk factor for cardiovascular disease (CVD) in women has not been extensively addressed. The Framingham Heart Study[176] has provided the only large prospective study of elevated levels and risk for CVD in women. In this study, the presence of a band representing sinking pre-beta lipoprotein was found to be a strong, independent predictor of myocardial infarction, intermittent claudication, and CVD in 3003 women observed for a mean period of 12 years. Interestingly, a recent study by Wild and co-workers[166] found little evidence for a relationship between Lp(a) level or apo(a) isoform size and risk for CVD in women. Clearly, this observation merits further investigation in larger studies.

Historically, the large majority of clinical studies relating Lp(a) to risk of disease have been performed in White populations. More recently, a number of investigators have begun to evaluate the clinical significance of Lp(a) in other ethnic groups.[68–70, 177–181] Sandholzer et al.[70] reported the results of a multicenter prospective case-control study that looked at apo(a) phenotypes and Lp(a) concentrations in six ethnic populations. These authors reported a consistent association of low-molecular-weight polymorphs with CHD across populations. However, plasma samples from all of the populations were not stored in the same way; the German samples were improperly stored at –20° C for 2 years and therefore were not analyzed for Lp(a) concentration, and the Israeli samples were stored at –20° C for 6 months. In addition, in one of the six populations, samples were from non-fasting individuals. This may be an important consideration if particles enriched with triglyceride containing Lp(a) react differently with antibodies used in Lp(a) assays. Abe and Noma found that the distribution of Lp(a) concentrations, apo(a) phenotype, and allele frequencies in healthy Japanese were not significantly different from White European populations, but were significantly different from other Asian populations, including Chinese, Indians, and Malaysians.[179] Further findings were that Lp(a) concentrations were significantly higher in patients with CHD compared to healthy controls, that there was a higher frequency of double-banded phenotypes in CHD patients, that the frequency of apo(a) alleles was not different from those in healthy individuals, and that Lp(a) concentrations in CHD patients were higher than those in healthy people who had the same phenotype.[180]

The most interesting and intriguing results are those obtained in the few studies in which the clinical significance of Lp(a) was evaluated in Black and White subjects. In The Bogalusa Heart Study, Lp(a) concentrations in White and Black children and incidence of MI in their parents were used as a measure of future risk for the children. Lp(a) concentrations in White children with parental MI were significantly higher than in White children without parental MI. In addition, the prevalence of parental MI in Whites was significantly higher in subjects with Lp(a) concentrations > 25 mg/dL. No relationship of Lp(a) concentration to incidence of parental MI was observed in Blacks. Guyton et al.[68] and Sorrentino et al.[181] studied the relationship between Lp(a) concentrations and CHD in Blacks and Whites and reported identical conclusions. White and Black patients with CHD had higher Lp(a) concentrations than Blacks and Whites without CHD. Although the Lp(a) concentrations in Blacks averaged twice those of Whites, the incidence of CHD was not different between the two racial groups, and Blacks did not appear to experience increased atherosclerotic progression and mortality. Based on these findings, Guyton et al. concluded that the atherogenicity of Lp(a) in Blacks is decreased or is counterbalanced by other factors.[68] Interestingly, a recent study by Marcovina and co-workers specifically demonstrated that Blacks have higher Lp(a) values than Whites in the range of intermediate apo(a) sizes.[85] This has led these authors to speculate that the high Lp(a) levels in Blacks are not predictive of CHD since the elevated levels are not associated with small apo(a) isoform sizes.

It is clear from these studies that the clinical significance of Lp(a) concentration and apo(a) isoform size in each ethnic group must be determined separately. Additionally, basic studies are required to investigate the reasons for the apparent difference in atherogenicity of Lp(a) in Blacks. Based on the recent study by Marcovina et al.[85]

the predictive value of small apo(a) isoform sizes clearly merits further investigation in prospective studies.

Lp(a) Concentrations in Patients with Diabetes

The literature is contradictory in describing the potential role of Lp(a) as a contributing risk factor to the development of cardiovascular complications in patients with diabetes mellitus.[182] Numerous groups have reported that Lp(a) concentrations are increased in patients with insulin-dependent diabetes (IDDM),[183-187] and that Lp(a) concentration was[183, 185, 188] or was not[189-191] related to the degree of glycemic control. However, other studies reported that Lp(a) concentrations were not increased in IDDM patients compared to healthy control subjects;[189, 192-194] one study found no significant difference in apo(a) phenotypes.[195] There seems to be general agreement, with two exceptions,[185, 196] that Lp(a) concentrations in non-insulin dependent (NIDDM) diabetes are not increased.[188, 189, 197-199] Increased concentrations of Lp(a) have also been reported in patients suffering from diabetic retinopathy.[200-202]

A number of studies have reported that other risk factors surpassed the significance of Lp(a) in diabetic patients. Ritter and co-workers studied the relationship between Lp(a) concentration and late diabetic complications, including diabetic polyneuropathy, autonomic neuropathy, nephropathy, peripheral occlusive disease, diabetic gangrene, CHD, and retinopathy.[203] No significant increases in Lp(a) correlated with any of these complications except for retinopathy, and this correlation was not significant when the duration of diabetes was factored into logistic regression analysis.[203] Similarly, in a more recent study Lp(a) levels were not found to be a significant risk factor for retinopathy in neither young- nor older-onset diabetic patients.[204] In a study of 45 identical twin pairs discordant for IDDM, Dubrey et al. reported no relationship between genetic susceptibility to IDDM and apo(a) phenotype or Lp(a) concentration; in this study, Lp(a) concentrations in diabetics were similar to those found in the control population.[205] In another study, Császár et al. reported no significant differences between Lp(a) concentration or phenotype frequencies between diabetic and non-diabetic subjects within two ethnic populations in Austria and Hungary.[206]

These studies collectively suggest that Lp(a) may not be a risk factor related to diabetes directly. Rather, Lp(a) concentrations may be increased in some individuals independent of the diabetic condition, and may pose an additional risk for atherosclerotic disease. Although the incidence of increased concentrations of Lp(a) in the diabetic population may be the same as in the normal population, it remains to be determined whether the atherogenecity of Lp(a) in patients with diabetes is increased, which may reflect altered biochemical properties of this lipoprotein in the diabetic condition.

Lp(a) Concentrations in Patients with Renal Disease

A number of studies have reported increased Lp(a) concentrations in patients with IDDM and proteinuria,[207-210] while others found no such association.[185, 190, 211] In three studies of subjects with NIDDM, one study found that microalbuminuria was associated with increased Lp(a) concentrations,[212] while the remaining two studies reported the opposite finding.[213, 214] Several authors reported increased Lp(a) concentrations in non-diabetic patients with various renal diseases;[215, 216] Stenvinkel reported significant reduction of Lp(a) concentrations in patients with nephrotic syndrome after remission.[217] Sato and coworkers demonstrated co-localization of apo(a) and apo B-100 in the mesangial area and capillary loops in glomeruli from patients with glomerular diseases, and proposed that Lp(a) might advance glomerular disease by interfering with activation of TGF-β, thereby interfering with repair of injured cells or tissue.[218] It was recently reported that the binding of Lp(a) to the extracellular mesangial matrix is enhanced relative to LDL.[219] Although the significance of Lp(a) trapping in the mesangial matrix is unclear at present, it has been demonstrated that Lp(a) has both stimulatory (at low concentrations) and cytotoxic (at high concentrations) effects on cultured mesangial cells, both of which may negatively impact the course of renal disease *in vivo.*[220]

The majority of these studies did not control for ethnicity; among the few that did, sample sizes within ethnic groups were too small to be meaningful. Most of these studies shared a similar finding that Lp(a) concentrations were higher in both diabetic and non-diabetic patients with proteinuria compared to those without proteinuria, suggesting that metabolic conditions in patients with renal disease and proteinuria may cause plasma Lp(a) concentrations to rise. Interestingly, however, a recent study by Yudkin and co-workers demonstrated that Lp(a) was not elevated in non-diabetic microalbuminuric patients compared to unaffected subjects.[221] Nonetheless, it has been hypothesized that elevated Lp(a) concentrations in renal disease may contribute to the increased risk of CHD which is often seen in these patients. Larger studies are needed to define the true role of Lp(a) in renal disease, both in diabetic and non-diabetic subjects.

Lp(a) Concentrations in Patients Receiving Renal Replacement Therapy

A number of recent studies have found significantly higher concentrations of Lp(a) in patients receiving hemodialysis, continuous ambulatory peritoneal dialysis (CAPD), or transplant therapy compared to healthy control subjects.[222-230]

Irish and co-workers reported significantly higher concentrations of Lp(a) in patients with chronic renal disease and in those undergoing CAPD compared to healthy controls, but found no difference between control subjects and patients undergoing hemodialysis or transplant therapy.[231] Black and Wilcken measured Lp(a) before and after kidney transplantation in 20 patients with end-stage renal failure and found a significant decrease in Lp(a) after transplantation[232] to a concentration comparable to values reported by others for renal transplant patients.[222, 231] The decrease in Lp(a) was significantly correlated with an increase in creatinine clearance. It has been suggested that cyclosporine may raise Lp(a) concentrations in transplant patients,[233, 234] but this conclusion has been contested.[235-237]

Cressman et al. reported that Lp(a) concentration and the presence of a previous CHD-related clinical event were the only independent risk factors for predicting CHD in hemodialysis patients in a multiple logistic regression model.[223] In a follow-up study, Lp(a) concentration was demonstrated to be an independent predictor of fatal events attributable to CHD.[238]

Dieplinger and coworkers reported increased Lp(a) values in patients with end-stage renal disease compared to controls, but found no difference in frequency of apo(a) isoforms between the groups. Concentrations of Lp(a) were increased two- to threefold in patients with high-molecular-weight apo(a) isoforms, while in patients with small isoforms, Lp(a) concentrations were comparable to those found in controls.[239] These results suggest that non-genetic factors related to renal insufficiency are responsible for increased Lp(a) concentrations in this population. Haffner et al. proposed that increased Lp(a) concentrations in chronic renal failure must occur early or contribute to its development, since Lp(a) concentration did not correlate with creatinine concentrations, was similarly increased in different ethnic groups, and was not affected by diet, hemodialysis, or CAPD treatment.[240] The release of tumor necrosis factor alpha, interleukin 1, and interleukin 6,[241] along with increased concentrations of C-reactive protein,[242] have been reported in hemodialysis patients. The release of cytokines has been attributed to chronic exposure to dialysis membranes.[243] Interleukin 6 is a potent activator of the synthesis of acute phase proteins by hepatocytes.[244, 245] Lp(a) has been shown to behave like an acute phase protein after MI, stroke, or CABG surgery,[156, 246–248] and may also play a role in inflammation.[249, 250]

These findings may explain why Lp(a) concentrations are increased in patients undergoing chronic hemodialysis. Similar cytokine production has been reported in CAPD patients.[251] These studies provide evidence that increased Lp(a) concentrations may contribute to the atherosclerotic disease associated with renal disease.

Requirements for Clinical Studies of Lp(a) and Atherosclerotic Disease

The lack of standardization of both Lp(a) measurement and apo(a) phenotype determination makes it difficult to compare clinical studies. Further, until the development of Lp(a) assays which are not sensitive to apo(a) size, no conclusion can be reached regarding the independent effects of Lp(a) concentration and apo(a) phenotype on the risk for atherosclerotic disease. The following guidelines are proposed for designing future studies of Lp(a) and atherosclerotic disease:

1. Sample size, estimated by appropriate power calculations, must be large enough to adequately represent the numerous apo(a) isoforms[31] and the most common of the possible polymorphic combinations. This will prevent possible selection bias due to phenotype.

2. Isoform studies should use the technique with the highest resolution,[30, 31] and a standardized approach for apo(a) phenotyping should be utilized.[252]

3. Antibodies used for the measurement of Lp(a) concentrations in clinical studies must be characterized with regard to the epitope recognized, and a clear demonstration of the effect of isoform size must be demonstrated in order to be able to interpret Lp(a) concentrations.

4. The ethnic composition of all study populations must be defined.

5. To avoid possible confounding effects of the acute phase response on Lp(a) concentrations, Lp(a) should not be measured during an active inflammatory state.

6. Because the non-Gaussian distribution of Lp(a) levels, medians should be reported rather than means.

7. Nonparametric statistics must be used for analysis of Lp(a) data.

SCREENING FOR LIPOPROTEIN(a) CONCENTRATIONS

Based on the contradictory results of the epidemiologic studies and the problems inherent in the immunochemical measurement of Lp(a), screening of the general population for Lp(a) concentration is not recommended. However, we recommend Lp(a) screening for patients with CHD or family history of CHD or stroke, siblings and offspring of individuals with increased concentrations of Lp(a), patients with FH, and patients with renal dysfunction accompanied by proteinuria. However, considering the numerous methodological problems, Lp(a) measurement on this high-risk group of subjects should be performed only by specialized lipid research laboratories. These laboratories should have population-based reference values determined by their method for different ethnic groups. To enable the physician to estimate the patient's risk, Lp(a) values should be reported with the indication of the corresponding percentile of the general population. Based on the outcome of the clinical studies, it appears reasonable to consider patients with Lp(a) values above the 80th percentile at increased risk for CHD.

With respect to clinical directives for patients with elevated Lp(a) levels, larger prospective studies utilizing Lp(a) measurement techniques that are insensitive to apo(a) isoform size variability are required in order to more clearly define the basis of the risk relationship between Lp(a) and atherosclerotic disease. Elucidation of the mechanism underlying the pathophysiology of Lp(a) will also be useful in suggesting directions for the design of therapeutic strategies specifically aimed at lowering Lp(a) levels. Currently, the most effective way to decrease Lp(a) concentrations by 50% or more is by LDL- or Lp(a)-apheresis procedures. However, these techniques are expensive and are reserved for the extreme cases of hetero- and homozygous FH.[253-255] Although several pharmacological agents have been identified which lower Lp(a) levels such as niacin and neomycin (either separately or in combination),[256-258] bezafibrate,[259] as well as estrogen, tamoxifen, and combination hormone therapy in healthy postmenopausal women,[260, 261] the long-term benefits of Lp(a) lowering therapy are currently unknown and as such their routine use cannot be recommended. There is, however, encouraging preliminary evidence to suggest that decreasing Lp(a) concentrations utilizing apheresis procedures before and after PTCA and during recovery after stroke may improve outcome.[253-255]

It is reasonable at this time to consider the use of therapeutic regimens for patients with a predisposition for developing atherosclerotic disease and with increased Lp(a) concentrations in order to minimize lipid- and non-lipid-related risk factors that can be modified; this may include the use of diet, hydroxymethylglutaryl-CoA (HMG-CoA) reductase inhibitors, bile acid sequestrants, and probucol, all of which do not affect Lp(a) concentrations.[262] Although it is a logical therapeutic goal to decrease Lp(a) in patients with multiple cardiovascular risk factors, specific goals or targets have not been established due to the lack of reference ranges for different ethnic groups.

SUMMARY

Lp(a), a cholesterol-rich plasma lipoprotein which is genetically controlled, is thought to be an independent risk factor for premature atherosclerosis. Although Lp(a) has been hypothesized to represent a bridge between the fields of atherosclerosis and thrombosis, studies of the effect of Lp(a) on fibrinolysis *in vitro* have been somewhat inconsistent, and no effect on fibrinolysis *in vivo* has been demonstrated. Standardization of Lp(a) measurement and apo(a) phenotype determination must be developed in order to provide clinical investigators with the tools they need to elucidate the true relationship of Lp(a) to atherosclerotic disease. Currently the majority of measurements of Lp(a) concentration reported in clinical studies in the literature is confounded by isoform size, making it difficult to come to a sound conclusion regarding the role of Lp(a) concentration in disease. Measurement of Lp(a) concentrations with methods not sensitive to isoform size and determination of apo(a) phenotypes in different ethnic groups are required before specific recommendations can be made regarding screening of the general population for Lp(a).

At the present time, screening for Lp(a) concentration is recommended for patients with, or with a family history of, CHD, stroke, MI, or FH and renal dysfunction accompanied by proteinuria. Management of patients with high Lp(a) concentrations should be directed at minimizing all other lipid- and non-lipid risk factors for atherosclerotic disease.   ✧

Acknowledgments. *The authors wish to express their gratitude to Dr. Daniel M. Levine and Dr. Giuseppe Lippi, who originally contributed to this chapter. Special thanks to Hal Kennedy for computer generation of the figures, and to Dorthy Westmoreland for typing the manuscript. Dr. Marcovina's original work cited in this review was supported by Program Project Grant HL 30086 from the National Heart, Lung, and Blood Institute, U.S. Public Service. Original work cited by Dr. Koschinsky was supported by the Medical Research Council of Canada and the Heart and Stroke Foundation of Ontario.*

REFERENCES

1. Berg K. A new serum type system in man: the Lp system. Acta Pathol Microbiol Scand 1963;59:362–82.
2. Berg K. The Lp system. [Review]. Ser Haemotol 1968;1:111–36.
3. Ernst A, Helmhold M, Brunner C, Petho-Schramm P, Armstrong VW, Muller H-J. Identification of two functionally distinct lysine-binding sites in kringle 37 and in kringles 32–36 of human apolipoprotein(a). J Biol Chem 1994;270:6227–34.
4. Trieu VN, McConathy WJ. A two-step model for lipoprotein(a) formation. J Biol Chem 1995;270:15471–4.
5. Gabel BR, May LF, Marcovina SM, Koschinsky ML. Lipoprotein(a) Assembly. Quantitative assessment of the role of apo(a) kringle IV types 2–10 in particle formation. Arterioscler Thromb Vasc Biol 1996;16:1559–67.
6. Albers JJ, Cabana VG, Warnick GR, Hazzard WR. Lp(a) lipoprotein: relationship to sinking pre-β lipoprotein, hyperlipoproteinemia, and apolipoprotein B. Metabolism 1975;24:1047–54.
7. Gaubatz JW, Heideman C, Gotto AM Jr, Morrisett JD, Dahlen GH. Human plasma lipoprotein(a): structural properties. J Biol Chem 1983;258:4582–9.

8.   Fless GM, Rolih CA, Scanu AM. Heterogeneity of human plasma lipoprotein(a): isolation and characterization of the lipoprotein subspecies and their apoproteins. J Biol Chem 1984;259:11470-8.

9.   Fless GM. Heterogeneity of particles containing the apo B-apo(a) complex. In: Scanu AM, ed. Lipoprotein(a). San Diego: Academic Press, 1990:41-51.

10.   Pfaffinger D, Schuelke J, Kim C, Fless GM, Scanu AM. Relationship between apo(a) isoforms and Lp(a) density in subjects with different apo(a) phenotype: a study before and after a fatty meal. J Lipid Res 1991;32:679-83.

11.   Cohn JS, Lam CWK, Sullivan DR, Hensley WJ. Plasma lipoprotein distribution of apolipoprotein(a) in the fed and fasted states. Atherosclerosis 1991;90:59-66.

12.   Fless GM, ZumMallen ME, Scanu AM. Physicochemical properties of apolipoprotein(a) and lipoprotein(a-) derived from the dissociation of human plasma lipoprotein(a). J Biol Chem 1986;261:8712-18.

13.   Hixson JE, Britten ML, Manis GS, Rainwater DL. Apolipoprotein(a) (Apo(a)) glycoprotein isoforms result from size differences in apo(a) mRNA in baboons. J Biol Chem 1989; 264:6013-16.

14.   Koschinsky ML, Beisiegel U, Henne-Bruns D, Eaton DL, Lawn RM. Apolipoprotein(a) size heterogeneity is related to variable number of repeat sequences in its mRNA. Biochemistry 1990;29:640-4.

15.   McLean JW, Tomlinson JE, Kuang W-J, et al. cDNA sequence of human apolipoprotein(a) is homologous to plasminogen. Nature 1987;330:132-7.

16.   Magnusson S, Sottrup-Jensen L, Petersen TE, Dudek-Wojciechowska G, Claeys H. Homologous "kringle" structures common to plasminogen and prothrombin: substrate specificity of enzymes activating prothrombin and plasminogen. In: Ribbons DW, Brew K. eds. Proteolysis and physiological regulation. New York: Academic Press, 1976:203-38.

17.   Castellino FJ, Beals JM. The genetic relationships between the kringle domains of human plasminogen, prothrombin, tissue plasminogen activator, urokinase, and coagulation factor XII. J Mol Evol 1987;26:358-69.

18.   Gabel BR, Koschinsky ML. Analysis of the proteolytic activity of a recombinant form of apolipoprotein(a). Biochemistry 1995;34:15777-84.

19.   Guevara J Jr, Knapp RD, Honda S, Northup SR, Morrisett JD. A structural assessment of the apo(a) protein of human lipoprotein(a). Proteins 1992;12:188-99.

20.   Guevara J Jr, Jan AY, Knapp R, Tulinsky A, Morrisett JD. Comparison of ligand-binding sites of modeled apo(a) kringle-like sequences in human lipoprotein(a). Arterioscler Thromb 1993;13:758-70.

21.   Lackner C, Cohen JC, Hobbs HH. Molecular definition of the extreme size polymorphism in apolipoprotein(a). Hum Mol Genet 1993;2:933-40.

22.   van der Hoek YY, Wittekoek ME, Beisiegel U, Kastelein JJ, Koschinsky ML. The apolipoprotein(a) kringle IV repeats which differ from the major repeat kringle are present in variably-sized isoforms. Hum Mol Genet 1993;2:361-66.

23.   Frank SL, Klisak I, Sparkes RS, et al. The apolipoprotein(a) gene resides on human chromosome 6q26-27, in close proximity to the homologous gene for plasminogen. Hum Genet 1988;79:352-6.

24.   Albers JJ, Wahl P, Hazzard WR. Quantitative genetic studies of the human plasma Lp(a) lipoprotein. Biochem Genet 1974;11:475-86.

25.   Iselius L, Dahlen G, DeFaire U, Lundman T. Complex segregation analysis of the Lp(a)/ pre-beta 1-lipoprotein trait. Clin Genet 1981;20:147-51.

26.   Morton NE, Berg K, Dahlen G, Ferrel RE, Rhoads GG. Genetics of the Lp lipoprotein in Japanese-Americans. Genet Epidemiol 1985;2:113-21.

27.   Utermann G, Menzel HJ, Kraft HG, Duba HC, Kemmler HG, Seitz C. Lp(a) glycoprotein phenotypes: inheritance and relation to Lp(a)-lipoprotein concentrations in plasma. J Clin Invest 1987;80:458-65.

28.   Utermann G, Duba C, Manzel HJ. Genetics of the quantitative Lp(a) lipoprotein trait. II. Inheritance of Lp(a) glycoprotein phenotypes. Hum Genet 1988;78:47-50.

29. Gaubatz JW, Ghanem KI, Guevara J Jr, et al. Polymorphic forms of human apolipoprotein(a): inheritance and relationship of their molecular weights to plasma concentrations of lipoprotein(a). J Lipid Res 1990;31:603–13.

30. Kamboh MI, Ferrell RE, Kottke BA. Expressed hypervariable polymorphism of apolipoprotein(a). Am J Hum Genet 1991;49:1063–74.

31. Marcovina SM, Zhang ZH, Gaur VP, Albers JJ. Identification of 34 apolipoprotein(a) isoforms: differential expression of apolipoprotein(a) alleles between American Blacks and Whites. Biochem Biophys Res Commun 1993;191:1192–6.

32. Lackner C, Boerwinkle E, Leffert CC, Rahmig T, Hobbs HH. Molecular basis of apolipoprotein(a) isoform size heterogeneity as revealed by pulsed-field gel electrophoresis. J Clin Invest 1991;87:2153–61.

33. Boerwinkle E, Leffert CC, Lin J, Lackner C, Chiesa G, Hobbs HH. Apolipoprotein(a) gene accounts for greater than 90% of the variation in plasma lipoprotein(a) concentrations. J Clin Invest 1992;90:52–60.

34. Trommsdorff M, Kochl S, Lingenhel A, Kronenberg F, Delport R, Vermaak H, Lemming L, Clausen IC, Faergeman O, Utermann G, Kraft H-G. A pentanucleotide repeat polymorphism in the 5′ control region of the apolipoprotein(a) gene is associated with lipoprotein(a) plasma concentrations in Caucasians. J Clin Invest 1995;96:150–57.

35. Utermann G, Hoppichler F, Dieplinger H, Seed M, Thompson G, Boerwinkle E. Defects in the low density lipoprotein receptor gene affect lipoprotein(a) levels: multiplicative interaction of two gene loci associated with premature atherosclerosis. Proc Natl Acad Sci USA 1989;86:4171–4.

36. Hegele RA, Sutherland S, Robertson M, Wu L, Emi M, Hopkins PN, Williams RR, Lalouel JM. The effect of genetic determinants of low density lipoprotein levels on lipoprotein(a). Clin Invest Med 1991;14:146–152.

37. Averna M, Marcovina SM, Noto D, Cole TG, Krul ES, Schonfeld G. Familial hypobetalipoproteinemia is not associated with low levels of lipoprotein(a). Arterioscler Thromb Vasc Biol 1995;15:2165–75.

38. Scanu AM, Pfaffinger D, Fless GM, Makino K, Eisenbart J, Hinman J. Attenuation of immunologic reactivity of lipoprotein(a) by thiols and cysteine-containing compounds: structural implications. Arterioscler Thromb 1992;12:424–9.

39. Guo H-C, Armstrong VW, Luc G, et al. Characterization of five mouse monoclonal antibodies to apolipoprotein(a) from human Lp(a): evidence for weak plasminogen reactivity. J Lipid Res 1989;30:23–37.

40. Naruszewicz M, Giroux L-M, Davignon J. Oxidative modification of Lp(a) causes changes in the structure and biological properties of apo(a). Chem Phys Lipids 1994;67/68:167–74.

41. Marcovina SM, Curtiss LK, Milne R, Albers JJ. Selection and characterization of monoclonal antibodies for measuring plasma concentrations of apolipoproteins A-I and B. Scientific Division, Committee on Apolipoproteins, Working Group on antibody reagents, IFCC document. JIFCC 1990;2:138–44.

42. Rainwater DL, Manis GS. Immunochemical characterization and quantitation of lipoprotein(a) in baboons: development of an assay depending on two antigenically distinct proteins. Atherosclerosis 1988;73:23–31.

43. Fless GM, Snyder ML, Scanu AM. Enzyme-linked immunoassay for Lp(a). J Lipid Res 1989;30:651–62.

44. Vu-Dac N, Mezdour H, Parra HJ, Luc G, Luyeye I, Fruchart JC. A selective bi-site immunoenzymatic procedure for human Lp(a) lipoprotein quantification using monoclonal antibodies against apo(a) and apo B. J Lipid Res 1989;30:1437–43.

45. Taddei-Peters WC, Butman BT, Jones GR, Venetta TM, Macomber PF, Ransom H. Quantification of lipoprotein(a) particles containing various apolipoprotein(a) isoforms by a monoclonal anti-apo(a) capture antibody and a polyclonal anti-apolipoprotein B detection antibody sandwich enzyme immunoassay. Clin Chem 1993;39:1382–9.

46. Kottke BA, Bren ND. A particle concentration fluorescence immunoassay for Lp(a). Chem Phys Lipids 1994;67/68:249–56.

47. Fless GM, Pfaffinger DJ, Eisenbart JD, Scanu AM. Solubility, immunochemical, and lipoprotein binding properties of apo B-100-apo(a), the protein moiety of lipoprotein(a). J Lipid Res 1990;31:909-18.

48. Zawadzki Z, Tercé F, Seman LJ, et al. The linkage with apolipoprotein(a) in lipoprotein(a) modifies the immunochemical and functional properties of apolipoprotein B. Biochemistry 1988;27:8474-81.

49. Gries A, Fievet C, Marcovina S, et al. Interaction of LDL, Lp(a) and reduced Lp(a) with monoclonal antibodies against apo B. J Lipid Res 1988;29:1-8.

50. Albers JJ, Hazzard WR. Immunochemical quantification of human plasma Lp(a) lipoprotein. Lipids 1974;9:15-26.

51. Marcovina SM, Albers JJ, Gabel B, Koschinsky ML, Gaur VP. Effect of the number of apolipoprotein(a) kringle 4 domains on immunochemical measurements of Lipoprotein(a) Clin Chem 1995;41:246-55.

52. Albers JJ, Marcovina SM, Lodge MS. The unique lipoprotein(a): properties and immunochemical measurement. Clin Chem 1990;36:2019-26.

53. Labeur C, Shepherd J, Rosseneu M. Immunological assays of apolipoproteins in plasma: methods and instrumentation. Clin Chem 1990;36:591-7.

54. Albers JJ, Adolphson JL, Hazzard WR. Radioimmunoassay of human plasma Lp(a) lipoprotein. J Lipid Res 1977;18:331-8.

55. Molinari E, Pichler P, Krempler F, Kostner G. A rapid screening method for pathological lipoprotein Lp(a) concentrations by counterimmunoelectrophoresis. Clin Chim Acta 1983;128:373-8.

56. Gaubatz JW, Cushing GL, Morrissett JD. Quantitation, isolation, and characterization of human lipoprotein(a). Methods Enzymol 1986;129:167-86.

57. Labeur C, Michiels G, Bury J, Usher DC, Rosseneu M. Lipoprotein(a) quantified by an enzyme-linked immunosorbent assay with monoclonal antibodies. Clin Chem 1989; 35:1380-4.

58. Abe A, Maeda S, Makino K, et al. Enzyme-linked immunosorbent assay of lipoprotein(a) in serum and cord blood. Clin Chim Acta 1988;177:31-40.

59. Wong WLT, Eaton DL, Berloui A, Fendly B, Hass PE. A monoclonal antibody-based enzyme-linked immunosorbent assay of lipoprotein(a). Clin Chem 1990;36:192-7.

60. Vu-Dac N, Chekkor A, Parra H, Duthilleul P, Fruchart JC. Latex immunoassay of human serum Lp(a+) lipoprotein. J Lipid Res 1985;26:267-9.

61. Cazzolato G, Prakasch G, Green S, Kostner GM. The determination of lipoprotein Lp(a) by rate and endpoint nephelometry. Clin Chim Acta 1983;135:203-8.

62. Levine DM, Sloan BJ, Donner JE, Lorenz JD, Henzerling R. Automated measurement of Lp(a) by immunoturbidimetric analysis. Int J Clin Lab Res 1992;22:173-8.

63. Albers JJ, Marcovina SM. Standardization of Lp(a) measurement. Chem Phys Lipids 1994;67/68:257-63.

64. Labeur C, Rosseneu M, Henderson O. International Lp(a) standardization. Chem Phys Lipids 1994;67/68:265-70.

65. Kulkarni KR, Garber DW, Marcovina SM, Segrest JP. Quantification of cholesterol in all lipoprotein classes by the VAP-II method. J Lipid Res 1994;35:159-68.

66. Seman LJ, Jenner JL, McNamara JR, Schaefer EJ. Quantification of lipoprotein(a) in plasma by assaying cholesterol in lectin-bound plasma fraction. Clin Chem 1994;40:400-3.

67. Austin MA, Sandholzer C, Selby JV, Newman B, Krauss RM, Utermann G. Lipoprotein(a) in women twins: heritability and relationship to apolipoprotein(a) phenotypes. Am J Hum Genet 1992;51:829-40.

68. Guyton JR, Dahlen GH, Patsch W, Kautz JA, Gotto AM, Jr. Relationship of plasma lipoprotein Lp(a) levels to race and to apolipoprotein B. Arteriosclerosis 1985;5:265-72.

69. Helmhold M, Bigge J, Muche R, et al. Contribution of the apo(a) phenotype to plasma Lp(a) concentration shows considerable ethnic variation. J Lipid Res 1991;32:1919-28.

70. Sandholzer C, Saha N, Kark JD, et al. Apo(a) isoforms predict risk for coronary heart disease: a study in six populations. Arterioscler Thromb 1992;12:1214-26.

71. Cobbaert C, Kesteloot H. Serum lipoprotein(a) levels in racially different populations. Am J Epidemiol 1992;136:441-9.

72. Parra HJ, Luyeye I, Bouramoue C, Demarquilly C, Fruchart JC. Black-White differences in serum Lp(a) lipoprotein levels. Clin Chim Acta 1987;168:27-31.

73. Srinivasan SR, Dahlen GH, Jarpa RA, Webber LS, Berenson GS. Racial (Black-White) difference in serum lipoprotein(a) distribution and its relation to parental myocardial infarction in children. Bogalusa Heart Study. Circulation 1991;84:160-7.

74. Brown SA, Hutchinson R, Morrisett J, et al. Plasma lipid, lipoprotein cholesterol, and apoprotein distributions in selected US communities: the Atherosclerosis Risk in Communities (ARIC) study. Arterioscler Thromb 1993;13:1139-58.

75. Marcovina SM, Albers JJ, Jacobs DR, Jr, et al. Lipoprotein(a) concentrations and apolipoprotein(a) phenotypes in Caucasians and African Americans: the CARDIA study. Arterioscler Thromb 1993;13:1037-45.

76. Rifai N, Heiss G, Doetsch K. Lipoprotein(a) at birth, in Blacks and Whites. Atherosclerosis 1992;92:123-9.

77. Wilcken DEL, Wang XL, Dudman NPB. The relationship between infant and parent Lp(a) concentrations. Chem Phys Lipids 1994;67/68:299-304.

78. Sandkamp M, Assmann G. Lipoprotein(a) in PROCAM participants and young myocardial infarction survivors. In: Scanu AM, ed. Lipoprotein(a). San Diego: Academic Press, 1990:205-9.

79. Nabulsi AA, Folsom AR, White A, et al. Association of hormone-replacement therapy with various cardiovascular risk factors in postmenopausal women. N Engl J Med 1993;328:1069-75.

80. Jenner JL, Ordovas JM, Lamon-Fava S, et al. Effects of age, sex, and menopausal status on plasma lipoprotein(a) levels: The Framingham Offspring Study. Circulation 1993;87:1135-41.

81. Henriksson P, Angelin B, Berglund L. Hormonal regulation of serum Lp(a) levels: opposite effects after estrogen treatment and orchidectomy in males with prostatic carcinoma. J Clin Invest 1992;89:1166-71.

82. Soma MR, Osnago-Gadda I, Paoletti R, et al. The lowering of lipoprotein(a) induced by estrogen plus progesterone replacement therapy in postmenopausal women. Arch Intern Med 1993;153:1462-8.

83. van der Mooren MJ, Demacker PN, Thomas CM, Rolland R. Beneficial effects on serum lipoproteins by 17 β-oestradiol-dydrogesterone therapy in postmenopausal women: a prospective study. Eur J Obstet Gynecol Reprod Biol 1992;47:153-60.

84. Seed M, Crook D. Postmenopausal hormone replacement therapy, coronary heart disease and plasma lipoproteins. Curr Opin Lipidol 1994;5:48-58.

85. Marcovina SM, Albers JJ, Wijsman E, Zhang Z-H, Chapman NH, Kennedy H. Differences in Lp(a) concentrations and apo(a) polymorphs between Black and White Americans. J Lipid Res 1996;37:2569-85.

86. Scanu AM. Lipoprotein(a): a potential bridge between the fields of atherosclerosis and thrombosis. Arch Pathol Lab Med 1988;112:1045-7.

87. Harpel PC, Gordon BR, Parker TS. Plasmin catalyzes binding of lipoprotein(a) to immobilized fibrinogen and fibrin. Proc Natl Acad Sci USA 1989;86:3847-51.

88. Gonzalez-Gronow M, Edelberg JM, Pizzo SV. Further characterization of the cellular plasminogen binding site: evidence that plasminogen 2 and lipoprotein(a) compete for the same site. Biochemistry 1989;28:2374-7.

89. Loscalzo J, Weinfeld M, Fless GM, Scanu AM. Lipoprotein(a), fibrin binding, and plasminogen activation. Arteriosclerosis 1990;10:240-5.

90. Rouy D, Koschinsky ML, Fleury V, Chapman J, Angles-Cano E. The binding of human recombinant apolipoprotein(a) and plasminogen to fibrin surfaces. Biochemistry 1992; 3:6333-39.

91. Miles LA, Fless GM, Levin EG, Scanu AM, Plow E. A potential basis for the thrombotic risks associated with lipoprotein(a). Nature 1989;339:301-3.

92. Hajjar KA, Gavish D, Breslow JL, Nachman RL. Lipoprotein(a) modulation of endothelial cell surface fibrinolysis and its potential role in atherosclerosis. Nature 1989;339:303-5.

93. Walton KW, Hitchens J, Magnani HN, Kahn M. A study of methods of identification and estimation of Lp(a) lipoprotein and of its significance in health, hyperlipidaemia and atherosclerosis. Atherosclerosis 1974;20:323-46.

94. Cushing, GL, Gaubatz JW, Nava ML, et al. Quantitation and localization of apolipo-proteins(a) and B in coronary artery bypass vein grafts at re-operation. Arteriosclerosis 1989;9:593-603.

95. Rath M, Niendorf A, Reblin T, Dietel M, Krebber HJ, Beisiegel U. Detection and quantification of lipoprotein(a) in the arterial wall of 107 coronary artery bypass patients. Arteriosclerosis 1989;9:579-92.

96. Niendorf A, Rath M, Wolf K, et al. Morphological detection and quantification of lipoprotein(a) deposition in atheromatous lesions of human aorta and coronary arteries. Virchows Archiv Pathol Anat 1990;417:105-11.

97. Beisiegel U, Niendorf A, Wolf K, Reblin T, Rath M. Lipoprotein(a) in the arterial wall. Eur Heart J 1990;11(supplement E):174-83.

98. Hoff HF, O'Neil J, Yashiro A. Partial characterization of lipoproteins containing apo(a) in human atherosclerotic lesions. J Lipid Res 1993;34:789-98.

99. Wolf K, Rath M, Niendorf A, Beisiegel U, Dietel M. Morphological co-localization of apoprotein(a) and fibrin(ogen) in human coronary atheromas. Circulation 1989;80:II-522.

100. Reblin T, Meyer N, Labeur C, Henne-Bruns D, Beisiegel U. Extraction of lipoprotein(a), apo B, and apo E from fresh human arterial wall and atherosclerotic plaques. Atherosclerosis 1995;113:179-88.

101. Etingin OR, Hajjar DP, Hajjar KA, Harpel PC, Nachman RL. Lipoprotein(a) regulates plasminogen activator inhibitor-1 expression in endothelial cells: a potential mechanism in thrombogenesis. J Biol Chem 1991;266:2459-65.

102. Levin EG, Miles LA, Fless GM, Scanu AM, Baynham P, Curtiss LK, Plow EF. Lipoproteins inhibit the secretion of tissue plasminogen activator from human endothelial cells. Arterioscler Thromb 1994;14:438-42.

103. Sangrar W, Bajzar L, Nesheim ME, Koschinsky ML. Antifibrinolytic effect of recombinant apolipoprotein(a) in vitro is primarily due to attenuation of tPA-mediated Glu-plasminogen activation. Biochemistry 1995;34:5151-7.

104. Palabrica TM, Liu AC, Aronovitz MJ, Furie B, Lawn RM, Furie BC. Antifibrinolytic activity of apolipoprotein(a) in vivo: human apolipoprotein(a) transgenic mice are resistant to tissue plasminogen activator-mediated thrombolysis. Nature Medicine 1995;1:256-9.

105. Biemond BJ, Friederich PW, Koschinsky ML, Sangrar W, Xia J, Levi M, Buller HR, ten Cate JW. Apolipoprotein(a) attenuates fibrinolysis in the rabbit jugular vein thrombosis model in vivo. Circulation 1996, in press.

106. Halvorsen S, Skjonsberg OH, Berg K, Ruyter R, Godal HC. Does Lp(a) lipoprotein inhibit the fibrinolytic system? Thromb Res 1992;68:223-32.

107. Mao SJ, Tucci MA. Lipoprotein(a) enhances plasma clot lysis in vitro. FEBS Lett 1990; 267:131-4.

108. Harpel PC, Chang VT, Borth W. Homocysteine and other sulfhydryl compounds enhance the binding of lipoprotein(a) to fibrin: a potential biochemical link between thrombosis, atherogenesis and sulfhydryl compound metabolism. Proc Natl Acad Sci USA 1992;89: 10193-7.

109. Harpel PC, Borth W. Fibrin, lipoprotein(a), plasmin interactions: a model linking thrombosis and atherogenesis. Ann NY Acad Sci 1992;667:233-8.

110. Kojima S, Harpel PC, Rifkin DB. Lipoprotein(a) inhibits the generation of transforming growth factor beta: an endogenous inhibitor of smooth muscle cell migration. J Cell Biol 1991;113:1439-45.

111. Grainger DJ, Kirschenlohr HL, Metcalfe JC, Weissberg PL, Wade DP, Lawn RM. The proliferation of human smooth muscle cells is promoted by lipoprotein(a). Science 1993;260:1655-8.

112. Grainger DJ, Kemp PR, Liu AC, Lawn RM, Metcalfe JC. Activation of transforming growth factor-beta is inhibited in transgenic apolipoprotein(a) mice. Nature 1994;370: 460-62.

113. Yashiro A, O'Neil J, Hoff HF. Insoluble complex formation of lipoprotein(a) with low density lipoprotein in the presence of calcium ions. J Biol Chem 1993;268:4709–15.

114. Smith EB, Cochran S. Factors influencing the accumulation in fibrous plaques of lipid derived from low density lipoprotein. II. Preferential immobilization of lipoprotein(a) (Lp(a)). Atherosclerosis 1990;84:173–81.

115. Maher VM, Brown BG, Marcovina SM, Hillger LA, Zhao XQ, Albers JJ. Effects of lowering elevated LDL cholesterol on the cardiovascular risk of lipoprotein(a). JAMA 1995;274:1771–4.

116. Scanu AM. Structural basis for the presumptive atherothrombogenic action of lipoprotein(a). Facts and speculations. Biochem Pharmacol 1993;46:1675–80.

117. Oshima S, Uchida K, Yasu T, Uno K, Nonogi H, Haze K. Transient increase of plasma lipoprotein(a) in patients with unstable angina pectoris: does lipoprotein(a) alter fibrinolysis? Arterioscler Thromb 1991;11:1772–7.

118. Donders SH, Lustermans FA, Van Wersch JW. Coagulation factors and lipid composition of the blood in treated and untreated hypertensive patients. Scand J Clin Lab Invest 1993;53:179–86.

119. Armstrong VW, Neubauer C, Schutz E, Tebbe U. Lack of association between raised serum Lp(a) concentration and unsuccessful thrombolysis after acute myocardial infarction. Lancet 1990;336:1077.

120. von Hodenberg E, Kreuzer J, Hautmann KJM, Nordt T, Kubler W, Bode C. Effects of lipoprotein(a) on success rate of thrombolytic therapy in acute myocardial infarction. Am J Cardiol 1991;67:1349–53.

121. Qiu S, Theroux P, Genest J Jr, Solymoss BC, Robitaille D, Marcil M. Lipoprotein(a) blood concentrations in unstable angina pectoris, acute myocardial infarction and after thrombolytic therapy. Am J Cardiol 1991;67:1175–9.

122. von Hodenberg, Pestel E, Kreuzer J, Freitag M, Bode C. Effects of lipoprotein(a) on thrombolysis. Chem Phys Lipids 1994;67/68:381–5.

123. Tranchesi B, Santos-Filho RS, Vinagre C, et al. Lipoprotein(a) concentrations do not influence the outcome of rt-PA therapy in acute myocardial infarction. Ann Hematol 1991;62;141–2.

124. Hegele RA, Freeman MR, Langer A, Connelly PW, Armstrong PW. Acute reduction of lipoprotein(a) by tissue-type plasminogen activator. Circulation 1992;85:2034–8.

125. Di Lorenzo M, Salvini P, Levi-Della-Vida M, Maddaloni E. Acute reduction of lipoprotein(a) by tissue-type plasminogen activator. Circulation 1993;87:1052–3.

126. Hervio L, Chapman MJ, Thillet J, Loyau S, Anglés-Cano E. Does apolipoprotein(a) heterogeneity influence lipoprotein(a) effects on fibrinolysis? Blood 1993;82:392–7.

127. Hervio L, Girard-Globia A, Durlach V, Anglés-Cano E. The antifibrinolytic effect of lipoprotein(a) in heterozygous subjects is modulated by the relative concentration of each of the apolipoprotein(a) isoforms and their affinity for fibrin. Eur J Clin Invest 1996;26: 411–17.

128. Dahlen G, Ericson C, Furberg C, Lundkvist L, Svardsudd K. Angina of effort and an extra pre-beta lipoprotein fraction. Acta Med Scan 192;531(Suppl):6.

129. Papadopoulos NM, Bedynek JL. Serum lipoprotein patterns in patients with coronary atherosclerosis. Clin Chim Acta 1973;44:153.

130. Insull W, Najmi M, Vloedman DA. Plasma pre-beta lipoprotein subfractions in diagnosis of coronary artery disease. Circulation 1972;45(suppl II):II-170.

131. Berg K, Dahlen G, Frick MH. Lp(a) lipoprotein and pre-beta1-lipoprotein in patients with coronary heart disease. Clin Genet 1974;6:230–5.

132. Dahlen G, Berg K, Gillnas T, Ericson C. Lp(a) lipoprotein/pre-beta1-lipoprotein in Swedish middle-aged males and in patients with coronary heart disease. Clin Genet 1975;7: 334–41.

133. Dahlen G, Frick MH, Berg K, Valle M, Wiljasalo M. Further studies of Lp(a) lipoprotein/pre-beta1-lipoprotein in patients with coronary heart disease. Clin Genet 1975;8: 183–9.

134. Kostner GM, Avogaro P, Cazzolato G, Marth E, Bittolo-Bon G, Qunici GB. Lipoprotein Lp(a) and the risk for myocardial infarction. Atherosclerosis 1981;38:51.

135. Dahlen GH, Guyton JR, Mohammad A, Farmer JA, Kautz JA, Gotto AM. Association of levels of lipoprotein Lp(a), plasma lipids, and other lipoproteins with coronary artery disease documented by angiography. Circulation 1986;74:758-65.

136. Armstrong VW, Cremer P, Eberle E, et al. The association between serum Lp(a) concentrations and angiographically assessed coronary atherosclerosis. Atherosclerosis 1986;62:249-57.

137. Hearn JA, DeMaio SJ Jr, Roubin GS, Hammarstrom M, Sgoutas D. Predictive value of Lipoprotein(a) and other serum lipoproteins in the angiographic diagnosis of coronary artery disease. Am J Cardiol 1990;66:1176-80.

138. Genest J Jr, Jenner JL, McNamara JR, et al. Prevalence of lipoprotein(a) [Lp(a)] excess in coronary artery disease. Am J Cardiol 1991;67:1039-45.

139. Genest JJ Jr, Martin-Munley SS, McNamara JR, et al. Familial lipoprotein disorders in patients with premature coronary artery disease. Circulation 1992;85:2025-33.

140. Genest JJ Jr, McNamara JR, Ordovas JM, et al. Lipoprotein cholesterol, apolipoprotein A-I and B and lipoprotein(a) abnormalities in men with premature coronary artery disease. J Am Coll Cardiol 1992;19:792-802.

141. Rosengren A, Wilhelmsen L, Eriksson E, Risberg B, Wedel H. Lipoprotein (a) and coronary heart disease: a prospective case-control study in a general population sample of middle aged men. BMJ 1990;301:1248-51.

142. Sandkamp M, Funke H, Schulte H, Kohler E, Assmann G. Lipoprotein(a) is an independent risk factor for myocardial infarction at a young age. Clin Chem 1990;36:20-23.

143. Kark JD, Sandholzer C, Friedlander Y, Utermann G. Plasma Lp(a), apolipoprotein(a) isoforms and acute myocardial infarction in men and women: a case-control study in the Jerusalem population. Atherosclerosis 1993;98:139-51.

144. Graziani MS, Zanolla L, Righetti G, et al. Lipoprotein(a) concentrations are increased in patients with myocardial infarction and angiographically normal coronary arteries. Eur J Clin Chem Clin Biochem 1993;31:135-7.

145. Hoff HF, Beck GJ, Skibinski CI, et al. Serum Lp(a) level as a predictor of vein graft stenosis after coronary artery bypass surgery in patients. Circulation 1988;77:1238-44.

146. Solymoss BC, Marcil M, Wesolowska E, Lesperance J, Pelletier LC, Campeau L. Risk factors of venous aortocoronary bypass graft disease noted at late symptom-directed angiographic study. Can J Cardiol 1993;9:80-84.

147. Hearn JA, Donohue BC, Baalbaki H, et al. Usefulness of serum lipoprotein(a) as a predictor of restenosis after percutaneous transluminal coronary angioplasty. Am J Cardiol 1992;69:736-9.

148. Tenda K, Saikawa T, Maeda T, et al. The relationship between serum lipoprotein(a) and restenosis after initial elective percutaneous transluminal coronary angioplasty. Jpn Circ J 1993;57:789-95.

149. Shimizu Y, Nishikawa H, Motoyasu M, et al. Influence of Lp(a) on restenosis after coronary angioplasty. Kokyu To Junkan 1991;39:687-90.

150. Seed M, Hopplicher F, Reaveley D, et al. Relation of serum lipoprotein(a) concentration and apolipoprotein(a) phenotype to coronary heart disease in patients with familial hypercholesterolemia. N Engl J Med 1990;322:1494-9.

151. Guo HC, Chapman MJ, Bruckert E, Farriaux JP, De-Gennes JL. Lipoprotein Lp(a) in homozygous familial hypercholesterolemia: density profile, particle heterogeneity and apolipoprotein(a) phenotype. Atherosclerosis 1991;86:69-83.

152. Hegele RA, Connelly PW, Cullen-Dean G, Rose V. Elevated plasma lipoprotein(a) associated with abnormal stress thallium scans in children with familial hypercholesterolemia. Am J Cardiol 1993;72:402-6.

153. Sorensen KE, Celermajer DS, Georgakopoulos D, Hatcher G, Betteridge DJ, Deanfield JE. Impairment of endothelium-dependent dilation is an early event in children with familial hypercholesterolemia and is related to the lipoprotein(a) level. J Clin Invest 1994;93:50-55.

154. Koltringer P, Jurgens G. A dominant role of lipoprotein(a) in the investigation and evaluation of parameters indicating development of cervical atherosclerosis. Atherosclerosis 1985;58:187-98.

155. Jurgens G, Koltringer P. Lipoprotein(a) in ischemic cerebrovascular disease: a new approach to the assessment of risk for stroke. Neurology 1987;37:513-15.

156. Woo J, Lam CWK, Kay R, Wong HY, Teoh R, Nicholls MG. Acute and long-term changes in serum lipids after acute stroke. Stroke 1990;21:1407-11.

157. Woo J, Lau E, Lam CWK, et al. Hypertension, lipoprotein(a), and apolipoprotein A-I as risk factors for stroke in the Chinese. Stroke 1991;22:203-8.

158. Pedro-Botet J, Senti M, Nogues X, et al. Lipoprotein and apolipoprotein profile in men with ischemic stroke: role of lipoprotein(a), triglyceride-rich lipoproteins, and apolipoprotein E polymorphism. Stroke 1992;23:1556-62.

159. Shintani S, Kikuchi S, Hamaguchi H, Shiigai T. High serum lipoprotein(a) concentrations are an independent risk factor for cerebral infarction. Stroke 1993;24:965-9.

160. Jovicic A, Ivanisevic V, Ivanovic I. Lipoprotein(a) in patients with carotid atherosclerosis and ischemic cerebrovascular disorders. Atherosclerosis 1993;98:59-65.

161. Nagayama M, Shinohara Y, Nagayama T. Lipoprotein(a) and ischemic cerebrovascular disease in young adults. Stroke 1994;25:74-78.

162. Averna MR, Barbagallo CM, Ocello S, et al. Lp(a) concentrations in patients undergoing aorto-coronary bypass surgery. Eur Heart J 1992;13:1405-9.

163. Yamaguchi H, Lee YJ, Daida H, et al. Effectiveness of LDL-apheresis in preventing restenosis after percutaneous transluminal coronary angioplasty (PTCA): LDL-apheresis angioplasty restenosis trial (L-ART). Chem Phys Lipids 1994;67/68:399-403.

164. Kanemitsu S, Tekekoshi N, Murakami E. Effects of LDL apheresis on restenosis after angioplasty. Chem Phys Lipids 1994;67/68:339-43.

165. Walzl M, Lechner H, Walzl B, Schied G. Improved neurological recovery of cerebral infarctions after plasmapheretic reduction of lipids and fibrinogen. Stroke 1993;24:1447-51.

166. Wild SH, Fortmann SP, Marcovina SM. A prospective case-control study of lipoprotein levels and apo(a) size and risk of coronary heart disease in Stanford Five-City Project participants. Arterioscler Thromb Vasc Biol 1997;17:239-45.

167. Sigurdsson G, Baldursdottir A, Sigvaldason H, Agnarsson U, Thorgeirsson G, Sigfusson N. Predictive value of apolipoproteins in a prospective survey of coronary artery disease in men. Am J Cardiol 1992;69:1251-4.

168. Schaefer EJ, Lamon-Fava S, Jenner JL, et al. Lipoprotein(a) levels and risk of coronary heart disease in men. JAMA 1994;271:999-1003.

169. Cremer P, Nagel D, Labrot B, Mann H, Muche R, Elster H, Seidel D. Lipoprotein Lp(a) as predictor of myocardial infarction in comparison to fibrinogen, LDL cholesterol and other risk factors: results from the prospective Gottingen Risk, Incidence and Prevalence Study (GRIPS). Eur J Clin Invest 1994;24:444-53.

170. Bostom AG, Cupples LA, Jenner JL, Ordovas JM, Seman LJ, Wilson PWF, Schaefer EJ, Castelli WP. Elevated plasma lipoprotein(a) and coronary heart disease in men aged 55 years and younger. JAMA 1996;276:544-8.

171. Jauhiainen M, Koskinen P, Ehnholm C, et al. Lipoprotein (a) and coronary heart disease risk: a nested case-control study of the Helsinki Heart Study participants. Atherosclerosis 1991;89:59-67.

172. Alfthan G, Pekkanen J, Jauhiainen M, Pitkdniemi J, Karvonen M, Tuomilehto J, Salonen JT, Ehnholm C. Relation of serum homocysteine and lipoprotein(a) concentrations to atherosclerotic disease in a prospective Finnish population based study. Atherosclerosis 1994;106:9-19.

173. Ridker PM, Hennekens CH, Stampfer MJ. A prospective study of lipoprotein(a) and the risk of myocardial infarction. JAMA 1993;270:2195-9.

174. Barnathan ES. Has lipoprotein "little" (a) shrunk? JAMA 1993;270:2224-5.

175. Gurewich V, Mittleman M. Lipoprotein(a) in coronary heart disease: is it a risk factor after all? JAMA 1994;271:1025-6.

176. Boston AG, Gagnon DR, Cupples A, Wilson PWF, Jenner FL, Ordovas JM, Schaefer EJ, Castelli WP. A prospective investigation of elevated lipoprotein(a) detected by electrophoresis and cardiovascular disease in women: The Framingham Heart Study. Circulation 1994;90:1688-95.

177. Kim JQ, Song JH, Lee MM, et al. Evaluation of Lp(a) as a risk factor of coronary artery disease in the Korean population. Ann Clin Biochem 1992;29:226-8.

178. Sandholzer CH, Boerwinkle E, Saha N, Tong MC, Utermann G. Apolipoprotein(a) phenotypes, Lp(a) concentration and plasma lipid levels in relation to coronary heart disease in a Chinese population: evidence for the role of the apo(a) gene in coronary heart disease. J Clin Invest 1992;89:1040-46.

179. Abe A, Noma A. Studies on apolipoprotein(a) phenotypes. Part 1. Phenotype frequencies in a healthy Japanese population. Atherosclerosis 1992;96:1-8.

180. Abe A, Noma A, Lee YJ, Yamaguchi H. Studies on apolipoprotein(a) phenotypes. Part 2. Phenotype frequencies and Lp(a) concentrations in different phenotypes in patients with angiographically defined coronary artery diseases. Atherosclerosis 1992; 96:9-15.

181. Sorrentino MJ, Vielhauer C, Eisenbart JD, Fless GM, Scanu AM, Feldman T. Plasma lipoprotein (a) protein concentration and coronary artery disease in black patients compared with white patients. Am J Med 1992;93:658-62.

182. Jenkins AJ, Best JD. The role of lipoprotein(a) in the vascular complications of diabetes mellitus. J Int Med 1995;237:359-65.

183. Bruckert E, Davidoff P, Grimaldi A, et al. Increased serum levels of lipoprotein(a) in diabetes mellitus and their reduction with glycemic control. JAMA 1990;263:35-36.

184. Haffner SM, Tuttle KR, Rainwater DL. Decrease of lipoprotein(a) with improved glycemic control in IDDM subjects. Diabetes Care 1991;14:302-7.

185. Guillausseau PJ, Peynet J, Chanson P, et al. Lipoprotein(a) in diabetic patients with and without chronic renal failure. Diabetes Care 1992;15:976-9.

186. Couper JJ, Bates DJ, Cocciolone R, et al. Association of lipoprotein(a) with puberty in IDDM. Diabetes Care 1993;16:869-73.

187. Salzer B, Stavljenic A, Jurgens G, Dumic M, Radica, A. Polymorphism of apolipoprotein E, lipoprotein(a), and other lipoproteins in children with type I diabetes. Clin Chem 1993;39:1427-32.

188. Nagashima K, Yutani S, Miyake H, Onigata K, Yagi H, Kuroume T. Lipoprotein(a) levels in Japanese children with IDDM. Diabetes Care 1993;16:846.

189. Ritter MM, Richter WO, Lyko K, Schwandt P. Lp(a) serum concentrations and metabolic control. Diabetes Care 1992;15:1441-2.

190. Maser RE, Usher D, Becker DJ, Drash AL, Kuller LH, Orchard TJ. Lipoprotein(a) concentration shows little relationship to IDDM complications in the Pittsburgh Epidemiology of Diabetes Complications Study cohort. Diabetes Care 1993;16:755-8.

191. Heller FR, Jamart J, Honore P, et al. Serum lipoprotein(a) in patients with diabetes mellitus. Diabetes Care 1993;16:819-23.

192. Levitsky LL, Scanu AM, Gould SH. Lipoprotein(a) levels in black and white children and adolescents with IDDM. Diabetes Care 1991;14:283-7.

193. Austin A, Warty V, Janosky V, Arslanian S. The relationship of physical fitness to lipid and lipoprotein(a) levels in adolescents with IDDM. Diabetes Care 1993;16:4215.

194. Winocour PH, Durrington PN, Bhatnagar D, et al. A cross-sectional evaluation of cardiovascular risk factors in coronary heart disease associated with type 1 (insulin-dependent) diabetes mellitus. Diabetes Res Clin Pract 1992;18:173-84.

195. Klausen IC, Schmidt EB, Lervang HH, Gerdes LU, Ditzel J, Faergeman O. Normal lipoprotein(a) concentrations and apolipoprotein(a) isoforms in patients with insulin-dependent diabetes mellitus. Eur J Clin Invest 1992;22:538-41.

196. Ramirez LC, Arauz-Pacheco C, Lackner C, Albright G, Adams BV, Raskin P. Lipoprotein(a) levels in diabetes mellitus: relationship to metabolic control. Ann Intern Med 1992;117:42-7.

197. Joven J, Vilella E. Serum levels of lipoprotein(a) in patients with well-controlled non-insulin-dependent diabetes mellitus. JAMA 1991;265:1113-14.

198. Wolffenbuttel BH, Leurs PB, Sels JP, Rondas-Colbers GJ, Menheere PP, Nieuwenhuijzen-Kruseman AC. Improved blood glucose control by insulin therapy in type 2 diabetic patients has no effect on lipoprotein(a) concentrations. Diabet Med 1993;10:427–30.
199. Velho G, Erlich D, Turpin E, et al. Lipoprotein(a) in diabetic patients and normoglycemic relatives in familial NIDDM. Diabetes Care 1993;16:742–7.
200. Maioli M, Tonolo G, Pacifico A, et al. Raised serum apolipoprotein (a) in active diabetic retinopathy. Diabetologia 1993;36:88–90.
201. Muller HM, Diekstall FF, Schmidt E, Marz W, Canzler H, Demeler U. Lipoprotein (a): a risk factor for retinal vascular occlusion. Ger J Ophthalmol 1992;1:338–41.
202. Tomikawa S, Mezawa M, Yoshida Y, Saiga T, Shimizu Y. Lipoprotein (a) and sclerotic changes in retinal arterioles. Nippon Ganka Gakkai Zasshi 1993;97:967–74.
203. Ritter MM, Loscar M, Richter WO, Schwandt P. Lipoprotein(a) in diabetes mellitus. Clin Chim Acta 1993;214:45–54.
204. Haffner SM, Klein BE, Moss SE, Klein R. Lp(a) is not related to retinopathy in diabetic subjects. Eur J Ophthalmol 1995;5:119–23.
205. Dubrey SW, Reaveley DA, Leslie DG, O'Donnell M, O'Connor BM, Seed M. Effect of insulin-dependent diabetes mellitus on lipids and lipoproteins: a study of identical twins. Clin Sci 1993;84:537–42.
206. Császár A, Dieplinger H, Sandholzer C, et al. Plasma lipoprotein (a) concentration and phenotypes in diabetes mellitus. Diabetologia 1993;36:47–51.
207. Takegoshi T, Haba T, Hirai J, et al. Alterations of lipoprotein(a) in patients with diabetic nephropathy. Atherosclerosis 1990;83:99–100.
208. Jenkins AJ, Steele JS, Janus ED, Best JD. Increased plasma apolipoprotein(a) concentrations in IDDM patients with microalbuminuria. Diabetes 1991;40:787–90.
209. Winocour PH, Bhatnagar D, Ishola M, Arrol S, Durrington PN. Lipoprotein(a) and microvascular disease in type I (insulin-dependent) diabetes. Diabet Med 1991;8:922–7.
210. Kapelrud H, Bangstad HJ, Dahl-Jorgensen K, Berg K, Hanssen KF. Serum Lp(a) lipoprotein concentrations in insulin dependent diabetic patients with microalbuminuria. BMJ 1991;303:675–8.
211. Gall MA, Rossing P, Hommel E, et al. Apolipoprotein(a) in insulin-dependent diabetic patients with and without diabetic nephropathy. Scand J Clin Lab Invest 1992;52:513–21.
212. Jenkins AJ, Steele JS, Janus ED, Santamaria JD, Best JD. Plasma apolipoprotein (a) is increased in type 2 (non-insulin-dependent) diabetic patients with microalbuminuria. Diabetologia 1992;35:1055–9.
213. Haffner SM, Morales PA, Gruber MK, Hazuda HP, Stern MP. Cardiovascular risk factors in non-insulin-dependent diabetic subjects with microalbuminuria. Arterioscler Thromb 1993;13:205–10.
214. Irish AB, Simons LA, Simons J. Lipoprotein(a) concentration in diabetes: relationship to proteinuria and diabetes control. Aust NZ J Med 1992;22:329–33.
215. Takegoshi T, Kotoh C, Haba T, et al. A study of the clinical significance of lipoprotein(a) in nephrotic syndrome. Jpn J Med 1991;30:21–5.
216. Thomas ME, Freestone A, Varghese Z, Persaud JW, Moorhead JF. Lipoprotein(a) in patients with proteinuria. Nephrol Dial Transplant 1992;7:597–601.
217. Stenvinkel P, Berglund L, Heimburger O, Pettersson E, Alvestrand A. Lipoprotein(a) in nephrotic syndrome. Kidney Int 1993;44:1116–23.
218. Sato H, Suzuki S, Ueno M, et al. Localization of apolipoprotein(a) and B-100 in various renal diseases. Kidney Int 1993;43:430–5.
219. Kramer-Guth A, Greiber S, Pavenstadt H, Quaschning T, Winkler K, Schollmeyer P, Wanner C. Interaction of native and oxidized lipoprotein(a) with human mesangial cells and matrix. Kidney Int 1996;49:1250–61.
220. Greiber S, Kramer-Guth A, Pavenstadt H, Gutenkunst M, Schollmeyer P, Wanner C. Effects of lipoprotein(a) on mesangial cell proliferation and viability. Nephrol Dial Transplant 1996;11:778–85.
221. Yudkin JS, Marcovina SM, Foyle WJ, Fernandez M. Lipoprotein(a) is not elevated in non-diabetic microalbuminuric subjects: a longitudinal study of lipoprotein(a) concentrations and apolipoprotein(a) size isoforms. Int J Clin Lab Res 1996;26:43–50.

222. Heimann P, Josephson MA, Felner SK, Thistlethwaite JR Jr, Stuart FP, Dasgupta A. Elevated lipoprotein(a) levels in renal transplantation and hemodialysis patients. Am J Nephrol 1991;11:470-4.

223. Cressman MD, Heyka RJ, Paganini EP, O'Neil J, Skibinski CI, Hoff HF. Lipoprotein(a) is an independent risk factor for cardiovascular disease in hemodialysis patients. Circulation 1992;86:475-82.

224. Barbagallo CM, Averna MR, Scafidi V, Galione A, Notarbartolo A. Increased lipoprotein(a) levels in subjects with chronic renal failure on hemodialysis. Nephron 1992;62:471-2.

225. Webb AT, Reaveley DA, O'Donnell M, O'Connor B, Seed M, Brown EA. Lipoprotein (a) in patients on maintenance haemodialysis and continuous ambulatory peritoneal dialysis. Nephrol Dial Transplant 1993;8:609-13.

226. Thillet J, Faucher C, Issad B, Allouache M, Chapman J, Jacobs C. Lipoprotein(a) in patients treated by continuous ambulatory peritoneal dialysis. Am J Kidney Dis 1993; 22:226-32.

227. Takegoshi T, Kitoh C, Shimada T, Kawai K, Yamazaki Y, Mabuchi H. Alterations of Lp(a) lipoprotein in patients with chronic renal failure treated by continuous ambulatory peritoneal dialysis. Nippon Jinzo Gakkai Shi 1993;35:757-63.

228. Anwar N, Bhatnagar D, Short CD, et al. Serum lipoprotein (a) concentrations in patients undergoing continuous ambulatory peritoneal dialysis. Nephrol Dial Transplant 1993;8: 71-74.

229. Webb AT, Plant M, Reaveley DA, et al. Lipid and lipoprotein(a) concentrations in renal transplant patients. Nephrol Dial Transplant 1992;7:636-41.

230. Murphy BG, McNamee P, Duly E, Henry W, Archbold P, Trinick T. Increased serum apolipoprotein(a) in patients with chronic renal failure treated with continuous ambulatory peritoneal dialysis. Atherosclerosis 1992;93:53-57.

231. Irish AB, Simons LA, Savdie E, Hayes JM, Simons J. Lipoprotein(a) concentrations in chronic renal disease states, dialysis and transplantation. Aust NZ J Med 1992;22: 243-8.

232. Black IW, Wilcken DE. Decreases in apolipoprotein(a) after renal transplantation: implications for lipoprotein(a) metabolism. Clin Chem 1992;38:353-7.

233. Webb AT, Reaveley DA, O'Donnell M, O'Connor B, Seed M, Brown EA. Does cyclosporin increase lipoprotein(a) concentrations in renal transplant recipients? Lancet 1993;341: 268-70.

234. Hilbrands LB, Demacker PN, Hoitsma AJ. Cyclosporin and serum lipids in renal transplant recipients. [Discussion]. Lancet 1993;341:765-6.

235. Kronenberg F, Konig P, Lhotta K, et al. Cyclosporin and serum lipids in renal transplant recipients. [Discussion]. Lancet 1993;341:765.

236. Irish A. Cyclosporin and serum lipids in renal transplant recipients. [Discussion]. Lancet 1993;341:766.

237. Segarra A, Chacon P, Vilardell M, Piera LL. Cyclosporin and serum lipids in renal transplant recipients. [Discussion]. Lancet 1993;341:766.

238. Cressman MD, Abood D, O'Neil J, Hoff HF. Lp(a) and premature mortality during chronic hemodialysis treatment. Chem Phys Lipids 1994;67/68:419-27.

239. Dieplinger H, Lackner C, Kronenberg F, et al. Elevated plasma concentrations of lipoprotein(a) in patients with end-stage renal disease are not related to the size polymorphism of apolipoprotein(a). J Clin Invest 1993;91:397-401.

240. Haffner SM, Gruber KK, Aldrete G Jr, Morales PA, Stern MP, Tuttle KR. Increased lipoprotein(a) concentrations in chronic renal failure. J Am Soc Nephrol 1992;3:1156-62.

241. Cavaillon JM, Poignet JL, Fitting C, Delons S. Serum interleukin-6 in long-term hemodialyzed patients. Nephron 1992;60:307-13.

242. Docci D, Bilancioni R, Buscaroli A, et al. Elevated serum levels of C-reactive protein in hemodialysis patients. Nephron 1990;56:364-7.

243. Mege JL, Olmer M, Purgus R, et al. Haemodialysis membranes modulate chronically the production of TNF alpha, IL1beta and IL6. Nephrol Dial Transplant 1991;6:868-75.

244. Le JM, Vilcek J. Interleukin-6: a multifunctional cytokine regulating immune reactions and the acute phase protein response. Lab Invest 1989;61:588-602.

245. Kishimoto T. The biology of interleukin-6. Blood 1989;74:1-10.

246. Sonoda M, Sakamoto K, Miyauchi T, et al. Changes in serum lipoprotein(a) and C4b-binding protein levels after acute myocardial infarctions. Jpn Circ J 1992;56:1214-20.

247. Slunga L, Johnson O, Dahlen GH, Eriksson S. Lipoprotein(a) and acute-phase proteins in acute myocardial infarction. Scand J Clin Lab Invest 1992;52:95-101.

248. Cobbaert C, Sergeant P, Meyns B, Szecsi J, Kesteloot H. Time course of serum Lp(a) in men after coronary artery bypass grafting. Acta Cardiol 1992;47:529-42.

249. Rantapaa-Dahlqvist S, Wallberg-Jonsson S, Dahlen G. Lipoprotein(a), lipids, and lipoproteins in patients with rheumatoid arthritis. Ann Rheum Dis 1991;50:366-8.

250. Maeda S, Abe A, Seishima M, Makino K, Noma A, Kawade M. Transient changes of serum lipoprotein(a) as an acute phase protein. Atherosclerosis 1989;78:145-50.

251. Steinhauer HB, Brugger U, Atmanspacher R, Lubrich-Birkner I, Schollmeyer P. Effect of CAPD dialysate on the release of eicosanoids and cytokines from human peritoneal macrophages. Adv Perit Dial 1992;8:47-52.

252. Marcovina SM, Hobbs HH, Albers JJ. Relationship between the number of apolipoprotein(a) kringle 4 repeats and mobility of the isoforms in agarose gel: bases for a standardized isoform nomenclature. Clin Chem 1996;42:436-9.

253. Armstrong VW, Schleef J, Thiery J, et al. Effect of HELP-LDL-apheresis on serum concentrations of human lipoprotein(a): kinetic analysis of the post-treatment return to baseline levels. Eur J Clin Invest 1989;19:235-40.

254. Pokrovsky SN, Adamova IY, Afanasieva OY, Benevolenskaya GF. Immunosorbent for selective removal of lipoprotein(a) from human plasma: in vitro study. Artif Organs 1991;15:136-46.

255. Gordon BG, Kelsey SF, Bilheimer DW, et al. Treatment of refractory familial hypercholesterolemia by low-density lipoprotein apheresis using an automated dextran sulfate cellulose adsorption system: The Liposorber Study Group. Am J Cardiol 1992;70:1010-16.

256. Gurakar A, Hoeg JM, Kostner GM, Papadopoulos NM, Brewer HB Jr. Levels of lipoprotein Lp(a) decline with neomycin and niacin treatment. Atherosclerosis 1985;57:293-301.

257. Kostner GM. The affection of lipoprotein-a by lipid lowering drugs. In: Widholm K, Naito HK, eds. Recent aspects of diagnosis and treatment of lipoprotein disorders: impact on prevention of atherosclerotic diseases. New York: Alan R. Liss, 1988:255-63.

258. Carlson LA, Hamsten A, Asplund A. Pronounced lowering of serum levels of lipoprotein Lp(a) in hyperlipidemic subjects treated with nicotinic acid. J Intern Med 1989;226:271-6.

259. Pelegri A, Romero R, Senti M, Nogues X, Pedro-Botet J, Rubies-Prat J. Effect of bezafibrate on lipoprotein(a) and triglyceride-rich lipoproteins, including intermediate-density lipoproteins, in patients with chronic renal failure receiving haemodialysis. Nephrol Dial Transplant 1992;7:623-6.

260. Shewmon DA, Stock JL, Rosen CJ, Heiniluoma KM, Hogue MM, Morrison A, Doyle EM, Ukena T, Weale V, Baker S. Tamoxifen and estrogen lower circulating lipoprotein(a) concentrations in healthy postmenopausal women. Arterioscler Thromb 1994;14:1586-93.

261. Soma MR, Meschia M, Bruschi F, Morrisett JD, Paoletti R, Fumagalli R, Crosignani P. Hormonal agents used in lowering lipoprotein(a). Chem Phys Lipids 1994;67/68:345-50.

262. Brewer HB. Effectiveness of diet and drugs in the treatment of patients with elevated Lp(a) levels. In: Scanu AM, ed. Lipoprotein(a). New York: Academic Press, 1990:211-20.

Immunological Assays of Apolipoproteins A-II, A-IV, C-I, C-II, and C-III in Plasma: Methods and Applications

16

Christine Labeur and Maryvonne Rosseneu

INTRODUCTION

❖   In atherosclerosis research, quantification of both the lipid and protein content of the lipoproteins has gained importance in the past ten years.[1-3] All of the major apolipoproteins have been isolated, purified, and sequenced, and most of their physiological functions have been elucidated.

Given the metabolic role of apolipoproteins as lipid carriers, as ligands for receptors, and as enzyme activators, the measurement of the apolipoprotein concentrations in plasma should usefully complement that of the lipids with which they are associated. Because several of these apolipoproteins are present on the same lipoprotein particles, they are best measured in whole plasma by immunological techniques requiring the use of monoclonal antibodies or polyclonal antisera.[4-6] These methods have already been applied to the quantification of most of the apolipoproteins in plasma, including apolipoprotein (apo) A-I, A-II, A-IV, B, C-I, C-II, C-III, D, E, and lipoprotein(a) [Lp(a)].[7-9] In general terms, the plasma concentration of the smaller apolipoproteins—apo C-I, C-II, C-III, A-II, A-IV, and E—are within the range of 5–50 mg/dL. This concentration range offers few difficulties for most of the current immunological techniques.

The various methodological aspects of immunological assays for apolipoproteins AII, AIV, CI, CII, and CIII and their current applications in research and clinical chemistry laboratories are described in this chapter.

GENERAL ASPECTS OF APOLIPOPROTEIN QUANTIFICATION

Immunological assays of apolipoproteins require some specific considerations.[4-6] Because of the lipid-binding properties of the apolipoproteins and their presence on the surface of lipoprotein particles, some of the antigenic sites are susceptible to partial or complete masking by lipids.[4, 5, 10] Therefore, accurate quantification of apolipoproteins requires pretreatment of the plasma or lipoprotein samples to completely expose the antigenic sites by delipidation or, on a more practical basis, by exposure to enzymes, denaturing agents, or detergents.[10] The presence of a given apolipoprotein on several lipoprotein fractions raises corollary problems. This effect is less pronounced for the smaller apolipoproteins, such as apo C-II and C-III, which are probably equally exposed at the surface of all particles.[11, 12]

Antisera for Apolipoprotein Assays

Immunological assays of apolipoproteins seem quite sensitive to the nature of the antisera used in the measurement; these vary with the kind of antigen used in the immunization procedure, the species of host animal, and the dose of antigen injected. Significant differences have been reported between antisera. Monoclonal antibodies have been investigated as a possible approach to circumventing this problem. Apparently, however, the exposure of epitopes may vary with the lipoprotein particles in different individuals. Optimal quantification of apolipoproteins will therefore require a mixture of several monoclonal antibodies.

Standards for Apolipoprotein Assays

Selection and quantification of a suitable primary standard has been a major problem in the development and standardization of apolipoprotein assays. Purified apolipoproteins have been chosen as primary standards for the apolipoproteins considered here. These purified apolipoprotein fractions were obtained from plasma lipoproteins separated by flotation ultracentrifugation.[7-10] For apo A-II isolation, the high-density lipoproteins (HDL) were isolated from normolipemic plasma, while for purification of the C apolipoproteins, the very-low-density lipoprotein (VLDL) fraction was recovered from hypertriglyceridemic plasma. All lipoproteins were subsequently delipidated with ether/ethanol,[9] and the HDL apolipoproteins and VLDL apolipoproteins were obtained. Apo A-II was further isolated from other HDL apolipoproteins by ion-exchange chromatography on a DEAE Sepharose column.[10] VLDL apolipoproteins were fractionated by gel filtration on a Sephacryl S200 column,[11, 12] yielding three major fractions. Apo C-III was isolated from the apo C-containing fraction by ion-exchange chromatography on a DEAE Sepharose column,[12] while apo C-II was recovered from the same fraction by chromatofocusing.[11]

A different purification strategy had to be applied for apo A-IV, as this apolipoprotein is only partially associated with lipoproteins in plasma.[13] Apo A-IV was purified from lymph chylomicrons obtained from a patient with lymph carcinoma,[13] or was recovered from plasma after adsorption on a triglyceride (TG) emulsion.[14] Further purification was performed by preparative gel electrophoresis in sodium dodecyl sulphate, and the protein was recovered by electroelution.[13] The mass of the primary standard was determined either by protein quantitation according to the method of Lowry[15] with bovine serum albumin as a standard, or preferably by quantitative amino acid analysis or by phenylalanine quantitation by high-performance liquid chromatography (HPLC).[16]

TECHNIQUES FOR THE QUANTIFICATION OF APO A-II, A-IV, C-I, C-II, AND C-III

Techniques for the quantification of apo A-II, A-IV, C-I, C-II and C-III include radioimmunoassay (RIA); enzyme immunoassays, particularly enzyme-linked immunosorbent assay (ELISA); electroimmunoassay (EIA); radial immunodiffusion (RID); and immunoprecipitin assays, including nephelometric and turbidimetric procedures. The characteristics of these assays are summarized in Table 16–1 and their advantages and disadvantages are given in Table 16–2.

Table 16–1 ✧ Characteristics of Immunological Assays for Apolipoproteins*						
	RIA	ELISA	EIA	RID	Nephel-ometry	Turbid-imetry
APO A-II						
Sensitivity (ng)	0.5	1	20	5	30	20
Intra-assay CV (%)	7	8	5	5	5	5
Inter-assay CV (%)	9	7	8	–	7	6
Normal values (mg/dL) mean ± SD	25 ± 4	35 ± 5	76 ± 2	29 ± 2	37 ± 9	38 ± 3
APO A-IV						
Sensitivity (ng)	5.0	0.2	20	–	25	–
Intra-assay CV (%)	5	4	5	–	2.0	–
Inter-assay CV (%)	7	8	9	–	2.4	–
Normal values (mg/dL) mean ± SD	17 ± 3	14 ± 5	14 ± 4	–	19 ± 3	–
APO C-I						
Sensitivity (ng)	1	5	50	–	–	–
Intra-assay CV (%)	7	3	5	–	–	–
Inter-assay CV (%)	9	5	8	–	–	–
Normal values (mg/dL) mean ± SD	5 ± 3	6 ± 2	6 ± 1	–	–	4 ± 1
APO C-II						
Sensitivity (ng)	1	0.3	45	–	–	10
Intra-assay CV (%)	6	3	6.5	–	–	3.3
Inter-assay CV (%)	10	8	8.2	–	–	6.2
Normal values (mg/dL) mean ± SD	4 ± 1	3 ± 1	4 ± 2	–	–	4 ± 1
APO C-III						
Sensitivity (ng)	0.3	10	20	–	15	–
Intra-assay CV (%	9	3.6	6	–	2.2	2.8
Inter-assay CV (%)	13	4.3	8	–	6.3	5.2
Normal values (mg/dL) mean ± SD	15 ± 6	16 ± 3	12 ± 4	–	12 ± 3	11 ± 3

*RIA = Radioimmunoassay
ELISA = Enzyme-linked Immunosorbent Assay
EIA = Electroimmunoassay
RID = Radial Immunodiffusion
CV = Coefficient of Variance
SD = Standard Deviation
— = No data available

Table 16–2 ✧ Advantages and Disadvantages of Immunological Assays for Apolipoproteins

Technique*	Advantages	Disadvantages
RIA	High sensitivity High specificity	High dilution Uses isotope
ELISA	High sensitivity High specificity No isotope	High dilution
RID	Easy Low dilution No isotope	Incubation time 48 h Not easy to automate
EIA	Low dilution No isotope	No monoclonal antibody 10 samples per plate Not easy to automate
Nephelometry	Low dilution No isotope Easy to automate	Special equipment No monoclonal antibody Specific polyclonal antibodies required
Turbidimetry	Low dilution No isotope Easy to automate	No monoclonal antibody Specific polyclonal antibodies required

*RIA = Radioimmunoassay
ELISA =Enzyme-linked Immunosorbent Assay
RID = Radial Immunodiffusion
EIA - Electroimmunoassay

Radioimmunoassay (RIA)

This technique, which can detect as little as a few nanograms of protein, has been applied to the assay of apo A-II,[17-20] A-IV,[21, 22] C-I,[23, 24] C-II,[23, 25, 26] and C-III.[23, 25] RIAs are of either the liquid or the solid-phase type and use either monoclonal antibodies or polyclonal antisera. However, RIAs require the iodination of pure apolipoprotein, a procedure that might decrease the reactivity of the standard compared to that of the lipoproteins, owing to self-association and aggregation of the isolated apolipoprotein. Another drawback of this technique is the need for high dilutions, which might lead to substantial experimental errors. The equipment needed for the RIA assay includes a gamma-counter for radioactivity measurement and an automated dilutor and pipetting station for precise handling of the high dilutions and small volumes. Calculation of the concentrations of the unknown samples is preferably carried out by a curve-fitting procedure after log-logit transformation of the measured values.

These assays can be easily automated, but are not convenient for clinical laboratories, owing to the safety requirements inherent to the handling and disposal of radioactive samples.

Enzyme Immunoassay

Several types of enzyme immunoassays, either direct or competitive, have been reported for the apolipoproteins. The sensitivity of these assays is similar to that of RIAs, but no radioactive tracers are required. These assays have enabled the quantification of apo A-II,[27-29] A-IV,[13] C-I,[30-32] C-II,[11, 30, 31] and C-III.[11, 30, 31] Most assays begin with the preparation of affinity-purified antibodies, which are subsequently labeled with either peroxidase or alkaline phosphatase, using either periodate or other classical coupling procedures.[9]

Recently, an enzyme-linked immunosorbent assay (ELISA) procedure involving monoclonal antibodies was reported for apo A-II.[29] The nature of the monoclonal antibody seems crucial for the recognition of all apo A-II present in plasma, so that a combination of several antibodies seems preferable to only one.

Two types of ELISA assays are currently used: the "sandwich" type and the competitive type. In the sandwich-type ELISAs, a polystyrene plate is coated with affinity-purified antibodies prepared against the apolipoprotein to be measured. After blocking all residual binding sites on the plate with either albumin or casein,[9] the plasma is incubated with the immobilized antibody for 2 h at 37° C. After extensive washing, the antibody-antigen complex on the plate is incubated with a second detecting antibody which is enzyme labeled. The amount of bound conjugated antibody is a direct measure of the antigen concentration. This assay is very sensitive, with a detection limit of 0.5–1 ng and has the major advantage of easy and stable coating of the plates with affinity-purified antibodies.[9, 10]

In the competitive type of assay, the plates are coated with the antigen and competition for the conjugated antibody takes place between the plasma antigen and the antigen immobilized on the plate. This assay is about 10–20 times less sensitive than the sandwich-type ELISA. Its major drawback for apolipoprotein measurement is the requirement for purified apolipoproteins for plate coating. As these apolipoproteins normally occur as lipid-bound components of lipoproteins, their antigenic properties when immobilized on the plate might differ from those in their native state.

ELISA assays, especially those of the sandwich type, are well suited to the quantification of apolipoproteins; they require a minimal amount of antiserum compared to nephelometry, radial immunodiffusion (RID), or electroimmunoassay (EIA), and have the great advantage of not being affected by sample turbidity.[10] They are also easy to automate, and their accuracy and reproducibility compares well to that of other assays, provided the dilutions are made accurately. These assays should become more widely used in the future, especially for quantification of the smaller apolipoproteins such as apo C-II, and C-III, whose plasma concentrations are around 10 mg/dL or less. ELISA processes can be partially or fully automated, including sample dilution, dispensing the samples into the plates, and plate washing. The plates can be read after the colorimetric reaction, either manually or by an automated reader which is connected to a personal computer or hard-wired to its own computing device.

Fully automated systems perform all operations automatically after programming for the application of the samples, the incubation times, wash cycles, volumes of reagents, etc.

Several types of calculations are available for computing results, depending upon the type of assay. In the sandwich-type direct assay, the curve can be fitted to a four-parameter equation[9] and the concentrations of the samples calculated from the fitted curve. For the competitive-type assay (as in RIAs), a log-logit transformation is used to linearize the curve before the concentration of test samples is calculated.

Electroimmunoassay (EIA)

This technique has also been used to quantify most apolipoproteins, including apo A-II,[33, 34] A-IV,[35-37] C-I,[38] C-II,[34, 38-40] and C-III.[34, 40, 41] The coefficient of variation (CV) for this assay is significantly higher than that obtained using other techniques. This method is difficult to automate and is therefore more limited in its application.

Radial Immunodiffusion (RID)

This method has been used to assay apo A-II,[42-45] C-I,[45] C-II,[44, 45] and C-III.[44, 45] Although RID is simple in principle, its applicability depends upon the ability to obtain sharp precipitin rings of sufficient diameter. However, silver staining of the immunoprecipitates can enhance the sensitivity tenfold, bringing the threshold level of detection to 10 ng.[45] The migration of VLDL is slow in comparison to that of low-density lipoprotein (LDL), and 72–96 h diffusion is required to reach an equilibrium. Although the technique is easy to perform, its accuracy is questionable; moreover, it is not readily applicable to large population studies that generate a large number of samples.

Immunoprecipitation Assays

These assays include both nephelometric and turbidimetric procedures and have been applied to the measurement of most apolipoproteins. Nephelometric assays have been described for apo A-II,[46, 47] apo AI-V,[48] and for apo C-III.[49] Both apolipoproteins were assayed by end-point nephelometry,[46-49] where the concentration is proportional to the turbidity after the formation of the antigen antibody complex is complete.

In the turbidimetric assay, the absorption of the antigen antibody complex is measured at 340 nm in a spectrophotometer. In the nephelometric assay, the intensity of the scattered light is measured at an angle of 30–90° to that of the incident beam. These techniques are fast, accurate, and reproducible.[10, 16] However, they have draw-backs in that they are extremely sensitive to the turbidity of the sample and require the use of enzyme or detergent when TG concentrations exceed 200 mg/dL. Measuring apo C-II, C-III, and A-IV in hyperlipemic samples by means of turbidimetry can be inaccurate. Turbidimetry has been used to quantify apo A-II,[50, 51, 53] C-II,[51-53] and C-III.[51, 53] This technique has been adapted to most of the available clinical analyzers and is especially suited to the measurement of large sample numbers with good reproducibility.

CLINICAL APPLICATIONS

Apolipoproteins and Cardiovascular Disease

Apolipoprotein assays have found three major fields of application: in the assessment of risk for cardiovascular disease in myocardial infarction survivors, in patients with evidence of coronary heart disease (CHD) as diagnosed by coronary angiography, and in offspring of patients with CHD. Apo A-I and B were the major parameters measured in most case-control studies, showing that the concentrations of these apolipoproteins differ significantly from the values measured in a control group.[8, 55] These studies were further extended to the measurement of apo A-II, C-II, and C-III.[10, 16]

In a case-control study[55] comparing 70 male survivors of myocardial infarction to an equal number of healthy controls matched for age and body-mass index, apo B was shown to be significantly increased and apo A-I significantly decreased in the cases compared to controls. A multivariate analysis indicated that the apo A-I/B ratio, HDL-cholesterol (HDL-C), and the apo A-I/A-II ratio contributed independently to the discrimination of cases from controls, with an overall classification of 82% of the cases. Similar results were obtained by other investigators (see Table 16–3). In most of these studies, the apo A-I/B ratio was the best discriminator between cases and controls, while apo A-II was a less powerful parameter.

Apolipoproteins were further measured in a group of patients with coronary lesions assessed by coronary angiography (see Table 16–3). In most studies, a statistically significant negative correlation between the apo A-I/B ratio and the severity of CHD was reported.[56-60] Other investigators found that apo A-I plasma concentrations relate

Table 16–3 ◆ Lipids and Apolipoprotein Measurements in Patients with Coronary Heart Disease

Author	Variables	Principal Findings
De Backer et al.[55]	apo A-I, A-II, B TC, TG, HDL-C	apo A-I, A-I/B, HDL-C lower apo B higher in cases
Leitersdorf et al.[54]	apo A-I, A-II, B, E HDL-C, TC, TG	apo AI lower apo B, E higher in cases
Riesen et al.[56]	apo A-I, A-II, B HDL-C, LDL-C, TC, TG	apo A-I, A-II lower apo B, LDL-C, TC higher in cases
Miller et al.[57]	apo A-I, A-II, E LDL$_2$-C, HDL$_2$-C, TC, TG	HDL$_2$-C lower in severe cases
Noma et al.[58]	apo A-I, A-II, B LDL-C, HDL-C, TC, TG	LDL/HDL-C higher in cases apo B/A-I, B/A-II higher in cases
Kottke et al.[60]	apo A-I, A-II, B TC, HDL-C, TG	apo A-I, A-II, B best discriminators
Sedlis et al.[59]	apo A-I, A-II, B, E HDL-C, TC, TG	apo A-I/B best discriminator apo E higher in cases with total occlusion
Labeur et al.[61]	apo A-I, A-II, B HDL-C, TC, TG	apo A-I/B best discriminator

better to the presence or absence of CHD than to the severity of the disease, while apo A-II was a poor discriminator.[57, 60]

In a study of 2020 patients aged 31–70 years who underwent coronary angiography, the patients were classified as having one-, two-, or three-vessel disease according to the extent of the lesions.[61] When compared to age-matched controls free of angiographically detected lesions, a significant decrease in the apo A-I/B ratio was observed in the cases with two- and three-vessel disease. Further, there was a tendency toward a decrease of the apo A-I/B ratio with an increasing severity of the lesions. Among the other apolipoproteins and lipids, apo B was the best discriminator, while apo A-I, A-II, total cholesterol (TC), and TG did not differ significantly between the four groups of patients.[61]

More recent studies which included the measurements of apo A-II, C-III, and A-IV in either plasma or lipoprotein particles[62–65] showed increased apo CIII concentrations in the patients. Studies conducted in patients with peripheral vascular disease[8] are difficult to evaluate due to complications such as diabetes, hypertension, and obesity which are often present in such patients.

A further application for plasma apolipoprotein assays is monitoring and early detection of an hereditary risk for CHD. In one study, young adults whose fathers suffered a well-documented myocardial infarction below age 50 were compared to an age- and sex-matched controls who had no familial history of CHD.[66] Lower apo A-I concentrations were the only significant difference in the lipid and apolipoprotein values between the cases and the controls. This difference in apo A-I concentrations is not reflected in either the HDL-C or apo A-II concentrations. In a comprehensive study based on the same design which was carried out in students of 12 European countries, results showed that apo B and LDL-C were the best discriminators between students with and without a paternal history of CHD.[67]

An early screening of neonates, including assays for apolipoproteins and TC, can be carried out on a minimal quantity of blood[68] to detect increased apo B and decreased apo A-I plasma concentrations. Other apolipoproteins, including A-II, C-II, C-III, and A-IV, can also be measured in newborns.[69–71]

Apolipoproteins and Primary Dyslipidemias

Patients with Type I dyslipidemia are characterized by significantly decreased plasma concentrations of apo A-I and apo B, but have normal apo A-I/B ratios. When lipoprotein lipase deficiency is responsible for this pattern, apo C-II and C-III are increased about threefold compared to normals. Apo C-II deficiency can also induce this type of dyslipidemia, in which case apo C-II concentrations are undetectable even by the most sensitive ELISA or RIA assays.[9, 10]

In Type II dyslipidemia, the plasma apo B concentrations are severely increased while the apo A-I concentrations are slightly decreased. A strong positive correlation between plasma TG and apo C-II and C-III concentrations exists in these hypercholesterolemic patients, so that a distinction between Type IIa and Type IIb patients can be made on the basis of the increased plasma concentrations of these apolipoproteins. In addition to a two- to threefold increase of plasma apo B concentrations, Type III patients are characterized by increased apo E concentrations, whereas apo C-II and apo C-III increase about fourfold above normal. In Type IV patients, the apo AI/B ratio is significantly reduced, whereas apo C-II and apo C-III are increased by a factor of two to three.

The most pronounced increase in plasma apolipoproteins is observed in Type V patients. In these patients, plasma TG are positively correlated with apo C-III and inversely correlated with apo C-II.

In hypobetalipoproteinemic patients, plasma apo B concentrations are strongly reduced, whereas apo A-I concentrations are normal. In addition, apo C-II concentrations are reduced by about 50%, whereas apo CIII concentrations are decreased about fourfold compared to normals.

Plasma concentrations of the C apolipoproteins are thus increased most significantly in the hypertriglyceridemic states, whereas apo A-IV concentrations are not significantly different in dyslipoproteinemic patients compared to controls.[13, 14] However, Brewer et al.[72] studied the *in vivo* metabolism of apo A-IV in severe hypertriglyceridemia and demonstrated that plasma levels of apo A-IV are significantly elevated in hypertriglyceridemic patients due to a delayed catabolism of apo A-IV. Apo A-IV concentrations seem sensitive to the state of alimentary lipemia,[73] and this apolipoprotein was reported to decrease food intake in rats.[74]

Well-controlled studies on the genetic polymorphism of apo A-IV and its influence on plasma lipid levels reported by the European Atherosclerosis Research Group[75] showed that the apo A-IV polymorphism does not influence HDL-C and apo A-IV plasma levels. Apo A-IV levels were lower in females than in males. In females, oral contraceptive users had significantly lower apo A-IV levels than non-users. When myocardial infarction survivors were compared to controls, no differences in apo A-IV levels and phenotypic distribution were observed, suggesting that the apo A-IV gene is not a major determinant of the risk for myocardial infarction and/or coronary heart disease.

Apolipoproteins and Secondary Dyslipidemias

In addition to the primary dyslipidemias, which are mostly due to genetic factors, a number of pathologies and dietary factors are responsible for inducing secondary dyslipidemias. These have essentially the same features and lead to the same phenotypes as the primary dyslipidemias. These are, however, reversible and should normalize upon treatment of the underlying disease. Secondary dyslipidemias can occur as a result of renal disease, alcohol consumption, liver disease, thyroid dysfunction, and diabetes mellitus.[7-10]

Chronic renal failure can be treated either by hemodialysis or by continuous ambulatory peritoneal dialysis (CAPD). Both types of treatment induce a decrease of the HDL fraction, which can be accompanied by an accumulation of VLDL and an increase of apo C-II and C-III.[76] The secondary dyslipidemia is usually more severe in CAPD patients, in whom a Type IIb or even a Type V dyslipidemia can occur.

In patients with nephrotic syndrome, pronounced secondary dyslipidemia develops readily due to decreased LDL-receptor synthesis and to apo B overproduction. HDL and especially apo AI are lost through the kidneys, accounting for the low apo AI and AII concentrations in these patients.[77]

Alcohol influences the lipoprotein patterns according to frequency and volume of consumption. Acute consumption increases HDL concentrations, especially that of apo A-II.

Secondary dyslipidemias can occur in diabetes mellitus. In Type I, insulin-dependent diabetes mellitus (IDDM), Type IV pattern is frequent, characterized by decreased apo A-I and A-II concentrations and increased apo B, C-II, and C-III concentrations.[7-10] In Type II, non-insulin dependent diabetes mellitus (NIDDM), a Type V hyperlipoproteinemia is frequently observed. In both cases, this secondary dyslipidemia results in CHD, which represents a major complication in diabetics. Apo A-IV levels and apo A-IV phenotypes were studied in NIDDM patients.[78, 79] Apo A-IV levels were higher both in male and female diabetic patients compared to controls, while there was no difference between the apo A-IV phenotypic distribution. Apo A-IV levels could be corrected with the hypertriglyceridemia in these patients.

Among liver diseases, acute hepatitis decreases the apo A-I and A-II concentrations due to impaired HDL synthesis, while a decrease in hepatic lipase activity increases the apo C-II and C-III concentrations. In chronic hepatitis, hepatic lipase activity is decreased while apo A-I and A-II synthesis is normal. In liver cirrhosis, protein synthesis is impaired and the concentrations of the liver-synthesized apolipoproteins—A-I, A-II, B, and the C apolipoproteins—are significantly decreased.

In thyroid disorders, hyperthyroidism is accompanied by a large decrease in apo B concentrations due to increased LDL catabolism. In non-obese hypothyroid patients, apo B is increased and a Type IIa phenotype is most common due to reduced LDL catabolism.[80] In obese hypothyroid patients, apo C-II and C-III can accumulate due to impaired IDL-to-LDL conversion, inducing a Type V dyslipidemia.

CONCLUSION

The apolipoprotein profiles can be routinely assessed by a variety of immunological procedures and can be usefully combined with lipid quantitation for the characterization of primary and secondary dyslipidemias. Since the apolipoproteins constitute the physiological carriers of the plasma lipids, their plasma concentration and lipoprotein distribution are sensitive to hormonal, functional, and dietary regulation. As a consequence, different patterns arise. The combination of apolipoprotein and lipid assays provides a more sensitive and accurate way of monitoring primary and secondary dyslipidemias, as well as of evaluating a patient's risk of developing cardiovascular diseases. ✧

REFERENCES

1. Rifkind BM. The Lipid Research Clinics Primary Prevention Trial results. I. Reduction in incidence of coronary heart disease. J Amer Med Assoc 1984;251:351–64.
2. Rifkind BM. The Lipid Research Clinics Coronary Primary Prevention Trial results. II. The relationship of reduction in incidence of coronary heart disease to cholesterol lowering. J Amer Med Assoc 1984;251:365–74.
3. De Backer G, Rosseneu M, Deslypeze JP. Discriminative value of lipids and apoproteins in coronary heart disease. Atherosclerosis 1982;42:197–203.
4. Steinberg KK, Cooper GR, Rosseneu M. Evaluation and standardization of apolipoprotein A-I immunoassays. Clin Chem 1983;29:415–26.

5. Rosseneu M, Vercaemst R, Steinberg KK, Cooper GR. Some considerations of methodology and standardization of apolipoprotein B immunoassays. Clin Chem 1983;29: 427-33.
6. Naito HK. The Clinical significance of apolipoprotein measurements. J Clin Immunoassay 1986;9:11-20.
7. Rosseneu M, Bury J. Apolipoproteins assays for the diagnosis of hyperlipidemias. In: Naito H, ed. Recent aspects on diagnosis and treatment of lipid disorders: Impact on prevention of atherosclerotic diseases. New York: A. R. Liss, 1988:143-5.
8. Kostner GM. Apolipoproteins and lipoproteins of human plasma: significance in health and disease. Adv Lipid Res 1983;20:1-43.
9. Bury J, Rosseneu M. Apolipoprotein quantitation by ELISA: technical aspects and clinical applications. Rev Immunoassay Techn 1988;1:1-25.
10. Labeur C, Shepherd J, Rosseneu M. Immunological assays of lipoproteins in plasma: Methods and instrumentation. Clin Chem 1990;36:591-7.
11. Bury J, Michiels G, Rosseneu M. Human apolipoprotein C-II quantitation by sandwich enzyme linked immunosorbent assay. J Clin Chem Clin Biochem 1986;24: 457-61.
12. Bury J, Rosseneu M. Enzyme immunosorbent assay for human apolipoprotein C-III. J Clin Chem Clin Biochem 1985;23:63-8.
13. Rosseneu M, Michiels G, De Keersgieter W, et al. Human apolipoprotein A-IV quantitation by sandwich enzyme linked immunosorbent assay. Clin Chem 1988; 34:739-43.
14. Weinberg RB, Scanu AM. Isolation and characterization of human apolipoprotein A-IV from lipoprotein-depleted serum. J Lipid Res 1983;24:54-9.
15. Lowry OH, Rosebrough NJ, Farr AL, Randall RJ. Protein measurement with the Folin reagent. J Biol Chem 1951;193:265-75.
16. Rosseneu MY, Labeur C. Apolipoprotein structure, function and measurement. Curr Opin Lipidol 1990;1:508-13.
17. Mordasini RC, Riesen WF. Electroimmunoassay and radioimmunoassay for the quantitation of high-density apolipoproteins AI and AII. J Clin Chem Clin Biochem 1980;18: 917-20.
18. Mao SJT, Gotto AM Jr, Jackson RL. Immunochemistry of human plasma high density lipoproteins: radioimmunoassay of apolipoprotein A-II. Biochemistry 1975;14:4127-31.
19. Schonfeld G, Chen J, McDonell WF, Jeng I. Apolipoprotein A-II content of plasma high density lipoproteins measured by radioimmunoassay. J Lipid Res 1977;18:645-54.
20. Goldberg RB, Karlin JB, Juhn DJ, Scanu AM, Edelstein C, Rubenstein AH. Characterization and measurement of human apolipoprotein A-II by radioimmunoassay. J Lipid Res 1980;21:902-12.
21. Ghiselli G, Krishnan S, Beigel Y, Gotto AM Jr. Plasma metabolism of apolipoprotein A-IV in humans. J Lipid Res 1986;27:813-27.
22. Bisgaier CL, Sachdev OP, Lee ES, Williams KJ, Blum CB, Glickman RM. Effect of lecithin:cholesterol acyltransferase on distribution of apolipoprotein A-IV among lipoproteins of human plasma. J Lipid Res 1987;28:693-703.
23. Bren ND, Rastogi A, Kottke BA. Quantification of human apolipoproteins C-I, C-II and C-III by radioimmunoassay. Mayo Clinic Proc 1993;68:657-64.
24. Polz E, Kotite L, Havel RJ, Kane JP, Sata T. Human apolipoprotein C-I: concentration in blood serum and lipoproteins. Biochem Med 1980;24:229-37.
25. Schonfeld G, George PK, Miller J, Reilly P, Witztum J. Apolipoprotein C-II and C-III levels in hyperlipoproteinemia. Metabolism 1979;28:1001-10.
26. Barr SI, Kottke BA, Chang JY, Mao SJT. Immunochemistry of human plasma apolipoprotein C-II as studied by radioimmunoassay. Biochem Biophys Acta 1981;663:491-505.
27. Dubois DY, Cantraine F, Malmendier CL. Comparison of different sandwich immunoassays for the quantitation of human apolipoproteins A-I and A-II. J Immunol Meth 1987;96:115-20.
28. Dufaux B, Ilsemann K, Assmann G. Competitive enzyme immunoassay for apolipoprotein A-II. J Clin Chem Clin Biochem 1983;21:39-43.

29. Stein EA, Dipersio L, Pesce AJ, et al. Enzyme-linked immunoabsorbent assay of apolipo-protein A-II in plasma with use of a monoclonal antibody. Clin Chem 1986;32:967-71.

30. Holmquist L. Quantitation of human serum very low density apolipoprotein B, C-I, C-II, C-III and E by enzyme immunoassay. J Immunol Meth 1980;34:243-51.

31. Carlson LA, Holmquist L. Concentrations of apolipoproteins B, C-I, C-II, C-III and E in sera from normal men and their relation to serum lipoprotein levels. Clin Chim Acta 1982;124:163-78.

32. Riesen WF, Sturzenegger E. Enzyme-linked immunosorbent assay for apolipoprotein C-I. J Clin Chem Clin Biochem 1986;24:723-7.

33. Curry MD, Alaupovic P, Suenram CA. Determination of apolipoprotein A and its con-stitutive A-I and A-II polypeptides by separate electroimmunoassays. Clin Chem 1976; 22:315-22.

34. Alaupovic P, Curry MD, McConathy WJ. Quantitative determination of human plasma apolipoproteins by electroimmunoassay. Intern Confer Atheroscl 1978;109-15.

35. Utermann G, Beisiegel U. Apolipoprotein A-IV: a protein occurring in human mesenteric lymph chylomicrons and free in plasma. Eur J Biochem 1979;99:333-43.

36. Green PHR, Glickman RM, Riley JW, Quinet E. Human apolipoprotein A-IV. J Clin Invest 1980;65:911-9.

37. Bisgaier CL, Sachdev OP, Megna L, Glickman RM. Distribution of apolipoprotein A-IV in human plasma. J Lipid Res 1985;26:11-25.

38. Curry MD, McConathy WJ, Fesmire JD, Alaupovic P. Quantitative determination of apolipoproteins C-I and C-II in human plasma by separate electroimmunoassays. Clin Chem 1981;27:543-8.

39. Jauhiainen M, Laitinen M, Penttilö I, Puhakainen E, Hietanen E. Determination of human apolipoprotein C-II by electroimmunoassay: studies on standardization and de-termination before and after physical training. Int J Biochem 1983;15:501-6.

40. Mörz W, Schenk G, Gross W. Apolipoproteins C-II and C-III in serum quantified by zone immunoelectrophoresis. Clin Chem 1987;33:664-9.

41. Curry MD, McConathy WJ, Fesmire JD, Alaupovic P. Quantitative determination of human apolipoprotein C-III by electroimmunoassay. Biochem Biophys Acta 1980;617: 503-13.

42. Albers JJ, Cheung MC, Wahl PW. Effect of storage on the measurement of apolipo-proteins A-I and A-II by radial immunodiffusion. J Lipid Res 1980;21:874-8.

43. Cheung MC, Albers JJ. The measurement of apolipoprotein A-I and A-II levels in men and women by immunoassay. J Clin Invest 1977;60:43-50.

44. Goto Y, Akanuma Y, Harano Y. Determination by the SRID method of normal values of serum apolipoproteins (A-I, A-II, B, CII, CIII and E) in normolipidemic healthy Japanese subjects. J Clin Biochem Nutr 1986;1:73-88.

45. Ishida BY, Paigen B. Silver-enhanced radial immunodiffusion assay of plasma apolipo-proteins. J Lipid Res 1992;33:1073-8.

46. Kuusi T, Palosuo T, Ehnholm C. Immunonephelometric measurements of human plasma apolipoproteins A-I and A-II: an assay performed by consecutive addition of the two antisera to a single specimen. Scand J Clin Lab Invest 1985;45:245-53.

47. Rosseneu M, Vinaimont N, Musliner TA, Bernier D, Herbert PN, Belpaire F. Immuno-nephelometry of apolipoprotein A-II in plasma. Clin Chem 1984;30:234-7.

48. Schwarz S, Haas B, Luley C, Schafer JR, Steinmetz A. Quantification of apolipoprotein A-IV in human plasma by immunonephelometry. Clin Chem 1994;40:1717-21.

49. Bury J, De Keersgieter W, Rosseneu M, Belpaire F, Christophe J. Immunonephelometric quantitation of the apolipoprotein C-III in human plasma. Clin Chim Acta 1985;145: 249-58.

50. Rifai N, King ME. Immunoturbidimetric assays of apolipoproteins A, AI, AII, and B in serum. Clin Chem 1986;32:957-61.

51. Noma A, Haras Y, Goto Y. Quantification of serum apolipoprotein A-I, A-II, B, C-II, C-III, and E by turbidimetric immunoassay: reference values and age- and sex-related dif-ferences. Clin Chim Acta 1991;199:147-57.

52. Rifai N, Silverman LM. Immunoturbidimetric techniques for quantifying apolipoproteins CII and CIII. Clin Chem 1986;32:1969–72.

53. Ikeda T, Shibuya Y, Senba U, et al. Automated immunoturbidimetric analysis of six plasma apolipoproteins: correlation with radial immunodiffusion assays. J Clin Lab Anal 1991;5:90–5.

54. Leitersdorf E, Gottehrer N, Fainaru M, et al. Analysis of risk factors in 532 survivors of first myocardial infarction hospitalized in Jerusalem. Atherosclerosis 1986;59:75–93.

55. De Backer G, Rosseneu M, Deslypere JP. Discriminative value of lipids and apoproteins in coronary heart disease. Atherosclerosis 1982;42:197–203.

56. Riesen WF, Mordasini R, Salzmann C, Theler A, Gurtner HP. Apolipoproteins and lipids as discriminators of severity of coronary heart disease. Atherosclerosis 1980;37:157–62.

57. Miller NE, Hammett F, Saltissi S, et al. Relation of angiographically defined coronary artery disease to plasma lipoprotein subfractions and apolipoproteins. British Med J 1981;282:1741–4.

58. Noma A, Yokosuka T, Kitmra K. Plasma lipids and apolipoproteins as discriminators for presence and severity of angiographically defined coronary artery disease. Atherosclerosis 1983;49:1–7.

59. Sedlis SP, Schechtman KB, Ludbrook PA, Sobel BE, Schonfeld G. Plasma apoproteins and the severity of coronary artery disease. Circulation 1986;73:978–86.

60. Kottke BA, Zinsmeister AR, Holmes DR, Kneller RW, Hallaway BJ, Mao ST. Apolipoproteins and coronary artery disease. Mayo Clin Proc 1986;61:313–20.

61. Labeur C, Vincke J, Muyldermans L, et al. Plasma lipoprotein (a) values and severity of coronary artery disease in a large population of patients undergoing coronary angiography. Clin Chem 1992;38:2261–6.

62. Genest JJ Jr, Bard JM, Fruchart JC, Ordovas JM, Wilson PF, Schaefer EJ. Plasma apolipoprotein A-I, A-II, B, E and CIII containing particles in men with premature coronary artery disease. Atherosclerosis 1991;90:149–57.

63. Kottke BA, Moll PP, Michels VV, Weidman WH. Levels of lipids, lipoproteins, and apolipoproteins in a defined population. Mayo Clin Proc 1991;66:1198–208.

64. Chivot L, Mainard F, Bigot E, et al. Logistic discriminant analysis of lipids and apolipoproteins in a population of coronary bypass patients and the significance of apolipoproteins C-III and E. Atherosclerosis 1990;82:205–11.

65. Ordovas JM, Civeira F, Genest J Jr, et al. Restriction fragment length polymorphisms of the apolipoprotein A-I, C-III, A-IV gene locus: relationships with lipids, apolipoproteins, and premature coronary artery disease. Atherosclerosis 1991; 87:75–86.

66. De Backer G, Hulstaert F, De Munck K, Rosseneu M, Van Parijs L, Dramaix M. Serum lipids and apoproteins in students whose parents suffered prematurely from a myocardial infarction. Am Heart J 1986;112:478–84.

67. Rosseneu, M, Fruchart JC, Bard JM, Nicaud V, Vinaimont N, Cambien F. On behalf of the EARS group: plasma apolipoprotein concentrations in young adults with a parental history of premature coronary heart disease and in controls: The EARS Study. Atherosclerosis 1994;108:127–36.

68. Van Biervliet JP, Vinaimont N, Caster H, Rosseneu M. A screening procedure for dyslipoproteinemia in newborns: apoprotein quantitation on dried-blood spots. Clin Chim Acta 1982;120:191–200.

69. Averna MR, Barbagallo CM, Di Paola G. et al. Lipids, lipoproteins and apolipoproteins AI, AII, B, CII, CIII and E in newborns. Biol Neonate 1991;60:187–92.

70. Boediman D, Murakami R, Nakamura H. Relationship between plasma triglycerides and apolipoprotein CII in infants during the first year of life. J Pediatr Gastroenterol Nutr 1993;17:82–5.

71. Van Biervliet JP, Rosseneu M, Bury J, Caster H, Stul MS, Lamote R. Apolipoprotein and lipid composition of plasma lipoproteins in neonates during the first month of life. Pediatric Res 1986;20:324–8.

72.   Verges B, Rader D, Schaefer J, Zech L, Kindt M. Fairwell T, Gambert P, Brewer HB Jr. In vivo metabolism of apolipoprotein A-IV in severe hypertriglyceridemia: a combined radiotracer and stable isotope kinetic study. J Lipid Res 1994;35:2280–91.

73.   Annuzzi G, Holmquist L, Carlson LA. Concentrations of apolipoproteins B, C-I, C-II, C-III, E and lipids in serum and serum lipoproteins of normal subjects during alimentary lipaemia. Scand J Clin Lab Invest 1989;49:73–81.

74.   Fujimoto K, Fukagawa K, Sakata T, Tso P. Suppression of food intake by apolipoprotein A-IV is mediated through the central nervous system in rats. J Clin Invest 1993;91: 1830–3.

75.   Ehnholm C, Tenkanen H, de Knijff P, Havekes L, Rosseneu M, Menzel JJ, Tiret L. Genetic polymorphism of apolipoprotein A-IV in five different regions of Europe. Relations to plasma lipoproteins and to history of myocardial infarction: the EARS study. European Atherosclerosis Study, Atherosclerosis 1994;107:229–38.

76.   Alsayed N, Rebourcet R. Abnormal concentrations of CII, CIII, and E apolipoproteins among apolipoprotein B-containing, B-free, and A-I-containing lipoprotein particles in hemodialysis patients. Clin Chem 1991;37:387–93.

77.   Muls E, Rosseneu M, Daneels R, Schurgers M, Boelaert J. Lipoprotein distribution and composition in the human nephrotic syndrome. Atherosclerosis 1985;54:225–37.

78.   Verges BL, Vaillant G, Goux A, Lagrost L, Brun JM, Gambert P. Apolipoprotein A-IV levels and phenotype distribution in NIDDM. Diabetes Care 1994;17:810-7.

79.   Verges B. Apolipoprotein A-IV in diabetes mellitus. Diabete Metab 1995;21:99–105.

80.   Muls E, Rosseneu M, Lamberigts G, De Moor P. Changes in the distribution and composition of high-density lipoproteins in primary hypothyroidism. Metabolism 1985; 34:345–53.

Apolipoprotein E: Laboratory Determinations and Clinical Significance

17

Lily H. Wu, James T. Wu, and Paul N. Hopkins

INTRODUCTION

❖ Apolipoprotein E (apo E) is a 299 amino acid, arginine-rich glycoprotein with an M_r of 34,200 daltons. Apo E is synthesized by many different cell types throughout the body. The major site of synthesis and secretion is liver parenchymal cells, which secrete apo E in association with very-low-density lipoprotein (VLDL) particles. Besides being associated with VLDL, apo E is a protein component of several other classes of plasma lipoproteins, including chylomicrons, chylomicron remnants, intermediate-density lipoproteins (IDL), and some cholesterol-rich subclasses of high-density lipoproteins (HDL), including apo E-HDL and HDL_1 (in humans and some rodents), and HDL_c (in cholesterol-fed animals).[1] Only a minute amount of apo E is found in low-density lipoproteins (LDL). A significant amount of apo E is also produced in astrocytes, peripheral nerves, and mature macrophages. Particles containing only apo E, cholesterol, and cholesterol ester may also exist at least transiently in interstitial fluid. Apo E serves as a ligand for at least two lipoprotein receptors: the LDL (or apo B/E) receptor and the putative hepatic apo E receptor (or the LDL receptor related protein, LRP).

It was found recently that the amount of apo E as well as the location of apo E on the lipoprotein particle are important for the interaction between apo E and its receptor.[2] The specific affinity of the apo E isoform with cellular surface proteoglycans facilitates the accumulation of lipoproteins at the cell surface, thereby reaching a critical concentration for optimal receptor-mediated uptake. Consequently, apo E plays an important role in lipoprotein metabolism.[3, 4]

The human apo E gene has been mapped to a single genetic locus on chromosome 19.[5] The structural gene for apo E is polymorphic, with three common alleles (ε2, ε3, ε4) coding for three isoforms of the apo E protein: E2, E3, and E4. The three isoforms differ in their amino acid sequence at positions 112 and 158. Apo E3, the most prevalent allele, contains cysteine at position 112 and arginine at position 158. In apo E2, a cysteine residue replaces the arginine at position 158 (Arg158→Cys or R158C), while apo E4 contains arginine at both positions (Cys112→Arg or C112R).[5] (See Figure 17-1.) Individuals inherit one apo E allele from each parent in simple Mendelian fashion with resulting genotypes. There are six genotypes (ε2/2, ε3/3, ε4/4, and ε2/3, ε3/4, ε3/4) which encode for the six common phenotypes (E2/2, E3/3, E4/4, E2/3, E3/4, or E2/4).

Figure 17–1 ✧ Specific Nucleotide Sequences and Their Coded Amino Acid Residues for the Three Common Apo E Alleles

Numbers at the top of the figure indicate the position of the amino acids in the protein sequence.

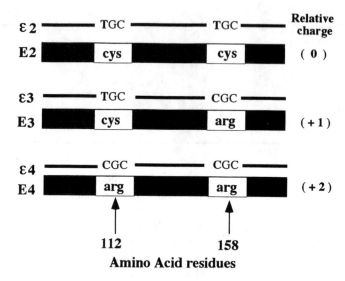

Amino Acid residues

Markedly different binding to the LDL receptor has been documented for the three common apo E isoforms. Apo E4 has a slightly higher affinity than apo E3, whereas apo E2 is clearly defective in its binding, having less than 2% of apo E3's affinity for the LDL receptor. Amino acid residues in the vicinity of 140–160 of the apo E molecule contain a high-affinity LDL receptor binding site. Surrounding residues may be responsible for the proper alignment of the receptor binding site and can also affect binding affinity. Loss of a positive charge as a result of amino acid substitutions in this region is thought to be the basis for the decrease in apo E2 binding. Homozygosity for apo E2 (an E2/2 phenotype or genotype) is the basis for Type III hyperlipidemia in most patients (see later discussion). In addition to the relatively common apo E2, there are a number of other rare isoforms with reduced binding of varying degrees to the LDL receptor, as shown in Table 17-1.[6-9] The potential differences in the tendency of apo E proteins to form homo- or mixed-disulfide protein dimers may also affect LDL receptor binding.[10, 11]

Consistent with the hyperlipidemia associated with defective or deficient apo E, a major role of this apolipoprotein appears to be the clearance of apo B-containing remnants. Accelerated catabolism of such remnants occurs when rabbits are injected or infused with purified apo E.[12, 13] When either rat[14, 15] or normal human[16] apo E3 is overexpressed in transgenic mice, lower concentrations of VLDL result with more efficient clearance of apo B-containing lipoproteins. Conversely, apo E null mice[17, 18] and transgenic mice overexpressing dysfunctional apo E[19, 20] develop severe hyperlipidemia resembling Type III hyperlipidemia in humans.

Table 17-1 ✧ Apolipoprotein E Alleles and Associations with Type III Hyperlipidemia

Position on IEF	Amino Acid Change	Receptor Binding (% normal)	Comments
COMMON			
E2	$Arg_{158} \rightarrow Cys$	< 2	Common cause of Type III (recessive). Also associated with reduced total and LDL cholesterol. Frequency 10%[*]
E3	None	100	Wild type allele. Frequency 75%[*]
E4	$Cys_{112} \rightarrow Arg$	> 100	Associated with increased total and LDL cholesterol. Frequency 15%[*]
RARE			
E1	$Lys_{146} \rightarrow Glu$	Unknown	Dominant Type III
E2	$Arg_{136} \rightarrow Ser$	40	Unknown mode of inheritance.
E2	$Arg_{136} \rightarrow Cys$	Unknown	Subtle position difference on IEF compared to common E2. Recessive for Type III.
E3	$Arg_{142} \rightarrow Cys$	< 4	Dominant Type III. Expression at an early age.
E2	$Arg_{145} \rightarrow Cys$	45	Unknown mode of inheritance.
E2	$Lys_{146} \rightarrow Gln$	40	Dominant Type III.
E3	Insertion	25	Leiden variant. 7 amino acids inserted (121–127). Dominant Type III.

[*]Gene frequencies vary in different populations.

The common polymorphisms of apo E influence plasma lipid and lipoprotein concentrations in human populations. Apo E4 imparts a tendency for modestly higher concentrations of total cholesterol (TC) and LDL cholesterol (LDL-C). Those with the E2 isoform tend to have lower LDL-C concentrations. Both apo E2 and E4 are associated with higher plasma triglyceride (TG) concentrations (see later section entitled "Clinical Significance"). There is no significant difference in the relative frequencies of the apo E alleles between men and women; however, the influence of apo E alleles on lipid variability appears to be greater in women.[21] A recent study by Schaefer et al.[22] found that, in men, the apo E4 affected the LDL-C levels, apo B levels, and LDL size, whereas in women it affected TC, LDL-C, and apo B levels. New data also indicated that the average effect of the ε2 allele on lowering LDL-C and the effect of the ε4 allele on increasing LDL-C levels are different between men and women. The ε2 allele lowered the LDL-C by 9.2 and 13.7 mg/dL (0.24 and 0.36 mmol/L) in men and women, whereas the ε4 allele increased the LDL-C by 2.6 and 5.4 mg/dL (0.7 and 0.14 mmol/L) in men and women, respectively.

Age was also found to have an impact. When men were divided into two groups according to age (< 50 and > 50 y old), the effect of the apo E phenotype on younger men was greater. For example, the average effect of the ε2 allele on lowering LDL-C levels was by 10.2 and 7.5 mg/dL (0.26 and 0.19 mmol/L) in the younger and older group, whereas the average effect of ε4 on increasing LDL-C levels was by 4.0 and 1.0 mg/dL (0.10 and 0.03 mmol/L) in younger men and older men, respectively. In women, the effect was opposite. The effect of apo E phenotypes on LDL-C and apo B levels was considerably greater in postmenopausal women than in premenopausal women. It was found that the ε2 allele lowered LDL-C by 8.2 and 20.4 mg/dL (0.21 and 0.53 mmol/L) in pre- and post-menopausal women, whereas the ε4 allele increased LDL-C by 1.6 and 7.1 mg/dL (0.04 and 0.18 mmol/L) in pre- and postmenopausal women, respectively. In addition, the E3/2, E3/3, and E3/4 phenotypes were associated with increases in LDL-C levels of 9%, 21%, and 26%, respectively, in postmenopausal women compared to premenopausal women.

Apo E also appears to play an important role in HDL metabolism and reverse cholesterol transport, the process by which excess cholesterol is removed from peripheral tissues and transported to the liver. Apo E facilitates the expansion of the HDL core, enhancing its cholesterol-carrying capacity.[23, 24] Furthermore, apo E can mediate hepatic removal and catabolism of cholesteryl-ester-enriched HDL.[25] Apo E secretion by macrophages is stimulated three- to eightfold by cholesterol loading. The apo E secreted becomes associated with phospholipid in a disc having a density of < 1.21 Kg/L. While the fate of these nascent particles is not clear, they may facilitate cholesterol removal from cells, possibly in conjunction with HDL.[26] Indeed, intravenous administration of purified apo E into Watanabe heritable hyperlipidemic rabbits 3 times per week for 8.5 months greatly decreased the cholesterol deposition into the aortas of these atherosclerosis-prone animals.[27]

It was also found recently that apo E synthesized by the macrophage appears to have several important effects on lipid metabolism and vascular disease. For example, macrophage-derived apo E modulates the cholesterol balance in the macrophage and in smooth muscle cells in the arterial wall, thereby impacting the progression or regression of the atherosclerotic lesion. It also modulates platelet aggregability and lymphocyte proliferation, and interacts with the extracellular matrix, the matrix affecting the retention of lipoproteins in the vessel wall, the bioavailability of sequestered cytokines and growth factors, and the regulation of arterial smooth muscle cell growth.[2]

Physiological functions of apo E are summarized as follows:

1. As a ligand for the LDL (apo B/E) and apo E (LRP) receptors, apo E is a key mediator in the clearance of TG-rich lipoproteins, including VLDL, chylomicrons, and chylomicron remnants, and may be required for the conversion of VLDL to LDL. It also appears to be responsible for the removal of apo-E-containing HDL from the blood circulation.[1]

2. By increasing the affinity of cholesterol ester transfer protein (CETP) for lipoproteins, apo E further helps regulate HDL-mediated reverse cholesterol transport.[28]

3. Apo E secreted by macrophages inhibits the unregulated uptake of oxidized-VLDL via the scavenger receptor and prevents transformation of macrophages into foam cells.[15] Furthermore, apo E secretion by macrophages may provide an additional pathway for reverse cholesterol transport.

4. Apo E may be involved in nerve regeneration, modulation of immune response, and the growth and/or differentiation of neuron and smooth muscle cells.[29]

APO E CONCENTRATION

Clinical Significance

Since Type III hyperlipoproteinemia is usually associated with a large increase in apo E concentration, measurement of apo E in the plasma may be useful for detection of this disorder.[30, 31] Surprisingly, in plasma from normal, fasting adults, 58% of the apo E was found in the HDL fraction (primarily the less-dense HDL) with most of the remainder in TG-rich lipoproteins. An even higher percentage of apo E was associated with HDL in cord blood.[32] Normal concentrations range from 1.0 to 9.0 mg/dL. In the hypertriglyceridemic state, apo E is redistributed to TG-rich lipoproteins. The concentration of apo E in one Type III patient was 66.4 mg/dL.[33] Theoretically, the measurement of apo E may be useful for monitoring the therapeutic response of Type III patients taking lipid-lowering medications. However, in clinical practice, the plasma TC and TG concentrations generally suffice for this purpose.

Total plasma apo E concentration does not appear to predict risk of coronary heart disease (CHD). However, increased concentrations of apo B- and E-containing lipoproteins were seen in coronary patients, while apo E in the HDL fraction was probably lower.[34] These findings suggest a protective role for apo E associated with HDL, while high concentrations of apo E in TG-rich particles indicate accumulation of remnant particles and therefore increased risk for CHD.

Since apo E synthesis in the central nervous system increases with remyelination, measurement of apo E in cerebrospinal fluid may be useful in the assessment of certain neurological conditions. In one study, an apo E index (comparing apo E and albumin in cerebrospinal fluid and serum) was much higher in multiple sclerosis patients in remission (when remyelination was active) compared to normal controls or patients in exacerbation.[35]

Methods of Determination

Reference values of serum or plasma apo E in fasting adult subjects range from 1.0 to 9.0 mg/dL. Lack of standardization of the various methods has contributed to the wide range of normal values found in the literature. Various immunological methods have been employed successfully for the measurement of plasma apo E concentration, including radial immunodiffusion (RID), electroimmunodiffusion (EID), immunoturbidimetric assay, immunonephelometric assay, radioimmunoassay (RIA), and enzyme-linked immunosorbent assay (ELISA).

It should be noted that apolipoprotein concentrations in serum samples are expected to be 3–5% higher than those obtained from EDTA plasma samples. (Heparinized samples give similar results as serum samples.) Ultracentrifugation may cause artifactual loss of apolipoproteins as free proteins or result in the redistribution of apo

E among lipoprotein particles. Discussed below are some available techniques and their major advantages and drawbacks.

Radial Immunodiffusion (RID)

Apo E concentration is estimated quantitatively by the diameter of the precipitation ring formed as the apo E present in a measured volume of sample placed in a central well diffuses outward and reacts with polyclonal antibody impregnated in an agarose gel.[36-40] This method is technically simple but can be time consuming. It may take as long as 72–96 h for apo E in VLDL to reach equilibrium and form a ring. In some cases, apo E never reaches equilibrium, resulting in spuriously low concentration estimates. The reading of the diameters can be somewhat subjective, and RID is less precise than other methods. The association of apo E with different sizes of lipoprotein particles may also alter the diffusion rate and the ring size. Finally, this method consumes rather large amounts of antibody.

Electroimmunodiffusion

Electroimmunodiffusion[41-43] is very similar to RID except that the height of a "rocket" formed as antigen-antibody complex after electrophoresis is used as a measure of concentration. As such, it shares most of the problems commonly encountered in RID. However, because of the use of electrophoresis to move the apo E antigen from the sample well into the gel in one direction, it is more sensitive and takes much less time to complete. Detergent is added to enhance the mobility of the VLDL fraction for apo E quantification.

Radioimmunoassay (RIA)

RIA[33, 44, 45] is very sensitive, capable of detecting as little as a few nanograms of protein. Either monoclonal or polyclonal antibody may be used. RIA uses either primary or secondary standards. Small amounts of antibody are used compared to other techniques. However, the large dilutions (> 10,000) employed can result in considerable imprecision and inaccuracy. RIA is not affected by turbidity—an important advantage. Competitive RIA requires the iodination of pure apolipoprotein, a procedure that might decrease the reactivity of apo E due to self-association and aggregation of the purified apolipoprotein.

Immunoprecipitation Assay

Immunoprecipitation assays[46-48] include immunonephelometry, which measures the light scattering of the particle, and immunoturbidimetry, which measures the decrease in light transmission. Both assays are fast, precise, and can be readily automated. High turbidity in samples with increased TG (> 600–1000 mg/dL [6.78–11.30 mmol/L]) can lead to erroneous results. Immunoturbidity appears to be slightly less affected by the presence of lipemia than immunonephelometry. Secondary standards are used.

Relatively large amounts of polyclonal or multiple monoclonal antibodies must be used.

Enzyme Immunoassay

Enzyme immunoassay[49-52] shares similar advantages and disadvantages with RIA. The sensitivity of this procedure is similar to that of RIA. There are several test formats for enzyme immunoassay, the most popular being the enzyme-linked immunosorbent assay (ELISA). With the microplate ELISA method, anti-apo E antibody is coated on polystyrene microplate wells for capturing apo E, and enzyme-conjugated anti-apo E antibody is then used to react with captured apo E for quantification.[53, 54] The microplate procedure can be semi-automated. Since the method is rapid, simple, and suitable for large population screening, the microplate ELISA format is the recommended method for measuring apo E concentration.

Apo E Standard

Purified apo E is recommended as the primary standard. However, pure apo E tends to aggregate over time, and the aggregate not only may have decreased immunoreactivity, but also migrates more slowly in a gel. Thus, using pure apo E as a standard may result in an overestimation of sample apo E concentration. To guard against this, plasma containing apo E calibrated against purified apo E should be used as a secondary standard for routine assays. The protein content of the highly purified apolipoproteins can be determined by the Lowry method or by amino acid analysis. Although in theory interaction of the proteins with lipids can mask antigenic determinants and affect immunoreactivity, in practice apo E epitopes in plasma lipoproteins appear to be fully exposed. Moreover, if a non-ionic detergent such as Tween 20 is included in the washing buffer with the ELISA method, delipidation of lipoprotein particles may occur without sample pretreatment and may help to expose all possible apo E antigenic sites.

PHENOTYPING AND GENOTYPING

Phenotyping

Because of their differences in charge, apo E isoforms can be conveniently separated by isoelectrofocusing (IEF). Earlier procedures for apo E phenotyping required an isolation of VLDL from the plasma before the separation by IEF. VLDL was usually isolated either by ultracentrifugation or by a specific precipitation method followed by the delipidation step. After IEF, the apo E isoforms were visualized by a protein stain. Recently, the procedure of phenotyping by IEF has been simplified due to the availability of the anti-apo E antibodies. Plasma specimens can be subjected to IEF directly and transferred to a nitrocellulose paper. The apo E pattern is then revealed by immunoblotting. Below are several electrophoretic procedures that have been used by various investigators.

Polyacrylamide Gel–IEF (PAG-IEF)

In the PAG-IEF method,[55-58] IEF is carried out in polyacrylamide gels (5% or 7.5% gel) containing 2% ampholytes (pH 4–7). This method requires isolation of VLDL from the plasma specimen by ultracentrifugation and delipidation of the isolated VLDL. This procedure typically requires 4 mL of plasma (8 mL of whole blood) and takes several days to complete. Only about 40–50% of the total plasma apo E can be recovered in the, VLDL fraction obtained by ultracentrifugation since the remainder is in the HDL fraction in normal subjects. Contamination by other proteins, such as serum amyloid protein A and apo AI in the isolated VLDL fraction, has been noted with this procedure, creating difficulties in interpretation of the phenotypes. The presence of sialylated apo E3 that focuses at the apo E2 position also can make reading difficult. Thus, the distinction between phenotypes E3/3 and E3/2 must be based on the relative intensities of the E2 and E3 bands, with band E3 > E2 in the E3/3 phenotype and E2 > E3 in the E3/2 phenotype. Band staining may be quantified by densitometric scanning. PAG-IEF also lacks sensitivity for samples containing low concentrations of VLDL or TG (see Figure 17–2).

IEF-Immobiline

The major difference between IEF-immobiline[59, 60] and PAG-IEF is the use of immobiline, a different form of ampholyte. Because the buffering groups are polymerized to the acrylamide gel matrix, forming an immobilized pH gradient, the pH gradient will not drift during electrofocusing. Utilizing immobiline allows the separation of proteins with very small differences in isoelectric point. This technique allows the separation of a rare E2 variant (Lys146→Gln) from the common apo E2. The IEF-immobiline separation

Figure 17–2 ✧ Polyacrylamide Gel Isoelectric Focusing Patterns for the Six Common Apo E Phenotypes Revealed by Coomassie Blue Stain

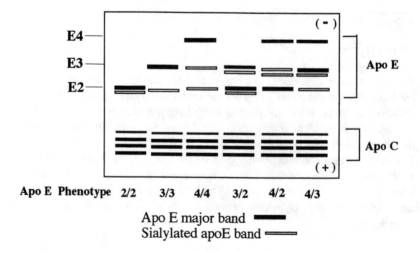

procedure can be combined with immunoblotting, thus eliminating the VLDL isolation procedure prior to IEF. Because of its high resolution, IEF-immobiline is a useful tool for the analysis of the structural integrity of apo E in various forms of dyslipoproteinemia.

SDS-PAGE

SDS-PAGE[61] accomplishes separation of common apo E isoforms and some rare mutants on polyacrylamide gel in the presence of sodium dodecyl sulfate (SDS).

PAG-IEF Immunoblotting

Availability of apo E antibodies and the need for a more rapid and reliable procedure for apo E phenotyping led to the application of immunoblotting to the analysis of apo E polymorphisms in unfractionated serum samples. Immunoblotting eliminates the need for VLDL isolation by ultracentrifugation. With the PAG-IEF method,[62-66] whole blood proteins are separated by IEF, transferred to nitrocellulose membranes, and then treated with anti-apo-E antibodies. An enzyme-conjugated second antibody is then added to visualize bands by substrate color development.

IEF-Agarose

With the IEF-agarose method,[67-69] PAG is replaced by agarose gel. After electrophoresis, apo E bands are visualized by immunoblotting or by the direct application of anti-apo E antibody to the gel without transferring apolipoproteins to nitrocellulose paper.

Additional Comments

Apo E variants with unusual amino acid composition or sequence may not be separated from common apo E isoforms by IEF if the isoelectric points of the variant proteins are similar to those of the three common isoforms of apo E.

Post-translational modifications, such as sialylation (enzymatic glycosylation) and glycation (nonenzymatic glycosylation), of apo E may alter the isoelectric point of the proteins and lead to erroneous interpretation of the phenotype.[58] For example, post-translational modifications can cause difficulties in the discrimination of phenotypes E4/3 from E4/4, and especially E3/2 from E3/3. Pretreatment of samples with neuraminidase to remove sialic acid residues or treatment with cysteinamine to add a positive charged group to cysteine helps to confirm the apo E phenotype.

Using "gel bond" for casting ultrathin gel plates for IEF allows up to 30 samples to be run at the same time. This minor modification makes it possible to screen phenotypes in a large population.

Combining IEF with immunoblotting reduces the sample requirement from 4 mL to a few microliters of plasma and also allows the entire procedure to be completed within a day.

Freezing serum samples at –70° C for as long as 15 years was found to have no effect on apo E phenotyping.[65]

Recommended Method:
PAG-IEF with Immunoblotting

PAG-IEF

Blood should be collected in EDTA-containing tubes (1 mg/mL) and kept at 4° C. Serum is not suitable for this procedure. The plasma should be separated within 2 h and stored at −70° C if not used within 4 days.

Before electrophoresis, the plasma should be pretreated by incubating with dithio-threitol (5 mmol/L) containing Tween 20 (2.5 mmol/L) at 4° C for at least 15 min or overnight. Electrophoresis is carried out in 5% PAG containing 1.5% pharmalyte (a mixture of one-third pH 4.5–5.4 and two-thirds pH 5–8 pharmalyte) containing 3 mol/L urea. For details on IEF conditions, see Kataoka et al.[66]

Immunoblotting

Following IEF, the proteins should be transferred to nitrocellulose or (PVDF) membranes by passive diffusion. The transfer buffer is 0.03 mmol/L Tris-HCl containing 0.25 mmol/L NaCl, pH 8.0. After blocking the membrane with nonfat dry milk, the apo E bands on the membrane are stained by mouse monoclonal anti-apo E antibody and then by anti-mouse IgG-peroxidase conjugated antibody. Polyclonal anti-E antibodies are also available from several commercial sources. The pattern of the major bands and sialylated isoforms is shown in Figure 17–3.[66]

Figure 17–3 ✧ Polyacrylamide Gel Isoelectric Focusing Patterns for the Six Common Apo E Phenotypes Identified by Immunoblotting Technique

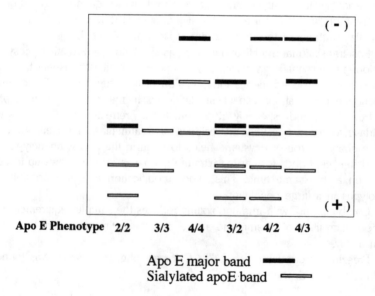

Apo E major band ━━━
Sialylated apoE band ═══

Comments

This method requires a very small amount of sample and does not require prior isolation of VLDL by ultracentrifugation or precipitation. The three common isoforms and their sialylated bands are well separated without having to be treated with neuraminidase or cysteinamine. This allows clear identification of phenotype by the band pattern rather than judging by the band intensities.

Genotyping

While DNA methods provide unambiguous results (assuming the amplification step is successful), they may not always be superior to protein separation (phenotyping). Genotyping is particularly helpful when the phenotype is difficult to interpret due to post-translational modification of apo E molecules, as in distinguishing phenotype E3/3 from E3/2. Genotyping methods may also complement phenotyping when certain structural variants of apo E have the same net charge as the three common isoforms. In this case, however, a genotyping method that specifically identifies rare variants must be employed. Indeed, most genotyping methods will omit new, rare variants that might be detected by IEF if a change in charge has occurred. The intralaboratory discrepancy between phenotype and genotype has been reported to vary between 0.2% and 24% depending on the method employed and the patient groups studied.

Apo E genotyping is based on the determination of nucleotide sequence variations. It requires less specimen than phenotyping. Direct determination of apo E genotype can be made with allele-specific oligonucleotides (ASO) or analysis of restriction enzyme digests after amplification of target sequences by the polymerase chain reaction (PCR). Various methods for genotyping are summarized below.

Southern Blotting and Hybridization with ASO Probes

Southern blotting was more widely used prior to the availability of PCR.[70-73] Relatively large amounts of genomic DNA is digested first with a restriction enzyme, separated by electrophoresis in agarose gels, and then transferred to nitrocellulose or nylon membranes. The DNA fragments are identified by hybridization with a radiolabeled probe. Different-sized DNA fragments (restriction fragment length polymorphisms [RFLP]) which hybridize with the probes are then visualized by autoradiography.

The introduction of PCR amplification allows for the use of much less specimen for genotyping. As little as 0.4–1.0 μg of DNA (10 μL of buffy coat, 100 μL of whole blood, or a 5 mm diameter spot of dried whole blood on filter paper) is sufficient for the identification of apo E phenotype. Methods based on PCR have essentially replaced Southern blotting.

PCR-RFLP

The PCR-RFLP[73-77] genotyping procedure for apo E takes advantage of Hha I RFLPs that are fortuitously introduced in the common apo E alleles. These alleles differ at amino acid residues 112 and 158 by the presence or absence of arginine. The Hha I enzyme cleaves at 5'...GCG|C...3' sites while the Arg codon is CGC. Initially, the target apo E DNA sequence is amplified by PCR. The amplified product is then digested with Hha I and then separated by agarose gel or PAG electrophoresis. The bands are visualized by ethidium bromide staining.

PCR-Dotting Method

The PCR-Dotting method[78] begins by spotting a PCR amplified apo E sequence on nitrocellulose or nylon membranes. The sequence on the membrane is then identified by hybridization with four different radioactively labeled ASO probes with sequences corresponding to the coding regions for cys 112, cys 158, arg 112, and arg 158 (see Figure 17–4). The major disadvantage of this otherwise excellent procedure is non-specific probe hybridization due to the high GC content of apo E. The procedure may be simplified by automating PCR and the hybridization procedure using non-radioisotopic, biotin-labeled probes.

Figure 17–4 ✧ Identification of Common Apo E Genotypes by Dot Blotting Technique Using ASO Probes

Apo E phenotypes of individual patients are shown on the left. A sample of the patient's amplified target DNA sequence is spotted onto each of four nitrocellulose strips. Each strip, in turn, is treated with radiolabeled ASO, which hybridizes to its matching sequence (shown at bottom). Dot patterns are revealed by autoradiography.

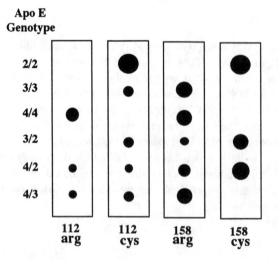

Adapted from Emi and Wu.[78]

PCR-DNA Melting Method

In the PCR-DNA melting method,[79, 80] a targeted apo E sequence is first amplified by PCR. Differences in DNA sequence are then detected by oligonucleotide "melting" or denaturing gradient gel. This procedure can detect single base substitutions and may facilitate the identification of new mutations. However, the procedure is technically very demanding.

Single Strand Conformational Polymorphism (PCR-SSCP)

In PCR-SSCP technique,[81] the PCR amplified products of the apo E gene are converted to single-strand DNA (SS DNA) by denaturation. The SS DNA is then separated by PAG electrophoresis (PAGE) under non-denaturing conditions. Differences in base pair sequence lead to changes in conformation of the folded molecule. After PAGE, these conformation polymorphisms are detected as discrete bands. This method is sensitive and can detect rare mutants. However, the particular conformation that a given sequence will take (and hence its band pattern) is highly sensitive to experimental conditions such as salt concentrations and temperature.

Amplification Refractory Mutation Systems (ARMS)

The ARMS procedure[82–84] takes advantage of ASO primers that are specific for different alleles of the apo E gene. Multiple primers, each specific for a given mutation site, are added to the PCR reaction mixture. Depending on the presence of sequences complementary to the primers, products of differing length will be produced during the PCR reaction. The genotype is then determined by the pattern produced after agarose gel electrophoresis of the PCR products and ethidium bromide staining.

Recommended Method: PCR-RFLP

Apo E Genotyping by PCR and Restriction Enzyme Digestion

This procedure uses Hha I RFLp polymorphisms that are present in the three common apo ε alleles. The target gene is first amplified by PCR. The amplified product is then exposed to Hha I and the digestion products separated by agarose or polyacrylamide gel electrophoresis. The bands are visualized by ethidium bromide staining as shown in Figure 17–5.

AMPLIFICATION OF GENOMIC DNA

Because of the high GC content of the apo E gene, successful PCR amplification can be difficult. We utilize rapid cycle DNA amplification techniques with an Air Thermo-cycler. With this technique, amplification can be completed in only 45 min. With rapid cycling capability and better temperature control, nonspecific amplification is reduced and cleaner digestion products result, allowing accurate genotyping by simple ethidium bromide staining.

Figure 17–5 ✦ Apo E Genotyping by PCR-Restriction Fragment Length Polymorphisms (RFLPs)

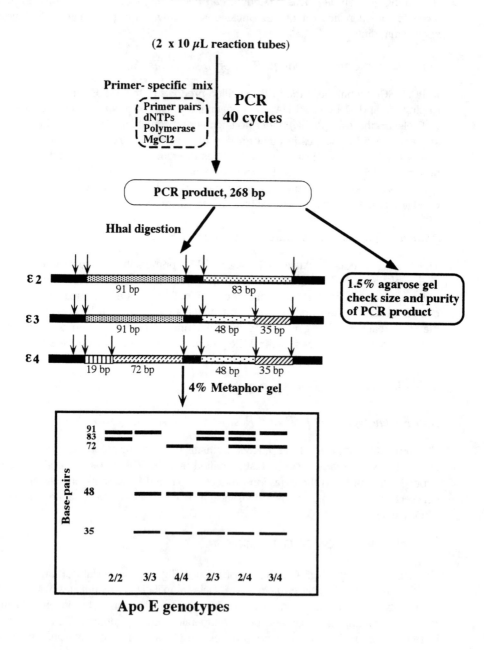

Apo E genotypes

Sample (Genomic DNA)

Source

a.   Fresh whole blood (collect in 1 mg/mL EDTA tube)

b.   Buffy coat (stored at –70° C)

c.   Whole blood on Whatman filter paper, dried and fixed with methanol and stored at room temperature.

DNA Isolation

a.   Use commercially available kits (e.g., QIAamp Blood Kit #29104, Qiagen Inc.)

b.   Standard proteinase K digestion, phenol/chloroform extraction

c.   Boil a 5 mm dried blood paper disc in 100 µL deionized sterile water for 5 min.

Primers

Primer 1. 5′-GGCACGGCTGTCCAAGGA-3′
Primer 2. 5′-CTCGCGGATGGCGCTGAG-3′

Summary of reaction constituents for each 10 µL reaction tube is as follows:

Component	Reagent Concentration	Volume Used	Final Concentration
DNA (human genomic)		50 ng/µL or A260 = 1.0	1µL 50 ng/µL
Primers	5 µmol/L	1 µL	0.5 µmol/L
Nucleotides	2 mmol/L dNTP	1 µL	200 µmol/L each
Buffer	500 mmol/L Tris pH 8.3 2.5 mg/mL BSA 20% (w/v) Sucrose 1 mmol/L Cresol Red 20 mmol/L MgCl$_2$	1 µL	500 mmol/L Tris pH 8.3 2.5 µg/mL BSA 2% (w/v) Sucrose 1 mmol/L Cresol Red 2 mmol/L MgCl$_2$
Polymerase	0.4 µU/L each	1 µL	0.4 U/10 µL
ddH$_2$0		4 µL	

Thermal Cycling Parameters (Idaho Technology #1605)

a.   Denature template DNA at 94° C for 1 min

b.   30–60 cycles:
Denaturation: 94° C for 2 sec
Annealing: 68° C for 25 sec
Elongation: 72° C for 0 sec

c.   Denature at 94° C for 2 sec

d.   Re-anneal final PCR products at 70° C for 5 min

e.   Let the reaction tubes cool to 40° C before removal.

IDENTIFICATION OF GENOTYPE BY RFLP PATTERNS

Restriction Enzyme Digestion (Hha I Gibco BRL #25212-010; 8–12 U/μL)

Dilute Hha I to 1 U/10 μL in enzyme diluent (10 mmol/L Tris Ph 8.3, 2.5 mg/mL BSA). Digest PCR products from one capillary tube with 10 μL of Hha I (1 U/10 μL). The Hha I enzyme recognizes the Arg codon CGC and cleaves at 5'...GCG|C...3' sites to produce DNA pieces of different length.

Gel Electrophoresis

Apply 20 μL digested PCR product to each well of a 4% metaphor agarose (FMC #50182) gel in 0.5% TBE/EtBr. The following DNA fragments are used for identifying each allele:

ε2   91 and 83 base pairs.

ε3   91, 48, and 35 base pairs.

ε4   72, 48, and 35 base pairs.

All six genotypes can be distinguished as shown in Figure 17–5.

Comments

Due to the high GC content of the apo E gene, genotyping for apo E is a very demanding procedure. Unsuccessful amplification is a frequent problem if PCR conditions are not rigorously controlled. The hybridization step using ASO probes can also be problematic. The recommended method avoids ASO hybridization, does not require radiolabeled probes, and requires only one PCR amplification process with one pair of primers.[73]

CLINICAL SIGNIFICANCE OF APO E PHENOTYPES AND GENOTYPES

Lipoprotein Metabolism and Cardiovascular Disease

As a ligand for both the LDL (apo B/E) receptor and LRP, apo E plays an important role in the catabolism of lipoproteins. Because of the different affinities of various apo E isoforms for these receptors, apo E polymorphisms will have an impact on plasma lipoprotein metabolism. Resultant changes in plasma lipoprotein concentrations can have a significant impact on atherosclerotic vascular disease.

In a meta-analysis utilizing studies that included 45 population samples from 17 countries, Dallongeville et al.[85] analyzed the relationship between apo E phenotype and plasma TC, TG, and HDL cholesterol (HDL-C) concentrations. The mean plasma values of TC, TG, and HDL-C of subjects with the E2/2, E3/2, E4/2, E4/3, E4/4 phenotypes were compared those of subjects with the E3/3 phenotype. Results are illustrated in Figure 17–6. TC was clearly increased in subjects with the E4/3 and E4/4 phenotypes, while significantly lower values were seen in those with the E3/2 and E2/2 phenotypes. A number of investigators have reported similar results as to the effect of apo E genotype on TC and LDL-C.[21, 86–91]

Figure 17–6 ✧ Effect of Apo E Phenotype on the Plasma Levels of Cholesterol, Triglycerides, and HDL Cholesterol

Shown are mean levels for each phenotype and 95% confidence intervals. Mean lipids (for age 20+, both sexes averaged together) from the LRC Prevalence Study were taken as apo E3/3 levels. Deviations from these references levels were estimated as the Z-score deviations reported by Dallongeville[85] multiplied by the estimated LRC standard deviations (taken as 28.6 mg/dL [0.74 mmol/L] for total cholesterol, 49.1 mg/dL [0.55 mmol/L] for triglycerides, and 11.3 mg/dL [0.29 mmol/L] for HDL cholesterol).

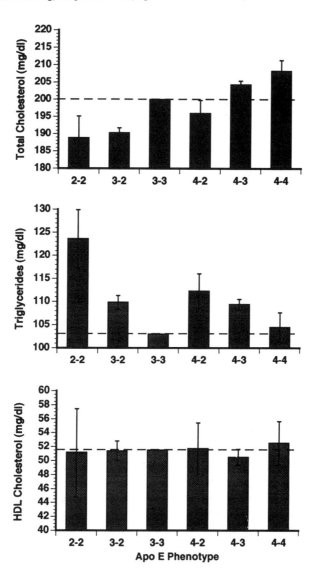

With respect to serum TG concentrations, possession of the E2 allele in either homozygous or heterozygous form clearly increased the serum concentrations above those seen with the E3 allele. In addition, apo E4/3 heterozygotes had higher concentrations of TG than E3/3 homozygotes, but E4 homozygotes did not have significantly higher TG concentrations. For HDL-C, where E4/3 heterozygotes had slightly lower concentrations, E4/4 homozygotes had similar concentrations compared to those individuals who were E3/3 homozygotes. Apo E2 had no effect upon HDL-C concentrations. All of these effects were consistent across ethnic and patient groups.[85]

In several studies, patients with CHD[91-93] and stroke[94] had greater frequency of the E4 allele than was normally found in healthy controls; in contrast, the E2 allele was less frequently present in the same group and could therefore be considered generally protective. In most of these studies, the excess risk associated with apo E4 appeared to be due to higher plasma TC or LDL-C concentrations. Dallongeville et al.[85] suggested that the increased cardiovascular risk associated with the E4/3 allele may also be mediated by higher TG and lower HDL-C concentrations. More CHD cases in the population appear to be attributable to these modest effects on plasma lipids compared to the relatively rare occurrence of Type III hyperlipidemia in apo E2/2 individuals.

Differences in the production and removal rates of VLDL$_1$, VLDL$_2$, IDL, and LDL were examined in normolipidemic (TC 195–240 mg/dL [5.05–6.22 mmol/L]) subjects homozygous for E2, E3, or E4. Compared to E3/3 subjects, E2/2 subjects produced less VLDL$_1$ (the precursor of VLDL$_2$) and exhibited delayed conversion of the more dense VLDL$_2$ to LDL. This resulted in higher concentrations of VLDL$_2$ and IDL and more direct catabolism of these particles prior to conversion to LDL. These alterations led to low LDL. The LDL fractional catabolic rate was not significantly affected by E2. In contrast, the LDL fractional catabolic rate was depressed in E4/4 subjects. Conversion of more dense VLDL to LDL was also increased in E4/4 subjects, suggesting down-regulation of LDL receptors.[95] Down-regulation of LDL receptors in individuals bearing an E4 allele may be due to increased efficiency of intestinal cholesterol absorption (order of efficiency: E4 > E3 > E2)[96, 97] and more rapid clearance of chylomicron remnants (order of clearance: E4 > E3 > E2).[98-100]

Type III Hyperlipidemia

Type III hyperlipidemia (or familial dysbetalipoproteinemia) is characterized by increased plasma concentrations of TC and TG due to marked accumulation of abnormal chylomicron and VLDL remnants (collectively referred to as β-VLDL) and IDL. Serum TC concentrations are typically in the range of 300–600 mg/dL (7.77–15.54 mmol/L), with roughly equal increases in TG concentration (when reported as mg/dL). Individual patient lipid values may fluctuate widely, especially in response to body weight changes or effective treatment. Thus, an initial TC value of 490 mg/dL (12.7 mmol/L) with TG of 550 mg/dL (6.22 mmol/L) may decrease to 250 mg/dL (6.5 mmol/L) and 230 mg/dL (2.60 mmol/L), respectively, with a ten-pound weight loss. The usual clinical laboratory estimation of LDL-C is invalid in Type III since the accumulated β-VLDL particles have roughly equal weights of cholesterol and TG (unlike VLDL, which has a TG to cholesterol ratio of 5:1). Patients with Type III hyperlipidemia develop accelerated atherosclerosis involving both coronary and peripheral arteries. Type III hyperlipidemia may account for as much as 5% of the early familial CHD.[101]

Over 95% of patients with Type III hyperlipidemia are found to have the apo E2/2 phenotype. Nevertheless, only 5% of E2/2 individuals in the general population will develop Type III hyperlipidemia. Apparently, manifestation of Type III hyperlipoproteinemia requires additional inciting factors such as familial combined hyperlipidemia, familial hypercholesterolemia, diabetes, hypothyroidism, obesity, estrogen deficiency, high-fat diet, or certain drugs.[51, 102, 103] Other rare apo E mutations that cause defective receptor binding may also cause accumulation of atherogenic β-VLDL and Type III hyperlipoproteinemia (reviewed in Table 17–1). Some of these mutations appear to be dominant, with only a single copy required for manifestation of hyperlipidemia.

Diagnosis of Type III hyperlipidemia can usually be confirmed by the identification of the apo E2/2 phenotype or a clear demonstration of a broad-beta band by electrophoresis of the isolated VLDL fraction (which normally shows only a pre-beta band). A measured ratio of VLDL cholesterol (VLDL-C) to total TG ≥ 0.30 (when measured in mg/dL; 0.68 when using mmol/L) is a specific but somewhat insensitive indicator of Type III hyperlipidemia.[102] Recognition of this relatively rare disease (1 to 10 individuals in 10,000) is important not only because of its association with a strong predisposition to coronary and peripheral vascular disease, but also because patients typically have an excellent response to appropriate diet and drug (niacin or fibrates) therapy.

Interaction of Apo E with Other Genetic and Environmental Factors

Interaction of apo E genotype with a defective receptor or other genetic or environmental factors can lead to measurable effects on lipoprotein metabolism. A few examples have been reported.[104, 105]

Gene-Gene Interaction

Typically, patients with Type III hyperlipidemia are homozygous for apo E2. However, about 26% of heterozygous familial hypercholesterolemic patients with a single copy of E2 (phenotypes E3/2 and E4/2) develop a Type III pattern as defined by a measured ratio of VLDL-C to total TG ≥ 0.30 (0.68 when using mmol/L) and TG > 150 mg/dL (1.70 mmol/L). Furthermore, estimated concentrations of β-VLDL-C in these patients increased markedly with age. Estimated β-VLDL-C concentrations were lower and did not rise with age in close relatives who did not have an apo E2 allele or in those without familial hypercholesterolemia.[106] Presumably, the inherited LDL receptor defect together with a diminished receptor binding (imparted by the presence of even a single apo E2 allele) resulted in defective clearance and accumulation of abnormal remnant particles. Familial hypercholesterolemia patients with the superimposed Type III pattern may be at increased risk for premature CHD.

Diabetes

Plasma concentrations of TG and VLDL were increased in diabetic patients with the E2 allele.[58, 107-110] Thus, the ε2 allele may be a marker for genetic susceptibility to hypertriglyceridemia in non-insulin-dependent diabetes mellitus patients.

Drug Response

There was a significant difference in the response to drug treatment associated with the apo E locus. Subjects carrying the ε4 allele had a significantly lower response, while the response was much greater in those carrying the apo ε2 allele. A meta-analysis utilizing data from five published studies indicated that the LDL response to HMG CoA reductase inhibitor therapy was influenced by apo E phenotypes.[111] The drug response for subjects with ε2, ε3/3, and ε4 were found to be 37%, 35%, and 33%, respectively. In familial hypercholesterolemia, patients with an apo E4 allele may respond better to probucol treatment than those without the E4 allele.[112] Plasma LDL response to other drugs in familial hypercholesterolemic patients appears not to be affected by apo E phenotype.[113-115]

Dietary Manipulation

Some recent studies have reported an association between apo E phenotype and the response to dietary manipulation. Persons with phenotypes E4/3 and E4/4 exhibited a significantly greater increase in plasma LDL-C concentrations when dietary cholesterol intake was increased, whereas patients with phenotypes E2/3 and E2/2 tended to be resistant to changes. There may be considerable heterogeneity with respect to the magnitude of the apo E allelic effects in different populations, since not all investigators have found a significant relationship between response to diet and apo E genotype.[116, 117] Nevertheless, there may be a metabolic basis for a differential dietary response. In other studies (reviewed in Abey[116] and Boerwinkle et al.[117]) persons with an apo E4 allele were observed to have enhanced cholesterol absorption and chylomicron remnant removal rates. As a result, more dietary cholesterol is presumably delivered to the liver by apo-E4-mediated uptake, which should result in down-regulation of hepatic LDL (apo B/E) receptors and cause increased LDL in plasma. Interestingly, familial hypercholesterolemia patients with the E3/2 phenotype responded poorly to soy-protein diets, while those with E3/3 or E4/3 experienced a mean 26% reduction in LDL-C.[118]

Recent studies investigating the association of apo phenotypes with dietary fat showed that the extent of increase in LDL cholesterol from a high fat diet differed among various phenotypes. The most profound effect was found to associate with E4 phenotype. However, the effect of dietary fat intake on both the reduction and increase of LDL cholesterol followed the same order in terms of phenotypes, with apo E4/3, 4/4 > apo E3/3 > apo E3/2.[119]

Alzheimer's Disease

Alzheimer's disease (AD), a devastating neurological disorder, is the leading cause of dementia in the elderly. It affects millions of individuals of all races and ethnic backgrounds. There are two major types of AD: sporadic (85%) and familial (15%). In sporadic AD, unlike the familial form, a well-defined hereditary cause cannot be established. Both versions of the disease follow the same progression: memory loss followed by loss of cognitive abilities. AD can also be differentiated by age of onset, with early-onset AD starting before age 65 and late-onset AD starting after age 65.

The apo ε4 allele has been found to be a risk factor in both sporadic and familial late-onset AD and appears to transmit risk as an autosomal co-dominant trait. A total of 80% of cases with familial AD and 45–64% of sporadic late-onset AD have at least one apo ε4 allele compared to controls, in whom frequency of an apo ε4 allele is about 15%.[120-122] The proportion of affected individuals increases with the number of ε4 alleles. For example, among individuals from AD-prone families with no ε4 allele, only 20% developed AD by age 75. The risk for AD increased to 47% in those having one copy (genotypes ε2/4 or ε3/4) and to 91% in those having two copies (genotype ε4/4).[123] Additional apo ε4 alleles also shift the time of onset of AD to younger ages. The mean age of onset was found to be 84.3 for individuals without an ε4 allele, 75.5 for those with one copy, and 68.4 for those with two copies.[123]

The apo E gene may be used to predict whether an individual is likely to develop late-onset Alzheimer's disease and at what age the first symptoms might appear, but keep in mind the apo E gene is not a disease locus with a specific mutation causing AD. The allele variation of the apo E locus affects the rate of disease progress. Studying the involvement of apo E in AD may help development of an intervention to slow the progress, delay the onset, or even prevent AD in the future.[124]

Presence of amyloid β-peptide (Aβ) deposition in senile plaques and cerebral vessels is a neuropathological feature of AD. Neurofibrillary tangles are made of bundles of abnormal fibers (modified protein) in the cytoplasm of certain neurons. Several additional proteins are associated with Aβ, including APP, α1-antichymotrypsin, complement factors, and immunoglobulins. Using immunochemical methods, apo E4 was recently found also in senile plaques in association with Alzheimer's Aβ deposits.[125] Apo E could also be seen in the vascular amyloid and neurofibrillary tangles of AD.

Evidence supporting the role played by apo E in the pathogenesis of AD is outlined below.[106, 113, 114]

1. Apo E plays an important role in nerve cell injury and regeneration.

2. The apo E gene is located on chromosome 19, within a region previously linked to late-onset AD.

3. Apo E can be detected in the senile plaques and the vascular and neurofibrillary tangles of AD.

4. The intensity of the immunohistochemical stain for apo E4 increases with the severity of AD.

5. Apo E was found to bind Aβ peptide in cerebrospinal fluid *in vitro*.

6. Apo E4 has a much higher affinity than apo E3 for Aβ.

7. Patients with one or two copies of apo E4 (phenotypes E2/4, E3/4, or E4/4) have greatly increased plaque amyloid deposits compared to individuals with the E3/3 phenotype.

The greatly increased risk of AD and the moderately increased risk of CHD in persons carrying an apo ε4 allele may help explain the decreased survival rate of older carriers which was found in one study that compared apo E allele frequencies of older and younger women.[126]

There are some 50 possible causes of dementia. AD accounts for 55% of all dementia in the elderly. Apo E4 is associated with late-onset familial and sporadic AD. It is most likely to act as a "chaperon" protein for amyloid plaques and fibrillary tangle formation. Apo E genotype/phenotype can be used as an adjunctive diagnostic test for AD among patients with dementia and positive family history for AD. Individuals without Apo E 4 may have AD, and individuals with E4 may never develop the disease. As for now, use of Apo E genotyping to predict AD risk in asymptomatic individuals is not recommended by the consensus statement published by the National Institute on Aging, the Alzheimer's Association (USA), and other organizations.[127] ✧

REFERENCES

1. Mahley RW, Innerarity TL. Apolipoprotein E: Cholesterol transport protein with expanding roles in cell biology. Science 1988;240:622-30.
2. Mazzone T. Apolipoprotein E secretion by macrophages: its potential physiological functions. Curr Opin Lipid 1996;7:303-7
3. Zannis VI, Breslow JL. Genetic mutations affect human lipoprotein metabolism. Adv Hum Gene 1985;14:125-215.
4. Getzs GS, Mazzone T, Soltys P, Bates SR. Atherosclerosis and apoprotein E. Arch Pathol Lab Med 1988;112:1048-55.
5. Rall SC, Weisgraber KH, Mahley RW. Human apolipoprotein E: the complete amino acid sequence. J Biochem 1982;247:4171-8.
6. Talmud P. Detection and physiological relevance of mutations in the apoprotein E, C-II, and B genes. In: Rosseneu M, ed. Structure and function of apolipoproteins. Boca Raton, FL: CRC Press, 1992:123-58.
7. Bhatnagar D, Durrington PN. Does measurement of apolipoproteins add to the clinical diagnosis and management of dislipidaemias? Curr Opin Lipidol 1993; 4:288-304.
8. Mahley RW, Innerarity TL, Rall SC, Weisgraber KH. Apolipoprotein E: genetic variants provides insights into its structure and function. Curr Opin Lipidol 1990; 1:87-95.
9. Walden CC, Huff MW, Leiter L, Connelly PW, Hegele RA. Variable expression of type III hyperlipidemia in compound heterozygotes for apolipoprotein E2 and a new mutant, R136C [abstract]. Circulation 1993;88(suppl I):461.
10. Weisgraber KH, Shinto LH. Identification of the disulfide-linked homodimer of apolipoprotein E3 in plasma. J Biol Chem 1991;266:12029-34.
11. Tozuka M, Yoshida Y, Tanigami J, Miyachi M, Katsuyama T, Masamitsu K. Development of an enzyme-linked immunosorbent assay of apolipoprotein E-AII complex in plasma. Clin Chem 1991;37:1645-8.
12. Yamada H, Shimano H, Mokuno H, et al. Increased clearance of plasma cholesterol after injection of apolipoprotein E into Watanabe heritable hyperlipidemic rabbits. Proc Natl Acad Sci USA 1989;86:665-9.
13. Mahley RW, Weisgraber KH, Hussain MM, Greenman B, Fisher M, Vobel T, Gorecki M. Intravenous infusion of apolipoprotein E accelerates clearance of plasma lipoproteins in rabbits. J Clin Invest 1989;83:2125-30.
14. Shimano H, Yamada N, Katsuki M, et al. Overexpression of apolipoprotein E in transgenic mice: marked reduction in plasma lipoproteins except high density lipoprotein and resistance against diet-induced hypercholesterolemia. Proc Natl Acad Sci USA 1992;89:1750-4.
15. Shimano H, Yamada N, Katsuki M, et al. Plasma lipoprotein metabolism in transgenic mice over-expressing apolipoprotein E. Accelerated clearance of lipoproteins containing apolipoprotein B. J Clin Invest 1992;90:2084.

16. de Silva HV, Lauer SJ, Wang J, et al. Opposing effects of human apolipoproteins E and C-II in lipoprotein remnant clearance in transgenic mice [abstract]. Circulation 1992;86(suppl I):471.

17. Zhang SH, Reddick RL, Piedrahita JA, Maeda N. Spontaneous hypercholesterolemia and arterial lesions in mice lacking apolipoprotein E. Science 1992;258: 468-71.

18. Plump AS, Smith JD, Hayek T, et al. Severe hypercholesterolemia and atherosclerosis in apolipoprotein E-deficient mice created by homologous recombination in ES cells. Cell 1992;71:343-53.

19. Fazio S, Lee Y-L, Ji Z-S, Rall SCJ. Type III hyperlipoproteinemic phenotype in transgenic mice expressing dysfunctional apolipoprotein E. J Clin Invest 1993; 92:1497-1503.

20. Fazio S, Horie Y Simonet, WS, Weisgraber KH, Taylor JM, Rall SC. Altered lipoprotein metabolism in transgenic mice expressing low levels of a human receptor-binding-defective apolipoprotein E variant. J Lipid Res 1994;35:408-16.

21. Xhignesse M, Lussier-Cacan S, Sing CF, Kessling AM, Davignon J. Influences of common variants of apolipoprotein E on measures of lipid metabolism in a sample selected for health. Arterioscler Thromb 1991;11:1100-10.

22. Schaefer EJ, Lamon-Fava S, Johnson S, Ordovas JM, Schaefer MM, Castelli WP, Wilson PWF. Effects of gender and menopausal status on the association of apolipoprotein E phenotype with plasma lipoprotein levels. Arterioscler Thromb 1994;14:1105-13/

23. Gordon V, Innerarity TL, Mahley RW. Formation of cholesterol- and apoprotein E-enriched high density lipoproteins in vitro. J Biol Chem 1983;258:6202-12.

24. Koo C, Innerarity TL, Mahley RW. Obligatory role of cholesterol and apolipoprotein E in the formation of large cholesterol-enriched and receptor-active high density lipoproteins. J Biol Chem 1985;260:11934-43.

25. Funke H, Boyles J, Weisgraber KH, Ludwig EH, Hui DY, Mahley RW. Uptake of apolipoprotein E-containing high density lipoproteins by hepatic parenchymal cells. Arteriosclerosis 1984;4:452-61.

26. Johnson WJ, Mahlberg FH, Rothblat GH, Phillips MC. Cholesterol transport between cells and high-density lipoproteins. Biochim Biophys Acta 1991;1085: 273-98.

27. Yamada N, Inoue I, Kawamura M, et al. Apolipoprotein E prevents the progression of atherosclerosis in Watanabe heritable hyperlipidemic rabbits. J Clin Invest 1992;89: 706-11.

28. Kinoshita M, Arai H, Fukasawa T, et al. Apolipoprotein E enhances lipid exchange between lipoproteins mediated by cholesteryl ester transfer protein. J Lipid Res 1993; 34:261-8.

29. Ishibashi S, Mori N, Shimada M, et al. Apolipoprotein E secreted by macrophage plays an important role in nerve injury and repair. Horm Metab Res 1993;25:82-7.

30. Gustafson S, Vessby B, Lindqvist OAM. Serum and interstitial fluid apolipoprotein E levels in the healthy and in hyperlipoproteinemia type III as studied by radioimmunoassay. Clin Chim Acta 1985;151:49-59.

31. Kushwaha RS, Hazzard WR, Wahl PW, Hoover JJ. Type III hyperlipoproteinemia: diagnosis in whole plasma by apolipoprotein E immunoassay. Ann Inter Med 1977;87: 509-16.

32. Blum CB, Davis PA, Forte TM. Elevated levels of apolipoprotein E in the high density lipoproteins of human cord blood plasma. J Lipid Res 1985;26:755-60.

33. Blum CB, Aron L, Sciacca R. Radioimmunoassay studies of human apolipoprotein E. J Clin Invest 1980;66:1240-50.

34. Genest JJ, Bard JM, Fruchart JC, Ordovas JM, Wilson PF, Schaefer EJ. Plasma apolipoprotein A-I, A-II, B, E and C-III containing particles in men with premature coronary artery disease. Atherosclerosis 1991;90:149-57.

35. Rifai N, Christenson RH, Gelman BB, Silverman LM. Changes in cerebrospinal fluid IgG and apolipoprotein E indices in patients with multiple sclerosis during demyelination and remyelination. Clin Chem 1987;33:1155-7.

36. Carlson LA, Holmquist L. Concentrations of apolipoproteins B, C-I, C-II, C-III and E in sera from normal men and their relation to serum lipoprotein levels. Clin Chim Acta 1982;124:163-78.

37. Oikawa S, Suzuki N, Sakuma E, et al. Abnormal lipoprotein and apolipoprotein pattern in lipoprotein glomerulopathy. Am J Kid Dis 1991;18:553-8.

38. Averna MR, Barbagallo CM, Di Paola G, et al. Lipids, lipoproteins and apolipoproteins AI, AII, B, CII, CIII and E in newborns. Biol Neonate 1991;60:187-92.

39. Senti M, Romero R, Pedro-Botet J, Pelegri A, Nogues X, Rubies-Prat J. Lipoprotein abnormalities in hyperlipidemic and normolipidemic men on hemodialysis with chronic renal failure. Kidney International 1992;41:1394-9.

40. Catalano M, Aronica A, Carzaniga G, Seregni R, Libretti A. Serum lipids and apolipoproteins in patients with essential hypertension. Atherosclerosis 1991; 87:17-22.

41. Curry MD, McConathy WJ, Alaupovic P, Ledford JH, Popovic M. Determination of human apolipoprotein E by electroimmunoassay. Biochim Biophys Acta 1976; 439: 413-25.

42. Bittolo BG, Cazzolato G, Saccardi M, Kostner GM, Avogaro P. Total plasma apo E and high density lipoprotein apo E in survivors of myocardial infarction. Atherosclerosis 1984;53:69-75.

43. Kuhl H, Marz W, Jung-Hoffman C, Weber J, Siekmeier R, Gross W. Effect on lipid metabolism of a biphasic desogestrel-containing oral contraceptive: divergent changes in apolipoprotein B and E and transitory decrease in Lp(a) levels. Contraception 1993 ;47:69-83.

44. Au YPT, Bren DN, Kottke BA. A rapid apolipoprotein E radioimmunoassay using solid phase Staphylococcus protein. Use of pooled plasma as a secondary standard. Biochim Biophys Res Comm 1986;138:455-62.

45. Mackie A, Caslake MJ, Packard CJ, Shepherd J. Concentration and distribution of human plasma apolipoprotein E. Clin Chim Acta 1981;116:35-45.

46. Weisweiler P, Schwandt P. Immunonephelometric quantitation of apolipoprotein E in human serum. J Clin Chem Clin Biochem 1983;21:227-30.

47. Noma A, Hata Y, Goto Y. Quantitation of serum apolipoprotein A-I, A-II, B, C-II, C-III and E in healthy Japanese by turbidimetric immunoassay: reference values, and age- and sex-related differences. Clin Chim Acta 1991;199:147-58.

48. Rifai N, Silverman LM. A simple immunotechnique for the determination of serum concentration of apolipoprotein E. Clin Chim Acta 1987;163:207-13.

49. Holmquist L. Quantitation of human serum very low density apolipoprotein C-I, C-II, C-III and E by enzyme immunoassay. J Immunol Methods 1980;34:243-51.

50. Bury J, Vercaemst R, Rosseneu M, Belpaire F. Apolipoprotein E quantified by enzyme-linked immunosorbent assay. Clin Chem 1986;32:265-70.

51. Koffigan M, Kora I, Clavey V, Bard JM, Chapman J. Quantification of human apolipoprotein E in plasma and lipoprotein subfractions by a non-competitive enzyme immuno-assay. Clin Chim Acta 1987;163:245-56.

52. Alsayed N, Rebourcet R, Chapman J. Concentrations of apoprotein CII, CIII, and E in total serum and in the apoprotein B-containing lipoproteins, determined by a new enzyme-linked immunosorbent assay. Clin Chem 1990;36:2047-52.

53. Leroy A, Vu-dac N, Koffigan M, Clavey V, Fruchart J-C. Characterization of a monoclonal antibody that binds to apolipoprotein E and to lipoproteins of human plasma containing apo E. Applications of ELISA quantification of plasma apo E. J Immunoassay 1988;9: 309-34.

54. Labeur C, van Huffel X, Rosseneu M. Evaluation of enzyme-linked immunoassays for the quantification of apolipoprotein E and B. In: Lentant C, et al., eds. Biotechnology of dyslipoproteinemias: application in diagnosis and control. New York: Raven Press, 1990:207-16.

55. Warnick GR, Mayfield C, Albers JJ, Hazzard WR. Gel isoelectric focusing method for specific diagnosis of familial hyperlipoproteinemia type 3. Clin Chem 1979;1979:279-84.

56. Eto M, Watanabe K, Ishii K. A rapid flat gel isoelectric focusing method for the determination of apolipoprotein E phenotypes and its application. Clin Chim Acta 1985; 149:21-8.

57. Wu LL. Apo E phenotype by ultra-thin isoelectrofocusing method on polyacrylamide gel. In: Sunderman FW, ed. Manual of procedures for the applied seminar on six major

advances in laboratory medicine and their clinical applications. Philadelphia: Institute for Clinical Science, 1990:71-5.

58.   Salzer B, Stavljenic A, Jurgens G, Dumic M, Radica A. Polymorphism of apolipoprotein E, lipoprotein (a), and other lipoproteins in children with type I diabetes. Clin Chem 1993;39:1427-32.

59.   Mailly F, Davignon J, Nestruck AC. Analytical isoelectric focusing with immobilized pH gradients of human apolipoprotein E from very low density lipoproteins and total plasma. J Lipid Res 1990;31:149-55.

60.   Marz W, Cezanne S, Gross W. Phenotyping of apolipoprotein E by immunoblotting in immobilized pH gradients. Electrophoresis 1991;12:59-63.

61.   Utermann G, Weisgraber KH, Weber W, Mahley RW. Genetic polymorphism of apolipoprotein E: a variant form of apolipoprotein E2 distinguished by sodium dodecylsulfate polyacrylamide gel electrophoresis. J Lipid Res 1984;25:378-82.

62.   Menzel HJ, Utermann G. Apolipoprotein E phenotyping from serum by Western blotting. Electrophoresis 1986;7:492-95.

63.   Havekes LM, de Knijff P, Beisiegel U, Havinga J, Smit M, Klasen E. A rapid micromethod for apolipoprotein E phenotyping directly in serum. J Lipid Res 1987; 28:455-63.

64.   Hill JS, Pritchard PH. Improved phenotyping of apolipoprotein E: application to population frequency distribution. Clin Chem 1990;36:1871-74.

65.   Eichner JE, Kuller LH, Ferrell RE, Kamboh ME. A simplified method for screening the apolipoprotein E polymorphism. Human Heredity 1991;41:61-4.

66.   Kataoka S, Paidi M, Howard BV. Simplified isoelectric focusing/immunoblotting determination of apoprotein E phenotype. Clin Chem 1994;40:11-3.

67.   Luley C, Baumstark MW, Wieland H. Rapid apolipoprotein E phenotyping by immunofixation in agarose. J Lipid Res 1991;32:880-3.

68.   Luley CH, Haas B, Buhrer B, Wieland H. Improvement of apolipoprotein E phenotyping by isoelectric focusing/immunofixation. Clin Chem 1992;38:168.

69.   McDowell IFW, Wisdom GB, Trimble ER. Apolipoprotein E phenotype determined by agarose gel electrofocusing and immunoblotting. Clin Chem 1989;35:2070-3.

70.   Smeets B, Poddighe J, Brunner H, Ropers HH, Wieringa B. Tight linkage between myotonic dystrophy and apolipoprotein E revealed with allele specific oligonucleotides. Hum Genet 1988;80:49-52.

71.   Weisgraber KH, Newhouse YM, Mahley RW. Apolipoprotein E genotyping using polymerase chain reaction and allele specific oligonucleotide probes. Biochem Biophys Res Commun 1988;157:1212-7.

72.   Houlston RS, Wenham PR, Humphries SE. Detection of apolipoprotein E polymorphisms using PCR/ASO probes and Southern transfer: application for routine use. Clin Chim Acta 1990;189:153-8.

73.   Richard P, Thomas G, de Zulueta MP, et al. Common and rare genotypes of human apolipoprotein E determined by specific restriction profiles of polymerase chain reaction-amplified DNA. Clin Chem 1994;40:24-9.

74.   Nassar BA, McPherson R, Lamothe EMF, Al Sultan AI, Zhang ZJ, Rosenblatt DS. Identification of variant apolipoprotein E by isoelectric focusing and restriction isotyping in a patient with type III hyperlipoproteinemia. Clin Chem 1991;37: 1308.

75.   Hixson JE, Vernier DT. Restriction isotyping of human apolipoprotein E by gene amplification and cleavage with Hha I. J Lipid Res 1990;31:545-48.

76.   Kontula K, Aalto-Setala K, Kuusi T, Hamalainen L, Syvanen AC. Apolipoprotein E polymorphism determined by restriction enzyme analysis of DNA amplified by polymerase chain reaction: convenient alternative to phenotyping by isoelectric focusing. Clin Chem 1990;36:2087-92.

77.   Wu LL. Apo E phenotyping by ultra-thin isoelectrofocusing method. Applied Seminar on Clinical Science of Aging, 1994:73.

78.   Emi M, Wu LL, Robertson MA, et al. Genotyping and sequence analysis of apolipoprotein E isoforms. Genomics 1988;3:373-9.

79.   Funke H, Rust S, Assmann G. Detection of apolipoprotein E variants by an oligonucleotide "melting" procedure. Clin Chem 1986;32:1285-9.

80. Parker S, Angelico MC, Laffel L, Krolewski AS. Application of denaturing gradient gel electrophoresis to detect DNA sequence differences encoding apolipoprotein E isoforms. Genomics 1993;16:245-47.

81. Tsai MY, Suess P, Schwichtenberg K, et al. Determination of apolipoprotein E genotypes by single-strand conformational polymorphism. Clin Chem 1993;39: 2121-4.

82. Main BF, Jones PJH, MacGillivray RTA, Banfield DK. Apolipoprotein E genotyping using the polymerase chain reaction and allele specific oligonucleotide primers. J Lipid Res 1991;32:183-7.

83. Green EK, Bain SC, Day PJR, et al. Detection of human apolipoprotein E3, E2 and E4 genotypes by an allele-specific oligonucleotide-primed polymerase chain reaction assay: development and validation. Clin Chem 1991;37:1263-8.

84. Wenham PR, Newton CR, Price WH. Analysis of apolipoprotein E genotypes by the amplification refractory mutation system. Clin Chem 1991;37:241-4.

85. Dallongeville J, Lussier-Cacan S, Davigon J. Modulation of plasma triglyceride levels by apo E phenotype: a meta analysis. J Lipid Res 1992;33:447-54.

86. Sing CF, Davignon J. Role of the apolipoprotein E polymorphism in determining normal plasma lipid and lipoprotein variation. Am J Hum Genet 1985;37:268-85.

87. Xu C-F, Talmud PJ, Angelico F, Ben MD, Savill J, Humphries SE. Apolipoprotein E polymorphism and plasma lipid, lipoprotein, and apolipoprotein levels in Italian children. Genetic Epidemiology 1991;8:389-98.

88. Hallman DM, Boerwinkle E, Saha N, et al. The apolipoprotein E polymorphism: a comparison of allele frequencies and effects in nine populations. Am J Hum Genet 1991;49:338-49.

89. Eichner JE, Kuller LH, Ferrell RE, Meilahn EN, Kamboh MI. Phenotypic effects of apolipoprotein structural variation on lipid profiles. III. Contribution of apolipoprotein E phenotype to prediction of total cholesterol, apolipoprotein B, and low density lipoprotein cholesterol in the Healthy Women Study. Arteriosclerosis 1990;10:379-85.

90. Eggertsen G, Tegelman R, Ericsson S, Angelin B, Berglund L. Apolipoprotein E polymorphism in a healthy Swedish population: variation of allele frequency with age and relation to serum lipid concentrations. Clin Chem 1993;39:2125-9.

91. Eto M, Watanabe K, Chonan N, Ishii K. Familial hypercholesterolemia and apolipoprotein E4. Atherosclerosis 1988;72:123-8.

92. Eichner JE, Kuller LH, Orchard TJ, et al. Relation of apolipoprotein E phenotype to myocardial infarction and mortality from coronary artery disease. Am J Cardiol 1993; 71:160-5.

93. Davignon J, Gregg RE, Sing CF. Apolipoprotein polymorphism and atherosclerosis. Arteriosclerosis 1988;8:1-21.

94. Couderc R, Mahieux F, Bailleul S, Fenelon G, Mary R, Fermanian J. Prevalence of apolipoprotein E phenotypes in ischemic cerebrovascular disease: a case-control study. Stroke 1993;24:661-4.

95. Demant T, Bedford D, Packard CJ, Shepherd J. Influence of apolipoprotein E polymorphism on apolipoprotein B-100 metabolism in normolipemic subjects. J Clin Invest 1991;88:1490-501.

96. Kesaniemi YA, Ehnolm C, Miettinen TA. Intestinal cholesterol absorption efficiency in man is related to apoprotein E phenotype. J Clin Invest 1987;80:578-81.

97. Gylling H, Kuusi T, Vanhanen H, Miettinen TA. Apolipoprotein E phenotype and cholesterol metabolism in familial hypercholesterolemia. Atherosclerosis 1989; 80:27-32.

98. Weintraub MS, Eisenberg S, Breslow JL. Dietary fat clearance in normal subjects is regulated by genetic variation in apolipoprotein E. J Clin Invest 1987;80:1571-7.

99. Brenninkmeijer BJ, Stuyt PMJ, Demacker PNM, Stalenhoef AFH, van't Larr A. Catabolism of chylomicron remnants in normolipidaemic subjects in relation to the apoprotein E phenotype. J Lipid Res 1987;28:361-70.

100. Brown AJ, Roberts DCK. The effect of fasting triacylglyceride concentration and apolipoprotein E polymorphism on postprandial lipemia. Arterioscler Thromb 1991;11: 1737-44.

101. Williams RR, Hopkins PN, Hunt SC, et al. Population-based frequency of dyslipidemia syndromes in coronary prone families in Utah. Arch Intern Med 1990;150:582-8.

102. Fredrickson DS, Morganroth J, Levy RI. Type III hyperlipoproteinemia: an analysis of two contemporary definitions. Ann Intern Med 1975;1975:150-7.

103. Mahley RW, Rall SC. Type III hyperlipoproteinemia (dysbetalipoproteinemia): the role of apolipoprotein E in normal and abnormal lipoprotein metabolism. In: Scriver CR, Beaudet AL, Sly WS, Velle D, eds. The metabolic basis of inherited disease, 6th ed. New York: McGraw Hill, 1989: 1195-213.

104. Utermann G. Diabetes, obesity and hyperlipidemia III. In: Crepaldi G, et al, eds. New York: Elsevier Science Publishers, 1985:1-28.

105. Berglund L, Wiklund O, Eggertsen G, et al. Apolipoprotein E phenotypes in familial hypercholesterolaemia: importance for expression of disease and response to therapy. J Intern Med 1993;233:173-8.

106. Hopkins PN, Wu LL, Schumacher MC, et al. Type III hyperlipoproteinemia in patients heterozygous for familial hypercholesterol and apolipoprotein E2: evidence for a gene-gene interaction. Arterioscler Thromb 1991;11:1137-46.

107. Imari Y, Koga S, Ibayashi H. Phenotypes of apolipoprotein E and abnormalities in lipid metabolism in patients with non-insulin dependent diabetes mellitus. Metabolism 1988; 37:1134-8.

108. Eto M, Watanabe K, Makino I, Ishii K. Apolipoprotein E allele frequencies in non-insu-lin-dependent diabetes mellitus with hypertriglyceridemia (type IIb, III, IV, and V hyper-lipoproteinemia). Metabolism 1991;40:776-80.

109. Sakurai T, Oka T, Hasegawa H, Igaki N, Miki S, Goto T. Comparison of lipids, apoproteins and associated enzyme activities between diabetic and nondiabetic end-stage renal disease. Nephron 1992;61:409-14.

110. Despres JP, Verdon MF, Moorjani S, et al. Apolipoprotein E polymorphism modifies relation of hyperinsulinemia to hypertriglyceridemia. Diabetes 1993; 42:1474-81.

111. Ordovas JM, Lopez-Miranda J, Perez-Jimenez F, Rodriguez C, Park JS, Cole T, Schaefer EJ. Effects of apolipoprotein E and A-IV phenotypes on the low density lipoprotein response to HMG CoA reductase inhibitor therapy. Atherosclerosis 1995;113:157-66.

112. Nestruck AC, Bouthillier D, Sing CF, Davignon J. Apolipoprotein E polymorphism and plasma cholesterol response to probucol. Metabolism 1987;36:743-7.

113. Gylling H, Vanhanen H, Miettinen TA. Effects of acipimox and cholestyramine on serum lipoproteins, non-cholesterol sterols and cholesterol absorption and elimination. Eur J Clin Pharmacol 1989;37:111-5.

114. Knijff PD, Stalenhoef AFH, Mol MJTM, et al. Influence of apo E polymorphism on the response to simvastatin treatment in patients with heterozygous familial hypercholes-terolemia. Atherosclerosis 1990;83:89-97.

115. O'Malley JP, Illingworth DR. The influence of apolipoprotein E phenotype on the re-sponse to lovastatin therapy in patients with heterozygous familial hypercholesterolemia. Metabolism 1990;39:150-4.

116. Abey M. The influence of apolipoprotein polymorphism on the response to dietary fat and cholesterol. Curr Opin Lipidol 1992;3:12-16.

117. Boerwinkle E, Brown SA, Rohrbach K, Gotto AMJ, Patsch W. Role of apolipoprotein E and B gene variation in determining response of lipid, lipoprotein, and apolipoprotein levels to increased dietary cholesterol. Am J Hum Genet 1991;49:1145-54.

118. Gaddi A, Ciarrocchi A, Matteucci A, et al. Dietary treatment for familial hypercholes-terolemia: differential effects of dietary soy protein according to the apolipoprotein E phenotypes. Am J Clin Nutr 1991;53:1191-6.

119. Dreon DM, Fernstrom HA, Miller B, Krauss RM. Apolipoprotein E isoform phenotype and LDL subclass response to a reduced-fat diet. Arterioscler Thromb Vasc Biol 1995; 15:105-111.

120. Strittmatter WJ, Saunders AM, Schmechel D, et al. Apolipoprotein E: high-avidity binding to β-amyloid and increased frequency of type 4 allele in late-onset familial Alzheimer's disease. Proc Natl Acad Sci USA 1993;90:1977-81.

121. Saunders AM, Strittmatter WJ, Schmechel DS, et al. Association of apolipoprotein E allele 4 with late-onset familial and sporadic Alzheimer's disease. Neurology 1993;43: 1467-72.
122. Saunders AM, Schmader K, Breitner JCS, et al. Apolipoprotein E ε4 allele distributions in late-onset Alzheimer's disease and in other amyloid-forming diseases. Lancet 1993; 342:710-1.
123. Corder EH, Saunders AM, Strittmatter WJ, et al. Gene dose of apolipoprotein E type 4 allele and the risk of Alzheimer's disease in late onset families. Science 1993;261: 921-3.
124. Poirier J, Davignon J, Bouthillier D, Kogan S, Bertrand P, Gauthier S. Apolipoprotein E polymorphism and Alzheimer's disease. Lancet 1993;342:697-9.
125. Wisniewski T, Golabek A, Matsubara E, Ghiso J, Frangione B. Apolipoprotein E: binding to soluble Alzheimer's β-amyloid. Biochem Biophys Res Comm 1993;192:359-65.
126. Cauley JA, Eichner JE, Kamboh MI, Ferrell RE, Kuller LH. Apo E allele frequencies in younger (age 42-50) vs. older (age 65-90) women. Genet Epidemiol 1993;10:27-34.
127. National Institute on Aging, the Alzheimer's Association Working Group. Apolipoprotein E genotyping in Alzheimer's disease. Lancet 1996;347:1091-95.

Laboratory Assessment of Lipoprotein Oxidation

18

Sridevi Devaraj and Ishwarlal Jialal

BACKGROUND AND INTRODUCTION

❖ Data continue to accrue supporting the hypothesis that the oxidative modification of low-density lipoprotein (LDL) is a key step in the genesis of the atherosclerotic lesion.

Figure 18-1 depicts the role of oxidatively modified LDL (OX-LDL) in foam cell formation. As shown in the figure, mildly oxidized LDL or minimally modified LDL (MM-LDL) is initially formed in the subendothelial space.[1,2] MM-LDL can induce the endothelium to express adhesion molecules for monocytes and to secrete monocyte chemotactic protein (MCP-1) and macrophage-colony stimulating factor (M-CSF).[3] This sequence of molecular events results in monocytes binding to the endothelium and their subsequent migration into the subendothelial space, where M-CSF promotes differentiation into tissue macrophages. Macrophages can further modify MM-LDL to a more oxidized form through a mechanism involving reactive oxygen species. OX-LDL then can be taken up by the scavenger receptor of monocyte-derived macrophages; this uptake is not regulated by the cellular cholesterol content.[4] The processing of OX-LDL by macrophages results in appreciable cellular accumulation of cholesterol and possible foam cell formation.

LDL can be oxidatively modified by incubation with endothelial cells, smooth muscle cells, macrophages, activated monocytes, and neutrophils or by incubation with metal ions, copper and iron in particular.[5] Several biological effects ascribed to OX-LDL may contribute to the initiation and progression of the atherosclerotic process.[5,6] The cytotoxicity of OX-LDL may be important in inducing dysfunction of endothelial cells, and/or in promoting the evolution of the fatty streak to a more complex and advanced lesion, which may be due, in part, to cytotoxicity of OX-LDL toward foam cells. OX-LDL is a potent chemo-attractant for the circulating monocytes. Since OX-LDL is recognized by the scavenger receptor, this could lead to cholesterol accumulation and foam cell formation. Because OX-LDL is a potent inhibitor of macrophage motility, it can also promote retention of macrophages in the arterial wall. OX-LDL could also promote atherogenesis by altering expression of other genes in the arterial wall. In addition to leukocyte adhesion molecules M-CSF and MCP-1, OX-LDL can stimulate interleukin-1 (IL-1) release from macrophages.[7]. IL-1b has been shown to induce smooth muscle

Figure 18–1 ◆ Schema Depicting the Role of OX-LDL in Atherogenesis

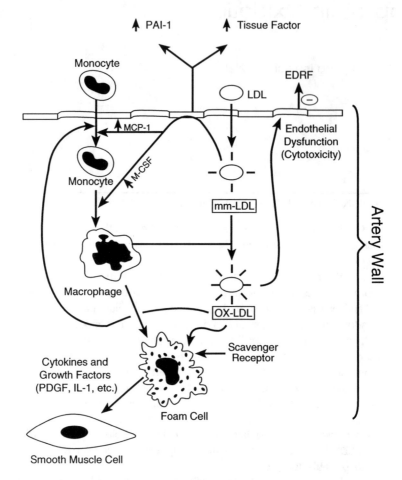

Adapted from: Jialal I, Devaraj S. Low-density lipoprotein oxidation, antioxidants and atherosclerosis: a clinical biochemistry perspective. Clin Chem 1996;42(4):498-506.

proliferation and endothelial adhesiveness to leukocytes.[8] Also, IL-1b mRNA has been found in atherosclerotic lesions.

OX-LDL can adversely affect the coagulation pathway by inducing tissue factor[9] and plasminogen activator inhibitor-1 synthesis.[10] Also, products of OX-LDL can impair expression of inducible genes such as tumor necrosis factor and platelet derived growth factor.[11] OX-LDL inhibits endothelium derived relaxation factor (EDRF)-mediated vasorelaxation.[12] EDRF appears to be crucial in maintaining coronary vasodilation and its activity is impaired in hypercholesterolemia and atherosclerosis. Another atherogenic property of modified LDL is its immunogenicity. Malondialdehyde-modified LDL has been shown to stimulate formation of autoantibodies, and immune complexes of LDL aggregates are efficiently internalized by macrophages via Fc receptors.[13] This could promote further cholesterol accumulation.

The oxidizability of LDL also depends on its size. Subjects with a predominance of small, dense LDL exhibit a greater risk of coronary artery disease compared to individuals with a predominance of large, more buoyant LDL.[14] Studies from numerous laboratories have shown that small, dense LDL is more susceptible to oxidation.[15] (For additional information on this subject, please refer to Chapter 14).

Furthermore, several lines of evidence support the *in vivo* existence of OX-LDL.[5, 6] Data has been presented for the occurrence of a modified form of LDL with many physical, chemical, and biological properties of OX-LDL in arterial lesions. Also, antibodies against epitopes on OX-LDL recognized material in atherosclerotic lesions, but not normal arteries, and circulating antibodies against epitopes of OX-LDL have been demonstrated in the plasma of humans. In fact, the titer of these antibodies correlates independently with the progression of atherosclerosis (carotid artery stenosis).[16] Additional support for the role of OX-LDL in atherosclerosis is found in the observation that antioxidants such as probucol, butylated hydroxytoluene, and vitamin E (α-tocopherol) can inhibit the development of atherosclerotic lesions in animal models.[17-19] Also, it was recently shown that the susceptibility of LDL to oxidation (the lag phase of oxidation) correlated with the severity of coronary atherosclerosis evidenced by angiography.[20] The precise mechanism(s) involved in the oxidative modification of LDL *in vivo* and its exact locality are unclear.

Human LDL comprises the population of lipoproteins (density range of 1.019–1.063 Kg/L) with diameter of 19–25 nm and molecular weight of 1.8–2.8 million Kd. The central lipophilic core consists mainly of cholesteryl esters and triglycerides surrounded by a monolayer of phospholipids and free cholesterol. The solubility of LDL in aqueous solutions is due to the location of the polar head of phospholipids at the surface of the particle. The apolipoprotein (apo) B-100, a large protein with molecular weight of 550 Kd, enfolds the whole surface of the LDL. About half of the fatty acids bound to the different lipids in LDL are polyunsaturated fatty acids (PUFA), but the content and distribution of the PUFA can vary widely, depending on dietary habits. The composition of PUFA modulates the susceptibility of LDL to oxidative modification. In fact, PUFA are much more susceptible to oxidation (due to the presence of double bonds) than mono-unsaturated and saturated fatty acids.

PUFA in LDL are protected from attack by reactive oxygen species (ROS) by several antioxidant compounds. On a molar basis, the major antioxidant is vitamin E, which is present in the LDL in a ratio of six molecules per particle.[21] Other antioxidants such as carotenoids, and ubiquinol-10 are present in smaller amounts.

EVALUATION OF LDL OXIDATIVE MODIFICATION

The evaluation of oxidative modification of LDL *in vivo* is very difficult. First, lipoprotein oxidation is likely to take place in the subendothelial space, outside the circulation. Second, the residence time of OX-LDL in plasma is short because of their affinity and rapid uptake by the scavenger receptor mechanism. Finally, the lack of sensitivity of the methods available make detecting the oxidative modification of lipoproteins at very low concentrations difficult.

While it has been suggested that there exists in plasma a more electronegative LDL which is more susceptible to oxidation, this methodology is tedious and is not easily applicable to routine use.[22] Thus, the more practical approach is to mimic the *in vivo* situation by subjecting LDL to an oxidative stress and to monitor its susceptibility to oxidation.

LDL is attacked by ROS in a series of steps, but the final results are the peroxidation of lipids and the oxidative modification of the major protein (apo B-100).[21] The latter phenomenon is caused by either the reaction with final products of lipid peroxidation or the direct effect of ROS. Some of the important properties of OX-LDL are described in Table 18-1. The various steps in oxidative modification of LDL can be monitored using different methodologies with varying degrees of complexity.

Table 18–1 ✧ Properties of Oxidized LDL*
✧ Decreased content of PUFA
✧ Loss of antioxidants
✧ Increased negative charge and density
✧ Increased content of lysolecithin
✧ Increased cholesterol oxidation products (7-keto-cholesterol)
✧ Fragmentation of apo B-100
✧ Increased fluorescence of apo B-100
✧ Increased content of aldehydes (MDA, HNE, etc.)
✧ Decreased uptake by LDL receptors
✧ Increased uptake by scavenger receptors
*LDL = low-density lipoprotein, PUFA = polyunsaturated fatty acids, apo B-100 = apolipoprotein B-100, MDA = malondialdehyde, HNE = hydroxynonenal

The initiation by ROS able to abstract an H• from a double bond in PUFA is followed by a molecular rearrangement, leading to the formation of conjugated double bonds referred to as conjugated dienes (CD). During this initial phase of lipid peroxidation of LDL, the rate of oxidation is suppressed by the endogenous antioxidants in LDL, resulting in a lag phase preceding the rapid propagation of lipid peroxidation. The length of this initial phase is largely determined by the antioxidant content and can be measured easily by spectrophotometry. The propagation phase starts only when antioxidants are depleted and results in the abstraction of H• by PUFA-peroxyl radical (LOO°) from another PUFA. This reaction results in the formation of lipid peroxides (LPO). Both CD and hydroperoxides are labile species.

A typical sequence of a lipid peroxidation reaction is shown in Figure 18-2. The propagation and degradation phases overlap, and the cleavage of carbon bonds during lipid peroxidation results in the formation of aldehydes. The major aldehydes produced include malondialdehyde (MDA), 4-hydroxynonenal (HNE), and hexanal. These can cross-link amino groups on apo B-100. MDA and other aldehydes are measured with the widely used thiobarbituric acid reactive substances method (TBARS).

Figure 18–2 ✧ The Peroxidation of Polyunsaturated Lipid

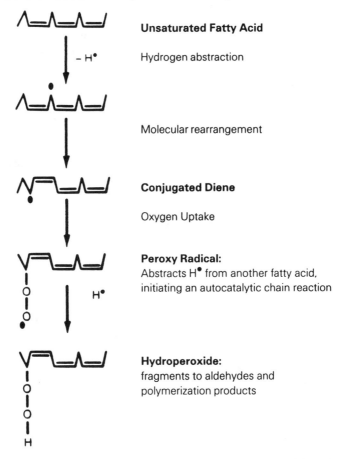

Unsaturated Fatty Acid

Hydrogen abstraction

Molecular rearrangement

Conjugated Diene

Oxygen Uptake

Peroxy Radical:
Abstracts H• from another fatty acid, initiating an autocatalytic chain reaction

Hydroperoxide:
fragments to aldehydes and polymerization products

Adapted from: Sinclair AJ, Barnett AH, Lunec J. Free radicals and antioxidants in health disease. Br J Hosp Med 1990;43:334-44.

HNE can be measured with high-performance liquid chromatography (HPLC) or with gas chromatography (GC).

Another characteristic of LDL following oxidation is an increase in the negative charge on the particle (measured by electrophoresis on agarose gel), which is possibly due to the derivatization of positively charged amino groups through Schiff's base formation with aldehydes. The derivatization of apo B-100 by reactive aldehydes can also result in increased fluorescence of OX-LDL, which can be easily measured at 430 nm, with excitation set at 360 nm. The attack of apo B-100 by reactive oxygen species results in fragmentation of apo B-100 by oxidative scission.

These changes in the lipid and protein moiety of OX-LDL result in new biological properties such as cytotoxicity and processing by the scavenger receptor mechanism.

METHODS USED TO ASSAY LDL OXIDATION

In plasma, LDL is efficiently protected by the extracellular antioxidant defense system, which includes ascorbate, bilirubin, and uric acid. In the course of isolation, a series of steps must be taken to minimize artifactual lipid peroxidation and maintain the integrity of LDL.

LDL is isolated from human plasma in EDTA (1 g/L), either by sequential ultracentrifugation in NaBr salt solutions as described by Havel,[23] or by rapid vertical spin gradient ultracentrifugation.[24] The isolated LDL is extensively dialyzed against a solution containing 150 mmol/L NaCl and 1 mmol/L EDTA (pH 7.4), filtered and stored at 4° C, under N_2. LDL is used within 7–10 days from the time of isolation. EDTA is present in excess to chelate transition metals and thus prevent LDL oxidation during isolation. Protein content is measured by the method of Lowry et al.[25] using bovine serum albumin as a standard.

To eliminate EDTA before oxidation experiments, LDL is dialyzed in the dark for 24 h at 4° C against two changes (1000-fold volume) of 0.01 mol/L phosphate-buffered saline (PBS) at pH 7.4, or passed through a Sephadex-G25 column (PD-10 column, Pharmacia, Piscataway, NJ).

Cell-Free System of LDL Oxidation

LDL can be oxidatively modified by co-incubation with cells or in a cell-free system by co-incubation with transition metals such as iron and copper or in a metal in-dependent system, by a free radical initiator, such as 2,2′-azobis(2-amidinopropane) (AAPH), a water-soluble azo compound that thermally decomposes, leading to the formation of peroxyl radicals at a constant rate.[26]

The oxidative modification of LDL by copper is thought to occur by the reaction of Cu^{++} with pre-existing endogenous lipid hydroperoxides (LOOH). The decomposition of LPO results in the production of several radical intermediates. Besides the initiation of lipid peroxidation, copper ions can form complexes with the ligand-binding sites of apo B-100, and it has been suggested that this binding is linked with structural modification of apo B-100.

OX-LDL is prepared by incubation of isolated LDL for 5 h or more in PBS supplemented with Cu^{++} ions at a concentration ranging from 1.66–10 μmol/L. We describe here the standard procedure generally used by most laboratories. LDL (200 μg protein/mL) is incubated at 37° C in PBS (0.01 mol/L) for a 6–8 h time-course experiment in the presence of 5 μmol/L Cu^{++} (incubation volume 1.0 mL).[27] A stock solution of 1 mmol/L Cu^{++} is made fresh in HPLC-grade water and diluted to give a final concentration of 5 μmol/L. Oxidation is stopped by refrigeration and addition of 0.01 mL EDTA (200 μmol/L) and butylated hydroxytoluene (40 μmol/L).

Cellular System of LDL Oxidation

A number of cells, including endothelial cells, monocyte-macrophages, and smooth muscle cells are able to oxidatively modify LDL to a degree that permits uptake by the macrophage scavenger receptor.[28-30] Cells generally require the presence of metal ions in the medium to induce LDL oxidative modification. A procedure for oxidatively modifying LDL by human monocyte-macrophages is described below.[31] It should be pointed out that mouse peritoneal macrophages or human macrophage cell lines, such as THP-1, can be used.

Human monocytes are isolated by density-gradient centrifugation from blood derived from fasting normolipidemic subjects. 20 mL of blood (anticoagulated with 10 IU/mL heparin) is layered over 15 mL of Ficoll-Hypaque and centrifuged at 1500 rpm for 30 min at room temperature. The mononuclear cell band is removed by aspiration. Cells are washed twice in RPMI-1640 media (GIBCO, BRL, Grand Island, New York), supplemented with 100 U/mL penicillin, 100 μg/mL streptomycin, and 2 mmol/L L-glutamine. Cells are diluted at the concentration of 5×10^6 cell/mL and 1 mL of the cell suspension is plated in a 35 mm dish in the same medium. After a 2 h incubation at 37° C in 5% CO_2/95% air, nonadherent cells are removed by three washes with serum-free medium. Finally, cells are incubated in RPMI 1640 containing 20% autologous serum and fed twice a week with the same medium. Monocyte-derived macrophages are used within 10–14 d of plating. Before use, cells are washed three times with serum-free RPMI 1640 medium.

For oxidation experiments, LDL (100 μg protein/mL) is incubated with mono-cyte-derived macrophages in Ham's F-10 medium for 24 h at 37° C in 5% CO_2/95% air (incubation volume 1.0 mL). Cell-free controls (LDL in Hams F-10 and RPMI-1640 media) are also undertaken. After incubation, medium is aspirated into tubes containing 200 μmol/L EDTA and 40 μmol/L BHT. The LDL solution is centrifuged at 1000 ×g for 10 min and the supernatant is collected.

INDICES USED TO MONITOR LDL OXIDATION

Conjugated Dienes

Oxidation of PUFA side-chains is accompanied by formation of conjugated dienes (CD) that absorb ultraviolet light in the wavelength range 230–235 nm (maximum at 234 nm). Measurement of this UV absorbance is a useful index of lipid peroxidation.[22] The CD peak appears after 3–4 h of incubation, depending on the incubation conditions. The second increase of absorbance does not correspond to newly formed CD but is due to the appearance of degradation products absorbing at the same wavelength. Since LDL is fully soluble in buffer, the generation of CD during LDL oxidation can be directly and continuously measured by recording the absorbance at 234 nm.

This procedure has been extensively described by Esterbauer et al.[32] The authors follow the kinetics of CD formation by incubating LDL (50 μg protein/mL) at 37° C in PBS with 1.66 μmol/L Cu^{++}. Usually the instrument is blanked with native LDL, the Cu^{++} is added, and the time course of oxidation is monitored. If other indices of LDL oxidation are also desired, then the reaction is stopped at selected times, an aliquot is diluted, and its absorbance is measured at 234 nm. CD formation generally cannot be used to assess cell-mediated LDL oxidation since ingredients in media can interfere with the assay. Currently, this method appears to be the most favored index of LDL oxidizability.

Spectrophotometric Assay for Lipid Peroxides

This is a quick and easy method for measuring lipid peroxides (LPO) in lipoprotein using a commercially available test kit for cholesterol determination. The method is based on the oxidation of iodide to iodine by lipid peroxides.[33] The problem with this assay is that its lower detection limit is similar to the reagent blank. Its advantage is the rapid determination of the total amount of lipid peroxides in LDL following LDL oxidation (e.g., with 5 µmol/L Cu^{++}). LDL (100 µL) is mixed on a vortex with 1 mL of the color reagent. (The constituents of the color reagent are detailed by El-Saadani et al.[33]) The sample is kept in the dark at room temperature for 30–60 min. Absorbance is measured at 365 nm against the reagent blank. The concentration of lipid peroxides is calculated using the molar absorption of iodide at 365 nm ($\varepsilon = 2.46 \times 10^4$ mol/L^{-1}).[33] Another method, the ferrous ion oxidation assay, in which ferrous ions are oxidized in the presence of xylenol orange (FOX assay) also seems to be relatively specific for lipid peroxides.[34]

Gas chromatography–mass spectrometry (GC/MS) methods are available to characterize single classes of lipid hydroperoxides (i.e., phosphatidylcholine hydroperoxides), but these methods are cumbersome and are not suitable for routine use.[35] A very sensitive and specific method for measuring total lipid hydroperoxides which utilizes HPLC with isoluminol chemiluminescence detection is also available.[36] However, these methods require additional instrumentation which is not always available to the clinical laboratory or to most investigators.

TBARS Assay

The thiobarbituric acid assay (TBA) is the most popular and easiest method used as an indicator of MDA formation during oxidation in biological samples. However, this test is not specific for MDA; in fact, many substances not related to lipid peroxidation–sugars, amino acids, etc.–may also form TBA adducts. Also, peroxides are formed during the heating phase of the assay. Thus, since this test not only measures MDA formed in the peroxidation system, it is more appropriately referred to as TBA-reactive substances, or TBARS. The chromogen is formed by reaction of one molecule of MDA with two molecules of TBA.

Basically, the sample is heated with TBA under acidic conditions and the amount of chromogen formed (MDA-TBA adduct) is measured at 532 nm. The absorbance is expressed in MDA equivalents/mg of LDL protein, using a standard curve for 1,1,3,3 tetramethoxypropane. A number of variations of the original TBA assay, differing in sample pretreatment, acid concentration, heating time, absence or presence of antioxidants, have been described.[37]

A spectrophotometric test (adapted for LDL samples) and a fluorometric test are described below.

Spectrophotometric Test

This method is a modification of the original procedure and includes the precipitation of protein (which interferes with the assay) using trichloracetic acid (TCA).[38] The assay is conducted in the presence of butylated hydroxytoluene (BHT) and EDTA to minimize the formation of TBARS activity during heating.[39]

LDL (500 μL, equivalent 100 μg and 50 μg LDL protein for copper-induced and cell-mediated oxidation, respectively) is combined with 1 mL of the TCA-TBA-HCl mixture (15% w/v TCA, 0.375% TBA, 25 mol/L HCl) and vortexed. The solution is heated for 20 min in a water bath at 100° C to precipitate protein. After cooling, samples are centrifuged at 2000 rpm for 20 min. The supernatant solution is carefully withdrawn and absorbance is determined at 532 nm against a blank containing all the reagents except LDL.

Fluorometric Test

In this procedure, protein is precipitated using phosphotungstic acid prior to carrying out the TBARS reaction.[40] BHT is added in the TBA reagent to minimize formation of new peroxides during the assay. For increased sensitivity, after reaction with TBA, the complex is extracted into butanol.

To 50 μL of LDL solution is added 0.5 mL phosphotungstic acid (10%) and 3.5 mL of water. Then 1 mL of TBA reagent (0.01% BHT in a mixture of equal volumes of 0.67% TBA and glacial acetic acid) is added to the sample. The solution is heated for 60 min in a water bath at 95° C. After cooling, the sample is combined with 5 mL of n-butanol and vortexed. The solution is centrifuged at 3000 rpm for 5 min. Fluorescence of the butanol layer is measured at 535 nm with 515 nm excitation against a blank containing all the reagents except LDL.

Relative Electrophoretic Mobility (REM)

This assay is based on the modification of LDL due to the derivatization of lysine residues of apo B-100 by certain reactive aldehydes (end products of lipid peroxidation) which lead to the increase in the negative charge of OX-LDL.

Commercially available reagents for electrophoretic separation of lipoproteins can be used. Electrophoresis is performed at pH 8.6 in 0.05 mol/L barbital buffer on 0.5% agarose gel. LDL (2–10 μg) is applied in each slot of a prepared agarose gel. After 5 min the gel is placed into the electrophoresis cell in barbital buffer and electrophoretic separation is performed for 30 min at 100 volts. The gel is then fixed in 1:3:6 solution of glacial acetic acid, water, and methanol and dried. The dried gel is placed for 10–15 min in the staining solution (Sudan Black B, 7%). After destaining in 45% methanol, the gel is rinsed with water and dried. The change in electrophoretic mobility is expressed relative to the mobility of native LDL. Figure 18–3 depicts the relative electrophoretic mobility (REM) during a typical time-course experiment of copper-catalyzed LDL oxidation.

Apo B-100 Fluorescence

The same process that alters the electrophoretic mobility of OX-LDL also generates fluorophors with a very strong fluorescence at 430 nm with excitation at 360 nm. The fluorescence has been attributed to the derivatization of apo B-100 lysine residues by

Figure 18–3 ✧ A Typical Time Course of LDL Oxidation

LDL (200 µg protein/mL) was incubated with 5 µmol/L Cu^{++} in PBS for 8 h.
LPO = Lipid Peroxides   REM = Relative Electrophoretic Mobility

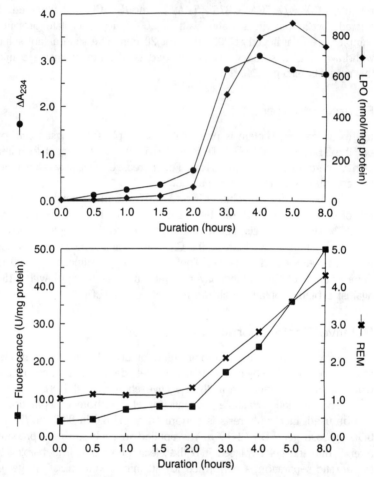

reactive aldehydes. A rapid method has recently been proposed in which the lipid extraction phase is omitted. This quick and simplified assay is useful to monitor apo B modification in time-course experiments,[41] as shown in Figure 18–3.

LDL solution is diluted to a concentration of 25 µg protein/mL in PBS. The emission is measured at 430 nm with excitation at 360 nm against a PBS blank. The fluorescence is corrected for protein concentration.

Loss of Endogenous Antioxidants and Fatty Acids

Measurements of the endogenous antioxidants and FA in LDL are important to have a better insight into the mechanism of LDL oxidative modification; however, they are difficult and need more complex instrumentation than the methods discussed above. The kinetics of disappearance of endogenous antioxidants during copper-catalyzed LDL oxidation can be monitored. As reported by Esterbauer et al.,[42] during oxidation, α-tocopherol is consumed first, followed by carotenoids. Measurement of α-tocopherol can be performed by HPLC with a reversed-phase column together with retinol.[43] Retinol and five carotenoids—lutein, cryptoxanthin, lycopene, and alpha- and beta-carotene—can be measured simultaneously by HPLC (reversed-phase column) with an isocratic solvent system.[44]

About half of FA in LDL are PUFA, mainly linoleic acid with minor amounts of arachidonic and docosahexaenoic acid. There is a high inter-individual variation in LDL FA composition, probably due to dietary habits. Such variation in PUFA content can lead to changes in the resistance of LDL toward oxidative modification. Usually the decrease in linoleic acid, arachidonic acid, and docosahexaenoic acid is monitored. The FA content of LDL is determined by GC following extraction and transmethylation.[45]

Fragmentation of APO B-100

Cell-induced and metal-catalyzed oxidative modification of LDL is accompanied by extensive breakdown of the major LDL protein (apo B-100) to small peptides.[46] The non-enzymatic oxidative cleavage of peptide bonds in apo B-100 leads to fragmentation, which is detectable by sodium dodecyl sulphate (SDS) polyacrylamide gradient gel electrophoresis.[47] Briefly, 20–30 μg of LDL protein is dissolved (1:3 v/v) with sample buffer containing 3% SDS, 10% glycerol, and 5% 2-mercaptoethanol in 0.5 mol/L Tris HCl at pH 6.8. The sample is incubated in boiling water for 5 min. Vertical gel electrophoresis is performed using 3–14% polyacrylamide gradient gel. The gel is fixed in 50% TCA and stained with Coomassie Blue R-250. Following LDL oxidation, the band of intact apo B-100 disappears with the formation of fragments.[46]

Oxysterols

It is also possible to evaluate the degree of modification of LDL by measuring oxidation products of cholesterol. Several oxysterols have been reported following LDL oxidation. Of these, 7-ketocholesterol has been identified by most laboratories as the main oxysterol produced during Cu^{++} catalyzed and cell-mediated LDL oxidative modification.[38, 48] Since GC and GC-MS methods are used, the availability of instrumentation confines oxysterol measurements to research laboratories.

Assays for the Biological Effects of OX-LDL

As discussed at the beginning of this chapter, OX-LDL has numerous biological effects. For the sake of brevity, only the two most common biological assays, ^{125}I-OX-LDL degradation by macrophages and cytotoxicity, are discussed in this review.

Degradation by Macrophages

LDL incubated at 37° C with macrophages is rapidly internalized and then delivered to lysosomes, where protein and cholesteryl esters are hydrolyzed. To measure ^{125}I-LDL degradation by the scavenger receptor on macrophages, ^{125}I-LDL is incubated with macrophages, usually for 5 h at 37° C in RPMI-1640 medium. ^{125}I-labeled LDL can be prepared by a modification of the iodine monochloride method.[49] The appearance of TCA-soluble (non-iodide) radioactivity formed by the cells and excreted in the media is determined by adding in order, albumin, TCA, H_2O_2, potassium iodide, and finally chloroform.[50] Degradation rates are corrected for cell-free controls incubated in parallel. Results are expressed as amount of protein degraded per milligram cell protein.

Cytotoxicity

The cytotoxicity of OX-LDL can be evaluated by incubating LDL with cells such as endothelial cells and embryonal fibroblasts, by monitoring the release of labeled chromium or lactate dehydrogenase released from the cells into the media or determining cell numbers or hexosaminidase activity of remaining target cells,[51, 52] one can obtain an estimate of cytotoxicity.

Other Approaches for Assessing Lipid Peroxidation

These measures are not specific for lipoprotein oxidation and cannot delineate the tissue of origin of lipid peroxidation.

Breakdown products of lipid hydroperoxides can be measured in exhaled breath as volatile hydrocarbons. This is a very sensitive yet non-invasive measure of lipid peroxidation in man. Ethane and pentane derived from hydroperoxides of ω-3 and ω-6 PUFA respectively can be quantitated by GC.[53, 54] It is essential to purify the inspired air because of the risk of hydrocarbon contamination arising from exogenous sources (motor vehicles, cigarette smoke, etc.) which create a high background. Thus, although this method is non-invasive, it is tedious and technically demanding because of its numerous pitfalls.[54] Its role in studying lipid peroxidation clearly needs to be established.

F2-isoprostanes are produced *in vivo* by humans by a noncyclo-oxygenase mechanism involving free radical-catalyzed peroxidation of arachidonic acid. The release of F2-isoprostanes is increased in LDL oxidized by macrophages, endothelial cells, or copper and can be measured by a solid-phase extraction procedure, followed by GC-MS.[55] The formation of F2-isoprostanes is induced in plasma and LDL exposed to oxidative stress *in vitro*.[56] Also, F2-isoprostanes and their metabolites recently were shown to be increased in plasma and urine of smokers.[57] However, although this is a measure of LDL oxidation, measurement in urine reflects whole body oxidation rather than LDL oxidation.

Another potential way to evaluate lipoprotein oxidation is by measurement of autoantibodies against epitopes on oxidized LDL.[58] A recent study has shown that the titer of these antibodies is an independent predictor of the progression of carotid atherosclerosis.[59] In the present form, most assays of antibodies to OX-LDL depend on differential reactions of immunoglobulin from patients' serum with antigen that either is in the native (unmodified) form (LDL) or has been oxidized. Thus, assays must be designed carefully to avoid changes in the LDL oxidation state during the assay, which could alter the results. The chances for antigen(LDL) oxidation could arise from different temperatures used in the various assay incubation steps. Once this assay is well-standardized, it could become an important and sensitive measure of LDL oxidation.

Nuclear magnetic resonance analysis of oxidized lipoproteins[60] could provide interesting information concerning the structural aspects of these modified lipoproteins.

Specific fluorescence patterns can be produced when certain amino acids react with lipid peroxides. It has been shown that dityrosine fluorescence is associated with the oxidation of linoleic acid.[61] Phagocytes generate myeloperoxidase to kill invading bacteria, and this may convert tyrosine to a radical catalyst that cross-links proteins. The stable oxidized product of the tyrosyl radical is dityrosine; its stability and intense fluorescence may allow it to also act as a marker for oxidatively damaged proteins in lesions. Exposure of LDL to L-tyrosine and activated human neutrophils has been shown to cause peroxidation of LDL lipids. The measurement of dityrosines could prove useful in evaluating the role of specific protein modifications that occur during lipoprotein oxidation. Also, reactive nitrogen intermediates such as peroxynitrite can modify proteins such as LDL. A useful marker of this reaction is nitrotyrosine. While measurement of dityrosine and nitrotyrosine appears to provide sensitive and accurate measures of oxidation, much further work is needed to assess their validity.

The total peroxyl radical trapping antioxidant parameter (TRAP) assay can be used as a measure of the antioxidant status of plasma.[62] Assessment of the relative contribution of the specific antioxidants—ascorbate, urate, protein sulphydryls, and α-tocopherol—requires that each be measured individually. Thus, while the TRAP assay may provide an index of antioxidant status, it only conveys part of the picture since the antioxidant deficiency is not defined. In fact, measurement of individual antioxidants such as ascorbate, α-tocopherol, and beta-carotene in plasma or LDL may, in their own right, provide very useful information with respect to antioxidant status. If the oxidation hypothesis is proved, these antioxidant assays could easily be incorporated into the repertoire for atherosclerosis screening and management.

CONCLUSION

The methods that are presently available to measure LDL oxidation were reviewed in this chapter. It is clear that no single method conveys the entire picture, and that each has its limitations. Thus, there is an urgent need for newer techniques that afford increased sensitivity and specificity. While the focus of this review has been on LDL oxidation, other lipoproteins also undergo lipid peroxidation. In fact, it has been shown that HDL can be oxidized, and that this impairs its ability to mediate cholesterol efflux.[63] It would appear that for the clinical laboratory, the ideal will be a standardized model system of plasma oxidation that parallels lipoprotein oxidation, yet is simple and rapid and thus available for routine use. Much further work is needed before measurement of lipoprotein oxidation becomes a routine clinical chemistry test. ✧

REFERENCES

1. Cushing S, Berliner J, Valente A, et al. Minimally modified LDL induces monocyte chemotactic protein I in human endothelial cells and smooth muscle cells. Proc Natl Acad Sci USA 1990;87:5134-8.

2. Berliner J, Territo M, Sevanian A, et al. Minimally modified LDL stimulates monocyte endothelial interaction. J Clin Invest 1990;85:1260-6.

3. Rajavashisth TB, Andalibi A, Territo MC, et al. Modified low density lipoproteins induce endothelial cell expression on granulocyte and macrophage colony stimulating factors. Nature 1990;344:254.

4. Sparrow CP, Parthasarathy S, Steinberg D. A macrophage receptor that recognizes oxidized low density lipoprotein but not acetylated low density lipoprotein. J Biol Chem 1989;264:2599-604.

5. Witztum JL, Steinberg D. Role of oxidized LDL in atherogenesis. J Clin Invest 1991;88: 1785-92.

6. Steinberg D, Parthasarathy S, Carew TE, Khoo JC, Witztum JL. Beyond cholesterol: modifications of low density lipoprotein that increase its atherogenicity. N Eng J Med 1989;320:915-24.

7. Thomas CE, Jackson RL, Ohlweiler DF, Ku J. Multiple lipid oxidation products in LDL induce IL-1b release from human blood mononuclear cells. J Lipid Res 1994;35:417-27.

8. Libby P, Hansson GK. Involvement of the human immune system in human atherogenesis: current knowledge and unanswered questions. Lab Invest 1991;64:5-15.

9. Drake TA, Hanani K, Fei H, Lavi S, Berliner JA. Minimally oxidized LDL induces tissue factor expression in cultured human endothelial cells. Am J Pathol 1991; 138:601-607.

10. Latron Y, Chautan M, Anfosso F, Alessi MC, Nalbone G, Lafont H, et al. Stimulating effect of oxidized LDL on plasminogen activator inhibitor-1 synthesis by endothelial cells. Arterioscler Thromb 1991;11:1821-9.

11. Hamilton TA, Ma GP, Chisolm GM. Oxidized LDL suppresses the expression of TNF alpha mRNA in stimulated murine peritoneal macrophages. J Immunol 1990;144: 2343-50.

12. Ohgushi m, Kygiyama K, Fukunaga K, Murohara T, Sugiyama S, Miyamoto E, et al. Protein kinase C inhibitors prevent impairment of endothelium dependent relaxation by oxidatively modified LDL. Arterioscler Thromb 1993;13:1525-32.

13. Gisinger C, Virella GT, Lopes Virella MF. Erythrocyte bound LDL immune complexes lead to cholesterol accumulation in human monocyte-derived macrophages. Clin Immunol Immunopathol 1991;59:37-52.

14. Austin MA, Breslow JL, Hennekens CH, Buring JE, Willett WC, Krauss RM. LDL subclass patterns and risk of myocardial infarction. JAMA 1988:260:1917-21.

15. Tribble DL, Holl LG, Wood PD, Krauss RM. Variations in oxidative susceptibility of LDL subfractions of differing density and particle size. Atherosclerosis 1992;93:189-99.

16. Salonen JT, Yla-Herttuala S, Yamamoto R, et al. Autoantibodies against oxidized LDL and progression of carotid atherosclerosis. Lancet 1992;339:883-7.

17. Kita T, Nagano Y, Yokode M, et al. Probucol prevents the progression of atherosclerosis in Watanabe heritable hyperlipidemic rabbit, an animal model for familial hypercholesterolemia. Proc Natl Acad Sci USA 1987;5928-31.

18. Björkhem I, Henriksson-Freyschuss A, Breuer O, Dicfalusy U, Berglund L, Henriksson P. The antioxidant butylated hydroxytoluene protects against atherosclerosis. Arterioscler Thromb 1991;11:15-22.

19. Verlangeri AJ, Bush M. Effects of d-alpha-tocopherol supplementation on experimentally induced primate atherosclerosis. J Am Coll Nutr 1992;11:131-8.

20. Regnstrom J, Nilsson J, Tornvall P, Landou C, Hamsten A. Susceptibility to low-density lipoprotein oxidation and coronary atherosclerosis in man. Lancet 1992;339:1183-6.

21. Esterbauer H, Gebicki J, Puhl H, Jürgens G. The role of lipid peroxidation and antioxidants in oxidative modification of LDL. Free Radic Biol Med 1992;13:341-90.

22. Cazzolato G, Avogaro P, Bittolo-Bon G. Characterization of a more electronegatively charged LDL subfraction by ion exchange HPLC. Free Rad Biol Med 1991;11:247-53.

23. Havel RJ, Eder HA, Bragdon JH. The distribution and chemical composition of ultra-centrifugally separated lipoproteins in human serum. J Clin Invest 1955;34:1345-53.

24. Chung BH, Wilkinson T, Geer JC, Segrest JP. Preparative and quantitative isolation of plasma lipoproteins: rapid single discontinuous density gradient ultracentrifugation in a vertical rotor. J Lipid Res 1980;21:284–91.

25. Lowry OH, Rosebrough NJ, Farr AL, Randall RJ. Protein measurements with the Folin phenol reagent. J Biol Chem 1951;193:265–75.

26. Frei B, Stocker R, Ames BN. Antioxidant defenses and lipid peroxidation in human plasma. Proc Natl Acad Sci USA. 1988;85:9748–54.

27. Jialal I, Grundy SM. Effect of dietary supplementation with alpha-tocopherol on the oxidative modification of low density lipoprotein. J Lipid Res 1992;33:899–906.

28. Henriksen T, Mahoney EM, Steinberg D. Enhanced macrophages degradation of low density lipoprotein previously incubated with cultured endothelial cells: recognition by receptor of acetylated low density lipoprotein. Proc Natl Acad Sci USA 1981;78:6499–503.

29. Parthasarathy S, Printz DJ, Boyd D, Joy L, Steinberg D. Macrophage oxidation of low density lipoprotein generates a modified form recognized by the scavenger receptor. Arteriosclerosis 1986;6:505–10.

30. Heinecke JW, Rosen H, Chait A. Iron and copper promote modification of low density lipoprotein by human arterial smooth muscle cells in culture. J Clin Invest 1984;84:1890–94.

31. Jialal I, Grundy SM. Preservation of the endogenous antioxidants in low density lipoprotein by ascorbate but not probucol during oxidative modification. J Clin Invest 1991;87:597–601.

32. Esterbauer H, Striegl G, Puhl H, Rotheneder M. Continuous monitoring of in vitro oxidation of human low density lipoprotein. Free Rad Res Comms 1989;6:67–75.

33. El-Saadani M, Esterbauer H, El-Sayed M, Goher M, Nasser AY, Jürgens G. A spectrophotometric assay for lipid peroxides in serum lipoproteins using a commercially available reagent. J Lipid Res 1989;30:627–30.

34. Jiang ZY, Hunt JV, Wolff SP. Ferrous ion oxidation in presence of xylenol orange for detection of lipid hydroperoxide in LDL. Anal Biochem, 1992;202:384:9.

35. Wang T, Yu W, Powell WS. Formation of monohydroxy derivative of arachidonic acid, linoleic acid, and oleic acid during oxidation of low density lipoprotein by copper ions and endothelial cells. J Lipid Res 1992;33:525–37.

36. Frei B, Yamamoto Y, Niclas D, Ames B. Evaluation of an isoluminol chemiluminescence assay for the detection of hydroperoxides in human blood plasma. Anal Biochem 1988;175:120–30.

37. Janero DR. Malondialdehyde and thiobarbituric acid-reactivity as diagnostic indices of lipid peroxidation and peroxidative tissue injury. Free Rad Biol Med 1990;9:515–40.

38. Buege JA, Aust SD. Microsomal lipid peroxidation. Methods Enzmol 1978;52:302–10.

39. Jialal I, Freeman D, Grundy SM. Varying susceptibility of different LDLs to oxidative modification. Arterioscler Thromb 1991;11:482–8.

40. Maseki M, Nishigaki I, Hagihara M, Tomoda Y, Yagi K. Lipid peroxide levels and lipid content of serum lipoprotein fractions of pregnant subjects with and without pre-eclampsia. Clin Chim Acta 1981;115:155–61.

41. Cominacini L, Garbin U, Davoli A, et al. A simple test for predisposition to LDL oxidation based on the fluorescence development during copper-catalyzed oxidative modification. J Lipid Res 1991;32:349–58.

42. Esterbauer H, Puhl H, Waeg G, Krebs A, Dieber-Rotheneder M. The role of vitamin E in lipoprotein oxidation. In Packer L, Fuchs J, eds. Vitamin E: biochemistry and clinical application. New York: Marcel Dekker, 1992:649–71.

43. Bieri JG, Talliver GT, Catignani LG. Simultaneous determination of alpha-tocopherol and retinol in plasma or red cells by high pressure liquid chromatography. Am J Clin Nutr 1979;32:2143–9.

44. Stacewicz-Sapuntzakis M, Bowen PE, Kikendal JQW, Burgess M. Simultaneous determination of serum retinol and various carotenoids: their distribution in middle-aged men and women. J Micronut Anal 1987;3:27–45.

45. Esterbauer H, Jürgens G, Quehenberger O, Koller E. Autoxidation of human low density lipoprotein: loss of polyunsaturated fatty acids and vitamin E and generation of aldehydes. J Lipid Res 1987;28:495-509.

46. Fong LG, Parthasarathy S, Witztum JL, Steinberg D. Nonenzymatic oxidative cleavage of peptide bonds in apoprotein B-100. J Lipid Res 1987;28:1466-77.

47. Laemmli UK. Cleavage of structural proteins during the assembly of the head of bacteriophage T4. Nature 1970;227:680-85.

48. Zhang H, Basra HJK, Steinbrecher U. Effects of oxidatively modified LDL on cholesterol esterification in cultured macrophages. J Lipid Res 1990;31:1361-9.

49. Grundy SM, Vega GL. Influence of mevinolin on metabolism of low sensitivity lipoproteins in primary moderate hypercholesterolemia. J Lipid Res 1985;26:1464-70.

50. Goldstein JL, Basu SK, Brown MS. Receptor-mediated endocytosis of low density lipoprotein in cultured cells. Meth Enzymol 1983;98:241-60.

51. Morel DW, Hessler JR, Chisolm GM. Low density lipoprotein cytotoxicity induced by free radical peroxidation of lipid. J Lipid Res 1983;24:1070-76.

52. Cathcart MK, McNally AK, Morel DW, Chisolm III, GM. Superoxide anion participation in human monocyte-mediated oxidation of low-density lipoprotein and conversion of low-density lipoprotein to a cytotoxin. J Immunol 1989;142(6):1963-9.

53. Jeejeebhoy KN. In vivo breath alkane as an index of lipid peroxidation. Free Rad Biol Med 1991;10:191-3.

54. Kneepkens CM, Ferreira C, Lepage G, Roy CC. The hydrocarbon breath test in the study of lipid peroxidation: principles and practice. Clin Invest Med 1991;15:163-86.

55. Gopaul NK, Nourooz-Zadeh J, Mallet AI, Anggard EE. Formation of F2-isoprostanes during aortic endothelial cell mediated oxidation of low density lipoprotein. FEBS Lett 1994;348:297-300.

56. Lynch SM, Morrow JD, Roberts LJ, Frei B. Formation of F2-isoprostanes in plasma and LDL exposed to oxidative stress in vitro. J Clin Invest 1994;93:998-1004.

57. Morrow JD, Frei B, Longmire AW, Gaziano JM, Lynch SM, Shyr Y, et al. Increase in circulating products of lipid peroxidation (F2 isoprostanes) in smokers. N Engl J Med 1995;332:1198-203.

58. Parums DV, Brown DL, Mitchinson MJ. Serum antibodies against LDL and ceroid in chronic periaortitis. Arch Pathol Lab Med 1990;114:383-7.

59. Maggi E, Chiesa R, Melissano G, Castellano R, Astore D, et al. LDL oxidation in patients with severe carotid atherosclerosis. Arterioscler Thromb 1994;14:1892-9.

60. Lodge JK, Sadler PJ, Kus ML, Winyard PG. Copper-induced LDL peroxidation investigated by NMR spectroscopy. Biochim Biophys Acta 1995;1256:130-140.

61. Kikugawa K, Kato T, Hayasaka A. Formation of dityrosine and fluorescent amino acids by reaction of amino acids with lipid hydroperoxides. Lipids 1991;26:922-9.

62. Wayner DDM, Burton GW, Ingold KU, Barklay LRG, Locke SJ. The relative contribution of vitamin E, urate, ascorbate, and proteins to the total peroxyl radical-trapping antioxidant activity of human blood plasma. Biochem Biophys Acta 1987;984:408.

63. Nagano Y, Arai H, Kita T. High density lipoprotein loses its effect to stimulate efflux of cholesterol from foam cells after oxidative modification. Proc Natl Acad Sci USA 1991;88:6457-61.

Determination and Clinical Significance of Lipoprotein Lipase and Hepatic Lipase

19

Thomas Olivecrona and Gunilla Olivecrona

INTRODUCTION

❖   Lipoprotein lipase (LPL) and hepatic triglyceride lipase (HTGL) are related enzymes that carry out the quantitatively major steps in lipoprotein metabolism. The delipidation process is illustrated in Figure 19–1. Note that HTGL can also hydrolyze phospholipids. LPL hydrolyzes triglycerides carried in chylomicrons and VLDL. This occurs at "binding-lipolysis sites" on the vascular endothelium, where the enzyme is anchored to heparan sulphate proteoglycans. The reaction releases fatty acids for use in cellular metabolic reactions and transforms the triglyceride-rich primary lipoproteins into cholesterol-rich remnant lipoproteins. This process is completed within minutes to a few hours after the lipoproteins have entered circulation. Some of the remnants are rapidly removed from the circulation by receptor-mediated endocytosis, but some are transformed into low-density lipoproteins (LDL) and high-density lipoproteins (HDL).

The role of HTGL remains somewhat enigmatic. Studies on lipoprotein kinetics in patients with HTGL deficiency[1] and studies on the effects of addition of purified HTGL to plasma[2] indicate that the enzyme acts on HDL and LDL and that it may be involved in the terminal stages of delipidation of chylomicron and VLDL remnants.

LPL action can be viewed as the general reaction in lipoprotein metabolism. In accord with this, LPL activity is high in most species. Table 19–1 shows the lipase activities in post-heparin plasma of man, rat, dog, guinea pig, and calf. Heparin (100 IU/kg b.w., about 0.65 mg) was injected i.v. and a plasma sample was taken 10 or 15 minutes later. HTGL was assayed using a gum arabic-stabilized triglyceride emulsion in the presence of 1 M NaCl to suppress LPL activity. LPL was assayed with a phosphatidylcholine-stabilized triglyceride emulsion using rat serum as source of activator. For assay of LPL activity in human and rat plasma, HTGL was suppressed by immunoinhibition using anti-HTGL serum. For dog, guinea pig, and calf plasma, LPL activity represents the difference in activity between samples treated with anti-LPL antibody and control serum.

Figure 19–1 ✧ Delipidation of Triglyceride-Rich Lipoproteins by the Lipases

A. Exogenous pathway.   B. Endogenous pathway

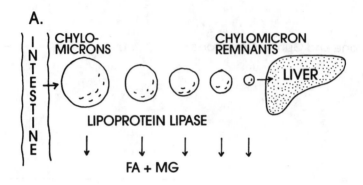

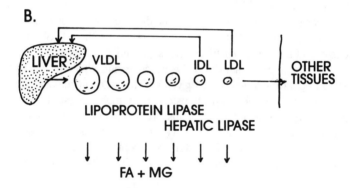

Source: Olivecrona and Bengtsson-Olivecrona[73]

Table 19–1 ✧ Lipase Activities in Post-Heparin Plasma of Some Species (values in mU/mL)		
	LPL	HTGL
Man	350	370
Rat	440	700
Dog	630	170
Guinea pig	790	70
Calf	530	< 5

HTGL can be seen to act upon the remnants formed by LPL for degradation or remodelling (see Figure 19-1). Its activity varies widely among species (see Table 19-1). It is high in humans and in rats, moderately high in dogs, low in guinea pigs and virtually non-existent in calves, fishes, and birds. Similar observations have been made for other factors involved in remodelling and metabolism of the cholesterol-rich lipoproteins. For instance, lipid transfer activity in plasma differs widely among species.[3] The concentrations of LDL and HDL in plasma also vary widely: LDL and HDL are both relatively high in humans, dogs have low LDL but high HDL, and guinea pigs have high LDL and low HDL. There is apparently considerable latitude in how animals handle metabolism of remnant particles and of LDL and HDL, and consequently in their need for HTGL activity. In contrast, the LPL reaction is indispensable.

There are many excellent reviews to which the reader is referred for information on the molecular structure, kinetic properties, physiological regulation, and postulated pathophysiological roles of the two lipases.[4-7] In this chapter we refer only to studies directly relevant to the measurement and clinical relevance of the lipases.

PROPERTIES OF LPL AND HTGL

LPL is present in most extrahepatic tissues. The enzyme is synthesized in parenchymal cells, transferred to the vascular endothelium, and anchored to heparan sulphate proteoglycans. The enzyme can move along the endothelium by jumping from one binding site to the next, and may perhaps move to other tissues with blood. Its life cycle is concluded by removal and degradation in the liver. This process is illustrated in Figure 19-2.

The enzyme requires apolipoprotein (apo) C-II for activity. It is strongly inhibited by fatty acids, which has been suggested to be a mechanism for feedback control of the enzyme activity. The main substrates for LPL are triglycerides in chylomicrons and VLDL. LPL is regulated in a tissue-specific manner, mainly by factors that relate to energy metabolism.

HTGL is present in the liver, in the adrenal cortex, and in ovaries but is absent in most other tissues. In contrast to LPL, it does not require apo C-II and acts on smaller, denser lipoproteins such as chylomicron remnants, intermediate-density lipoproteins (IDL), LDL, and HDL. HTGL activity is regulated by steroid and other hormones.

Non-catalytic Functions

LPL enhances binding of lipoproteins to cells. This enhancement of binding can be very substantial, several hundred-fold, and involves at least two separate mechanisms. In one mechanism, LPL binds to cell surface heparan sulphate and to the lipoprotein particle.[8] This bridging is of obvious physiological importance for the transient binding of chylomicrons and VLDL to "binding-lipolysis sites" at the endothelium. However, bridging also can be demonstrated for LDL and HDL with a large variety of cells as well as the intercellular matrix.[8] The physiological and/or pathophysiological importance of this mechanism is yet not established, but some authors ascribe to it an important role in atherogenesis.[7]

Figure 19–2 ✧ Transport of LPL in Blood

The enzyme is produced in parenchymal cells, illustrated here by an adipocyte on the right. It is released from these cells and transferred to the binding sites at the nearby vascular endothelium. From here, LPL can dissociate into the circulating blood and bind to endothelial sites in other tissues, as illustrated in the left part of the figure. Avid uptake by the liver keeps the blood concentration of LPL low.

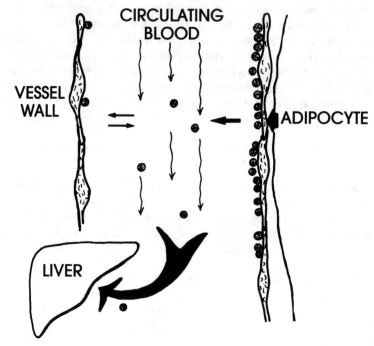

Source: Olivecrona and Bengtsson-Olivecrona[74]

In the other mechanism, LPL binds to a group of cell surface receptors in the LDL-receptor family.[9] Most studied is the binding of LPL to the low-density lipoprotein receptor related protein (LRP). This mechanism is believed to play an important role for catabolism of remnant lipoproteins.

LPL in Adipose Tissue

Some of the fatty acids generated by LPL action are directly taken up into the subjacent tissue, but some are released back into blood as albumin-bound free fatty acids (FFA). This split must reflect a balance between LPL-mediated lipolysis and metabolic processes in the cells. In the fed state, fatty acids from chylomicrons are taken up and stored in adipose tissue much more efficiently than albumin-bound FFA.[10, 11] In this sense, LPL directs fatty acids to the adipose tissue. For fatty acid storage to take place, other signals must make the tissue ready to esterify the fatty acids into triglycerides.[12, 13] The regulation of these processes, which are obviously central to regulation of energy metabolism and for the size of adipose tissue, has generated much interest.

LPL activity in adipose tissue is regulated by several mechanisms acting at different levels. For example, there is long-term regulation of LPL mRNA by hormones such as insulin[14] and cortisol.[15] There are differences between adipose tissue localities, and these have been suggested to be affected by sex steroid hormones, perhaps contributing to the male and female patterns of obesity. Two mechanisms for short-term regulation have been described. There is a protein in adipocytes which binds specifically to the 3'-untranslated region of LPL mRNA and prevents its translation into protein.[16] This process is triggered by adrenergic stimulation. Another mechanism affects the maturation of LPL. The default pathway, which operates in other tissues and in adipose tissue in the fed state, processes newly synthesized enzyme into its active form. During fasting, however, a mechanism is switched on in the adipose tissue that channels the enzyme into an inactive form which is then degraded.[17]

LPL as a Possible Rate-Limiter for the Turnover of Triglyceride-Rich Lipoproteins

Triglyceride clearance is usually a very efficient process. Results from studies employing oral fat loads imply that most individuals can easily transport 10 g triglyceride per hour. This is more than enough to cover resting energy expenditure and about 100 times the LDL cholesterol transport rates. The question arises whether LPL activity sets the upper limit for the transport rate. As a first approximation one could use post-heparin LPL activity as a measure of LPL available at endothelial sites. A recent study showed an activity of 483 ± 180 mU/mL for a group of middle-aged, healthy, normolipidemic men.[18] This assay was performed with a phospholipid-stabilized triglyceride emulsion at 25° C and pH 8.5. The activity would be higher at 37° C but lower at pH 7.4; these factors roughly equal out. The activity is somewhat higher with rat chylomicrons than with the synthetic emulsion. Nonetheless, the value should give an estimate of the capacity for triglyceride hydrolysis *in vivo*.

For each triglyceride molecule, two ester bonds are split by the enzyme. Therefore, the activity corresponds to clearing of roughly 250 nmol triglyceride per mL and minute, or about 40 g of triglyceride per hour. The concentrations of triglyceride-rich lipoproteins in normal plasma are well above the K_m values measured *in vitro*. Hence, if the particles had free access to the lipase, the system would be close to saturation and would operate at a rate much above the observed rates for triglyceride transport. Perhaps the most direct evidence for this is that plasma triglyceride levels quickly drop after heparin injection, demonstrating that the limiting factor is not the amount of lipase but its access to the lipoprotein particles.[19] The simple fact is that lipoproteins spend most of their time in the circulating blood where there is little or no LPL; lipase action requires that the particles bind to the endothelium. In most cases, this "margination" of lipoproteins to endothelial sites may be the limiting factor. Whether it is related to the amount of LPL available at the sites is presently not known.

LPL Deficiency

More than 40 mutations in LPL that result in inactive enzyme have been described.[6] Some are major rearrangements of the gene, but most are point mutations. Homozygotes or compound heterozygotes develop massive hypertriglyceridemia.[20] This illustrates that the LPL reaction is necessary for normal clearance of triglyceride-rich lipoproteins. Predictably, the patients have low levels of LDL and HDL. Other clinical signs include eruptive xanthomas and lipemia retinalis. The major pathology is related to recurrent episodes of pancreatitis. Otherwise, the patients are relatively healthy and there is no evidence that they develop premature atherosclerosis.

Heterozygotes should have half-normal LPL activity. Studies to date indicate that most of the heterozygotes have normal lipid levels, but they tend to develop hyperlipid-emia when exposed to other metabolic stress situations such as obesity[21] and pregnancy.[22] Hence, half-normal LPL activity is usually compatible with relatively normal lipoprotein metabolism. Interestingly, the lipoprotein phenotype that the heterozygotes tend to develop is similar to that encountered in the so-called metabolic syndrome[23] and is quite different from the phenotype seen in homozygotes. Along the same line, in mice with targeted inactivation of the LPL gene, the heterozygotes had a mild phenotype with moderate elevation of plasma triglyceride and a decrease of HDL cholesterol.[24]

Post-heparin LPL activity varies a great deal among individuals. A three-fold range of activities is not unusual in a population sample. Some years ago Babirak et al. measured post-heparin LPL activity and mass in 56 individuals with familial combined hyperlipidemia.[25] In 20 of them LPL activity and mass were in the same range as obligate heterozygotes for LPL deficiency, and the authors concluded that heterozygosity for LPL deficiency was a likely contributing factor in familial combined hyperlipidemia. The LPL genes in these 20 individuals have now been examined.[26] One regulatory mutant was found but no mutation in the structural gene which would predict inactive LPL. Gagné et al. studied the LPL genes in another group of 31 unrelated individuals with familial combined hyperlipoproteinemia and likewise found no significant structural mutations.[27] Hence, the original prediction of a high frequency of heterozygosity for LPL deficiency in patients with familial combined hyperlipoproteinemia has not been borne out. On the other hand, the finding that many patients with familial combined hyperlipoproteinemia have low post-heparin LPL activity has been confirmed.[28]

Individuals with defects in apo C-II have a similar clinical picture as those with defects in LPL.[20] Heterozygotes for C-II defects do not present any clinical symptoms.

HTGL Deficiency

Fewer cases of HTGL deficiency have been described than of LPL deficiency. This is probably because the phenotype is less dramatic,[29] and therefore identifying individuals for DNA sequence analysis has not been so easy.

Accessing Lipases for Measurement

LPL is present in many extrahepatic tissues, but its main sites of action are in muscles and adipose tissue. It is therefore logical to measure the enzyme in these tissues if biopsies can be obtained. Theoretically, HTGL could be measured in the liver, but it is not realistic to obtain liver biopsies for this purpose.

Fortunately, there is a simpler method to sample the lipases. Heparin releases them from their tissue binding sites in the form of enzyme-heparin complexes. Therefore, post-heparin plasma provides convenient access to the lipases for clinical studies.

LPL and HTGL activity are interesting parameters in population studies but generally do not yield information that is relevant to treatment strategies for individual patients. The only situation in which the clinician needs a measure of the lipases is when a deficiency state is suspected from the plasma lipoprotein profile. In general, patients with genetic deficiencies have no or very low activity in post-heparin plasma. For LPL, the differential diagnosis is to find whether the case is a deficiency of the enzyme or of its activator, apo C-II.

HTGL in Pre- and Post-Heparin Plasma

HTGL activity in plasma is low but significant. Heparin increases the activity several hundred-fold. A positive, linear correlation exists between the plasma HTGL activities before and after injection of heparin.[30, 31] This suggests that plasma HTGL is in equilibrium with HTGL in the liver, and that the effect of heparin is to shift the equilibrium towards soluble complexes in blood. In accord with this, a study in which human HTGL was injected in mice showed that the enzyme rapidly became bound in the liver, from which it could be released again by heparin.[32] The turnover rate for HTGL is relatively slow; the $T_{1/2}$ has been estimated to 4.6 hours in rats[33] and 3 hours in mice.[32] Hence, relatively small amounts would be expected to turn over during the 15–60 minutes that are usually studied after heparin injection. Plasma HTGL curves tend to follow the heparin concentration fairly closely.[34] HTGL remains in blood for as long as heparin remains.

Because of the strong linear correlation between HTGL activity before and after heparin injection, one could measure this enzyme in regular plasma samples. However, the activity is so low that it is at or beyond the limit of current methodologies. Since the uncertainties in measuring HTGL activity in regular plasma are so great, we recommend that it be measured in post-heparin plasma.

Clinical Significance of Post-Heparin HTGL Activity

Many studies have demonstrated an inverse relationship between HTGL activity and HDL cholesterol levels.[18, 35, 36] Based on the observation that HTGL acts on HDL, it has been argued that high HTGL activity leads to a generally enhanced catabolism of the particles.[35] Alternatively, it has been suggested that the major impact of high HTGL activity is to enhance hydrolysis of triglyceride transferred into the particles with cholesteryl ester transfer protein (CETP), and hence drive depletion of HDL core lipids through exchange with triglyceride-rich lipoproteins.[37-39]

LPL Activity in Pre- and Post-Heparin Plasma

As with HTGL, the level of LPL activity in plasma is very low. The origin and fate of plasma LPL is more complex than for HTGL. LPL is produced in extrahepatic tissues, taken up from blood, and degraded in the liver. The concentration of LPL in plasma does not reflect an equilibrium situation but represents a continuous flow of lipase molecules.[7] The processes involved are likely influenced by a number of physiological parameters. Although one early study claimed a correlation between LPL activity in pre- and post-heparin plasma,[31] most studies have not supported this finding.[18, 40] It is now clear that LPL activity in pre- and post-heparin plasma are two separate parameters, the more useful of which is the activity in post-heparin plasma. The activity in pre-heparin plasma is difficult to measure with precision, and its clinical significance has not been established.[18]

LPL is thought to be anchored to the vessel walls by interaction with heparan sulphate proteoglycans on endothelial cells. An additional 116 kDa protein may be involved in the binding. The enzyme at the endothelium is often referred to as "functional LPL" because it can act on lipoproteins, in contrast to LPL located within cells or in transit to the endothelium.

Studies with perfused rat hearts have led to the concept that heparin-releasable LPL is equal to functional LPL. Borensztajn and Robinson reported that when rat hearts are perfused and heparin is added to the medium, a burst of LPL activity occurs during the first two minutes.[41] It is reasonable to assume that this is the enzyme that was directly exposed at the endothelium. If the perfusion continues, the enzyme continues to be released, but at a much lower level.[42] Hence, heparin can recruit LPL from sites not immediately exposed to blood. This may represent the pool of LPL located along cell surfaces in the tissue, as shown by electron microscopic immunostaining,[43] and perhaps LPL recycling in the endothelial cells.[44] Translating this mechanism to the whole animal, we might expect to see a quick rise of LPL activity after heparin injection, followed by a continued rise. This is exactly what one sees in animals in which the liver has been excluded from the circulation.[45] In an intact animal, the situation is more complex: The liver extracts LPL even in the presence of heparin,[46] so that post-heparin LPL soon reaches a plateau value. This value does not represent all the LPL that was exposed at endothelial sites, but a balance between release from peripheral tissues and extraction in liver.

Heparin is a polydisperse mixture of molecules varying in length and degree of sulfation. We have recently compared the effects of size-fractionated heparins on LPL.[19, 34] Shorter heparins were quite effective in releasing the enzyme from peripheral tissues, but were relatively less efficient in retarding the uptake of the enzyme by the liver. Hence, plasma LPL activity fell off more rapidly after the shorter heparins. This led to a period of depletion of functional LPL, with impeded triglyceride clearing ability.

In conclusion, it is not clear how post-heparin LPL relates to functional LPL. The activity in a sample of post-heparin plasma underestimates functional, endothelium-bound LPL because some of the released enzyme has been extracted by the liver. On the other hand, heparin recruits enzyme from deeper layers in the tissue. The balance between these processes depends on the type of heparin used. In particular, low-molecular-weight heparin preparations yield different results compared to regular heparin.

Clinical Significance of Pre- and Post-Heparin LPL Activity

If LPL activity were the major determinant for catabolism of triglyceride-rich lipoproteins, one would expect a strong association between measures of LPL activity and plasma triglyceride. However, in most studies this relationship was found to be weak or non-significant.[18, 28, 40,47-51] Taskinen et al. found a strong correlation between postprandial triglyceride and post-heparin LPL activity in normal individuals.[47] In men with NIDDM, the relationship was weaker and not statistically significant, and in men with NIDDM and coronary artery disease no relationship was found. Likewise, Tornvall et al. found a rather strong inverse correlation between fasting plasma triglyceride and post-heparin LPL activity in normal men, but no relation in young survivors of myocardial infarction.[18] These results reinforce the hypothesis that metabolic factors can override LPL activity as the rate-limiting factor in triglyceride lipolysis.

Increases of LPL activity by several mechanisms have been found to result in lowering of plasma triglyceride, improved capacity to handle lipid loads, and increases in HDL levels. This is true in transgenic mice overexpressing LPL,[52-54] in mice treated with a novel drug, NO-1886,[55] which increases tissue LPL mRNA and activity, and in humans treated with fenofibrate.[56, 57]

In the general population, the parameter that correlates most consistently with LPL activity has been HDL cholesterol, particularly HDL_2 cholesterol.[36, 57-59] The molecular mechanisms behind this relation have been discussed extensively.[3, 36, 37, 60] One line of thought is based on the fact that surface components transfer from triglyceride-rich lipoproteins to HDL as a result of LPL-mediated hydrolysis of core triglyceride. Hence, efficient delipidation, as opposed to early receptor-mediated particle removal, would channel more phospholipids, cholesterol, and apolipoproteins to HDL. Another line of thought stresses the role of CETP, which catalyzes homo- and hetero-exchange of cholesteryl esters and triglyceride between lipoproteins. Increased levels of triglyceride-rich lipoproteins (basal or post-prandial) would cause increased flow of cholesteryl esters from LDL and HDL into the triglyceride-rich lipoproteins. On the other hand, triglyceride transferred to LDL and HDL would be susceptible to hydrolysis by HTGL. The result would be a preponderance of small HDL (HDL_3), and small LDL (pattern B). Recent studies, in fact, have demonstrated an association between LPL activity and small, dense LDL.[49, 61, 62]

LPL Mass in Pre- and Post-Heparin Plasma

There is more LPL protein mass in plasma than corresponds to the active enzyme.[18, 63, 64] LPL mass can be separated into two fractions by chromatography on heparin-agarose. One fraction corresponds to a small amount of active lipase. The other fraction is a larger amount of catalytically inactive lipase protein, probably in monomeric form.[64] The origin and turnover of this inactive lipase is not clear. The level is increased only about two-fold by heparin. Most of it is bound to lipoproteins, predominantly to LDL in fasting plasma.[65] The amount corresponds to about one lipase monomer for each 500 to 1000 apo B molecules. Model experiments have shown that monomeric LPL bound to lipoproteins enhances their interaction with heparan sulphate but does not mediate binding to LRP. The monomer has much lower affinity for heparin/heparan sulphate than the dimer.

LPL mass is readily measured by an ELISA.[65] The clinical significance of this measure has not been established. Much research remains before we understand the physiology of this inactive mass. One study found a strong correlation between this measure and the level of HDL cholesterol in myocardial infarct survivors.[18, 36]

LPL activity and mass in post-heparin plasma correlate rather closely.[18] This suggests that LPL released by heparin is almost exclusively the active species. These relationships are illustrated in Figure 19–3, which shows separation of pre- and post-heparin plasma on heparin-agarose. In post-heparin plasma, peaks of lipase activity and mass coincided at around 0.9 M NaCl in the gradient. There was also an earlier peak of inactive lipase that eluted around 0.5 M NaCl. In pre-heparin plasma only the inactive peak was seen, since the amount of active lipase in pre-heparin plasma after distribution into the chromatography fractions is below the limit of detection in the assays. In this experiment, the ratio between the mass of active LPL and the mass of inactive LPL in post-heparin plasma was 3.6. Though the lipase activity in plasma increased 325-fold after heparin, the inactive LPL mass increased only two-fold. In analysis of post-heparin plasma from six individuals, the ratio between the active peak and the inactive peak was 2.9 ± 0.5. The inactive LPL peak increased 3.0 ± 0.4 fold after heparin infusion.

Description and Discussion of Current Methods

Different assay procedures result in widely varying values for lipase activities. For instance, Taskinen[66] made a survey of the literature and found that values reported for LPL in post-heparin plasma from normal individuals differed about ten-fold between laboratories. The difference for adipose tissue LPL was even greater, at 6–110 mU/g.

We recommend that the clinical laboratory measure LPL and HTGL activities in post-heparin plasma as the first choice. For studies on patients suspected to have deficiency of either LPL or HTGL, we recommend that the samples be shipped to a laboratory experienced in this methodology. For this purpose, post-heparin plasma can be frozen. For research projects, it is often more appropriate to study LPL in tissue extracts. For this, one cannot recommend one single method (see discussion below). We refer readers to the literature for conditions suitable for the particular project. The two main approaches to estimating tissue LPL activity are to measure total activity and/or heparin-releasable activity. The latter is assumed to be the sum of endothelial LPL and some intracellular LPL which has been secreted during the extraction, balanced by inactivation/degradation in the medium. The most efficient extraction/solubilization of total tissue LPL is obtained with buffers containing detergents. A further advantage is that LPL is usually stable for hours at 4° C in these buffers.

Several different detergent cocktails have been described. Most of these contain protease inhibitors. The one we use is 25 mM ammonia adjusted with HCl to pH 8.2 containing 5 mM EDTA and, per mL, 10 mg Triton X-100, 1 mg SDS, 5 IU heparin, 10 µg leupeptin (Boehringer), 1 µg pepstatin, and 25 KIU Trasylol (Sigma). Stock solutions of leupeptin and pepstatin (1 mg/mL) are made in ethanol (95%). Higher

Figure 19–3 ✧ Separation of Active and Inactive Forms of LPL in Plasma by Chromatography on Heparin-Agarose

Ten mL of plasma were loaded on a small column of heparin-agarose and eluted using a gradient of NaCl. LPL mass was determined by ELISA.

○   LPL mass in pre-heparin plasma
●   LPL mass in plasma obtained 10 minutes after i.v. injection of 100 IU heparin/kg body weight
◆   LPL activity in post-heparin plasma.

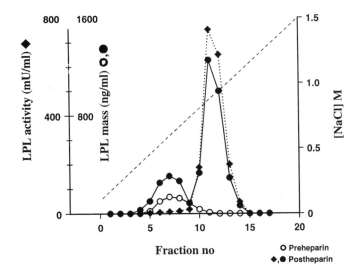

Source: Olivecrona et al.[64]

proportions of SDS will denature LPL. This buffer is suitable also for immunoassay and immunoprecipitation. It is excellent for dilution of purified LPL, and therefore for assay purposes. LPL solubilized as described above can bind to heparin-agarose, but for this purpose heparin should be omitted from the buffer. Whenever the protein concentrations of the extracts are low, increased recovery and stability is obtained if bovine serum albumin (1 mg/mL) is included in the buffer. The heparin-detergent buffer also works well for extraction of HTGL from liver and steroid-producing glands.

Substrate Emulsions

The substrates commonly used for measurement of LPL and HTGL are long-chain triglycerides emulsified with phospholipids or other surface-active components (e.g., gum arabic). For LPL, the reaction rates with synthetic emulsions are comparable to those obtained with VLDL or chylomicrons. For convenience, and to increase assay sensitivity, labelled triglycerides (^{3}H or ^{14}C in the fatty acid moiety) are often used. Triolein is preferable to saturated triglycerides (e.g., tripalmitin), since it is melted at assay temperatures, and is preferable to more unsaturated triglycerides (e.g., trilinolein) because it is less prone to oxidative damage.

Emulsions stabilized by gum arabic are recommended for assay of HTGL and can also be used for measurement of LPL. This emulsion is prone to absorption of non-specific proteins (e.g., from tissue homogenates), which may inhibit lipase activity by covering the oil-water interface. With LPL, the basal activity (in the absence of apo C-II or serum) is high. The stimulation by apo C-II is consequently less (1.5 to 2.5-fold) than with other types of emulsions.

To prepare such an emulsion, mix 25 mg unlabelled triolein (e.g., from a heptane solution containing 25 mg/mL) with ^{3}H-labelled triolein (~50 × 10^6 d.p.m.) in a round-bottom, 30 mm diameter glass vessel suitable for sonication. Evaporate solvent under N_2 at room temperature. Then add 1 mL 10 % (w/v) gum arabic in water (Sigma). Gum arabic takes some time to dissolve with magnetic stirring. Add 1.25 mL 1 M Tris-HCl buffer pH 8.5 and 2 mL water. Chill the vessel in ice water and sonicate for 10 minutes in a 50% pulsed mode (Soniprep 150, MSE, Crawley, Sussex, UK) with a 9.5 mm diameter flat tip probe at medium setting placed a few mm below the surface of the liquid. It is important to standardize conditions of vessel geometry, volume, tip placement, energy, and time. Inspect the emulsion. If oil droplets float on the surface, sonication is insufficient. Try other settings. The emulsion is now ready to be mixed with other constituents of the incubation medium. Use this emulsion on the same day it is prepared.

Zilversmit et al.[67] pointed to the possibility of dispersing triglyceride in glycerol with phospholipids as stabilizers. Nilsson-Ehle and Schotz[68] used this to develop a stable stock emulsion for assay of LPL. This convenient method is now widely used. In our laboratory, the most reproducible measurements of LPL are obtained with the commercial emulsion Intralipid® and manual titration of the released fatty acids. The sensitivity in such assays is too low for many applications. This can be overcome by incorporation of a labelled triglyceride into Intralipid by sonication. The activities obtained by quantitating release of labelled fatty acids are comparable to those obtained by titration. This indicates that the labelled triolein mixes well with the Intralipid lipids. The sonicated emulsion is stable for about 2 weeks. Intralipid 10% is an emulsion of soya bean triglycerides in egg yolk phosphatidyl choline used for parenteral nutrition. It contains 100 g triglycerides and 12 g phospholipid per liter. Presumably, other lipid emulsions for parental nutrition can be used.

To incorporate the labeled lipid, evaporate labelled triolein (~10^6 d.p.m.) under N_2 on the walls of a round-bottom, 30 mm diameter glass vessel suitable for sonication. Add 5 mL Intralipid (10%, Pharmacia & Upjohn, Stockholm, Sweden). Chill the vessel in ice water and sonicate for 10 minutes in a 50% pulsed mode (MSE Soniprep 150 at medium setting with a flat tip 9.5 mm probe placed a few mm below the surface of the liquid). As for the gum arabic emulsion, it is important to standardize conditions of vessel geometry, volume, tip placement, energy, and time. After sonication, the emulsion is less stable, but can be stored at 4° C for 1–2 weeks without change in substrate properties.

The reactions involved in lipase assays are complex. Triglycerides are sequentially hydrolyzed to diglycerides, monoglycerides, and free glycerol. The action on each of these intermediary products differs, due to properties of the enzyme's active site (low activity against 2-monoglycerides but high activity against 1,3-monoglycerides) and also because of the different physical properties of the products. Usually the rate-limiting step is hydrolysis of the first ester bond in the triglyceride.

Substrate Concentration

The relevant factor is the amount of lipid-water interface, not the total amount of emulsified lipid. One cannot use data on substrate requirements from the literature; one must determine this experimentally, because it depends on the physical properties of the home-made emulsion.

Albumin

Both LPL and HTGL are inhibited by fatty acids. It is therefore necessary to include albumin in the reaction mixture, to bind the fatty acids. Furthermore, albumin at concentrations of a few mg per mL is useful to prevent adsorption of the lipases to glass. The molar ratio of free fatty acids to albumin should not exceed 5:1 at any time. Incubation systems for hydrolysis of triglycerides usually contain 30–60 mg albumin per mL. For most purposes it is not necessary to use fatty acid-free albumin.

pH

The activity of both lipases is usually measured at alkaline pH (8.2–8.6) because the higher rate makes the assays more sensitive. It should be pointed out, however, that the enzymes have a relatively high activity also at physiological pH (7.4) which is approximately half of that observed at pH 8.5. Other aspects of the reaction may be sensitive to pH, such as lipid packing, lipid-protein interactions, and the rate at which partial glycerides/lysophospholipids are isomerized. Therefore, pH 7.4 is recommended for studies that explore physiological reactions, such as lipoprotein interconversions.

Temperature

In an early study,[69] it was noted that LPL-catalyzed release of fatty acids was linear with time at room temperature, but not at 37° C under the assay conditions used. This important observation has been overlooked in many subsequent studies. Unless there is a specific reason to use 37° C, such as studying lipid transitions, it is recommended that the incubation temperature be 25° C.

Buffer Composition

It is considered a characteristic of LPL, "the salt-sensitive lipase," that it is inhibited by 0.5–1 M NaCl. This is due to an irreversible denaturation of the enzyme molecule and depends on a combination of the high salt concentration and a high temperature (e.g., 37° C). If this is avoided, for instance by incubating at low temperature, the enzyme can exert full catalytic activity even in the presence of 1 M NaCl. For most purposes, NaCl concentrations of 0.05–0.15 result in optimal activity and stability of LPL for kinetic studies. The activity of HTGL, "the salt-resistant lipase," is not affected much by 1.0 M NaCl.

Activator

With triglyceride emulsions as substrates, the activity of LPL (but not of HTGL) is increased several fold by apo C-II. For assay purposes, whole serum or HDL can be used to provide activation. Similar results are obtained with plasma as with serum. Due to the presence of low lipase activities, the serum should be heat-inactivated at 56° C for 30 min. Serum from most mammals, with the exception of cows and guinea pigs, can probably be used, but the most common sources are fasting humans or rats. Due to individual variation in the amounts of activator, it is recommended that the laboratory prepare a large pool of serum and test out the optimal amount to be used in the assay (usually 5–10% v/v). The serum can be stored at –20° C for years.

Heparin

The LPL-heparin complex is more stable and soluble than the enzyme alone and is catalytically active.[70] Therefore, heparin is included in most buffers used for extraction of LPL from tissues and for incubation of the enzyme in kinetic studies. Plasma samples for analysis should preferentially be collected in heparinized tubes.

Selective Measurement of LPL and HTGL

There are two approaches to measurement of LPL and HTGL: either to use assay conditions which favor one of the enzymes, or to use antibodies that inhibit the activity of one of them. The activity of LPL can be readily suppressed by 1 M NaCl. The remaining activity, measured using the gum arabic–stabilized emulsion in the absence of serum or apo C-II, is a good measure of HTGL. We advocate the latter method. Note that the mechanism of suppression is an irreversible conformation change in LPL. For this to work, the pH should be relatively high (8.5–8.6), the temperature should be at least 25° C, and the emulsion should not contain phospholipids.

We advocate immunoinhibition of HTGL for routine assays of LPL. This is accomplished by mixing the sample with an appropriate amount of antiserum, or preferably immune IgG, and incubating for 2 h on ice. LPL in plasma or in tissue extracts in the heparin-detergent buffer does not lose appreciable activity during this time. Centrifugation before assay is not needed and does not change the results. As a control, incubate some samples after immunoinhibition under conditions used for HTGL determination. There should be little or no activity. Otherwise, one has to determine whether the immunoinhibition was complete (> 95%) and/or whether the LPL was fully suppressed by 1 M NaCl.

Sometimes there is a need to differentiate LPL from other lipases—in tissue homogenates, for instance. Some information can be obtained by testing the effects of including 1 M NaCl in the assay, and/or excluding serum (apo C-II). This should suppress the LPL activity. A more direct approach is to pretreat the enzyme source with antibodies to LPL.

For assay of LPL, we recommend the following method: Prepare a batch of assay medium which can then be stored in suitable aliquots at –20° C. The composition is 0.3 M Tris with 0.2 M NaCl, 0.02% (w/v) heparin and 12% (w/v) bovine serum albumin. Adjust the pH to 8.5 with HCl. Mix appropriate volumes of assay medium, heat-inactivated serum, and labelled emulsion at room temperature. This solution is stable for one day. A typical ratio of components is 10 parts assay medium, 1 part rat serum, and 1 part ^{3}H-labelled Intralipid. Pipette 120 µL into each assay tube. The total volume should be 200 µL. Hence, a maximum of 80 µL sample can be added. For plasma and tissue homogenates, one should preferably use less than 10 µL to avoid interference by other sample components. The rest of the volume can be made up with water. Incubate the tubes at 25° C for 5 minutes before adding the enzyme source. Continue incubation in a shaking water bath. For longer times (1–2 h), it may be necessary to cover the tubes to prevent evaporation. Run blank incubations (without lipase) for each assay and preferably also reference sample(s). Assay samples in duplicate or triplicate. Stop the reaction after the desired time by addition of solvents for extraction of fatty acids.[71, 72]

To assay HTGL, mix one batch of the gum arabic-stabilized emulsion with 2.5 mL each of 5 M NaCl and of 10 % (w/v) bovine serum albumin in water (titrated to pH 8 with NaOH, stored frozen). Add 3.25 mL water, for a total volume of 12.5 mL. Use on the same day only. Pipette 150 µL substrate into each tube. Add water and/or buffer to make 200 µL when the sample has been added. Incubate at 25° C for 5 minutes before the enzyme source is added. Continue as under assay for LPL.

Units

Unfortunately, several different units are used to express lipase activities. We advocate the definition of a mU as the release of 1 nmol fatty acid per minute at 25° C and pH 8.5. This is becoming the most frequently used unit.

Standardization of the Assay and Quality Control

Using the procedures described above, the intra-assay variation is usually ± 5%. However, due to the complex nature of the substrate, the inter-assay variation can be substantial: up to ±25%. It is important to quantify the specific radioactivity of the substrate accurately (d.p.m. per nmol fatty acid). As a quality control, one should occasionally determine the amount of fatty acids released in some samples by manual titration, and compare this to the release of fatty acids calculated from radioactivity. One should also check the efficiency of the extraction procedure for fatty acids by adding a known amount of labelled fatty acid to some samples and performing the assay procedure. It is advisable to include a reference sample in each assay and to use this to correct for between-assay variation. Whenever the reference sample activity deviates by more than 25% from the expected value, one should review the optimization of the assay.

Due to the instability of the enzymes, a good standard is hard to find. For LPL, we and others use bovine skim milk frozen in portions at –70° C. For HTGL, and for assays of LPL in human pre- or post-heparin plasma, a batch of human post-heparin plasma stored at –70° C is the best reference. Our experience is that the assay has to be kept under thorough control continuously, since many components of the system may vary. ✧

REFERENCES

1. Holmquist L, Karpe F, Nilsson-Ehle P, Packard CJ, Shepherd J. Lipoprotein metabolism in hepatic lipase deficiency: studies on the turnover of apo B and on the effect of hepatic lipase on high density lipoprotein. J Lipid Res 1989;30:1603–12.

2. Clay MA, Hopkins GJ, Ehnholm C, Barter PJ. The rabbit as an animal model of hepatic lipase deficiency. Biochim Biophys Acta 1989;1002:173–81.

3. Barter PJ. Enzymes involved in lipid and lipoprotein metabolism. Curr Opin Lipidol 1990;1:518–23.

4. Goldberg IJ. Lipoprotein lipase and lipolysis: central roles in lipoprotein metabolism and atherogenesis. J Lipid Res 1996;37:693–707.

5. Bensadoun A, Berryman DE. Genetics and molecular biology of hepatic lipase. Curr Opin Lipidol 1996;7:77–81.

6. Santamarina-Fojo S, Dugi KA. Structure, function and role of lipoprotein lipase in lipoprotein metabolism. Curr Opin Lipidol 1994;5:117–25.

7. Olivecrona G, Olivecrona T. Triglyceride lipases and atherosclerosis. Curr Opin Lipidol 1995;6:291–305.

8. Eisenberg S, Sehayek E, Olivecrona T, Vlodavsky I. Lipoprotein lipase enhances binding of lipoproteins to heparan sulfate on cell surfaces and extracellular matrix. J Clin Invest 1992;90:2013–21.

9. Beisiegel U. Receptors for triglyceride-rich lipoproteins and their role in lipoprotein metabolism. Curr Opin Lipidol 1995;6:117–22.

10. Bragdon JH, Gordon RS. Tissue distribution of C[14] after the intravenous injection of labeled chylomicrons and unesterified fatty acids in the rat. J Clin Invest 1958;37:574–78.

11. Hultin M, Savonen R, Olivecrona T. Chylomicron metabolism in rats: lipolysis, recirculation of triglyceride-derived fatty acids in plasma FFA, and fate of core lipids as analyzed by compartmental modelling. J Lipid Res 1996;37:1022–36.

12. Sniderman AD, Baldo A, Cianflone K. The potential role of acylation stimulating protein as a determinant of plasma triglyceride clearance and intracellular triglyceride synthesis. Curr Opin Lipidol 1992;3:202–7.

13. Frayn KN, Coppack SW, Fielding BA, Humphreys SM. Coordinated regulation of hormone-sensitive lipase and lipoprotein lipase in human adipose tissue *in vivo:* implications for the control of fat storage and fat mobilization. Advan Enzyme Regul 1995;35:163–78.

14. Farese RV, Jr., Yost TJ, Eckel RH. Tissue-specific regulation of lipoprotein lipase activity by insulin/glucose in normal-weight humans. Metabolism 1991;40:214–16.

15. Ottosson M, Vikman-Adolfsson K, Enerbäck S, Olivecrona G, Björntorp P. The effects of cortisol on the regulation of lipoprotein lipase activity in human adipose tissue. J Clin Endocrinol Metab 1994;79:820–25.

16. Ranganathan G, Vu D, Kern PA. Translational regulation of lipoprotein lipase by epinephrine involves a trans-acting binding protein interacting with the 3′ untranslated region. J Biol Chem 1997;272:2515–19.

17. Bergö M, Olivecrona G, Olivecrona T. Forms of lipoprotein lipase in rat tissues: in adipose tissue the proportion of inactive lipase increases on fasting. Biochem J 1996; 313:893–8.

18. Tornvall P, Olivecrona G, Karpe F, Hamsten A, Olivecrona T. Lipoprotein lipase mass and activity in plasma and their increase after heparin are separate parameters with different relations to plasma lipoproteins. Arterioscler Thromb Vasc Biol 1995;15: 1086–93.

19. Chevreuil O, Hultin M, Østergaard PB, Olivecrona T. Biphasic effects of low-molecular-weight and conventional heparins on chylomicron clearance in rats. Arterioscler Thromb 1993;13:1397–1403.

20. Brunzell JD. Familial lipoprotein lipase deficiency and other causes of the chylomicronemia syndrome. In: Scriver CR, Beaudet AL, Sly WS, Valle D., eds. Metabolic basis of inherited disease, 7th ed. New York: McGraw-Hill, 1995:1913–32.

21. Julien P, Vohl M-C, Lévesque G, Després J-P, Murthy MRV, Gagné C, et al. Effect of obesity on plasma triglyceride levels in familial lipoprotein lipase deficiency. [Abstract]. Atherosclerosis 1995;115(Suppl.):S8

22. Ma Y, Ooi TC, Liu M-S, Zhang H, McPherson R, Edwards AL, et al. High frequency of mutations in the human lipoprotein lipase gene in pregnancy-induced chylomicronemia: possible association with apolipoprotein E2 isoform. J Lipid Res 1994;35:1066–75.

23. Wilson DE, Emi M, Iverius P-H, Hata A, Wu LL, Hillas E, et al. Phenotypic expression of heterozygous lipoprotein lipase deficiency in the extended pedigree of a proband homozygous for a missense mutation. J Clin Invest 1990;86:735–50.

24. Coleman T, Seip RL, Gimble JM, Lee D, Maeda N, Semenkovich CF. COOH-terminal disruption of lipoprotein lipase in mice is lethal in homozygotes, but heterozygotes have elevated triglycerides and impaired enzyme activity. J Biol Chem 1995;270: 12518–25.

25. Babirak SP, Brown BG, Brunzell JD. Familial combined hyperlipidemia and abnormal lipoprotein lipase. Arterioscler Thromb 1992;12:1176–83.

26. Nevin DN, Brunzell JD, Deeb SS. The LPL gene in individuals with familial combined hyperlipidemia and decreased LPL activity. Arterioscler Thromb 1994;14:869–73.

27. Gagne E. Analysis of DNA changes in the LPL gene in patients with familial combined hyperlipidemia. Arterioscler Thromb 1994;14:1250–57.

28. Seed M, Mailly F, Vallance D, Doherty E, Winder A, Talmud P, et al. Lipoprotein lipase activity in patients with combined hyperlipidaemia. Clin Investig 1994;72:100–6.

29. Hegele RA, Little JA, Vezina C, Maguire GF, Tu L, Wolever TS, et al. Hepatic lipase deficiency: clinical, biochemical, and molecular genetic characteristics. Arterioscler Thromb 1993;13:720–8.

30. Karpe F, Olivecrona T, Walldius G, Hamsten A. Lipoprotein lipase in plasma after an oral fat load: relation to free fatty acids. J Lipid Res 1992;33:975–84.

31. Glaser DS, Yost TJ, Eckel RH. Preheparin lipoprotein lipolytic activities: relationship to plasma lipoproteins and postheparin lipolytic activities. J Lipid Res 1992;33:209–14.

32. Peterson J, Bengtsson-Olivecrona G, Olivecrona T. Mouse preheparin plasma contains high levels of hepatic lipase with low affinity for heparin. Biochim Biophys Acta 1986; 878:65–70.

33. Schoonderwoerd K, Hülsmann WC, Jansen H. Stabilization of liver lipase in vitro by heparin or by binding to non-parenchymal liver cells. Biochim Biophys Acta 1981; 665:317–21.

34. Chevreuil O, Hultin M, Østergaard P, Olivecrona T. Heparin-decasaccharides impair the catabolism of chylomicrons. Biochem J 1996;320:437–44.

35. Taskinen M-R, Kuusi T. Enzymes involved in triglyceride hydrolysis. In: Shepherd J., ed. Clinical endocrinology and metabolism: lipoprotein metabolism. London: W. B. Saunders, 1987:639–66

36. Tornvall P, Karpe F, Proudler A, Bavenholm P Landou C, Olivecrona T, et al. High-density lipoprotein: relations to metabolic parameters and severity of coronary artery disease. Metabolism: Clinical and Experimental 1996;45:1375–82.

37. Deckelbaum RJ, Olivecrona T, Eisenberg S. Plasma lipoproteins in hyperlipidemia: roles of neutral lipid exchange and lipase. In: Carlson LA, Olsson AD., eds. Treatment of hyperlipoproteinemia. New York: Raven Press, 1984:85–93.

38. Miesenböck G, Patsch JR. Postprandial hyperlipemia: the search for the atherogenic lipoprotein. Curr Opin Lipidol 1992;3:196-201.

39. Clay MA, Newnham HH, Barter PJ. Hepatic lipase promotes a loss of apolipoprotein A-I from triglyceride-enriched human high density lipoproteins during incubation in vitro. Arteriosclerosis 1991;11:415-22.

40. Watson TDG, Tan C-E, McConnell M, Clegg SK, Squires LF, Packard CJ. Measurement and physiological significance of lipoprotein and hepatic lipase activities in preheparin plasma. Clin Chem 1995;41:405-12.

41. Borensztajn J, Robinson DS. The effect of fasting on the utilization of chylomicron triglyceride fatty acids in relation to clearing factor lipase (lipoprotein lipase) releasable by heparin in the perfused rat heart. J Lipid Res 1970;11:111-17.

42. Liu G, Olivecrona T. Synthesis and transport of lipoprotein lipase in perfused guinea pig hearts. Am J Physiol 1992;263:H438-46.

43. Blanchette-Mackie EJ, Masuno H, Dwyer NK, Olivecrona T, Scow RO. Lipoprotein lipase in myocytes and capillary endothelium of heart: immunocytochemical study. Am J Physiol 1989;256:E818-28.

44. Saxena U, Klein MG, Goldberg IJ. Transport of lipoprotein lipase across endothelial cells. Proc Natl Acad Sci USA 1991;88:2254-8.

45. Ehnholm C, Schröder T, Kuusi T, Bång B, Kinnunen PKJ, Kahma K, et al. Studies on the effect of hepatectomy on pig post-heparin plasma lipases. Biochim Biophys Acta 1980;617:141-9.

46. Vilaró S, Llobera M, Bengtsson-Olivecrona G, Olivecrona T. Lipoprotein lipase uptake by the liver: localization, turnover, and metabolic role. Am J Physiol 1988;254:G711-22.

47. Taskinen M-R. Postprandial lipemia and lipoprotein lipase. In: Woodford FP, Davignon J, Sniderman A., eds. Atherosclerosis X. Amsterdam: Elsevier, 1995:758-62.

48. Jansen H, Hop W, Van Tol A, Bruschke AVG, Birkenhäger JC. Hepatic lipase and lipoprotein lipase are not major determinants of the low density lipoprotein subclass pattern in human subjects with coronary heart disease. Atherosclerosis 1994;107:45-54.

49. Campos H, Dreon DM, Krauss RM. Associations of hepatic and lipoprotein lipase activities with changes in dietary composition and low density lipoprotein subclasses. J Lipid Res 1995;36:462-72.

50. St-Amand J, Després J-P, Lemieux S, Lamarch B, Moorjani S, Prud'homme D, et al. Does lipoprotein or hepatic lipase activity explain the protective lipoprotein profile of premenopausal women? Metabolism 1995;44:491-8.

51. Jeppesen J, Hollenbeck CB, Zhou M-Y, Coulston AM, Jones C, Chen Y-DL, et al. Relation between insulin resistance, hyperinsulinemia, postheparin plasma lipoprotein lipase activity, and postprandial lipemia. Arterioscler Thromb Vasc Biol 1995;15:320-24.

52. Shimada M, Ishibashi S, Yamamoto K, Kawamura M, Watanabe Y, Gotoda T, et al. Overexpression of human lipoprotein lipase increases hormone-sensitive lipase activity in adipose tissue of mice. Biochem Biophys Res Commun 1995;211:761-6.

53. Liu M-S, Jirik FR, LeBoeuf RC, Henderson H, Castellani LW, Lusis AJ, et al. Alteration of lipid profiles in plasma of transgenic mice expressing human lipoprotein lipase. J Biol Chem 1994;269:11417-24.

54. Zsigmond E, Scheffler E, Forte TM, Potenz R, Wu W, Chan L. Transgenic mice expressing human lipoprotein lipase driven by the mouse metallothionein promoter: a phenotype associated with increased perinatal mortality and reduced plasma very low density lipoprotein of normal size. J Biol Chem 1994;269:18757-66.

55. Tsutsumi K, Inoue Y, Shima A, Murase T. Correction of hypertriglyceridemia with low high-density lipoprotein cholesterol by the novel compound NO-1886, a lipoprotein lipase-promoting agent, in STZ-induced diabetic rats. Diabetes 1995;44:414-17.

56. Simpson HS, Williamson CM, Olivecrona T, Pringle S, MacLean J, Lorimer AR, et al. Postprandial lipemia, fenofibrate and coronary artery disease. Atherosclerosis 1990; 85:193-202.

57. Föger B, Drexel H, Hopferwieser T, Miesenböck G, Ritsch A, Lechleitner M, et al. Fenofibrate improves postprandial chylomicron clearance in II B hyperlipoproteinemia. Clin Investig 1994;72:294–301.

58. Patsch JR, Prasad S, Gotto AM Jr., Patsch W. High density lipoprotein 2: relationship of the plasma levels of this lipoprotein species to its composition, to the magnitude of postprandial lipemia, and to the activities of lipoprotein lipase and hepatic lipase. J Clin Invest 1987;80:341–7.

59. Kuusi T, Ehnholm C, Viikari J, Härkönen R, Vartiainen E, Puska P, et al. Postheparin plasma lipoprotein and hepatic lipase are determinants of hypo-and hyperalphalipoproteinemia. J Lipid Res 1989;30:1117–26.

60. Miesenböck G, Patsch JR. Postprandial hyperlipemia: the search for the atherogenic lipoprotein. Curr Opin Lipidol 1992;3:196–201.

61. Karpe F, Tornvall P, Olivecrona T, Steiner G, Carlson LA, Hamsten A. Composition of human low density lipoprotein: effects of postprandial triglyceride-rich lipoproteins, lipoprotein lipase, hepatic lipase and cholesteryl ester transfer protein. Atherosclerosis 1993;98:33–49.

62. Miesenböck G, Hölzl B, Föger B, Brandstätter E, Paulweber B, Sanhofer F, et al. Heterozygous lipoprotein lipase deficiency due to a missense mutation as the cause of impaired triglyceride intolerance with multiple lipoprotein abnormalities. J Clin Invest 1992;91:448–55.

63. LaDu MJ, Kapsas H, Palmer WK. Regulation of lipoprotein lipase in adipose and muscle tissues during fasting. Am J Physiol Regul Integr Comp Physiol 1991;260:R953–9.

64. Olivecrona G, Hultin M, Savonen R, Skottova N, Lookene A, Tugrul Y, et al. Transport of lipoprotein lipase in plasma and lipoprotein metabolism. In: Woodford FP, Davignon J, Sniderman AD., eds. Atherosclerosis X. Amsterdam: Elsevier, 1995:250–53.

65. Vilella E, Joven J, Fernández M, Vilaro S, Brunzell JD, Olivecrona T, et al. Lipoprotein lipase in human plasma is mainly inactive and associated with cholesterol-rich lipoproteins. J Lipid Res 1993;34:1555–64.

66. Taskinen M-R. Lipoprotein lipase in hypertriglyceridemias. In: Borensztajn J., ed. Lipoprotein lipase. Chicago: Evener Publishers, 1987:201–28.

67. Corey JE, Zilversmit DB. Validation of a stable emulsion for the assay of lipoprotein lipase activity. J Lab Clin Med 1977;89:666–74.

68. Nilsson-Ehle P, Schotz MC. A stable, radioactive substrate emulsion for assay of lipoprotein lipase. J Lipid Res 1976;17:536–41.

69. Greten H, Levy RI, Fredrickson DS. A further characterization of lipoprotein lipase. Biochim Biophys Acta 1968;164:185–94.

70. Olivecrona T, Bengtsson-Olivecrona G. Heparin and lipases. In: Lane D, Lindahl U., eds. Heparin. London: Edward Arnold Publishers, 1989:335–61.

71. Belfrage P, Vaughan M. Simple liquid-liquid partition system for isolation of labeled oleic acid from mixtures with glycerides. J Lipid Res 1969;10:341–4.

72. Bengtsson-Olivecrona G, Olivecrona T. Assay of lipoprotein lipase and hepatic lipase. In: Converse CA, Skinner ER., eds. Lipoprotein analysis: a practical approach. New York: Oxford University Press, 1992:169–85.

73. Olivecrona T, Bengtsson-Olivecrona G. Lipoprotein lipase and hepatic lipase. In: Schettler G, Habenicht AJR., eds. Handbook of experimental pharmacology. Volume 109: Principles and treatment of lipoprotein disorders. Heidelberg: Springer-Verlag, 1993.

74. Olivecrona T, Bengtsson-Olivecrona G. Lipoprotein lipase from milk: the model enzyme in lipoprotein lipase research. In: Borensztajn J., ed. Lipoprotein lipase. Chicago: Evener Publishers, 1987:15–58.

Determination and Clinical Significance of Cholesterol Ester Transfer Protein

20

Christopher J. Fielding

BACKGROUND AND INTRODUCTION

❖   Cholesteryl ester transfer protein (CETP) is a 74-kda glycoprotein catalyzing the equilibration of nonpolar lipids (particularly triglyceride [TG] and cholesteryl ester [CE]) between plasma lipoprotein particles.[1, 2] Genomic and cDNA base sequences have been reported.[3, 4]

CETP is one member of a family of mammalian lipid transfer proteins including plasma phospholipid transfer protein (PLTP), lipopolysaccharide binding protein, and permeability increasing factor.[5] CETP mRNA is widely expressed in sites including adipose tissue, muscle, liver, and placenta. The major part of circulating CETP probably originates from the liver. It is possible that CETP plays an intracellular role in neutral lipid transfer between lipid droplets and other organelles; however, individuals with genetic CETP deficiency, who completely lack neutral lipid transfer activity in plasma, had no reported defect in cellular neutral lipid metabolism.[6] CETP may contribute to the transfer of phospholipids between plasma lipoproteins, although the greatest part of phospholipid transfer is now assigned to PLTP.[7] CETP is active in the "idle" exchange of CE between all lipoprotein classes. It is mainly because of CETP activity that the cholesteryl ester fatty acyl composition of very-low-density lipoproteins (VLDL), low-density lipoproteins (LDL), and high-density lipoproteins (HDL) is identical in human plasma. In terms of *net* lipid transfer, the exchange of HDL-CE for VLDL- and LDL-TG has the greatest magnitude.[8]

The clinical significance of CETP has been controversial.[9] This is in part, because the protein seems to play two separate roles in plasma lipid metabolism. When CETP catalyzes the net exchange of VLDL-TG for HDL-CE, the TG-rich HDL produced are a substrate for hepatic triglyceride lipase. Hydrolysis of this TG by hepatic lipase leads to a reduction in HDL "core" volume, accompanied by an excess of "surface" protein and phospholipid. HDL protein (apolipoprotein A-I [apo A-I]) is released. The small pre-beta-migrating HDL produced are an effective acceptor of free cholesterol (FC) unloaded from peripheral cells, and promote reverse cholesterol transport.[10] Other reactions also contribute to prebeta-HDL production. For example, the transfer of phospholipid to HDL by PLTP can displace pre-beta-migrating, lipid-poor apo A-I from HDL.[11] Nevertheless, on present evidence, the role of CETP in HDL metabolism would be considered anti-atherogenic, because of the potentially protective effect against cellular cholesterol accumulation.

The second product of the CETP reaction is a CE-enriched VLDL or LDL. VLDL newly secreted from the liver contains some CE, but this mass is significantly increased by CETP-mediated transfer from HDL. As a result, human LDL contain about twice the CE content (relative to LDL protein, apo B) as VLDL.[12] CE-enriched LDL react relatively poorly with hepatic LDL receptors.[13] As a result, increased levels of CETP would be expected to lead to the appearance of large CE-rich LDL. These "beta-VLDL" are usually considered pro-atherogenic. However, several other factors complicate this picture. Only part of VLDL is converted to LDL; the balance is removed by the liver as soon as TG hydrolysis is complete.[14] CE-rich VLDL bind apo E more effectively than normal VLDL.[15] Apo E-rich VLDL are cleared more efficiently than normal VLDL by hepatic LDL receptors.[16] This reaction sequence could counteract the effect of increased CETP activity, by decreasing the proportion of VLDL converted to LDL.

Large, CE-rich LDL with the expected properties are induced in cholesterol-fed lower primates.[17] CETP activity is increased in the plasma of these animals.[18] However, similar particles are not normally seen in human plasma. In fact, in the presence of documented coronary heart disease (CHD), small, dense LDL are typically observed.[19] Finally, in most individuals, the mass of CETP protein in plasma does not determine the rate of CETP activity.[20] Instead, this more often reflects the composition of the donor and acceptor lipoprotein classes, HDL and VLDL.

In summary, a cause-and-effect relationship between increased CETP concentrations and human atherosclerosis has not yet been convincingly shown. Consistent with this lack of relationship, the incidence of CHD in CETP-deficient human subjects was no less than that of controls.[21, 22]

CLINICAL RELEVANCE, FREQUENCY DISTRIBUTION, REFERENCE RANGES, AND INTERPRETATION

CETP protein concentration in normolipemic human plasma has been assayed with monoclonal antibodies by several laboratories. Mean values ranged from a high of 2.8 ± 0.6 mg/dL[23] to a low of 0.9 ± 0.4 mg/dL.[24] Most studies used the same proprietary monoclonal antibody (TP-2). The weighted mean in different studies was about 1.8 mg/dL. The plasma concentration of CETP protein was mildly elevated (less than twofold) in several hyperlipidemic syndromes, including combined hyperlipidemia, hypercholesterolemia, dysbetalipoproteinemia, and hyperchylomicronemia. The mean of plasma CETP mass in these groups was generally within two standard deviations of normal values.[25]

CETP mass in plasma has also been measured indirectly.[25, 26] This assay uses exogenous donor and recipient lipoproteins, usually HDL and LDL, which were isolated by ultracentrifugal flotation. In most studies, HDL was directly labeled with ^{3}H-cholesteryl oleate. The correlation coefficient of activity and mass assays was about 0.85.[25, 26] Unlabeled cholesteryl ester in plasma will dilute isotopically labeled HDL-CE by CETP-mediated exchange as a function of time. As a result, the kinetics of this assay are potentially quite complex. Because of difficulties in isolating and storing fully active CETP protein, indirect measurement of CETP mass is made relative to a normal plasma pool.

Endogenous plasma CETP activity reflects the net rate at which CE mass is transferred in native plasma samples between lipoprotein classes. This rate has been assayed enzymatically, as the rate of change in CE mass in donor and acceptor lipoproteins as a function of time.[27] It has also been measured isotopically, in plasma in which CE has been prelabeled to equilibrium.[28]

Much of the net transfer of CE represents an exchange with TG. It is still unclear whether CETP can catalyze unidirectional neutral lipid transfer. CETP also catalyzes the nonproductive (bidirectional) exchange of CE between lipoprotein particles. As a result, endogenous CETP activity is strongly influenced by plasma TG concentration. As plasma TG concentration rises, an increased proportion of nonproductive CE exchange is transformed to the productive transfer of CE for TG.

Endogenous CETP activity is conventionally defined as the net rate at which HDL-CE mass is transferred to VLDL and LDL. Using this definition, CETP rate can sometimes have a zero or negative value.[29] This reflects net transfer of VLDL and LDL-CE to HDL.

A second influence on CETP activity which is independent of CETP protein levels is the activity of lecithin:cholesterol acyltransferase (LCAT).[10] Essentially the whole of HDL-CE is generated by the LCAT. As a result, regardless of the level of CETP protein in plasma, the molar rate of CETP-mediated transfer of HDL-CE cannot exceed that of LCAT because HDL-CE levels would become zero. In normal fasting plasma, the molar rate of net transfer of HDL-CE to VLDL and LDL was 10–50% of the rate of LCAT (5–25 nmol/mL/h).[27, 30] The balance of LCAT-derived CE remains in HDL. It is probably removed by the liver via the selective transfer pathway.[31]

CETP activity is increased postprandially, but CETP mass was not significantly increased.[32, 33] The postprandial stimulation of CETP activity in normal plasma was coincident with, and probably entirely dependent on, the postabsorptive rise in VLDL-TG. In nephrotic syndrome[34] and combined hyperlipidemia,[35] hypertriglyceridemia was also associated with a change in CETP activity.

ADVANTAGE AND DISADVANTAGES OF CURRENT METHODOLOGIES

Measurements of plasma CETP mass have been carried out with monoclonal antibodies directed against the intact purified protein[23-25] or against a synthetic polypeptide representing residues 131–142 of the CETP amino acid sequence.[36] The mAb against CETP protein can be obtained from Dr. Y. L. Marcel, Ottawa Heart Institute, and the antipeptide mAb is available from Affinity Bioreagents, Golden, Colorado. Both assays use standard ELISA procedures[23] and measure CETP protein mass at 20–400 ng/well.

In view of the availability of CETP mABs, and the widespread use of automated immunoassay procedures in the analytical laboratory, assays of CETP mass using purified labeled exogenous lipoproteins offer no obvious advantage. These assays are empirical, difficult to standardize between laboratories, expensive in isotope costs, and time-consuming.

Measurement of CETP activity in native plasma, particularly if coupled with assay of LCAT activity, offers insight into the flow of cholesterol between plasma lipoproteins not available from other procedures. It would be interesting to make measurements of this kind under conditions where plasma lipoprotein concentrations were modified, for example during cholesterol lowering by diet or drugs. Three methodologies have been described. Two involve the enzymatic measurement of CE mass in HDL or VLDL+LDL as a function of time. The third measures the movement of ^{3}H-cholesteryl esters in prelabeled plasma.

Enzymatic Method 1[30]

The principle of this method is that when LCAT activity is inhibited, total CE in plasma is unchanged during incubation at 37° C. The CETP-mediated transfer of CE from HDL to VLDL+LDL can be conveniently determined as the rate of decrease in HDL-CE mass. This can be measured in a standard laboratory chemistry analyzer as the difference between total and free cholesterol in the soluble (HDL) fraction of plasma following precipitation of VLDL and LDL with heparin-MnCl$_2$ or MgCl$_2$-dextran sulfate.[36] This assay depends on the assumption that CETP activity is independent of HDL-CE mass, and the accumulation of CE in VLDL, over the period of assay. It also assumes that CETP activity is unaffected by the inhibition of LCAT. In practice, rates are often only briefly linear, as the compositional gradient between HDL and VLDL becomes dissipated as a function of time, and in the absence of hepatic lipase activity.

Enzymatic Method 2[27]

The principle of this method is that the increase in CE measured in plasma incubated *in vitro* as a result of LCAT activity is associated with an equivalent molar *decrease* in FC. The rate of CETP-mediated transfer of CE from HDL to VLDL and LDL is then the difference between the rate of *decrease* in FC in whole plasma, and the rate of *increase* of CE in HDL, as a function of time.

$$
\begin{aligned}
\text{Molar CETP activity} &= [\text{Total increase in plasma CE}] - [\text{Increase in HDL-CE}] \\
&= [\text{Decrease in plasma FC}] - [\text{Increase in HDL-CE}] \\
&= [(\text{Initial plasma FC} - \text{final plasma FC})] - [(\text{final HDL-TC} \\
&\quad - \text{final HDL-FC}) - (\text{initial HDL-TC} - \text{initial HDL-FC})]
\end{aligned}
$$

where CE is cholesteryl ester, FC is free cholesterol, HDL is high-density lipoprotein, and TC is total cholesterol,

While these measurements can all be made with a standard laboratory chemistry analyzer, the variances are additive. Six assays are needed at each time point, compared to the four needed in the first enzymatic method. Nevertheless, this assay provides unique information on the interplay between the LCAT and CETP reactions.

Isotopic Method[28]

Plasma FC is pre-equilibrated with ^{3}H-FC in the presence of a sulfhydryl inhibitor of LCAT, to prevent synthesis of labeled CE during equilibration. LCAT activity is restored by adding excess mercaptoethanol or dithiothreitol. A portion of the labeled CE synthesized is transferred by CETP to VLDL+LDL. At intervals, total labeled CE, and labeled CE in VLDL+LDL are determined. Because FC is also labeled in this method, esterified and ^{3}H-FC must be separated by thin-layer chromatography prior to determination of CETP activity.

This assay relies on the assumption that the activity of CETP, and the gradient of CE between HDL and VLDL, are not modified by the pre-equilibration of plasma with ^{3}H-FC in the presence of DTNB.

DISCUSSION OF RECOMMENDED METHODS

For determination of CETP mass, immunoassay using available reagents is clearly preferable to the less direct isotopic method. Each of the three methods to determine CETP activity gave qualitatively similar results in individual studies in the assay of normal plasma, but there has been to date no systematic comparison between them, either with normal or with hyperlipidemic plasma samples. Methodological details are given in the individual references cited. ✧

REFERENCES

1. Tall A. Plasma lipid transfer proteins. Ann Rev Biochem 1995;64:235-57.
2. Lagrost L. Regulation of cholesteryl ester transfer protein (CETP) activity: review of in vitro and in vivo studies. Biochim Biophys Acta 1994;1215:209-36.
3. Drayna D, Jarnagin AS, McLean J, Henzel W, Kohr W, Fielding C, Lawn R. Cloning and sequencing of human cholesteryl ester transfer protein cDNA. Nature 1987;327: 632-4.
4. Agellon L, Quinet E, Gillette T, Drayna D, Brown M, Tall AR. Organization of the human cholesteryl ester transfer gene. Biochemistry 1990;29:1372-6.
5. Day JR, Albers JJ, Lofton-Day CE, Gilberg TL, Ching AFT, et al. Complete cDNA encoding human phospholipid transfer protein from human endothelial cells. J Biol Chem 1994; 269:9388-91.
6. Inazu A, Brown ML, Hesler CB, Agellon LB, Koizumi J, Takata K, Moruhama Y, et al. Increased high density lipoprotein levels caused by a common cholesteryl ester transfer gene mutation. N Engl J Med 1990;323:1234-8.
7. Speijer H, Groener JEM, van Ramshorst E, van Tol A. Different locations of cholesteryl ester transfer protein and phospholipid transfer protein activities in plasma. Atherosclerosis 1991;90:159-68.
8. Morton RE, Zilversmit DB. Interrelationship of lipids transferred by the lipid transfer protein isolated from human lipoprotein-deficient plasma. J Biol Chem 1983; 258: 11751-7.
9. Fielding CJ, Havel RJ. Cholesteryl ester transfer protein: friend or foe? J Clin Invest 1996 97:2687-8.
10. Fielding CJ, Fielding PE. Molecular physiology of reverse cholesterol transport. J Lipid Res 1995;36:211-28.
11. Von Eckardstein A, Jauhiainen M, Huang YD, Metso J, Langer C, Pussinen P, Wu SL, et al. Phospholipid-transfer protein mediated conversion of high density lipoprotein generates prebeta(1) HDL. Biochim Biophys Acta 1996;1301:255-62.
12. Fielding PE, Ishikawa Y, Fielding CJ. Apolipoprotein E mediates binding of normal very low density lipoprotein to heparin but is not required for high affinity receptor binding. J Biol Chem 1989;264:12462-6.
13. Schechtman G, Boerboom LE, Hannah J, Howard BV. Dietary fish oil decreases low density lipoprotein clearance in nonhuman primates. Am J Clin Nutr 1996;64:215-21.

14. Kesaniemi YA, Vega G, Grundy SM. Kinetics of apolipoprotein B in normal and hypertri-glyceridemic man: review of current data. In: Berman M, Grundy SM, Howard BV, eds. Lipoprotein kinetics and modelling. New York: Academic Press, 1982:181–205.

15. Pagnan A, Havel RJ, Kane JP, Kotite L. Characterization of human very low density lipoproteins containing two electrophoretic populations: double prebeta lipoproteinemia and primary dysbetalipoproteinemia. J Lipid Res 1977;18:613–22.

16. Windler EET, Kovanen PT, Chao YS, Brown MS, Havel RJ, Goldstein JL. The estradiol-stimulated lipoprotein receptor of rat liver: a binding site that mediates the uptake of rat lipoproteins containing apolipoproteins B and E. J Biol Chem 1980;255:10464–71.

17. Tall AR, Small DM, Atkinson D, Rudel L. Studies on structure of low density lipoprotein isolated from *Macaca fascicularis* fed an atherogenic diet. J Clin Invest 1978;62:1354–63.

18. Quinet E, Tall AR, Ramakrishnan R, Rudel L. Plasma lipid transfer protein as a deter-minant of the atherogenicity of monkey plasma lipoproteins. J Clin Invest 1991;87:1559–66.

19. Krauss RM. Low-density lipoproteins and coronary artery disease. Am J Cardiol 1995;75:53B–57B.

20. Mann CJ, Yen FT, Grant AM, Bihain BE. Mechanism of plasma cholesteryl ester transfer in hypertriglyceridemia. J Clin Invest 1991;88:2059–66.

21. Hirano KS, Yamashita S, Kuga Y, Sakai N, Nozahi S, Kihara T, Arai K, et al. Atherosclerotic disease in marked hyperalphalipoproteinemia: combined reduction of cholesteryl ester transfer protein and hepatic lipase. Arterio Thromb Vasc Dis 1995;15:1840–56.

22. Zhong S, Sharp DS, Grove JS, Bruce C, Yano K, Curb JB, Tall AR. Increased coronary artery disease in Japanese-American men with mutation in the cholesteryl ester transfer protein gene despite increased HDL levels. J Clin Invest 1996;97:2917–23.

23. Glenn KC, Melton MA. Quantification of cholesteryl ester transfer protein: activity and immunochemical assays. Methods Enzymol 1996;263:339–51.

24. Guyard-Dangrement V, Lagrost L, Gambert P, Lallemand C. Competitive enzyme-linked immunoabsorbent assay of the human cholesteryl ester transfer protein. Clin Chim Acta 1995;231:147–60.

25. McPherson R, Mann CJ, Tall AR, Hogue M, Martin L, Milne RW, Marcel YL. Plasma concentrations of cholesteryl ester transfer protein in hyperlipoproteinemia. Arterio Thromb 1991;11:797–804.

26. Tato F, Vega GL, Tall AR, Grundy SM. Relation between cholesteryl ester transfer protein activities and lipoprotein cholesterol in patients with hypercholesterolemia and combined hyperlipidemia. Arterio Thromb Vasc Biol 1995;15:112–20.

27. Fielding CJ, Havel RJ, Todd KM, Yeo KE, Schloetter MC, Weinberg V, Frost PH. Effects of dietary cholesterol and fat saturation on plasma lipoproteins in an ethnically diverse population of healthy young men. J Clin Invest 1995;95:611–18.

28. Channon KM, Clegg RJ, Bhatnagar D, Ishola M, Arrol S, Durrington PN. Investigation of lipid transfer in human serum leading to the development of an isotopic method for the determination of endogenous cholesterol esterification and transfer. Atheroscle-rosis 1990;80:217–26.

29. Van Tol A, Schenk LM, Groener JEM. Net mass transfer of cholesteryl esters from low density lipoproteins to high density lipoproteins in plasma from normolipemic subjects. Arterio Thromb Vasc Biol 1994;11:55–63.

30. Fielding PE, Fielding CJ, Havel RJ, Kane JP, Tun P. Cholesterol net transport, esterifi-cation and transfer in human hyperlipemic plasma. J Clin Invest 1983;71:449–60.

31. Acton S, Rigotti A, Lanschutz KT, Xu S, Hobbs HH, Krieger MM. Identification of scavenger receptor SB-1 as a high density lipoprotein receptor. Science 1996;271:518–20.

32. Castro GR, Fielding CJ. Effects of postprandial lipemia on plasma cholesterol metab-olism. J Clin Invest 1985;75:874–82.

33. Tall A, Sammett D, Granot E. Mechanisms of enhanced cholesteryl ester transfer from high density lipoproteins to apolipoprotein B-containing lipoproteins during alimentary lipemia. J Clin Invest 1986;77:1163–72.

34. Moulin P, Appekl GB, Ginsberg HN, Tall AR. Increased concentration of plasma cholesteryl ester transfer protein in nephrotic syndrome: role in dyslipoproteinemia. J Lipid Res 1992;33:1817-22.
35. Guerin ME, Bouchert E, Dolphin PJ, Chapman MJ. Absence of cholesteryl ester transfer protein-mediated cholesteryl ester mass transfer from high density lipoprotein to low density lipoprotein particles is a major feature of combined hyperlipidemia. Eur J Clin Invest 1996;26:485-94.
36. Thomas AP, Cumming RI, Jones C, Thomas RC, Pleasant KT, Barakat H. Mouse monoclonal antipeptide antibodies specific for cholesteryl ester transfer protein (CETP). Hybridoma 1996;15:359-64.

Lecithin:Cholesterol Acyltransferase

21

P. Haydn Pritchard

INTRODUCTION

❖   Lecithin:cholesterol acyltransferase (LCAT) is the enzyme responsible for the synthesis of the majority of plasma cholesteryl esters in plasma by the transfer of fatty acid from phosphatidylcholine to the 3-hydroxyl group of cholesterol (see Figure 21–1).

A great deal of information on the biochemistry and pathophysiology of this enzyme is now available, and it has been the topic of numerous reviews.[1, 2, 3] It is generally believed that LCAT regulates the transport of cholesterol between extravascular and intravascular pools. In the theoretical pathway, known as reverse cholesterol transport, cholesterol is moved from peripheral tissues to the liver for catabolism. The esterification of cholesterol by LCAT in plasma serves to maintain a chemical concentration gradient for unesterified cholesterol between peripheral cells and the plasma.[4] LCAT therefore plays a central role in the initial steps of this process. Studies on patients with the familial LCAT deficiency have clearly identified the central role this enzyme plays in plasma cholesterol homeostasis.[5] However, the exact role LCAT plays in reverse cholesterol transport is far from clear.

The purpose of this chapter is to describe how determination of LCAT activity in plasma can be used in the differential diagnosis of familial LCAT deficiency and its variant, fish-eye disease.[6, 7] In addition, the chapter discusses how LCAT activity might be used as a biological probe to predict HDL particle size and, potentially, the risk of coronary artery disease (CAD).[8]

BIOCHEMISTRY OF LECITHIN:CHOLESTEROL ACYLTRANSFERASE

LCAT is a glycoprotein with an apparent molecular weight of 67 kD, and the human enzyme has been purified to homogeneity in a number of laboratories. In plasma. LCAT protein is bound to high-density lipoproteins (HDL) and it esterifies cholesterol primarily in this class of lipoproteins. However, several investigators have provided evidence that plasma or recombinant LCAT may act directly on lower density lipoproteins.[9-11] The major structural protein of HDL, apolipoprotein (apo) A-I, is believed to be the principal activator of LCAT. In addition, our observation that 90% of LCAT

Figure 21–1 ✧ Cholesterol Esterification by Lecithin:Cholesterol Acyltransferase

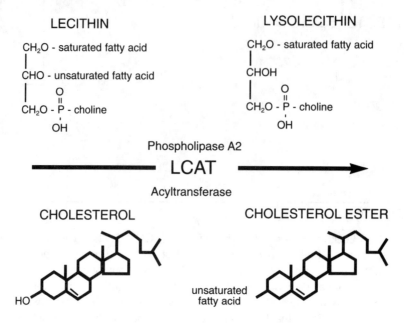

activity is removed from plasma by anti-A-I immunoaffinity column chromatography[12] suggests a physical association and functional interdependence.

The gene for the human LCAT has been sequenced.[13, 14] It consists of 6 exons and 5 introns and encodes an mRNA of 1,550 nucleotides, which is expressed primarily in the liver. The mature protein contains 416 amino acids and a hydrophobic lead sequence of 24 amino acids. Amino acid sequence analysis indicates homology with the active site of a variety of other lipases.[15] This suggests that serine 181 is the reactive residue of LCAT. Francone and Fielding[16] used site-directed mutagenesis and *in vitro* expression to probe the role of these two serine residues. Exchange of serine 181 for either threonine, glycine, or alanine resulted in the complete loss of activity. Substitution of serine 216 with threonine resulted in only a modest decrease in LCAT activity. Remarkably, substitution of serine 216 by an alanine residue resulted in a ten-fold increase in activity. Yang and Pownall[17] have analyzed the secondary structure based on the amino acid sequence and the identification of disulfide bridges. Spectro-fluorometric studies have demonstrated that a substantial portion of the tryptophan residues are exposed on the outside of porcine LCAT. These hydrophobic residues are usually assumed to be within inner domains of proteins. The high degree of glycosylation may account for this unusual structure. The LCAT protein is readily soluble in water, yet its hydropathic index is far greater than that of the plasma apolipoproteins such as apo A-I. The carbohydrate groups of LCAT may therefore play a major role in the structure and function of this protein. We have demonstrated by site-directed mutagenesis[18, 19] that LCAT is glycosylated at all four potential N-glycosylation sites. No data exists on the tertiary structure of LCAT, and no crystals of purified plasma LCAT have been reported in the literature.

MOLECULAR PATHOLOGY OF THE LCAT GENE

It is now 35 years since a Norwegian patient with familial lecithin:cholesterol acyltransferase (LCAT) deficiency was described by Kare Norum and collaborators. Since that time, the study of LCAT deficiency has received a great deal of attention from clinical and basic scientists. These research efforts have provided information on the clinical presentation and laboratory findings in affected individuals which have led to a better understanding of the pathological changes that are common in this rare yet instructive disease process. Accordingly, a number of review articles have been published.[4, 20, 21]

Familial LCAT deficiency is characterized biochemically by the absence of LCAT activity in plasma. This results in a grossly abnormal lipoprotein structure and, most significantly, HDL deficiency. Extensive genetic studies have clearly demonstrated that both LCAT deficiency and its related disorder, fish-eye disease, are caused by one of a number of mutations that occur within the LCAT gene. In affected individuals, LCAT in plasma is either absent, present but inactive, or present but dysfunctional.[20]

Over the last ten years, several laboratories have reported the gene defects that appear to be causative for LCAT deficiency and fish-eye disease. In our recent review[20] we identified all the published mutations of the LCAT gene and classified them according to the biochemical phenotype. The causative nature of these mutations has been established from the fact that none of these defects have been identified in a normal population and, in most cases, the observed mutation was the only one found on each allele analyzed. The absolute assignment of these mutations to either LCAT deficiency or fish-eye disease is not straightforward, and caution should be used in such a segregation. This is especially true in cases where the clinical phenotype appears to be caused by compound heterozygosity. In the first instance, however, the relationship between the structural defect and the function of LCAT is more easily studied in patients who are homozygous for a single genetic defect.

In general, mutations which are likely to have a major effect on the structure of LCAT, such as frame shifts, premature stop codons, or the introduction of a proline residue, appear to be associated with a near absence of LCAT enzyme protein in plasma; consequently, LCAT activity is absent. By contrast, single amino acid changes are more often associated with higher levels of LCAT mass and activity. The ability of some LCAT mutants to utilize lipoproteins other than HDL to synthesize cholesteryl esters, as reflected by a higher proportion of endogenous activity, is directly related to the clinical phenotype. In addition, mutations of this type, particularly the fish-eye disease defects, would not be expected to disrupt the structural integrity of the catalytic site but may represent abnormalities associated with the binding of LCAT to HDL. It is possible that this class of mutation may prevent LCAT from making a conformational change which is necessary for normal interaction with HDL but not with LDL. Several mutations have been identified in compound heterozygotes, indicating that the number of mutations of the LCAT gene is greater than originally predicted.

The number of different molecular defects identified in the LCAT gene so far is consistent with heterogeneity of the phenotypic expression seen in these disorders. However, it is likely that the additional effects of the environment and other genes will also influence the expression of the clinical and biochemical phenotypes. The presence of widely spaced mutations throughout the LCAT gene, and the knowledge that the sequence of the LCAT gene is virtually conserved in humans, suggest that the normal function of LCAT is very sensitive to changes throughout its primary amino acid sequence From the biochemical analysis of fish-eye disease defects, it appears that LCAT has at least two functionally important domains, the catalytic center and the recognition site for HDL substrates. However, without the knowledge of the three-dimensional structure of this protein and the definition of specific structural domains, it remains difficult to resolve how mutations that are seemingly very close to one another can result in dramatic differences in the properties of this enzyme.

TYPES OF ASSAYS USED IN THE ASSESSMENT OF LCAT ACTIVITY

The three assays for the measurement of LCAT activity described below were established initially for the differential diagnosis of HDL deficiency syndromes. We have previously reported a process for investigating such conditions; the discussion herein is confined to the specific methods used. It is important, however, that the investigator be clear in understanding the different types of assays used and the limitations of the results obtained. This is especially important in choosing the correct assay to use for studying LCAT activity in patients who are not being investigated for LCAT deficiency syndromes. A summary of the methods and their uses is presented in Table 21–1.

Table 21–1 ✧ Summary of Methods Used to Measure Cholesterol Esterification

Assay	Source of LCAT	Substrate	Interpretive Use	Comments
LCAT Activity	plasma	exogenous HDL analog	Determination of homozygous or heterozygous LCAT deficiency	Activity generally reflects the amount of wild type LCAT in plasma.
Cholesterol Esterification Rate (CER)	plasma	endogenous lipoproteins	Low normal activities in the absence of LCAT activity are diagnostic for fish-eye disease.	This method has limited use with the exception of differential diagnosis of LCAT deficiency syndromes. The method likely overestimates the true molar rate of esterification in plasma.
Fractional Esterification Rate in HDL (FER$_{HDL}$)	Phosphotungstic acid-treated plasma (i.e., plasma which has been depleted of VLDL and LDL)	HDL in plasma	Activity measure is proportional to the relative amount of small HDL particles.	Potentially, a highly informative assay. High activities are associated with small HDL, low levels of HDL, and the presence or risk of CAD.

LCAT Activity

In this assay, the methods employed are used to define the activity of LCAT in plasma using an exogenous substrate (specifically an HDL analogue) which has been labeled with ^{3}H-cholesterol. The results obtained are generally equivalent to the amount of LCAT enzyme present in the plasma. In most individuals, the LCAT activity measured by this method varies very little between individuals. The assay is based on the ability of a sample of plasma to esterify ^{3}H-cholesterol in an exogenously provided analog of HDL which also contains a known amount of unlabelled unesterified cholesterol (UC), phosphatidylcholine, and apo A-I. The calculation of the activity assumes that during the incubation, the ^{3}H-cholesterol does not equilibrate with the endogenous cholesterol pool of the plasma sample. This is generally acceptable for most individuals, but isotope dilution might occur in samples with very high lipid levels. Such problems can be exacerbated by the precipitation of LDL and VLDL by phosphotungstic acid treatment of the plasma prior to the addition of the substrate. Since greater than 95% of the LCAT protein is bound to HDL or is free in plasma, the LCAT is not significantly reduced by removal of the less dense lipoproteins.

Cholesterol Esterification Rate (CER)

In this assay, the rate of observed cholesterol ester synthesis is a function of both the amount and activity of LCAT in plasma, together with the endogenous plasma lipoprotein substrate composition and properties. The principle of the assay is straight-forward. The sample of plasma is equilibrated with a trace amount of ^{3}H-cholesterol, incubated at 37° C, and the amount of ^{3}H-cholesterol ester produced is measured as a function of the total radioactivity. This fractional rate of esterification depends on a number of factors, most importantly the availability of the ^{3}H-cholesterol for esterification by LCAT. Thus, if the plasma sample has high levels of total cholesterol (and hence of unesterified cholesterol), the relative rate of esterification will fall since proportionally more of the cholesterol will be less available for esterification due to its location in larger lipoproteins. This "isotope dilution effect" also has impact on the calculated rate of (endogenous) cholesterol esterification.

   In the calculation described below,[7] the CER is calculated from the fractional esterification rate (FER) and the total amount of unesterified cholesterol in the plasma sample. This calculation makes the assumption that all molecules of cholesterol are equally available for esterification during the incubation. This is not accurate and the true rate of esterification is likely far lower than that estimated by this method. In my opinion, the only method that can definitively measure the true rate of esterification is one which chemically measures the increase in cholesterol esters or the decrease in unesterified cholesterol during the incubation. Such methods are not yet available. Thus, I believe that the primary use of measuring LCAT activity and the CER is in the differential diagnosis of LCAT deficiency syndromes.

FER$_{HDL}$

As indicated above, all assays of LCAT function that use ^{3}H-cholesterol as a marker for the esterification of the total UC pool in the assay may yield erroneous results.

This fact was observed by Dobiasova, who correctly identified the fraction esterification rate (FER) as having great potential for the study of cholesterol esterification in individuals who are not being investigated for LCAT deficiency syndromes.[6, 22-25] Dobiasova's strategy has been to measure the FER in only the HDL fraction of plasma. This is achieved by removal of the lower density lipoproteins by precipitation with phosphotungstic acid prior to labeling the endogenous lipoproteins with ^{3}H-cholesterol. Thus, all of the radiolabel is confined to the HDL particles and the assumption that all of the radiotracer is available for esterification is more valid. This has revealed more significant changes in apparent LCAT activity in conditions where there is proven CAD or increased risk of disease. Specifically, the FER_{HDL} is significantly higher in patients with CAD or at risk of CAD from hyperlipidemia or hypertension. In contrast, octogenarians who have no evidence of CAD have very low levels, as do women compared to age-matched men.

These changes in FER_{HDL} appear to be related to the size distribution of the HDL, i.e., the smaller the size of the HDL particles, the higher the FER_{HDL}. This makes sense since LCAT prefers to esterify cholesterol in smaller particles. This unique property of LCAT can be used as a biological probe for the estimation of lipoprotein particle size. Since smaller HDL particles are seen in patients at risk of CAD, this assay may merely be a measure of size heterogeneity of HDL rather than reflect a true increase in the rate of cholesterol esterification in the plasma of such subjects. This notion, however, should not be forgotten: If the high FER_{HDL} does indeed reflect a high endogenous esterification rate in the HDL fraction, this finding disagrees with the generally accepted opinion that LCAT activity is beneficial to the process of reverse cholesterol transport. Such a paradox requires further investigation.

METHODS

LCAT Activity

This assay uses ethanolosome (proteoliposome) substrates to measure LCAT activity in plasma. The results obtained generally reflect the amount of LCAT protein in plasma and hence do not vary greatly between normal individuals. A normal range of 25–35 nmol/h/mL plasma can be expected; however, this *must* be established in-house since preparations of apo A-I vary in their ability to activate LCAT. Both familial LCAT activity and fish-eye disease will give values < 2 nmol/h/mL. Heterozygotes for both disorders will be approximately 50% of normal. Usually, an LCAT of < 20 nmol/h/mL in a first-degree relative of a patient with LCAT deficiency or fish-eye disease will be indicative of the heterozygous state. Care should be taken in interpreting low (but not absent) LCAT activity since this can also be associated with extremely high triglyceride levels or with poor sample storage. It is crucial that the samples have been frozen only once prior to analysis.

Stock Solutions and Equipment

✥ Egg yolk phosphatidylcholine (EYPC): Sigma Type III-E, 5 mg/mL in absolute ethanol. Store at –20° C.

❖ Unesterified cholesterol (UC): Sigma CH-S, 1 mg/mL in absolute ethanol. Store at −20° C.

❖ Tritiated unesterified cholesterol ([7(n)-^{3}H] cholesterol, 1 m Ci/mL) (Amersham Catalog No. TRK 122).

❖ Apo A-I (purified by PBE 94 chromatofocusing), 1.5 mg/mL in 0.15 mol/L NaCl, 1 mmol/L EDTA, 0.03% azide. Store at 4° C.

❖ Assay buffer: 10 mmol/L Tris-HCl, pH 7.4 (1.211 g/L), 5 mmol/L EDTA (1.861 g/L), 0.15 mol/L NaCl (8.783 g/L). Store at 4° C.

❖ 8% BSA: 0.8 of BSA (essentially fatty acid free) dissolved in 10 mL assay buffer. Store at 4° C.

❖ 0.1 M β-mercaptoethanol: 35 μL undiluted β-mercaptoethanol in 5 mL freshly made assay buffer

❖ UC/CE standard: 20 mg cholesterol and 20 mg cholesteryl oleate (or palmitate) 98% pure in 10 mL chloroform.

❖ TLC plates: Merck 20 × 20 cm silica gel 60 F_{254}.

❖ Amicon ultrafiltration cell, model 12, and Amicon YM30 membranes.

❖ Fisher disposable culture tubes (borosilicate glass, Catalog No. 14-961-26).

Production of Ethanolosomes

1. Mix 260 μL EYPC, 150 μL UC, 12 μL ^{3}H-UC (1 m Ci/mL) in a 12 × 75 mm test tube and dry under nitrogen gas. This gives a PC:UC molar ratio of 4:1.

2. Place 10 mL of assay buffer in a test tube. Dissolve the dried lipid residue in 125 μL absolute ethanol. Take this up in a 1 mL syringe with a small gauge needle (> 25) and, while vortexing, inject this solution in the 10 mL assay buffer.

3. Concentrate the solution on an Amicon YM-30 membrane:

4. Place the Amicon ultrafiltration cell (model 12) on a stirrer.

5. Place a YM-30 membrane (carefully check that the membrane is intact!) in the ultrafiltration cell, shiny part up. (Be careful. The filter is very fragile.)

6. Wash the membrane twice with 1 volume Milli-Q water (MQ) under nitrogen pressure of ± 18–20 psi (with slow gas flow and slow stirring).

7. After the second wash step, apply the sample solution and let the sample flow through (under the same conditions as for wash steps) until no more than 2 mL is left on the membrane. Collect the buffer which flows through.

8. Take up the remaining 2 mL using a pipette fitted with a small piece of rubber tubing to prevent damage to the membrane.

9. Store the membrane in 70% ethanol.

10. Adjust to a final volume of 2.5 mL with assay buffer. This solution should be water clear or slightly turbid.

11. Check that all activity is retained in the sample by counting 10 μL of the filtered sample solution and 10 μL of the "flow-through."

12. Store ethanolosomes at 4° C and use within 14 days.

Assay Procedure

1. Run duplicates for each sample, including quality controls (15 μL serum).

2. Determine the number of samples to be measured. Make a premix containing liposomes, apo A-I, and assay buffer, according to Table 21-2.

Table 21-2 ❖ Assay Parameters and Conditions	
Liposomes	30 μL
Apo A-I	± 10 μL*
Assay buffer	85 μL
BSA/β-mercaptoethanol mix	60 μL
Plasma sample	15 μL
Incubation temperature	37° C
Incubation time	30 minutes

*The amount of apo A-I to be used depends on the optimal activation of the apo A-I preparation, which varies from batch to batch.

3. Add 100 μL of the premix to each test tube and incubate for 30 minutes at 37° C to allow for possible association of apo A-I with liposomes. Do not place the samples on ice after incubation; leave them at room temperature.

4. Make a mixture of 5 volumes 8% BSA and 1 volume 0.1 mol/L β-mercaptoethanol (5:1 ratio), enough for all samples (see Table 21-2). Add 60 μL of this mixture to each tube.

5. Add 15 μL of plasma sample to each tube and incubate at 37° C for the time indicated in Table 21-2.

6. Terminate the reaction by adding 1 mL of 100% ethanol. Leave the samples at room temperature for 15 minutes.

7. Vortex the samples and centrifuge at 4,000 rpm for 20 minutes at room temperature in a standard table-top centrifuge to separate phases.

8. Pour the liquid phase in new test tubes and evaporate to dryness under N_2.

9. While the samples are drying, set up a glass tank for the chromatography of TLC plates. Make a mixture of 105 mL petroleum ether, 18 mL diethyl ether, and 1.56 mL acetic acid. Mix well, pour into the tank and close the lid tightly to obtain saturation in the tank.

       Caution: Pour in the middle, not on the wall, and do not apply grease to the lid of the tanks.

10.   Prepare the TLC plates: Mark the 1.5, 9.0, 10.0, 11.0, and 18.5 cm points on two ends of the plates. Draw corresponding lines by connecting the points (the middle line is used to cut the plate in half.) Mark 2.5 cm segments for each line, for 8 segments per plate.

11.   When the samples are completely dry, add 10 µL UC/CE standard and 50 µL of chloroform to each sample to visualize the bands and to provide a carrier for more efficient extraction.

12.   Apply the samples to the TLC plate as streaks (20 µL at a time) in the fume hood. Include a control lane (UC/CE standard) on each plate.

13.   Run in the glass tank until the solvent front reaches the top line. This may take approximately 10 minutes. Dry the plates in the fume hood.

14.   The cholesterol and cholesteryl ester bands can be visualized with the aid of light or iodine vapor (use I_2 crystals).

15.   Outline the UC and CE bands with pencil. The highest band is the cholesteryl ester band, which is the most hydrophobic. If iodine vapor was used to visualize the bands, leave the plates in the fume hood until the iodine has completely disappeared. Presence of I_2 will quench the counts.

16.   Carefully cut out squares containing the UC and CE bands and place them in 5 mL scintillation vials. Add 5 mL scintillation fluid (toluene containing 4 g/L omnifluor or xylene-based Instafluor), preferably in the fume hood. Leave the samples at room temperature for at least 1 hour before starting to count, or, if you are in a hurry, shake well and count.

Calculation

LCAT activity is expressed in nmol of cholesterol esterified per hour per mL plasma. It is calculated from:

$$[CE/(CE + UC)] \times 1/l \times 4.66 \times 1000/sv$$

where CE is the disintegrations per minute (DPM) recovered in cholesteryl ester after the incubation, UC is the DPM recovered in cholesterol after the incubation, l is the time of incubation (usually 0.5 h), sv is the sample volume (usually 15 µL), and 4.46 is the total amount of unesterified cholesterol (in nmols) added to the incubation in the ethanolosome substrate.

Cholesterol Esterification Rate (CER) in Plasma

The methods by which this assay is used to investigate families with fish-eye disease has been extensively reported.[26-31] Specifically, in patients with LCAT deficiency, both the LCAT activity and the CER are virtually nonexistent. However, in the case of fish-eye disease, the LCAT activity is close to zero, yet the CER remains at 50–70% of normal. *This paradoxical esterification of cholesterol in the plasma of patients with fish-eye disease is diagnostic.*

Reagents

✦   [7(n)^{3}H] cholesterol (specific activity 5 Ci/mmol) (Amersham Corp.).

✦   Unesterified cholesterol assay kit (Wako Chemicals, Richmond VA).

✦   Tris Buffer, pH 7.4

Labeling of Plasma

1.   Prepare paper disc from Whatmann 1 filter paper using a hole punch.

2.   Dry 10 μL of ^{3}H-cholesterol under N_2.

3.   Reconstitute in 200 μL of absolute ethanol.

4.   Add 3 μL to each disc and allow the discs to air dry for 10 minutes.

5.   Transfer the discs into 12×75 glass tubes.

6.   Close the tubes with parafilm. Store at 4° C. (These discs will last 3 months at 4° C.)

7.   Add a minimum of 100 μL of plasma sample to each tube. Seal with parafilm and incubate overnight on ice.

8.   Transfer 50 μL of the labeled sample to a new tube.

9.   Incubate at 37° C for 30 minutes.

10. Terminate the reaction by adding 1 mL of 100% ethanol. Leave the samples at room temperature for 15 minutes.

11. Vortex the samples and centrifuge at 4,000 rpm for 20 min at room temperature in a standard table-top centrifuge to separate phases.

12. Pour the liquid phase into new test tubes and evaporate to dryness under N_2.

13. While the samples are drying, set up a glass tank for the chromatography of TLC plates. Make a mixture of 105 mL petroleum ether, 18 mL diethyl ether, and 1.56 mL acetic acid. Mix well. Pour the mixture into the tank and close the lid tightly to obtain saturation in the tank.

      Caution: Pour in the middle, not on the wall, and do not apply grease to the lid of the tanks.

14. Prepare the TLC plates: Mark the 1.5, 9.0, 10.0, 11.0, and 18.5 cm points on two ends of the plates. Draw corresponding lines by connecting the points (the middle line is used to cut the plate in half). Mark 2.5 cm segments for each line, for 8 segments per plate.

15. When the samples are completely dry, add 10 μL UC/CE standard and 50 μL of chloroform to each sample to visualize the heights of the bands and to provide a carrier medium for a more efficient way of extraction.

16. Apply the samples to the TLC plate as streaks, 20 µL at a time, in the fume hood. Include a control lane (UC/CE standard) on each plate.

17. Run in the glass tank until the solvent front reaches the top line. This may take approximately 10 minutes. Dry the plates in the fume hood.

18. The cholesterol and cholesteryl ester bands can be visualized with the aid of light or iodine vapor (use I_2 crystals). Outline the UC and CE bands with pencil. The highest band is the cholesteryl ester band, which is the most hydrophobic. If iodine vapor was used to visualize the bands, leave the plates in the fume hood until the iodine has completely disappeared. Presence of I_2 will quench the counts.

19. Carefully cut out squares containing the UC and CE bands and place them in 5 mL scintillation vials. Add 5 mL scintillation fluid (toluene containing 4 g/L omnifluor), preferably in the fume hood. Leave the samples at RT for at least 1 hour before starting to count.

Calculation

The plasma cholesterol esterification rate (CER) is expressed in nmols/h/mL plasma. It requires prior knowledge of the concentration of unesterified cholesterol in the test sample. CER is calculated as follows:

$$[CE/(CE+UC)] \times 1/I \times puc \times 1000/sv$$

where CE is the DPM (disintegrations per minute) recovered in cholesteryl ester after the incubation, UC is the DPM recovered in cholesterol after the incubation, I is the time of incubation (usually 0.5 h), sv is the sample volume, and puc is the total amount of unesterified cholesterol (in nmol) added to the incubation mixture with the plasma sample.

Fractional Esterification Rate (FER$_{HDL}$) in HDL

Preparation of VLDL and LDL Depleted Plasma

Reagents:

❖ Phosphotungstate solution (PTA): 4 g of phosphotungstic acid and 16 mL of 1 mol/L NaOH. Make it up to 100 mL with deionized distilled water.

❖ 2 mol/L $MgCl_2$

Precipitation Procedure:

To 1 mL of plasma (in 1.5 mL eppendorf tubes) add 100 µL of PTA and vortex. Add 25 µL of 2 mol/L $MgCl_2$ and vortex. Incubate at 4° C for 20 minutes. Centrifuge at 12,000 rpm at 4° C (precise temperature is important) for 10 minutes. Remove supernate to a new tube. This fraction contains the HDL particles; always store on ice.

Determination of FER in PTA Treated Plasma

This procedure is conducted exactly as that described for CER above.

Calculation

Since the FER$_{HDL}$ is independent of the amount of unesterified cholesterol in the incubation, the calculation simply reflects the fraction of the total radiolabel that was esterified. It is calculated as follows:

$$[CE/(CE+UC)] \times 1/I \times 100$$

where CE is the DPM recovered in cholesteryl ester after the incubation, UC is the DPM recovered in cholesterol after the incubation, and I is the time of incubation (usually 0.5 h)

SUMMARY

LCAT is clearly an important plasma enzyme that plays a major role in cholesterol metabolism. The assay of LCAT activity and the cholesterol esterification rate described in this chapter are primarily used in the differential diagnosis of HDL deficiency syndromes. However, for the assessment of patients at risk of CAD, the measurement of FER$_{HDL}$ has greater potential use in the clinical management and in the elucidation of the true role of LCAT in the protection against CAD.   ✧

Acknowledgments: *These studies have been funded through grants from the British Columbia Heart and Stroke Foundation.*

REFERENCES

1. Jonas A. Lecithin-cholesterol acyltransferase in the metabolism of high-density lipoproteins. Biochim Biophys Acta 1991;1084:205–20.
2. Applebaum-Bowden D. Lipases and lecithin:cholesterol acyltransferase in the control of lipoprotein metabolism. Curr Opin Lipidol 1995;6:130–5.
3. Marcel YL, Vezina CA, Weech PK, et al. Lecithin:cholesterol acyltransferase: a review and immunochemical studies. Adv Exper Med Biol 1986;201:163–79.
4. Fielding CJ. Factors affecting the rate of catalyzed transfer of cholesteryl esters in plasma. Am Heart J 1987;113:532–7.
5. Frohlich J, McLeod R. Lecithin:cholesterol acyltransferase (LCAT) deficiency syndromes. Adv Exper Med & Biol 1986;201:181–94.
6 Frohlich JJ, Pritchard PH. The clinical significance of serum high density lipoproteins. Clin Biochem 1989;22:417–23.
7. Frohlich J, Westerlund J, Sparks D, Pritchard PH. Familial hypoalphalipoproteinemias. Clin Invest Med 1990;13:202–10.
8. Dobiasova M, Frohlich J. Measurement of fractional esterification rate of cholesterol in plasma depleted of apoprotein B containing lipoprotein: methods and normal values. Phys Res 1996;45:65–73.

9. Rajaram OV, Barter PJ. Reactivity of human lipoproteins with purified lecithin: cholesterol acyltransferase during incubations in vitro. Biochim Biophys Acta 1985;835:41-49.

10. Carlson LA, Holmquist L. Evidence for the presence in human plasma of lecithin:cholesterol acyltransferase activity (beta-LCAT) specifically esterifying free cholesterol of combined pre-beta- and beta-lipoproteins: studies of fish eye disease patients and control subjects. Acta Med Scand 1985;218:197-205.

11. OK Hill JS, Wang X, Pritchard PH. Recombinant lecithin:cholesterol acyltransferase containing a Thr123→Ile mutation esterifies cholesterol in low density lipoprotein but not in high density lipoprotein. J Lipid Res 1993;34:81-8.

12. Pritchard PH, McLeod RM, Frohlich JJ, et al. Lecithin:cholesterol acyltransferase in familial HDL deficiency (Tangier disease). Biochem Biophys Acta 1988;958:227-34.

13. McLean J, Fielding C, Drayna D, et al. Cloning and expression of human lecithin-cholesterol acyltransferase cDNA. PNAS USA 1986;83:2335-9.

14. McLean J, Wion K, Drayna D, et al. Human lecithin-cholesterol acyltransferase gene: complete gene sequence and sites of expression. Nucl Acid Res 1986;14:9397-406.

15. Warden CH, Langner CA, Gordon JI, et al. Tissue-specific expression, developmental regulation, and chromosomal mapping of the lecithin:cholesterol acyltransferase gene: evidence for expression in brain and testes as well as liver. J Biol Chem 1989;264:21573-81.

16. Francone OL, Fielding CF. Structure-function relationships in human lecithin:cholesterol acyltransferase: site-directed mutagenesis at serine residues 181 and 216. Biochem 1991;30:1074-7.

17. Yang CY, Mangoogian D, Pao Q, et al. Lecithin:cholesterol acyltransferase: functional regions and a structural model of the enzyme. J Biol Chem 1987;262:3086-91.

18. OK Hill JS, Wang X, McLeod R, Pritchard PH. Lecithin:cholesterol acyltransferase: role of N-linked glycosylation in enzyme function. Biochem J 1993;294:879-84.

19. OK Hill JS, Pritchard PH. Role of N-linked glycosylation of lecithin:cholesterol acyltransferase in lipoprotein substrate specificity. Biochim Biophys Acta 1995;1254:193-7.

20. Kuivenhoven JA, Pritchard PH, Hill JS, Frohlich J, Assmann G, Kastelein JJ. The molecular pathology of lecithin:cholesterol acyltransferase deficiency syndromes. J Lipid Res 1997;38:191-205.

21. Kuivenhoven JA, Stalenhoef AF, Hill JS, Demacker PN, Errami A, Kastelein JJ, Pritchard PH. Two novel molecular defects in the LCAT gene are associated with fish eye disease. Arterioscler Thromb Vasc Biol 1996;16:294-303.

22. Dobiasova M, Stribrna J, Sparks DL, et al. Cholesterol esterification rates in very low density lipoprotein- and low density lipoprotein-depleted plasma: relation to high density lipoprotein subspecies, sex, hyperlipidemia, and coronary artery disease. Arterioscler Thromb 1991;11:64-70.

23. Dobiasova M, Stribrna J, Pritchard PH, et al. Cholesterol esterification rate in plasma depleted of very low and low density lipoproteins is controlled by the proportion of HDL2 and HDL3 subclasses: study in hypertensive and normal middle-aged and septuagenarian men. J Lipid Res 1992;33:1411-8.

24. Dobiasova M, Frohlich JJ. Structural and functional assessment of high-density lipoprotein heterogeneity. Clin Chem 1994;40:1554-8.

25. Dobiasova M, Stribrna J, Frohlich JJ. Relation of cholesterol esterification rate to the plasma distribution of high-density lipoprotein subclasses in normal and hypertensive women. Clin Invest Med 1995;18:449-54.

26. Funke H, von Eckardstein A, Pritchard PH, et al. The molecular defect causing fish eye disease. Proc Natl Acad Sci 1991;88:4855-9.

27. Klein H-G, Lohse P, Pritchard PH, et al. Two different allelic mutations in the lecithin:cholesterol acyltransferase (LCAT) gene associated with the fish eye syndrome. J Clin Invest 1992;89:499-506.

28. Funke H, von Eckardstein A, Pritchard PH, et al. Genetic and phenotypic heterogeneity in familial lecithin:cholesterol acyltransferase (LCAT) deficiency: six newly identified defective alleles further contribute to the structural heterogeneity in this disease. J Clin Invest 1993;91:677-83.

29. Kastelein JJP, Pritchard PH, Erkelens DW, et al. Familial high density lipoprotein deficiency causing corneal opacities (fish eye disease) in a kindred of Dutch descent. J Intern Med 1992;231:413-19.

30. Kuivenhoven JA, Weibusch H, Pritchard PH, et al. An intronic mutation in the lariate branch point sequence is a direct cause of an inherited human disorder (fish eye disease). J Clin Invest 1996;98:358-64.

31. Kuivenhoven JA, Voorst tot Vorst E, Weibusch H, et al. A unique genetic and biochemical presentation of fish eye disease. J Clin Invest 1995;96:2783-91.

Determination and Clinical Significance of Phospholipids

Papasani V. Subbaiah

22

Background and Introduction

❖   Phospholipids are integral and essential components of all lipoproteins and cell membranes. In quantitative terms, the phospholipids in fact exceed triglycerides (TG) as well as cholesterol in normal human plasma. However, phospholipids are chemically more diverse than the neutral lipids, and are composed of several subclasses with distinct physicochemical properties. The two major classes of phospholipids in plasma lipoproteins are: glycerophospholipids, which have a glycerol backbone, and sphingo-phospholipids, which have a sphingosine backbone. Five subclasses of glycero-phospholipids are found in plasma: phosphatidyl choline (PC), lysophosphatidyl choline (LPC), phosphatidyl ethanolamine (PE), phosphatidyl serine (PS), and phosphatidyl inositol (PI), and one sphingophospholipid: sphingomyelin (SPH). Each subclass of phospholipids is actually composed of several molecular species which differ from one another in their fatty acid composition. The structures of the major phospholipids in human plasma and their normal concentrations are shown in Figure 22–1.

Despite the high concentration of phospholipids in plasma, their measurement is not routinely performed in the clinical chemistry laboratory. One reason is that most methods for the determination of total phospholipids have been rather time consuming, tedious, and less amenable to automation than methods for the determination of the neutral lipids. Another reason is that the phospholipid concentration in plasma is not altered as markedly as that of cholesterol and triacylglycerol (TG) in various pathological conditions. However, the following considerations show that the estimation of lipoprotein phospholipids provides information which is not merely supplemental to the neutral lipid values, but at times more important than either cholesterol or TG concentration.

1.   Only 10–20% of the total weight of high-density lipoproteins (HDL) is cholesterol, but 25–30% of it is phospholipids.[1] Although HDL concentration is expressed routinely in terms of its cholesterol content, it is obvious that the phospholipid content reflects the concentration of HDL much more accurately.

2.   Functionally, the phospholipids of HDL are more important than cholesterol or even apoprotein A-I in the reverse cholesterol transport.[2] Abnormalities in phospholipid composition would affect the function of HDL more than the abnormalities in TG or cholesterol concentration.

Figure 22–1 ✦ Structures of Major Phospholipids of Normal Plasma

General Structure of Phosphoglyceride

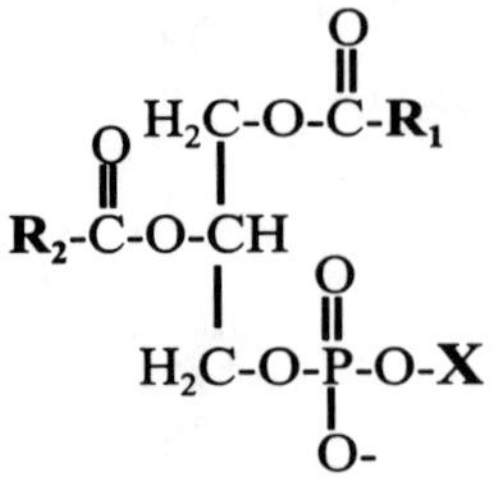

$$\begin{array}{l}
\quad\quad\quad\quad O \\
\quad\quad\quad\quad \parallel \\
\quad O\;\; H_2C\text{-}O\text{-}C\text{-}R_1 \\
\quad \parallel\quad\;\; | \\
R_2\text{-}C\text{-}O\text{-}CH \\
\quad\quad\quad | \quad\; O \\
\quad\quad\quad\quad\quad \parallel \\
\quad\; H_2C\text{-}O\text{-}P\text{-}O\text{-}X \\
\quad\quad\quad\quad\; | \\
\quad\quad\quad\quad\; O\text{-}
\end{array}$$

R_1 = Usually saturated fatty acid

R_2 = Usually unsaturated fatty acid
(absent in LPC)

Phosphoglyceride	Structure of X	Conc. in normal plasma mmol/L (% of total)
Phophatidyl choline (PC)	$H_2C\text{-}H_2C\text{-}\overset{+}{N}(CH_3)_3$	1.795 (68.4)
Lysophosphatidyl choline (LPC)	$H_2C\text{-}H_2C\text{-}\overset{+}{N}(CH_3)_3$	0.178 (6.8)
Phosphatidyl ethanolamine (PE)	$H_2C\text{-}H_2C\text{-}\overset{+}{N}H_3$	0.115 (4.4)
Phosphatidyl serine (PS)	$H_2C\text{-}HC\text{-}\overset{+}{N}H_3$ COO-	0.021 (0.8)
Phosphatidyl inositol (PI)	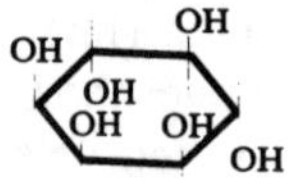 (inositol ring: OH OH OH OH OH OH)	0.060 (2.3)

Structure of Sphingomyelin (SPH)

0.454 (17.3)

$$\begin{array}{l}
H_3C(CH_2)_{12} \\
\quad HC\text{=}CH \quad\quad\quad\quad O \\
\quad\quad CH\text{-}CH\text{-}CH_2O\text{-}P\text{-}O\text{-}CH_2\text{-}CH_2\text{-}N(CH_3)_3 \\
\quad\quad OH\;\; NH\text{-}R_3 \quad\; O\text{-}
\end{array}$$

R_3 = Long-chain saturated fatty acid

3. Phospholipids are substrates for several important enzymes in plasma, such as lecithin:cholesterol acyltransferase (LCAT), lipoprotein lipase, and hepatic lipase; therefore, changes in their composition may affect the activities of these enzymes.

4. Unlike the TG or cholesteryl esters, the phospholipids exchange more readily with the cell membranes, and therefore alterations in plasma phospholipid composition likely reflect possible alterations in cell membrane composition and function in various pathological states.

Table 22-1 lists some of the pathological conditions in which the plasma phospholipid composition has been shown to be altered.

Table 22-1 ✦ Pathological Significance of Plasma Phospholipids		
Disease	*Effects on Plasma Phospholipids*	*Reference*
Coronary heart disease	PC/free cholesterol ratio significantly lower in ischemic heart disease	31
	HDL phospholipids correlate with atherogenic risk even in normolipidemics	32
	PC/SPH ratio decreased in HDL	33, 34
	Decrease in HDL phospholipids is more significant than the decrease in HDL cholesterol	35
	Free cholesterol/PL ratio increased in HDL in ischemic heart disease	36
Hyperlipidemia	35% increase in cholesterol/PL ratio in LDL (Type IIa hyperlipidemia)	37
Insulin-dependent diabetes	Decrease in choline PL in apoprotein B-containing lipoproteins	38
	Free cholesterol/PL ratio increased	39
Liver diseases	HDL-PL correlate better than HDL cholesterol with liver disease	40
	Free cholesterol and PL increased in cholestatic liver disease	41
Cancer	Decreased PL in hematologic cancer	42
	Decrease in plasma PL in acute leukemia and malignant lymphoma. LPC peak most sensitive indicator for monitoring treatment	18
Cerebrovascular disease	HDL PL significantly decreased	43

Abbreviations: HDL: = high-density lipoproteins, LDL = low-density lipoproteins, LPC = lysophosphatidyl choline, PC = phosphatidyl choline, PL = phospholipids, SPH = sphingomyelin

Review of Existing Methods for Phospholipid Estimation

The methods for phospholipid estimation can be divided into two groups: (1) estimation of the total phospholipid concentration in plasma or lipoproteins, and (2) estimation of the composition of individual phospholipid subclasses. In addition, there are special methods (which will not be discussed here) to determine the molecular species composition of individual phospholipid subclasses,[3] and to estimate the concentration of minor phospholipids with specific biological functions, such as platelet-activating factor,[4] disaturated PC,[5] plasmalogens,[6] and phospholipid-hydroperoxides.[7]

Total Phospholipids of Plasma

The only unique structural feature common to all phospholipids is the presence of lipid-bound phosphate. Therefore, most of the methods originally designed to determine plasma phospholipids depended upon the estimation of lipid phosphorus. In general, the total lipids are first extracted from the plasma, the lipid phosphorus is released by acid-digestion, and then the released phosphorus is estimated by colorimetric methods. The various methods differ from one another in the reagents used for the release of the inorganic phosphate (Pi), including: sulfuric acid and hydrogen peroxide, perchloric acid, mixtures of perchloric and sulfuric acids, with vanadium pentoxide as catalyst. The most common reagent used for the development of color is ammonium molybdate, which forms a phosphomolybdate complex with the phosphate, which is then reduced by stannous chloride–hydrazine sulfate or aminonapthol sulfonate at high temperature.

Phospholipids have also been estimated without acid digestion, by complexing the intact lipids with chromogenic reagents such as ammonium ferrothiocyanate[8] and prussian blue complex,[9] or with fluorogenic reagents such as diphenylhexatriene.[10]

Since about 95% of the total plasma phospholipids contain choline as the base (PC, LPC, SPH), many laboratories use the determination of lipid-bound choline as a close approximation of total phospholipids. The method is based on the release of choline by phospholipase D from *Streptomyces chromofuscus*, which acts on all three choline-containing phospholipids. The released choline is oxidized with choline oxidase to produce betaine and hydrogen peroxide. The hydrogen peroxide is then reacted with peroxidase in the presence of 4-amino antipyrine and phenol to produce a red quinone complex, which is measured at 505 nm.

$$PC \xrightarrow{\text{Phospholipase D}} \text{Phosphatidic acid} + \text{choline}$$

$$LPC \xrightarrow{\text{Phospholipase D}} \text{Lysophosphatidic acid} + \text{choline}$$

$$SPH \xrightarrow{\text{Phospholipase D}} \text{Ceramide phosphate} + \text{choline}$$

$$\text{Choline} \xrightarrow{\text{Choline oxidase}} \text{Betaine} + H_2O_2$$

$$2 H_2O_2 + \text{Phenol} + \text{4-aminoantipyrene} \xrightarrow{\text{Peroxidase}} \text{Quinineimine} \,(\lambda Dmax\ 505\ nm) + 2H_2O$$

This method has the advantage of not requiring lipid extraction and not involving the corrosive reagents such as perchloric acid or a special fume hood. The drawback of the method is that it does not measure PS, PI, and PE. High concentrations of bilirubin and ascorbic acid have been reported to interfere in color development, although the concentrations encountered in most clinical samples are without effect. Interference by the high concentration of EDTA in plasma has been reported,[11] but this can be overcome by including sufficient $CaCl_2$ in the buffer.

Choline can also be estimated by the use of choline kinase by the following sequence of reactions:

$$\text{Choline} + \text{ATP} \xrightarrow{\text{Choline kinase}} \text{Choline phosphate} + \text{ADP}$$

$$\text{ADP} + \text{phosphoenol pyruvate} \xrightarrow{\text{Pyruvate kinase}} \text{ATP} + \text{Pyruvate}$$

$$\text{Pyruvate} + \text{NADH} + \text{H}^+ \xrightarrow{\text{Lactate dehydrogenase}} \text{Lactate} + \text{NAD}^+$$

The NADH consumed is measured at 340 nm. The main advantage of this method is that it can be used on dilute solutions where the interference from bilirubin and ascorbate may be more problematic with the choline oxidase method. A disadvantage is that additional enzymes and a UV range spectrophotometer are required.

Quantitation of Individual Phospholipid Classes

As mentioned earlier, the total PC *concentration* of whole plasma or lipoproteins does not change as dramatically as either cholesterol or TG, and therefore the quantitation of phospholipids as potential markers of the disease has been neglected. However, the *composition* of phospholipids may be more important than the total phospholipids in some cases. The importance of determining the SPH/PC ratio in the amniotic fluid for the estimation of lung maturity of the fetus is well established.[12] Because some pathological conditions are characterized by abnormalities in individual phospholipid subclasses (see Table 22–1), estimation of the phospholipid composition may be more useful than the total phospholipids. About 70% of plasma PE is in the plasmalogen form,[13] which is considered to have strong anti-oxidant properties. Therefore, the estimation of plasma PE provides an indirect measure of the anti-oxidant reserve of the plasma. Furthermore, since LPC is the product of lipolytic actions in the plasma, an increase in its concentration may indicate the improper storage of plasma.

The separation of phospholipids into individual classes has been performed by classical chromatographic procedures using silicic acid column, silicic acid-impregnated paper, and silica gel thin-layer chromatography (TLC),[14] as well as high-performance liquid chromatography (HPLC),[15] and capillary gas-liquid chromatography (GLC).[16] In addition, nuclear magnetic resonance (NMR) methods have been developed which do not require the physical separation of the phospholipids from each other before their quantitation.[17, 18] At present, the TLC and HPLC methods are the most widely used.

TLC separation is performed on silica gel-coated plates, with a variety of solvent systems, the most effective being those containing chloroform, methanol, and water. The quantitation of individual phospholipid spots after TLC separation is performed either by densitometry after color development on the plate[19] or by determining the lipid phosphorus in individual spots after scraping them from the plate.[20] In the Iatroscan method, a combination of TLC and flame ionization detection employing silica-coated chromarods is used.[21] While this method has high sensitivity, in our experience it suffers from poor reproducibility.

HPLC separation is usually carried out on normal-phase silica columns with a variety of solvent systems, the choice of which is dictated by the detection method used. The various methods for quantitation following HPLC separation include UV absorbance,[15] post-column fluorescence derivatization,[22] electrochemical detection,[23] flame ionization,[24] mass spectroscopy,[25] light-scattering detection,[26] and refractive index.[27] Although the UV detection method has been used by several investigators, its main drawback is that it is dependent on the number of double bonds in the acyl chains, which causes highly variable results. In addition, the choice of solvents is limited because the most effective solvents interfere with UV measurements at low wavelengths. The molar extinction coefficients are also very low, and therefore the sensitivity is not high. However, if the fatty acid composition is not significantly different among samples, one can use calibrated standards of similar composition and quantitate the phospholipids quite accurately.

The refractive index method is not dependent on the structure of the phospholipid, but its sensitivity is very low and it is unsuitable for gradient separation of the phospholipids. The electrochemical method is also independent of the phospholipid structure, but suffers from poor reproducibility and interference from other solutes.[23] Mass spectroscopy yields detailed information which is not obtainable with other methods, but the instrumentation is expensive and difficult to operate. The flame ionization technique is very sensitive and allows the use of most solvents for HPLC separation. Although this method is promising, it has not yet gained wide acceptance for phospholipid estimations. In our experience the light-scattering detection method is more practical and reproducible and the results correlate highly with the estimation of lipid phosphorus.

Enzymatic methods to estimate the major phospholipids of plasma without prior chromatographic separation have also been reported. Blaton et al.[28] used phospholipase C and sphingomyelinase from *B. cereus*, which release choline phosphate specifically from PC and SPH respectively, to determine these phospholipids separately. LPC concentration can be determined as the difference between the total lipid-bound choline as estimated by the phospholipase D method, and the PC and SPH values as determined by this procedure. One drawback of this procedure is that since both phospholipase C and sphingomyelinase are from the same source, the possible cross-contamination of the enzymes can give rise to spurious results for PC, SPH, or both.

Recommended Methods for Total Phospholipid Estimation

ESTIMATION OF LIPID PHOSPHORUS BY CHEMICAL METHOD

Apparatus required:

Heating block with thermostatic control
Spectrophotometer
Perchloric acid fume hood
Water bath
N_2 evaporator

Reagents:

Perchloric acid (70%)

Ammonium molybdate (2.5% w/v in de-ionized water)

ANSA (1-amino-naphthol-4-sulfonic acid) reagent: Dissolve 12 g of $NaHSO_3$ in about 80 mL de-ionized water by stirring at room temperature. Then add 2.4 g of Na_2SO_3 and 0.2 g of ANSA and stir for about 10 min to dissolve all ingredients. Next, filter the solution through a Whatman No. 1 filter paper and add de-ionized water to bring the volume to 100 mL. Store at 4° C in a brown bottle, protected from light. The solution is stable for a least 1 month.

Standard solution: Dissolve 43.9 g of KH_2PO_4 (10 mg Pi) in de-ionized sterile water in a 100 mL volumetric flask. Add deionized water to bring the volume to 100 mL and store at 4° C. If kept sterile, the solution is stable for at least 6 months.

Working solution: Dilute 2.5 mL stock phosphorus standard to 25 mL with de-ionized sterile water and store at 40° C. The solution is stable for 1 month. This solution contains 10 µg Pi/mL.

Lipid extraction:

Extract the total lipids from the plasma or lipoprotein samples by the modified Bligh and Dyer procedure[29] as follows:

Dilute aliquots of plasma or lipoproteins sample (equivalent to 25–100 µL plasma) to 0.4 mL with 0.15 mol/L NaCl-1 mmol/L EDTA in 13 × 100 mm disposable glass tubes. Add 1.0 mL methanol to each tube and vortex briefly (10 sec). Then add 0.5 mL chloroform and vortex for 15 sec. Add another 0.5 mL chloroform and 0.5 mL water, mixing briefly after each addition. Centrifuge the tubes at 1000 ×g at room temperature to separate the chloroform and aqueous layers. Using a Pasteur pipet, transfer the chloroform layer into a clean glass tube. Add another 0.5 mL of chloroform to the original tube, vortex, and centrifuge as above. Combine the chloroform layer from this extract with the first extract. Evaporate the combined extracts under N_2 and redissolve in 100 µL of chloroform:methanol (2:1 v/v).

Lipid digestion and color development:

Take aliquots of lipid extract (equivalent to 25 µL whole plasma) into disposable glass tubes (13 × 100 mm) and evaporate the solvent completely under a stream of nitrogen. Take KH_2PO_4 standards containing 0.5–5.0 µg Pi and a reagent blank containing 100 µL water. Add 0.4 mL of 70% perchloric acid to each tube, including the standards and blanks, using a glass pipet and a Pipet-Aid dispenser. Place all tubes in a block heater which has been preheated to 200° C, in a perchloric acid hood, and digest the samples for 20 min, or until all the yellow color disappears from the sample tubes. Cool the tubes to room temperature (in the fume hood), and add 3 mL de-ionized water, followed by 0.2 mL of ammonium molybdate solution and 80 µL of the ANSA reagent. Mix the tubes by vortexing and place them in a boiling water bath for 10 min. Remove the tubes from the water and allow to cool to room temperature. Take the readings in a spectrophotometer at 830 nm, against the reagent blank. The blue color is stable for at least 24 h; therefore, analysis of several samples in the same batch is possible without loss of sensitivity or accuracy.

Calculations:

From the optical density (OD) values of the standards, calculate the absorbance units per µg phosphorus. Divide the OD of the unknown sample by the above value to obtain the µg of lipid phosphorus in the unknown sample (25 µL plasma). Since there is one atom of phosphorus per mole of phospholipid, dividing the phosphorus value by 31 (atomic weight of phosphorus) gives the µmol/L of phospholipid in the sample. To convert the µg phosphorus into mg weight percentage of phospholipids, multiply it by 25 (use 775 as the average mol weight of the phospholipid) and by the dilution factor.

$$\frac{\text{OD of unknown (25 µL plasma)}}{\text{OD of standard per µg Pi}} \times \frac{40}{31} = \text{mmol/L of plasma}$$

$$\frac{\text{OD of unknown (25 µL plasma)}}{\text{O.D of standard per µg Pi}} \times \frac{25 \times 40 \times 100}{1000} = \text{mg phospholipid / dL plasma}$$

ESTIMATION OF LIPID-BOUND CHOLINE
BY ENZYMATIC METHOD

Reagents:

All reagents described here are based on the "phospholipids B" kit supplied by Wako Chemicals Inc. (Richmond, VA). These reagents can be purchased in kit form from this company, or can be prepared in the laboratory using the ingredients purchased from other manufacturers (e.g., Sigma Chemical Co., St. Louis, MO; Boehringer Mannheim, Indianapolis, IN).

1. Buffer (200 mL): 0.5 mol/L Tris-Cl buffer, pH 8.0, containing 50 µg/mL $CaCl_2 \cdot H_2O$ and 0.05% phenol. Store at 4° C. The solution is stable for at least 2 months.

2. Color reagent (50 mL):

Phospholipase D from *Streptomyces chromofuscus* (EC 3.1.4.4) 24 units

Choline oxidase (EC 1.1.3.17) 100 units

Horseradish peroxidase (EC 1.11.1.7) 270 units

4-amino antipyrine 750 mg

Make up all the ingredients in 50 mL of the above buffer solution.[1] This solution is stable for at least 2 weeks at 4° C

3. Standard solution (10 mL):

Choline chloride: 3.87 mmol/L (equivalent to 300 mg/dL of phospholipid)

Phenol: 0.1% (w/v)

The solution is stable for at least 1 month at 4° C.

Procedure:

Place 20 μL aliquots of plasma, standard solution, and 0.15 mol/L NaCl (reagent blank) into disposable glass tubes (13 × 100 mm). Add 3.0 mL of color reagent and mix the contents by vortexing. Place all the tubes in a water bath at 37° C for 10 min. Take the readings at 505 nm in a spectrophotometer against the reagent blank. The color is stable for more than 2 h at room temperature.

Calculation:

$$\frac{\text{OD of sample}}{\text{OD of standard}} \times 300 = \text{mg phospholipid/dL}$$

The above value may be converted to SI units by dividing with 77.5:

$$\text{phospholipids (mg/dL)} \times 77.5 = \text{phospholipids (mmol/L)}$$

When the lipoprotein fractions are estimated, use samples equivalent to 50 μL of plasma.

Interfering substances:

Bilirubin in amounts up to 20 mg/dL (342 μmol/L) does not affect the reaction. However, ascorbic acid above 5 mg/dL (284 μmol/L) inhibits the color development. The presence of free choline in plasma gives spuriously high values, but less than 1% of total choline in plasma is known to be in free form. The reported inhibition of color development by EDTA in plasma samples[11] is overcome by the presence of $CaCl_2$ in the dilution buffer.

Recommended Methods for Determination of Phospholipid Composition

While there are several methods for the quantitation of phospholipid subclasses, especially following their separation by HPLC, the following two methods are recommended, based on experience in the author's laboratory.

TLC SEPARATION AND PHOSPHORUS ESTIMATION

Apparatus and Reagents:

Same as used for the estimation of total phospholipids by the phosphate assay. Additional equipment needed are a TLC chamber, an iodine chamber, a dry-air oven, and silica gel-coated TLC plates (commercially obtained from American Scientific Products).

Activate the TLC plate by placing it in a dry-air oven at 105° C for 30 min. Cool to room temperature. Make lanes of 2 cm each on the plate by scoring with a needle. Using a capillary pipet, spot the lipid extract equivalent to 100 μL of whole plasma on each lane. Standards (50 μg each) of PC, LPC, and PE should be spotted on a separate lane for the purpose of identification of the spots. To develop the plate, place it in a TLC chamber containing about 100 mL of the solvent mixture of chloroform: methanol:water (65:25:4 v/v) and let the solvent run until it reaches about 2 cm from the top of the plate. Lining the TLC chamber with filter paper increases the saturation of the chamber with solvent vapors and improves the reproducibility.

Remove the plate from the chamber and let it dry in a fume hood for a few minutes, until the solvent smell is gone. Place the plate in an iodine chamber; a TLC chamber with about 50 g of iodine crystals in the bottom and a glass lid should serve well as an iodine chamber. After about 30 sec the lipids will display as yellow spots. Mark the spots corresponding to standard PC, LPC, and PE with a needle. The spot between LPC and PC is SPH, which usually appears as a double spot (see Figure 22–2). The faint spot between PE and PC is the mixture of PI and PS. These two lipids do not separate from each other in this solvent system. Since their concentrations in human plasma are very low, we routinely estimate them together.

After the iodine color disappears, use a razor blade to scrape the spots into individual glass tubes (13 × 100 mm). Add 0.4 mL of 70% perchloric acid to each tube and digest the lipids and determine phosphorus as described for the total phospholipids. The presence of silica gel does not interfere with the color development. The only extra step needed is to centrifuge the tubes at 1000 ×g for 5 min to sediment the silica gel before taking the readings of the supernates in a spectrophotometer. For

Figure 22–2 ✧ Schematic Diagram of Thin-Layer Chromatographic Separation of Plasma Phospholipids (not drawn to scale)

Abbreviations:

LPC = lysophosphatidyl choline

PC = phosphatidyl choline

PE = phosphatidyl ethanolamine

PI = phosphatidyl inositol

PS = phosphatidyl serine

SPH = sphingomyelin

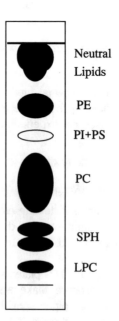

each batch of plates, estimate phosphorus from a 4 sq. cm area of the blank plate to correct for any interference from silica gel. Most commercially available plates do not show any phosphorus.

Calculations:

$$\frac{\text{OD of unknown (100 } \mu\text{L of plasma)}}{\text{OD / } \mu\text{g of Pi standard}} \times \frac{10}{31} = \text{mmol/L of plasma}$$

To calculate the mg/dL value, multiply the above value (mmol/L) by 77.5 for PC, PE, PI + PS, and SPH, and by 50 for LPC.

HPLC SEPARATION AND QUANTITATION BY A LIGHT-SCATTERING DETECTOR

Apparatus:

HPLC machine with gradient capabilities

Evaporative light-scattering detector (ELSD) (Varex Corporation, Burtonsville, MD)

HPLC column (46 × 250 mm) silica column (5 μ), with a guard column

Solvent Mixture:

Use only HPLC grade solvents. All solvents must be filtered through 0.45 μ filters and degassed by bubbling helium or nitrogen before use.

The gradient system described by Becart et al.[30] is recommended, with the flow rate set at 1.0 mL/min throughout.

Solvent A: chloroform:methanol:30% ammonium hydroxide (80:19.5:0.5 v/v)

Solvent B: chloroform:methanol:water:30% ammonium hydroxide (60:34:5.5:0.5 v/v)

Set the gradient program as follows.

Time (min)	% of A	% of B
0	100	0
14	0	100
23	0	100
29	100	0
34	100	0

The last step returns the column to the initial setting, ready for the injection of the next sample.

ELSD detector settings: N_2 gas flow, 1.6 mL/min; drift tube temperature, 50° C.

Inject total lipid extract corresponding to 50 μL plasma into the column and record the detector output using a computer-based data management system.

The response factor for each phospholipid should be determined by using standards, and the concentrations of various phospholipids should then be calculated by entering the predetermined response factors into the program. Figure 22–3 shows a typical chromatogram for the separation of human plasma phospholipids (corresponding to 50 μL plasma). The peak for PS, between PC and PI, is barely visible at this concentration. Both SPH and LPC appear as double peaks, and the two peaks are combined for the calculation.

The concentrations determined by this method agree closely with those determined with the TLC method. However, since the factors are non-linear and vary significantly between different phospholipids, it is important to determine these factors in the ranges expected in the samples, and with the specific data management program employed. It should be pointed out that the response factors for the phospholipids normally present in low concentrations in human plasma (PI, PS, LPC) are lower than those for PC, PE, and SPH. ✧

Acknowledgments: The research reported in this chapter was supported by a grant from the National Institutes of Health (#HL 52597) and by a grant from the American Heart Association of Metropolitan Chicago. The technical assistance of Mr. Wilfred Buchanan is gratefully acknowledged.

Figure 22–3 ✧ High-Performance Liquid Chromatographic Separation of Human Plasma Phospholipids, and Quantitation by a Light-Scattering Detector

A: Neutral lipids, including free and esterified cholesterol, and triglycerides.
B: Free fatty acids and unidentified neutral lipids.
The detector response is in arbitrary units.

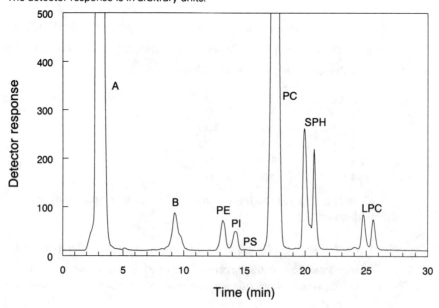

REFERENCES

1. Edelstein C. General properties of plasma lipoproteins and apolipoproteins. In: Scanu AM, Spector AA., eds. Biochemistry and biology of plasma lipoproteins, New York: Marcel Dekker, 1986:495–505.

2. Fournier N, de la Llera Moya M, Burkey BF, et al. Role of HDL phospholipid in efflux of cell cholesterol to whole serum: studies with human apo A-I transgenic rats. J Lipid Res 1996;37:1704–11.

3. Blank ML, Robinson M, Fitzgerald V, Snyder F. Novel quantitative method for determination of molecular species of phospholipids and diglycerides. J Chromatogr 1984; 298:473–82.

4. Shinozaki K, Kawasaki T, Kambayashi J, et al. A new method of purification and sensitive bioassay of platelet-activating factor (PAF) in human whole blood. Life Sci 1994;54:429–37.

5. Sestak TL, Subbaiah PV, Jaskowiak NT, Bagdade JD. A high-performance liquid chromatographic procedure for the determination of disaturated phosphatidylcholine in human plasma. Anal Biochem 1990;191:156–9.

6. Schulz R, Strynadka KD, Panas DL, Olley PM, Lopaschuk GD. Analysis of myocardial plasmalogen and diacyl phospholipids and their arachidonic acid content using high-performance liquid chromatography. Anal Biochem 1993;213:140–46.

7. Miyazawa T, Fujimoto K, Oikawa S. Determination of lipid hydroperoxides in low density lipoprotein from human plasma using high performance liquid chromatography with chemiluminescence detection. Biomed Chromatogr 1990;4:131–4.

8. Stewart JCM. Colorimetric determination of phospholipids with ammonium ferrothiocyanate. Anal Biochem 1980;104:10–14.

9. Sandhu RS. Serum phospholipids determined without acid digestion. Clin Chem 1976; 22:1973–5.

10. Jouanel P, Motta C, Delattre J, Dastugue B. A rapid and sensitive fluorometric assay of serum phospholipid. Clin Chim Acta 1980;105:173–81.

11. Cham BE, Mahon M, Kostner K, Dwivedy A, Fang NX, Iannuzzi C. Phospholipids in EDTA-treated plasma and serum. Clin Chem 1993;39:2347–8.

12. Gluck L, Kulovich MW, Borer RC. Diagnosis of the respiratory distress syndrome by amniocentesis. Am J Obstet Gynecol 1971;109:440–45.

13. Myher JJ, Kuksis A, Pind S. Molecular species of glycerophospholipids and sphingomyelins of human plasma: Comparison to red blood cells. Lipids 1989;24:408–18.

14. Kates M. Techniques of lipidology. Isolation, analysis, and identification of lipids. 1972; 393–465.

15. Patton GM, Fasulo JM, Robins SJ. Analysis of lipids by high performance liquid chromatography: Part I. J Nutr Biochem 1990;1:493–500.

16. Kuksis A, Myher JJ, Geher K, et al. Effect of saturated and unsaturated fat diets on lipid profiles of plasma lipoproteins. Atherosclerosis 1982;41:221–40.

17. Nourisorkhabi MH, Agar NS, Sullivan DR, Gallagher C, Kuchel PW. Phospholipid composition of erythrocyte membranes and plasma of mammalian blood including Australian marsupials; Quantitative P-31 NMR analysis using detergent. Comp Biochem Physiol [B] 1996;113:221–7.

18. Kuliszkiewicz-Jaus M, Janus W, Baczynski S. Application of ^{31}P NMR spectroscopy in clinical analysis of changes of serum phospholipids in leukemia, lymphoma, and some other non-haematologic cancers. Anticancer Res 1996;16:1587–94.

19. Bovet P, Darioli R, Essinger A, Golay A, Sigwart U, Kappenberger L. Phospholipids and other lipids in angiographically assessed coronary artery disease. Atheroscler 1989; 80:41–7.

20. Subbaiah PV, Davidson MH, Ritter MC, Buchanan W, Bagdade JD. Effects of dietary supplementation with marine lipid concentrate on the plasma lipoprotein composition of hypercholesterolemic patients. Atherosclerosis 1989;79:157–66.

21. Sebedio JL. Utilization of thin-layer chromatography-flame ionization detection for lipid analysis. In: Sebedio JL, Perkins EG., eds. New trends in lipid and lipoprotein analyses, Champaign, IL: AOCS Press, 1995:24-37.

22. Bernhard W, Linck M, Creutzburg H, et al. High performance liquid chromatographic analysis of phospholipids from different sources with combined fluorescence and ultraviolet detection. Anal Biochem 1994;220:172-8.

23. Boswart J, Schmidt T, Kostiuk P, Pacakova V, Stulik K. High-performance liquid chromatographic determination of some polar phospholipids in serum. J Chromatogr 1989; 495:61-70.

24. Maxwell RJ, Nungesser EH, Marmer WN, Foglia TA. HPLC with flame ionization detection: class separation, linearity of response, and quantification of sterols, glycerides, and phospholipids. LC-GC 1987;5:829-33.

25. Kuypers FA, Bütikofer P, Shackleton CHL. Application of liquid chromatography-thermospray mass spectrometry in the analysis of glycerophospholipid molecular species. J Chromatogr Biomed Appl 1991;562:191-206.

26. Christie WW. Rapid separation and quantification of lipid classes by high performance liquid chromatography and mass (light-scattering) detection. J Lipid Res 1985;26:507-12.

27. Porter NA, Wolf RA, Nixon JR. Separation and purification of lecithins by high pressure liquid chromatography. Lipids 1978;14:20-24.

28. Blaton V, DeBuyzere M, Spincemaille J, Declercq B. Enzymic assay for phosphatidylcholine and sphingomyelin in serum. Clin Chem 1996;29:806-9.

29. Bligh EG, Dyer WJ. A rapid method of total lipid extraction and purification. Can J Biochem Physiol 1959;37:911-17.

30. Becart J, Chevalier C, Biesse JP. Quantitative analysis of phospholipids by HPLC with a light scattering evaporative detector. Application to raw materials for cosmetic use. J High Res Chromatogr 1990;13:126-9.

31. Kuksis A, Myher JJ, Geher K, et al. Decreased plasma phosphatidyl choline/free cholesterol ratio as an indicator of risk for ischemic vascular disease. Arteriosclerosis 1982; 2:296-302.

32. PerovIA, Nechaev AS, Nikitina NA, Metel'skaia VA. Indicators of the atherogenic properties of plasma lipoproteins and coronary atherosclerosis (selective angiography data). Kardiologiia 1985;25:91-5.

33. Mai FT, Liakishev AA, Polesskii VA, Sidorenko BA, Gerasimova EN. Phospholipid content of subfractions of high density lipoproteins in women with angiographically documented coronary arteriosclerosis. Kardiologiia 1983;23:33-7.

34. Ozerova IN, Gerasimova EN, Mai FT, Kurdanov KhA. Esterifying activity of the plasma in patients with ischemic heart disease. Vopr Med Khim 1984;30:118-23.

35. Kunz F, Pechlaner C, Erhart R, Fend F, Muhlberger V. HDL and plasma phospholipids in coronary artery disease. Arterioscler Thromb 1994;14:1146-50.

36. Pham TM, Torkhovskaia TI, Ozerova IN, Polesskii VA, Kurdanov KhA. Changes in the indices affecting the phospholipid structure of high density lipoprotein subfractions in ischemic heart disease. Vopr Med Khim 1981;27:701-6.

37. Shattil SJ, Bennett JS, Colman RW, Cooper RA. Abnormalities of cholesterol-phospholipid composition in platelets and low-density lipoproteins of human hyperbetalipoproteinemia. J Lab Clin Med 1977;89:341-53.

38. Ziegler O, Mejean L, Igau B, Fruchart JC, Drouin P, Fievet C. Accessibility of human apolipoprotein B-100 epitopes in insulin-dependent diabetes: relation with the surface lipid environment of atherogenic particles. Diabetes Metab 1996;22:179-84.

39. Bagdade JD, Subbaiah PV. Abnormal high-density lipoprotein composition in women with insulin-dependent diabetes. J Lab Clin Med 1989;113:235-40.

40. Akaike M, Kikuchi K, Aramaki T, Okumura H. High density lipoprotein phospholipid concentrations in serum of patients with liver disease. Clin Chem 1985;31:1083-4.

41. Miller JP. Dyslipoproteinaemia of liver disease. Baillieres Clin Endocrinol Metab 1990;4: 807-32.

42. Dessi S, Batetta B, Spano O, et al. Clinical remission is associated with restoration of normal high-density lipoprotein cholesterol levels in children with malignancies. Clin Sci 1995;89:505-10.

43. Sall ND, Toure M, Fall S, et al. Phospholipid levels in exploration of cerebral atherosclerosis in African Senegalese population. Dakar Medical 1994;39:77-80.

Determination and Clinical Significance of Nonesterified Fatty Acids

Henry J. Pownall, Diane H. Bick, and John B. Massey

23

INTRODUCTION

❖   Nonesterified fatty acids (NEFA), also referred to as free fatty acids, are fundamental units in the structure of lipids in membranes and lipoproteins. The NEFA form esters of cholesterol and glycerol, which ultimately form the fatty inclusions of liver cells[1] and adipocytes, the cores of low-density and very-low-density lipoproteins (LDL and VLDL),[2] and the fat droplets that give monocyte-derived macrophages in atherosclerotic lesions their foamy appearance.[3] NEFA are also an important source of energy that is used by heart and aerobically conditioned skeletal muscle.

Plasma NEFA concentrations are increased in three related pathological states that tend to cluster in individuals and that have been implicated in premature coronary artery disease: obesity, non-insulin-dependent diabetes mellitus (NIDDM), and hypertriglyceridemia.[4-8] The cluster of factors also includes reduced plasma concentrations of high-density lipoprotein (HDL) cholesterol, a reduction that occurs through the exchange of HDL cholesteryl esters for the triglycerides in VLDL and chylomicrons.[9, 10] In NIDDM, insulin resistance in multiple tissue sites, especially adipose tissue, leads to impaired NEFA uptake and a rise in plasma NEFA and triglyceride concentrations.[11-13] *In vitro* studies have shown that several important cell types exhibit an active NEFA metabolism that may be impaired in pathological states. These cells include hepatocytes,[14] adipocytes,[6, 7, 12, 13] smooth muscle cells,[15] and neutrophils.[16]

The mechanism of NEFA transfer among lipoproteins and between lipoproteins and cell membranes is important to our understanding of lipid metabolism. There appears to be some consensus that fatty acids transfer between lipid and protein surfaces by means of rate-limiting desorption followed by diffusion-controlled uptake by an acceptor lipid surface or protein. This rate increases and decreases, respectively, with the degree of unsaturation and the chain length of the fatty acids.[17-19] The mechanism of lipid translocation across cell membranes remains unresolved. Some evidence favors a protein-mediated mechanism, and a fatty acid transport protein has been cloned from adipocytes.[20] Other evidence suggests that fatty acids spontaneously transfer across cell membranes and that differences in rates of transfer of fatty acids are simply a reflection of the metabolic state of the cell.[11]

In humans, the major fatty acids contain an even number of carbon atoms in straight chains that contain 14 to 22 carbon atoms. These chains may have from zero to six double bonds; fatty acids with zero, one, two, and three or more are called saturated, monounsaturated, diunsaturated, and polyunsaturated, respectively. The physical effect of an increase in the number of double bonds in a fatty acid is a reduction in the melting point. The physiological effects of unsaturation are much broader. Many of the acyltransferases that utilize fatty acids or their acyl–coenzyme A analogues have a specificity that varies according to unsaturation and chain length. In addition, some fatty acids are precursors for other bioregulatory molecules such as the eicosanoids and prostaglandins.

Fatty acids are usually described in terms of the number of carbon atoms (n) and the number of double bonds (m); they are named according to the location of the double bonds, with carboxyl-carbon being C_1. In humans consuming a diet of cold-water fish such as salmon, a group of polyunsaturated long-chained fatty acids have been found. Another nomenclature has been applied to these fatty acids, under which they are called omega-3 or n-3 fatty acids. In this system, the location of double bonds is indicated by counting from the last carbon (omega or n = 1), which is typically in a methyl group, to the position of the first carbon atom in each double bond.

Examples of fatty acids found in human plasma and tissues are shown in Table 23–1. In humans, the fatty acid compositions of plasma NEFA, plasma lipoproteins, and, to a lesser extent, adipose tissue are a function of the fatty acid composition of the diet. The effects of diets enriched in saturated, monounsaturated, polyunsaturated, and omega-3 fatty acids on plasma NEFA and on lipid compositions of individual plasma lipoprotein classes have been reported;[21] for the sake of brevity and illustration, effects only on plasma NEFA are shown in Table 23–2. The reported data show that the fatty acid compositions of plasma NEFA and lipoprotein lipids contain a higher fraction of those fatty acids that are found in the diet. These effects are likely to be connected to the cholesterol-lowering effects of diets in which polyunsaturated fatty acids replace saturated fatty acids, and according to the Hegsted equation,[22] the change in total plasma cholesterol (ΔTPC, mg/dL) in response to a change in the composition of the diet is given by:

$$\Delta TPC = 2.16\ \Delta S - 1.65\ \Delta P + 0.068\ \Delta C$$

where S and P are the percentages of calories derived from saturated and polyunsaturated fatty acids and C is the daily consumption of cholesterol (mg/day).

EXPERIMENTAL PLAN AND SAMPLING

From the brief summary given above, it is clear that fatty acid analyses provide important information about lipid metabolism in both clinical and basic research. In particular because of the possible roles of NEFA in the pathogenesis of obesity and NIDDM, and ultimately atherosclerosis, accuracy in measurement *in vitro* and *in vivo* is crucial. Relevant analyses include those that provide the fatty acid compositions of total NEFA,

Table 23–1 ✧ Structures of Typical Fatty Acids Found in Human Diets, Plasma, and Tissues

Fatty Acid		Structure
Saturated	Palmitic	$CH_3(CH_2)_{14}COOH$
	Stearic	$CH_3(CH_2)_{16}COOH$
Monounsaturated	Oleic	$CH_3(CH_2)_7CH=CH(CH_2)_7COOH$
	Linoleic	$CH_3(CH_2)_7CH=CH(CH_2)_7COOH$
Omega-6 polyunsaturated	Linoleic	$CH_3(CH_2)_4(CH=CHCH_2)_2(CH_2)_6COOH$
	Linolenic	$CH_3(CH_2)_4(CH=CHCH_2)_3(CH_2)_3COOH$
	Arachidonic	$CH_3(CH_2)_4(CH=CHCH_2)_4(CH_2)_2COOH$
Omega-3 polyunsaturated	Eicosapentaenoic	$CH_3(CH_2)_4(CH=CHCH_2)_5(CH_2)_2COOH$
	Docosahexaenoic	$CH_3(CH_2)_4(CH=CHCH_2)_6(CH_2)_2COOH$

Table 23–2 ✧ Nonesterified Fatty Acids in Plasma Following Four Dietary Interventions in Normolipidemic Men (N = 20)

Fatty Acid[a]	Dietary Fat (30% of Calories) Consisting Mainly of			
	Saturated Fat	Monounsaturated Fat	Polyunsaturated Fat	Polyunsaturated Fat + n-3 Fatty Acids
14:0 (S)	2.49	2.14	1.94	2.17
16:0 (S)	23.95	25.10	23.03	27.78
16:1 (M)	3.40	2.42	2.93	3.02
18:0 (S)	9.07	8.10	10.13	8.26
18:1 (M)	38.43	38.15	32.17	31.69
18:2 (P)	19.71	20.07	23.47	19.20
18:3 (P)	0.22	0.07	0.60	0.48
18:4 (P)	0.00	0.00	0.52	0.07
20:3 (P)	0.73	0.00	0.99	0.00
20:4 (P)	0.54	1.82	1.99	1.51
20:5 (n)	0.20	1.25	0.00	2.73
22:6 (n)	1.24	0.89	0.24	3.10

Source: Data from Pownall et al.[21]
[a] S = Saturated, M = Monounsaturated, P = Polyunsaturated, n = Omega-3

of unbound NEFA, and of cholesteryl, glyceryl, and phosphoglyceryl esters. These analyses may be performed in tissue culture media, plasma, and cell membranes, each of which may require special handling to prevent changes in fatty acid composition. Such changes can result from a variety of lipolytic processes occurring between the time of sampling and analysis. For longitudinal trials in which some analytes are not measured for several weeks or even months after collection, it is important to collect and store samples under conditions that minimize degradation.

Zambon et al. assessed for reliability a number of techniques for analyzing plasma NEFA.[23] One of the problems that had to be resolved was the artifactual elevation of plasma NEFA as the result of *in vitro* lipolysis following blood collection; this problem was particularly acute in hypertriglyceridemic plasma or following the administration of heparin. To minimize *in vitro* lipolysis, paraoxon, a cholinesterase inhibitor, was added to the plasma sample immediately following blood collection and separation. Paraoxon proved to be an effective inhibitor of lipolysis in preheparin plasma at room temperature for 2 h and in postheparin plasma stored immediately at $-20°$ C. Inhibition with paraoxon was not necessary for preheparin samples that were collected and immediately transferred to ice and assayed, or stored at $-70°$ C for up to 60 days before assaying.

Thus, it is advisable to use paraoxon as an inhibitor of lipolytic activity in postheparin plasma and to store these samples at $-70°$ C if analyses are to be performed at a later date. If plasma is to be analyzed for NEFA after long-term storage, it is advisable to verify that the analyte concentration remains stable for the term of storage. Optimal handling would probably involve blood collection in paraoxon-coated tubes, immediate transfer to ice, separation at $0°$ to $4°$ C, and storage at $-70°$ C.

CAUTION: Paraoxon is a nerve agent. Use a fume hood.

NEFA concentrations are highly variable intra-individually according to nutritional state, smoking, and exercise.[12] Values should be determined from triplicate samples. Subjects need to have fasted, without smoking immediately before sampling and preferably without having exercised. Exercise before sampling (as recently as the night before) would need to be repeated before any sampling. NEFA concentrations are low compared with other plasma risk markers; a typical NEFA value is 0.3 mmol/L with a range of 0.1–0.7 mmol/L daily in a healthy adult, compared with, for example, 5 mmol/L with a daily range of 4.9–5.1 mmol/L for cholesterol.[12] NEFA turnover is extremely rapid, with a typical turnover of 6 µmol/min/kg, compared with 0.03 µmol/min/kg for cholesterol and 10 µmol/min/kg for glucose.[12]

NEFA ANALYSIS

Several methods are commonly used for NEFA analysis; each has its advantages and disadvantages. Before a method is chosen, consideration must be given to the skill of the technical personnel, the cost of reagents, the instrumentation needed, and the precision and accuracy of the method. For clinical studies, each of the methods should be considered to determine which best addresses the study aims.

Direct Chemical Analysis

The titration method of Dole[24] remains a proven method. It involves the extraction of plasma with 40 parts 2-propanol, 10 parts heptane, and 1 part sulfuric acid. The acid provides the protons that give NEFA the neutrality necessary for solubilization in the organic phase. Typically, 5 parts of the extraction mixture are mixed with 1 part plasma by vortexing. The organic phase is collected, and thymol blue indicator blanks without fatty acids and palmitic acid standards within the range of normal, hypertriglyceridemic, or diabetic plasma (0.3–1.0 mmol/L) are treated in the same way. Freshly prepared NaOH in absolute ethanol is used to titrate the samples while the sample is gently agitated. The volume of the titrant is recorded at the endpoint, and the NEFA concentration determined on the basis of the calibration curve that is recorded with a range of palmitic acid concentrations.

The advantages of this method are that it requires very little specialized equipment and it is a direct chemical method in which the stoichiometry between titrant and NEFA is known. The disadvantages are that it is time-consuming, requires greater technical skill than some other methods, and does not give the concentration of individual fatty acid species.

High-Performance Liquid Chromatographic Analysis of Fluorescent NEFA Esters

Several methods in which NEFA are derivatized with a fluorescent reagent have been described. The reagents include 5-bromomethyl fluorescein,[25] 9-anthryldiazomethane (ADAM),[26] 4-(2-carbazoylpyrrolidin-1-yl)-7-(*N,N*-dimethylaminosulfonyl)-2,1,3-benzoxadiazole,[27] 2-(4-hydrazinocarbonylphenyl)-4,5-diphenylimidazole,[28] and *p*-bromophenacyl bromide.[29] All these derivatives are suitable for the determination of total fatty acid concentration and fatty acid composition. However, the conditions have been best detailed for ADAM[26] and *p*-bromophenacyl bromide.[29] Both procedures begin with a Dole extraction followed by derivatization to the fluorescent ester, which can be detected by monitoring the fluorescence of the effluent from a reverse-phase high-performance liquid chromatography column.

The limits of sensitivity are a function of the absorption and fluorescence properties of the derivative. An optimal derivatizing agent would selectively react with fatty acids, and it would have a high extinction coefficient in a spectral range where light sources have their most intense outputs. Furthermore, the fluorescence of the derivatized fatty acid should have a high quantum yield that is independent of the structure of the acyl chain, and should appear in a spectral range where detectors have high sensitivity. As the cost of lasers falls and their power and reliability improve, it is likely that more commercial instruments will use a laser source.[25]

The advantages of high-performance liquid chromatographic methods combined with fluorescence detection are high sensitivity and discrimination of most fatty acid species. As technology improves, it is likely that newer methods with improved molecular species discrimination and sensitivity will be developed. The disadvantages of these methods are that they require expensive instrumentation and sophisticated technical support, and their results may be confounded by other carboxyl-containing species that form fluorescent derivatives. Before these methods are embraced for any study, they should be thoroughly evaluated in systems with a predetermined fatty acid composition and concentration.

Analysis of Unbound Fatty Acids

In plasma most NEFA are associated with albumin and the plasma lipoproteins, and the fraction that is associated with lipoproteins is greatly increased in physiological states (such as diabetes) in which there are high plasma concentrations of fatty acids.[30] However, as with all sparingly soluble substances, a small proportion of the NEFA circulate in the hydrated and unbound state. The concentration of this fraction may be very important physiologically because the rate of transport is very close to diffusion controlled. As a consequence, the concentration of unbound NEFA is an important determinant of fatty acid flow into cells. In the past, the concentration of unbound fatty acids could be determined only by such methods as equilibrium dialysis, gel filtration, and ultracentrifugation, all of which are model dependent and require some expensive instrumentation.

Richieri and Kleinfeld recently described a fluorescence method that gives the concentration of unbound NEFA.[31] The method uses intestinal fatty acid–binding protein that has been tagged with the fluorescent probe acrylodan. The labeled protein, ADIFAB, is nonfluorescent in the absence of NEFA and exhibits increasing fluorescence as the NEFA concentration increases. On the basis of this method, the mean concentration of unbound NEFA in serum was 7.5 nmol/L, which was six orders of magnitude lower than the mean concentration of total serum NEFA.[31] Because the concentration of unbound NEFA increases exponentially with the ratio of total NEFA to albumin, the method is a sensitive one for assessment of physiological status. It is anticipated that these measurements will be increasingly applied to the study of obesity, diabetes, and atherosclerosis.

Gas Chromatographic Analysis

Several methods for the gas chromatographic analysis of fatty acids have been described. Most are laborious because they involve an extraction method.[32-35] A more recent report describes a procedure in which plasma NEFA are directly esterified by a 2% solution of acetyl chloride in methanol that contains an internal standard.[36] The resulting esters are extracted into hexane and an aliquot is injected into a gas chromatograph. The concentrations of the fatty acids were calculated by comparing the integrated area under their respective peaks with an internal standard (tridecanoic acid) of known concentration.

This procedure has the advantages of relative simplicity and providing the concentrations of individual fatty acid classes. The disadvantages are that it requires a gas chromatograph and it is not as sensitive as some of the fluorescence-based assays. In addition, according to one report[37] and our experiences with this assay, the treatment of plasma with methanolic acetyl chloride is associated with some hydrolysis of plasma acyl esters. Nevertheless, the procedure is useful if the spontaneous hydrolysis is less than the amount of analyte being estimated. Additional method development is needed to improve this otherwise convenient assay.

Enzymatic Analysis

Several procedures for the enzymatic determination of NEFA have been reported,[38-40] and with the availability of commercial kits these methods have enjoyed wide use. Like other kits, the one supplied by Wako involves a complex and yet reliable chemistry. The method relies on the formation of acyl–coenzyme A from NEFA and coenzyme A in the presence of acyl–coenzyme A synthase. The resulting acyl–coenzyme A is treated with acyl–coenzyme A oxidase, thereby liberating hydrogen peroxide, which in the presence of peroxidase leads to the oxidative condensation of 3-methyl-*N*-ethyl-*N*-(β-hydroethyl)-aniline, with 4-aminoantipyrine giving a colored adduct that can be quantified spectrophotometrically. The amount of NEFA in the sample can be calculated on the basis of absorption at 550 nm, and a calibration curve prepared with standards having known concentrations.

The advantages of this procedure are its simplicity and the requirement of only a spectrophotometer. The disadvantages are the low sensitivity (> 0.1 mmol/L) and the inability to quantify individual NEFA species. In addition, there is reduced sensitivity against long-chain polyunsaturated fatty acids such as arachidonate, eicosapentaenoate, and docosahexaenoate, so that the plasma NEFA of patients on diets containing long-chain omega-3 fatty acids will be underreported.

Colorimetric Methods

Several colorimetric methods have been reported.[41-43] These are generally indirect methods based on the partitioning of copper into soaps formed by fatty acids. They are time-consuming and not very sensitive. Any future development of a NEFA assay that might employ an absorbance measurement is likely to be displaced by a more sensitive fluorescence method based on similar chemistry.

FINAL PERSPECTIVES

Some of the methods cited are also applicable to the analysis of fatty acids liberated from esters by treatment with base or with an enzyme. However, gas chromatographic analysis of fatty acid methyl esters liberated by treatment with methanolic base and boron trifluoride is likely to be simpler than fluorescence or colorimetric methods. Given the relatively high concentrations of fatty acid esters compared with NEFA in most biological fluids, much smaller sample volumes can usually be used.

The choice of method in a given application will depend on the number of samples to be run, the amount of sample available, and the possible need to measure all NEFA species. In all cases it is advisable to collect samples and cool immediately with an ice bath to minimize lipolysis. If samples cannot be analyzed immediately, they should be stored in the presence of paraoxon at $-70°$ C, particularly if they are from hypertriglyceridemic and/or postheparin plasma. If an enzymatic method is used, the paraoxon could interfere with the assay, and storage will have to be at −70° C in the absence of paraoxon. For small studies, it is economically feasible to separate fatty acids from other lipids by thin-layer or high-performance liquid chromatography and to analyze the respective band or peak by gas chromatography of methyl esters or similarly formed fluorescent derivatives. For large studies, it is usually more economical to use one of the enzymatic kits. In all cases, the appropriate quality assurance and quality control measures should be in place before the study is begun.   ✧

REFERENCES

1. Goldblatt PJ, Gunning WT III. Ultrastructure of the liver and biliary tract in health and disease. Ann Clin Lab Sci 1984;14:159-67.
2. Miller KW, Small DM. Structure of triglyceride-rich lipoproteins: an analysis of core and surface phases. In: Gotto AM Jr, ed. Plasma lipoproteins: new comprehensive biochemistry, Vol. 14. Amsterdam: Elsevier, 1987:1-75.
3. Tabas I. The stimulation of the cholesterol esterification pathway by atherogenic lipoproteins in macrophages. Curr Opin Lipidol 1995;6:260-8.
4. Schneider DJ, Sobel BE. Synergistic augmentation of expression of plasminogen activator type-1 induced by insulin, very-low-density lipoproteins, and fatty acids. Coron Artery Dis 1996;7:7813-7.
5. Lewis GF, Uffelman KD, Szeto LW, Weller B, Steiner G. Interaction between free fatty acids and insulin in the acute control of very low density lipoprotein production in humans. J Clin Invest 1995;95:158-66.
6. Egan BM, Hennes MMI, Stepniakowski KT, O'Shaughnessy IM, Kissebah AH, Goodfriend TL. Obesity hypertension is related more to insulin's fatty acid than glucose action. Hypertension 1996;27:723-8.
7. Laws A. Free fatty acids, insulin resistance and lipoprotein metabolism. Curr Opin Lipidol 1996;7:172-7.
8. Hopkins PN, Hunt SC, Wu LL, Williams GH, Williams RR. Hypertension, dyslipidemia, and insulin resistance: links in a chain or spokes on a wheel? Curr Opin Lipidol 1996;7:241-53.
9. Deckelbaum RJ, Granot E, Oschry Y, Rose L, Eisenberg S. Plasma triglyceride determines structure-composition in low and high density lipoproteins. Arteriosclerosis 1984;4:225-31.
10. Patsch JR, Prasad S, Gotto AM Jr, Patsch W. High density lipoproteins2: relationship of the plasma levels of this lipoprotein species to its composition, to the magnitude of postprandial lipemia, and to the activities of lipoprotein lipase and hepatic lipase. J Clin Invest 1987;80:341-7.
11. Civelek N, Hamilton JA, Tornheim K, Kelly KL, Corkey BE. Intracellular pH in adipocytes: effects of free fatty acid diffusion across the plasma membrane, lipolytic agonists, and insulin. Proc Natl Acad Sci USA 1996;93:10139-44.
12. Frayn KN, Williams CM, Arner P. Are increased plasma non-esterified fatty acid concentrations a risk marker for coronary heart disease and other chronic diseases? Clin Sci 1996;90:243-53.
13. Schwartz MW, Brunzell JD. Regulation of body adiposity and the problem of obesity. [Review]. Arterioscler Thromb Vasc Biol 1997;17:233-8.
14. Dixon JL, Furukawa S, Ginsberg HN. Oleic acid stimulates secretion of apolipoprotein B-containing lipoproteins from HepG2 cells by reducing intracellular degradation of apolipoprotein B. [Abstract]. Arteriosclerosis 1990;10:763a.
15. Lu G, Morinelli TA, Meier KE, Rosenzweig SA, Egan BM. Oleic acid–induced mitogenic signaling in vascular smooth muscle cells: a role for protein kinase C. Circ Res 1996;79:611-8.

16. Li Y, Ferrante A, Poulos A, Harvey DP. Neutrophil oxygen radical generation: synergistic responses to tumor necrosis factor and mono/polyunsaturated fatty acids. J Clin Invest 1996;97:1605–9.

17. Zhang F, Kamp F, Hamilton JA. Dissociation of long and very long chain fatty acids from phospholipid bilayers. Biochemistry 1996;35:16055–60.

18. Pownall HJ, Hickson DL, Smith LC. Transport of biological lipophiles: effect of lipophile structure. J Am Chem Soc 1983;105:2440–5.

19. Massey JB, Bick DH, Pownall HJ. Spontaneous transfer of monoacyl amphiphiles between lipid and protein surfaces. Biophys J, in press.

20. Schaffer JE, Lodish HF. Expression cloning and characterization of a novel adipocyte long chain fatty acid transport protein. Cell 1994;79:427–36.

21. Pownall HJ, Raynaud AS, Harper E, Choi S, Rohrbach K, Pao Q, et al. Effects of 12 weeks of dietary fish oil, polyunsaturated fat, monounsaturated fat, and saturated fat on human plasma lipoprotein structure and composition. In: Pownall HJ, Spector AS, eds. Proceedings from the Scientific Conference on Omega-3 Fatty Acids in Nutrition, Vascular Biology, and Medicine. Dallas: American Heart Association, 1995:64–78.

22. Hegsted DM, McGandy RB, Myers ML, Stare FJ. Quantitative effects of dietary fat on serum cholesterol in man. Am J Clin Nutr 1965;17:281–95.

23. Zambon A, Hashimoto SI, Brunzell JD. Analysis of techniques to obtain plasma for measurement of levels of free fatty acids. J Lipid Res 1993;34:1021–8.

24. Dole VP. A relation between non-esterified fatty acids in plasma and the metabolism of glucose. J Clin Invest 1956;35:150–4.

25. Mukherjee PS, DeSilva KH, Karnes HT. 5-Bromomethyl fluorescein (5-BMF) for derivatization of carboxyl containing analytes for use with laser-induced fluorescence detection. Pharm Res 1995;12:930–6.

26. Tojo H, Ono T, Okamoto M. Reverse-phase high-performance liquid chromatographic assay of phospholipases: application of spectrophotometric detection to rat phospholipase A$_2$ isozymes. J Lipid Res 1993;34:837–44.

27. Toyo'oka T, Takahashi M, Suzuki A, Ishii Y. Determination of free fatty acids in blood, tagged with 4-(2-carbazoylpyrrolidin-1-yl)-7-(N,N-dimethylaminosulfonyl)-2,1,3-benzoxadiazole, by high-performance liquid chromatography with fluorescence detection. Biomed Chromatogr 1995;9:162–70.

28. Nakashima K, Taguchi Y, Kuroda N, Akiyama S, Duan G. 2-(4-Hydrazinocarbonylphenyl)-4,5-diphenylimidazole as a versatile fluorescent derivatization reagent for the high-performance liquid chromatographic analysis of free fatty acids. J Chromatogr 1993;619:1–8.

29. Püttmann M, Krug H, von Ochsenstein E, Kattermann R. Fast HPLC determination of serum free fatty acids in the picomole range. Clin Chem 1993;39:825–32.

30. Cistola DP, Small DM. Fatty acid distribution in systems modeling the normal and diabetic human circulation: a ^{13}C nuclear magnetic resonance study. J Clin Invest 1991;87:1431–41.

31. Richieri GV, Kleinfeld AM. Unbound free fatty acid levels in human serum. J Lipid Res 1995;36:229–40.

32. MacGee J, Allen KG. Preparation of methyl esters from the saponifiable fatty acids in small biological specimens for gas–liquid chromatographic analysis. J Chromatogr 1974;100:35–42.

33. Tserng K-Y, Kliegman RM, Miettinen E-L, Kalhan SC. A rapid, simple, and sensitive procedure for the determination of free fatty acids in plasma using glass capillary column gas–liquid chromatography. J Lipid Res 1981;22:852–8.

34. Lefèvre G, Tallet F, Baassou S, Agneray J, Yonger J, Raichvarg D. Free fatty acid microdetermination by gas–liquid chromatography without transmethylating effects of methylation procedure. J Biochem Biophys Methods 1985;11:133–6.

35. Höckel M. A microliter method for the gas chromatographic determination of long-chain non-esterified fatty acids in human serum or plasma. J Chromatogr 1980;221:205–14.

36. Lepage G, Roy CC. Specific methylation of plasma nonesterified fatty acids in a one-step reaction. J Lipid Res 1988;29:227–35.

37. Hallaq Y, Becker TC, Manno CS, Laposata M. Use of acetyl chloride/methanol for assumed selective methylation of plasma nonesterified fatty acids results in significant methylation of esterified fatty acids. Lipids 1993;28:355-60.

38. Mulder C, Schouten JA, Popp-Snijders C. Determination of free fatty acids: a comparative study of the enzymatic versus the gas chromatographic and the colorimetric method. J Clin Chem Clin Biochem 1983;21:823-7.

39. Ramirez I. A problem with enzymatic determination of free fatty acids in rat and mouse blood. J Lipid Res 1984;25:92.

40. Degen AJM, Van Der Vies J. Enzymatic microdetermination of free fatty acids in plasma of animals using paraoxon to prevent lipolysis. Scand J Clin Lab Invest 1985;45: 283-5.

41. Lauwerys RR. Colorimetric determination of free fatty acids. Anal Biochem 1969;32: 331-3.

42. Regouw BJM, Cornelissen PJHC, Helder RAP, Spijkers JBF, Weeber YMM. Specific determination of free fatty acid in plasma. Clin Chim Acta 1971;31:187-95.

43. Brunk SD, Swanson JR. Colorimetric method for free fatty acids in serum validated by comparison with gas chromatography. Clin Chem 1981;27:924-6.

Determination and Clinical Significance of Lipoprotein Particles LpA-I and LpA-I:A-II

24

Patrick Duriez and Jean-Charles Fruchart

INTRODUCTION

❖   Many epidemiological studies have indicated that the plasma level of high-density lipoproteins (HDL) is inversely correlated with the risk for coronary heart disease.[1] It has been hypothesized that HDL exerts this protective effect by the "reverse" transport of excess cholesterol from peripheral tissues to the liver.[2]

Conventionally, HDL are isolated by ultracentrifugation in the density range of 1.063 to 1.21 kg/L. Two main subfractions have been identified as HDL2 (1.063 < d < 1.125 kg/L) and HDL3 (1.155 < d < 1.21 kg/L).

Ultracentrifugation is a valuable tool for HDL isolation, but this procedure alters the structure and composition of the particles.[3] Moreover, ultracentrifugation does not take into account the protein component of the lipoproteins, which plays a key role in their metabolism. The discovery of essential metabolic role of apolipoproteins led to the realization that they could be used as specific markers for the identification of lipoprotein particles and as a new means for the characterization and classification of lipoproteins.[4] The availability of antibodies directed against specific apolipoproteins allowed the isolation and characterization of lipoprotein particles based on their apolipoprotein composition.

The purpose of this chapter is to review the clinical significance of HDL subfractions according to the apolipoprotein composition.

ISOLATION AND COMPOSITION OF HDL PARTICLES

Lipoproteins can be distinguished on the basis of their apolipoprotein composition. According to concept developed by Alaupovic,[4] lipoproteins can be separated into simple lipoprotein particles that contain one apolipoprotein (LpB, LpA-I, etc.), and complex lipoprotein particles that contain two or more apolipoproteins (LpB:E, LpB:C-III, LpB:C-III:E, LpA-I:A-II, etc.).

We purified HDL particles from plasma of normolipidemic subjects according to their content of apolipoproteins A-I, A-II, and A-IV using sequential immunoaffinity chromatography.[5] A flowchart of the process is given in Figure 24-1. The result was isolation of four types of particles: LpA-I, LpA-I:A-II, LpA-IV, and LpA-IV:A-I. As shown in Table 24-1, all types had a similar proportion of protein but differed significantly

Figure 24–1 ◆ Flow Diagram of Sequential Immunoaffinity Chromatography

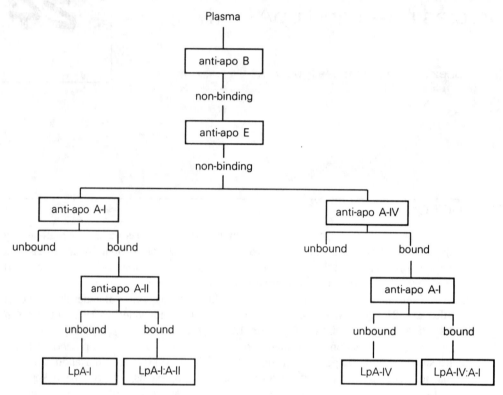

Table 24–1 ◆ Protein, Lipid, and Apolipoprotein Composition of LpA-I, LpA-I:A-II, LpA-IV, and LpA-IV:A-I Particles (Mass %)

Component	LpA-I	LpA-I:A-II	LpA-IV	LpA-IV:A-I
Proteins	62.0 ± 7.4	65.2 ± 7.3	70.2 ± 20.1	61.3 ± 9.4
LIPIDS				
Total cholesterol	11.8 ± 4.1	11.5 ± 3.9	4.2 ± 3.5	8.0 ± 3.8
Free cholesterol	2.8 ± 1.1	1.6 ± 1.1	0.4 ± 0.2	1.2 ± 1.1
Triglycerides	5.0 ± 2.2	3.8 ± 1.8	9.4 ± 6.8	9.6 ± 5.7
Phospholipids	21.2 ± 4.4	19.5 ± 4.3	16.2 ± 10.5	21.1 ± 6.9
APOLIPOPROTEINS				
A-I	97.6 ± 2.5	67.4 ± 13.3	—	57.8 ± 14.4
A-II	—	31.4 ± 13.5	0.4 ± 0.7	10.2 ± 2.7
A-IV	2.1 ± 2.4	1.0 ± 1.9	99.6 ± 0.8	31.5 ± 21.0
C-III	0.3 ± 0.3	1.2 ± 0.2	0.1 ± 0.1	0.4 ± 0.1

All values are given as mean ± SD

in cholesterol and triglyceride content. LpA-I and LpA-I:A-II particles were found to contain more cholesterol (approximately 11% of total weight) than LpA-IV and LpA-IV:A-I (4% and 8%, respectively). Conversely, the apo A-IV–containing particles had more triglyceride (10%).[6]

Particles were defined by their major apolipoprotein content: LpA-I and LpA-IV contained a single major apolipoprotein. LpA-I:A-II and LpA-IV:A-I were more complex particles, but both still had apo A-I as the major apolipoprotein. LpA-I:VA-I particles contained apo A-I and apo A-II in a molar ratio of 4:3, whereas LpA-IV:A-I contained apo A-I, apo A-IV, and apo A-II in a molar ratio of approximately 3.5:1:1.

Of the total recovered weight of apo A-I, 65% was found in LpA-I:A-II, 25% in LpA-I, and only 1–2% in LpA-IV:A-I particles. Most of the apo A-II was found in LpA-I:A-II, with a small proportion in LpA-IV. Of the total recovered weight of apo A-IV, 92% was found in LpA-IV and LpA-IV:A-I particles, 5% was associated with LpA-I:A-II, and 3% was associated with LpA-I. All particles contained a small proportion of apo C-III. In addition, sodium dodecylsulphate–polyacrylamide gel electrophoresis (SDS-PAGE) of the isolated particles revealed the presence of other proteins. The proline-rich protein lecithin-cholesterol acyltransferase (LCAT), cholesteryl ester-transfer protein (CETP), and apo D were visualized using immunoblotting with specific antibodies for each type of isolated particle[6] and quantified.

The LCAT activity of the particles was measured by the method of Chen and Albers.[7] The specific activity of LCAT was expressed as the percentage of cholesterol esterified per 100 μg of protein. Under these conditions, and using the value for the LpA-I particle to represent 100% activity, cholesterol esterification never exceeded 16%. The LpA-IV particles demonstrated most activity, followed by LpA-IV:A-I and LpA-I. LpA-I:A-II particles showed little LCAT activity. Of considerable significance was the finding that CETP was present in LpA-I, LpA-IV:A-I, and LpA-IV, but not in LpA-I:A-II particles (unpublished data).

Analysis of phospholipids revealed differences in the type of phospholipid constituents between the particles. The phosphatidylcholine/sphingomyelin ratio was 3.9:1 and 5.3:1 for LpA-I and LpA-I:A-II, respectively, and approximately 1:1 for the apo A-IV–containing particles.

PHYSIOLOGICAL ROLE OF APO A-I–CONTAINING PARTICLES

One of the key questions is whether the different HDL particles differ in their physiological roles. To gain some insight into the mechanisms of cholesterol movement in peripheral cells, cultured adipose cells were used. Adipose tissue is the main organ of cholesterol storage in the body and contains mostly non-esterified cholesterol. Moreover, rat adipocytes can accumulate and release, on feeding and fasting respectively, large amounts of cholesterol, suggesting that these peripheral cells may represent a relaxed form of control of cholesterol homeostasis. This observation has been advantageous in the study of cholesterol efflux from cholesterol-preloaded adipose cells in culture, using Ob1771 adipose cells.

A subclone of Ob17 cells established from the epididymal fat pad of the Ob/Ob mouse was used as a model of peripheral cells. In the presence of low-density lipoprotein (LDL), these cells accumulate cholesterol via the LDL receptor pathway. After cholesterol preloading with LDL, long-term exposure to LpA-I particles promoted cho-lesterol efflux. Such efflux was not observed in the presence of LpA-I:A-II.[8] The ligands that recognize the cell surface HDL binding sites have been identified as apo A-I, apo A-IV, and apo A-II.[9, 10]

It has been proposed that apo A-I and apo A-IV play the role of agonists and apo A-II that of antagonist of cholesterol efflux.[10] It has been reported that HDL3 induces protein kinase C-dependent translocation of cholesterol from intracellular mem-brane to the cell surface in human fibroblasts or bovine endothelial cells.[11] We recently demonstrated that cholesterol efflux from adipose cells is coupled to diacylglycerol production and to protein kinase C activation.[12] The role of apo A-II as an antagonist in the generation of cholesterol efflux is strongly supported by the fact that the binding of apo A-I liposomes, but not apo A-II liposomes, results in diacylglycerol production. It has been recently reported that both LpA-I and LpA-I:A-II demonstrate equal ability to promote efflux of cholesterol from several types of cells, such as fibroblasts, smooth muscle cells, and Fu5AH cells.[13, 14]

QUANTIFICATION OF LpA-I AND LpA-I:A-II PARTICLES

Quantification of LpA-I and LpA-I:A-II lipoprotein particles is possible using techniques such as immunoprecipitation,[15] two-phase electroimmunoassay,[16] enzyme-linked differ-ential antibody immunosorbent assay,[5] and differential electroimmunoassay.[17] The two latter methods have been adapted for routine analysis and are described below.

Enzyme-Linked Differential Antibody Immunosorbent Assay

An enzyme-linked immunosorbent assay (ELISA) method has been described for the measurement of LpA-I:A-II particles.[5] The method consisted of two steps: measurement of LpA-I:A-II and measurement of total apo A-I.

To measure LpA-I:A-II, wells of the plates were coated with rabbit antibodies to apo A-II (50 μL per well, diluted 100-fold in deionized water) for 18 h at 25° C in a humidified chamber. After blocking the non-reacted sites, and three washes with 1% rabbit serum in deionized water, 50 μL samples of non-delipidated plasma, diluted in 150 mmol/L Na_2HPO_4 buffer, pH 6.5, containing 1% of rabbit serum, were added to the wells and incubated for 18 h at 4° C. During this incubation step, only LpA-I:A-II were retained; LpA-I were removed during the subsequent washing with Na_2HPO_4 buffer.

After incubation with peroxidase-labeled antibodies to apo A-I, the measurement of retained peroxidase activity by addition of peroxidase substrate allowed determination of the amount of apo A-I associated with apo A-II. Quantitative recovery of known amounts of LpA-I:A-II isolated by immunoaffinity chromatography added to plasma varied from 95 to 102% (n = 7). The intra- and interassay coefficients of variation were 4.8% and 9.2%, respectively.

Total apo A-I was measured using the non-competitive enzyme-linked immuno-assay. Here, the plates were coated with antibodies to apo A-I. After incubation with various dilutions of non-delipidated plasma, the total amount of apo A-I retained by these antibodies was evaluated using peroxidase-labeled antibodies to apo A-I (LpA-I:A-II + LpA-I). The difference between total apo A-I (LpA-I:A-II + LpA-I) and apo A-I associated with apo A-II (LpA-I:A-II) represented the apo A-I (LpA-I) associated with particles without apo A-II. Addition of LpA-I isolated by immunoaffinity chromatography to the plasma with a known concentration of LpA-I resulted in an average recovery of 95% (93–103%, *n* = 7). Intra- and interassay coefficients of variation were 5.1 and 9.6%, respectively.

Differential Electroimmunoassay

A rocket electroimmunoassay procedure has been developed to quantify LpA-I particles containing apo A-I but free of apo A-II.[17]

Preparation of Plates

Suitable concentrations of polyclonal antisera to apo A-I and to apo A-II were incorporated in a 9 g/L solution of buffered (electrophoresis buffer, pH 8.6) agarose at 55° C, poured onto plastic films, and allowed to gel at room temperature. Wells were punched in the gel (16 per film), and the plates were then ready to use. Samples were diluted 50-fold in isotonic saline, and 5 µL of the solution were placed in each well. Electrophoresis was carried out at 12.5 V/cm for 4 h in a pH 8.6 buffer containing Tris 7.05 g/L, glycine 5.65 g/L, barbital 0.285 g/L, and sodium barbital 1.62 g/L . When anti-apo A-II was used in very high amounts that exceed anti-apo A-I, the LpA-I:A-II particles were retained near the wells, whereas LpA-I particles continued to migrate and react with anti-apo A-I. After electrophoresis, the remaining proteins were absorbed by placing on the gels one layer of thin filter paper soaked with isotonic saline and two layers of thick of filter paper, all held in place under a pressure of 1 kg for 20 minutes. Thereafter, gels were vertically washed in isotonic saline for 60 minutes and absorption process was repeated for 10 minutes. Plates were dried and stained with Coomassie Brilliant Blue. After destaining, "rockets" corresponding to LpA-I:A-II particles (low peaks) and to LpA-I particles (less-intensely colored high peaks) were visible.

LpA-I:A-II can be calculated as the difference between total apo A-I and LpA-I levels. LpA-I:A-II levels can be routinely measured using a commercialized kit (Sebia, Issy les Moulineaux, France).[17]

Primary and Secondary Standards

LpA-I particles isolated by immunoaffinity chromatography were used as a primary standard. They were concentrated under reduced pressure, and the concentration of apo A-I was determined by electroimmunoassay. This primary standard was used to measure the concentration of LpA-I in a lyophilized normolipidemic plasma, which was subsequently used as a secondary standard.

Precision

Within-run precision was estimated by repeated measurements (*n* = 32) of LpA-I concentrations in three plasma samples containing high, medium, and low amounts; resulting CVs were 1.51%, 2.57% and 3.72%, respectively. The between-run precision was assessed by performing 10 measurements of LpA-I in the same samples on four consecutive days; resulting CVs were 3.01%, 4.12% and 4.56% for the high, medium, and low concentrations, respectively.

Sample Storage

The effect of freezing was investigated by comparing LpA-I results for fresh plasma samples and samples frozen (−20° C) for a four-month period ($n = 80$). Results were similar after the first freeze-thaw cycle. After the second freeze-thaw cycle, the results on frozen samples were significantly lower compared to fresh samples.

Comparison of the Two Methods

The ELISA method to measure LpA-I:A-II is very sensitive but difficult to implement in a routine laboratory. In our view, its use is limited to research laboratories. On the other hand, the differential immunoassay method is easy to use, is highly reproducible, and comparable results are obtained among different routine laboratories. We think that this method is better suited for the clinical laboratories, but it is relatively expensive and difficult to automate.

CLINICAL SIGNIFICANCE OF LpA-I AND LpA-I:A-II LEVELS

Distribution in Normolipidemic Men

HDL-cholesterol (HDL-C), apo A-I, and LpA-I were measured in 233 healthy normolipidemic young men (cholesterol < 250 mg/dL and triglycerides < 200 mg/dL).[18] Among these subjects, the composition of HDL was highly variable: the 10th and the 90th percentile values for the HDL-C/apo A-I ratio were 0.32 and 0.49, respectively. The 10th and 90th percentiles for apo A-I and LpA-I:A-II concentrations were 126 and 167 mg/dL and 83 and 116 mg/dL, respectively. On the other hand, LpA-I showed a much larger variation: the 10th and 90th percentiles were 33 and 62 mg/dL, respectively. The distribution of individual values of LpA-I showed that this fraction of apo A-I–containing particles was highly variable among subjects; the LpA-I/apo A-I ratio varied from 0.18 to 0.58. Triglyceride, LpA-I, and LpA-I:A-II concentrations correlated with HDL-C, but there was no correlation between apo A-I–containing particles and plasma triglyceride level.

Longevity

We hypothesized that octogenarians survive the age when the incidence of coronary heart disease (CHD) is very high due to several protective factors. We compared HDL-C, HDL2-cholesterol (HDL2-C), HDL3-cholesterol (HDL3-C), apo A-I, and apo A-II in octogenarians and younger control subjects who smoked less than 10 cigarettes per day and were not taking drugs known to affect lipid metabolism.[19] We also compared the levels of LpA-I and LpA-I:A-II in these individuals using the differential immunoassay procedure. In men, the total HDL-C was similar in octogenarians and in controls aged 38 ± 8 years, while HDL2-C was higher and HDL3-C, apo A-I, and A-II were lower in octogenarians than in controls. In women, the levels of HDL-C and apo A-I were similar in premenopausal and octogenarian subjects, but were higher in postmenopausal women than in octogenarians. HDL2-C and apo A-II were similar in all three groups. In contrast, HDL3-C was higher in premenopausal and postmenopausal control women than in octogenarians. However, LpA-I was significantly elevated in octogenarian men and women (men: 61 ± 14 mg/dL; women 70 ± 14 mg/dL) compared to younger control subjects (men: 48 ± 12 mg/dL; premenopausal women: 53 ± 11 mg/dL; postmenopausal women: 63 ± 19 mg/dL). On the other hand, LpA-I:A-II was clearly lower in octogenarians. The distribution of LpA-I and LpA-I:A-II values also appeared to be modified by age, with a shift of the distribution toward higher values of LpA-I and lower values of LpA-I:A-II in octogenarians as compared with younger subjects. This could mean that individuals with low levels of LpA-I have a higher frequency of CHD during the sixth or seventh decade of life.

Brewer et al.[20] recently investigated LpA-I and LpA-I:A-II in a kindred with hyper-alphalipoproteinemia and a decreased risk of CHD. The selective increase in LpA-I in the 60-year-old putative homozygote proband with a family history of longevity supports the concept that these particles may represent the "anti-atherogenic" fraction of HDL.

Coronary Heart Disease

LpA-I, but not LpA-I:A-II, was found to be lower in normolipidemic patients with an-giographically documented CHD, compared to asymptomatic subjects and a group of patients with angiographically normal coronary arteries.[21] However, in a recent study which found triglyceride levels to be higher in the patients than in the controls, both LpA-I and LpA-I:A-II were reduced to a similar degree in patients with CHD.[22]

A case-control study of apo A-I–containing particles has been carried out in three populations with different CHD risk.[23] Male patients with myocardial infarction and controls were recruited in two French centers, Strasbourg and Toulouse, and in Belfast in Northern Ireland. The standardized CHD mortality rates in Belfast, Strasbourg, and Toulouse were, respectively, 348, 102, and 78 per 100,000. In Northern Ireland and France, patients had lower levels of HDL cholesterol, apo A-I, apo A-II, LpA-I and LpA-II:A-I in comparison to controls. In control subjects and in patients, the level of LpA-I was lower in Northern Ireland than in France. A high-risk profile, characterized by a low LpA-I level, was more frequent in Northern Ireland. Furthermore, the multi-variate analyses suggest that LpA-I/HDL cholesterol ratio is a significant marker of CHD risk. We have recently observed that the level of LpA-I (but not LpA-I:A-II) is lower in children whose parents had premature CHD than in a control group with no family history of CHD.[24]

Primary and Secondary Dyslipidemias

Some dyslipidemias have characteristic patterns of apo A-I particles. For instance, Type III dyslipidemia is characterized by a decrease of LpA-I and an increase of LpA-I:A-II.[25] The HDL decrease observed in patients with chronic renal failure treated with hemo-dialysis is mainly due to a decrease in LpA-I:A-II.[26] Non-insulin dependent diabetes mellitus is characterized by a specific decrease in LpA-I particles.[27]

Diet

Diet can also modify the LpA-I concentration. The effect of the ratio of dietary polyunsaturated fat to saturated fat (P/S) on apo A-I–containing particles has been investigated. With total fat and cholesterol intake kept constant, a high P/S diet led to a decrease in LpA-I but not LpA-I:A-II particles, compared to a low P/S diet.[28]

Alcohol consumption increases circulating levels of HDL. Some authors suggest a beneficial effect of chronic alcohol consumption on CHD. We investigated the relationships between LpA-I and LpA-I:A-II concentrations and alcohol consumption in 344 men and found that LpA-I:A-II levels increased and LpA-I levels decreased with an increasing alcohol intake.[29]

Studies with octogenarians and patients with CHD suggest that LpA-I is the main anti-atherogenic particle. Therefore, it seems unlikely that chronic alcohol consumption would have an anti-atherogenic effect, at least due to changes in LpA-I and LpA-I:A-II levels.

Effects of Drugs on Apo A-I Particles

Considering that LpA-I is a potent marker of cardiovascular risk in clinical and in epidemiological studies, it is interesting to study the effect of drug therapy on LpA-I level. Two main questions concerning the effects of drugs arise:

❖ Do compounds with various mechanisms of action have different effects on HDL particles?

❖ Does pharmacological modulation of LpA-I concentration change cardiovascular morbidity and mortality?

We now have some data to answer the former question, but further research is still needed to answer the latter.

Atmeh et al.[16] showed that the use of nicotinic acid may increase LpA-I concentration, whereas probucol leads to a decrease in the concentration of this particle. In contrast, nicotinic acid decreased LpA-I:A-II and probucol had no major effect. We have shown that fenofibrate decreases LpA-I and increases LpA-I:A-II,[30] whereas hydroxymethylglutaryl-CoA reductase inhibitors such as simvastatin and pravastatin have different effects. Simvastatin increased LpA-I, particularly when baseline levels were low,[30] but had no effect on LpA-I:A-II. Pravastatin increased both LpA-I and LpA-I:A-II.[31] The bile acid sequestrant, cholestyramine, also increased the concentration of these two particle types.

It has been suggested that LpA-I may represent the particle that is involved in cholesterol efflux from peripheral cells. We speculate that the observed increase in LpA-I may potentiate the beneficial cardiovascular effect of low-density lipoprotein cholesterol reduction observed on statin measurement. Conversely, the decrease caused by fenofibrate might be considered a potentially harmful effect. However, kinetic studies are necessary to determine whether HMG-CoA reductase inhibitors and cholestyramine increase, and fenofibrate decreases, LpA-I level by inducing an excess synthesis of the particle or by inhibiting its catabolism.

CONCLUSION

The introduction of immunological methods that allow the separation of various apo A-I–containing lipoprotein particles revealed the existence of their subpopulations with different lipid and apolipoprotein composition and with different metabolic functions. Quantification of LpA-I and LpA-I:A-II particles might allow more accurate prediction of the risk of developing premature atherosclerosis. This approach might also provide a new basis for the classification of dyslipidemias and for the study of the effects of lipid-lowering drugs.   ❖

REFERENCES

1. Gordon T, Castelli WP, Hjortland MC, Kannel WB, Dawber TR. High density lipoprotein as a protective factor against coronary heart disease: The Framingham Study. Am J Med 1977; 62:707–14.
2. Glomset JA. The plasma lecithin-cholesterol acyltransferase reaction. J Lipid Res 1968; 9:155–67.
3. Castro GR, Fielding CF. Evidence for the distribution of apolipoprotein E between lipoprotein classes in human normocholesterolemic plasma and for the origin of unassociated apolipoprotein E (LpE). J Lipid Res 1984;25:58–67.
4. Alaupovic P. The role of apolipoproteins in the lipid transport process. Ric Clin Lab 1982;12:3–21.
5. Koren E, Puchois P, Alaupovic P, Fesmire J, Kandoussi A, Fruchart JC. Quantification of two different types of apolipoprotein A-I containing lipoprotein particles in plasma by enzyme-linked differential antibody immunosorbent assay. Clin Chem 1987;33:38–43.
6. Duverger N, Ghalim N, Theret N, Duchateau P, Aguie G, Ailhaud G, Castro G, Fruchart JC. Lipoprotein A-I containing particles. In: Malmendier CL et al., eds. Hypercholesterolemia, hypocholesterolemia, hypertriglyceridemia. New York: Plenum Press, 1990:93–99.
7. Chen CC, Albers JJ. Characterization of proteoliposomes containing apolipoprotein A-I: a new substrate for the measurement of lecithin-cholesterol acyltransferase activity. J Lipid Res 1982;23:680–91.
8. Barkia A, Puchois P, Ghalim N, Torpier G, Ailhaud G, Fruchart JC. Differential role of apolipoprotein A-I containing particles in cholesterol efflux from adipose cells. Atherosclerosis 1991;87:135–46.
9. Steinmetz A, Barbaras R, Ghalim N, Clavey V, Fruchart JC, Ailhaud G. Human apolipoprotein A-IV binds to apolipoprotein A-I/A-II receptor sites and promotes cholesterol efflux from adipose cells. J Biol Chem 1990;265:7859–63.
10. Barbaras R, Puchois P, Fruchart JC, Pradines-Figueres A, Ailhaud G. Purification of an apolipoprotein A binding protein from mouse adipose cells. Biochem J 1990;269:767–73.
11. Slotte JP, Oram JF, Bierman EL. Binding of high density lipoproteins to cell receptors promotes translocation of cholesterol from intracellular membranes to the cell surface. J Biol Chem 1987;262:12904–7.
12. Theret N, Delbart C, Aguie G, Fruchart JC, Vassaux G, Ailhaud G. Cholesterol efflux from adipose cells is coupled to diacylglycerol production and protein kinase C activation. Biochem Biophys Res Commun 1990;173:1361–8.
13. Oikawa S, Mendez AJ, Cheung MC, Oram JF, Bierman EL. Effect of apo A-I and apo A-I:A-II HDL particles in intracellular cholesterol efflux. [Abstract 2711]. Circulation 1991;84(Suppl II):682.
14. Johnson WJ, Kilsdonk EPC, Van Tol A, Phillips MC, Rothblat GH. Cholesterol efflux from cells to immunopurified subfractions of human high density lipoprotein: LpA-I and LpA-I:A-II. J Lipid Res 1991;32:1993–2000.

15. Cheung MC, Albers JJ. Distribution of high density lipoprotein particles with different apoprotein composition: particles with AI and AII and particles with AI but no AII. J Lipid Res 1982;23:747-53.

16. Atmeh RF, Shepherd J, Packard CJ. Subpopulations of apolipoprotein AI in human high density lipoproteins: their metabolic properties and response to drug therapy. Biochim Biophys Acta 1983;751:175-88.

17. Parra HJ, Mezdour H, Ghalim N, Bard JM, Fruchart JC. Differential electroimmunoassay of human LpAI lipoprotein particles on ready-to-use plates. Clin Chem 1990;36:1431-5.

18. Luc G, Parra HJ, Zylberberg G, Fruchart JC. Plasma concentrations of apolipoprotein A-I containing particles in normolipidemic men. Eur J Clin Invest 1991;21:118-22.

19. Luc G, Bard JM, Lussier-Cacan S, Bouthillier D, Parra HJ, Fruchart JC, Davignon J. High-density lipoprotein particles in octogenarians. Metabolism 1991;40:1238-43.

20. Brewer HB, Rader D, Fojo S, Hoeg JM. Frontiers in the analysis of HDL structure, function, and metabolism. In: Carlson LA, ed. Disorders of HDL. London: Smith-Gordon, 1990:51-58.

21. Puchois P, Kandoussi A, Fiévet P, Fourrier JL, Bertrand M, Koren E, Fruchart JC. Apolipo-protein A-I containing lipoproteins in coronary artery disease. Atherosclerosis 1987;68: 35-40.

22. Genest JJ, Bard JM, Fruchart JC, Ordovas JM, Wilson PFW, Shaefer GJ. Plasma apolipo-proteins (a), A-I, A-II, B, E and C-III containing particles in men with premature coronary artery disease. Atherosclerosis 1991;90:149-57.

23. Cambien F, Parra HJ, Arveiler D, Cambou JP, Evans A, Bingham A. Lipoprotein particles in patients with myocardial infarction and controls. [Abstract 1380]. Circulation 1990; 82(Suppl III):348.

24. Amouyel P, Isorez D, Bard JM, Goldman M, Lebel P, Zylberberg G, Fruchart JC. Par-enteral history of early myocardial infarction is associated with decreased levels of lipoparticle A-I in adolescents. Arterioscler Thromb 1993;13:1640-4.

25. Lussier-Cacan S, Bard JM, Boulet L, Nestruck AC, Grother AM, Fruchart JC, Davignon J. Lipoprotein composition changes induced by fenofibrate in dysbetalipoproteinemia type III. Atherosclerosis 1989;78:167-82.

26. Cachera C, Kandoussi A, Equagoo K, Fruchart JC, Tacquet A. Evaluation of apolipoprot-ein A-I containing particles in chronic renal failure patients undergoing hemodialysis. Am J Nephrol 1990;10:171-2.

27. Fruchart JC. Insulin resistance and lipoprotein abnormalities. Diabet Metab 1991;17: 244-8.

28. Fumeron F, Brigant L, Parra HJ, Bard JM, Fruchart JC, Apfelbaum M. Lowering of HDL_2 cholesterol and lipoprotein A-I particle levels by increasing the ratio of polyun-saturated to saturated fatty acids. Am J Clin Nutr 1991;53:655-9.

29. Puchois P, Ghalim N, Zylberberg G, Fiévet P, Demarquilly C, Fruchart JC. Effect of alcohol intake on human apolipoprotein A-I containing lipoprotein subfractions. Arch Intern Med 1990;150:1638-41.

30. Bard JM, Parra HJ, Camare R, Luc G, Ziegler O, Dachet C, Bruckert E, Douste-Blazy P, Drouin P, Jacotot B, De Gennes JL, Keller U, Fruchart JC. A multicenter comparison of the effects of simvastatin and fenofibrate therapy in severe primary hypercholesterole-mia, with particular emphasis on lipoproteins defined by their apolipoprotein compo-sition. Metabolism 1992;4:498-503.

31. Bard JM, Parra HJ, Douste-Blazy P, Fruchart JC. Effect of pravastatin, an HMG CoA reductase inhibitor, and cholestyramine, a bile acid sequestrant, on lipoprotein particles defined by their apolipoprotein composition. Metabolism 1990;39:269-73.

Triglyceride-Rich Lipoprotein Remnants

25

Richard J. Havel

INTRODUCTION

❖ Plasma triglycerides are contained predominantly in two major lipoprotein classes: very-low-density lipoproteins (VLDL) and chylomicrons.[1] Triglyceride concentration is closely correlated with the concentration of these two triglyceride-rich lipoproteins (TRL). TRL have a density of < 1.006 Kg/L and can therefore be separated by ultra-centrifugal flotation at the non-protein solvent density of plasma. The clinical utility of plasma triglyceride concentrations, measured in the post-absorptive state, remains some-what controversial, although increasing evidence indicates that this analyte is an in-dependent risk factor for coronary heart disease (CHD) and other atherosclerotic diseases.[2] Plasma triglycerides are quantified clinically for this reason and also to permit estimation of low-density lipoprotein cholesterol (LDL-C) by the Friedewald formula.[3]

TRL comprise a heterogeneous group of particles of differing origin (chylomicrons from the intestine and VLDL from the liver), size (ranging in diameter from 300–800 Å or greater), and lipid and apolipoprotein composition.[1] (For additional information on lipoprotein composition, refer to Chapter 1.) Moreover, as described below, they include nascent particles and particles that have been partially metabolized by lipases (principally lipoprotein lipase and, to a lesser extent, hepatic lipase). The latter particles are generally referred to as remnants.[4] During the last twenty years, evidence has accumulated to suggest that remnant particles may constitute the atherogenic compo-nent of TRL.[5] Such particles, as compared with nascent TRL, are depleted of triglyc-erides, phospholipids, and apolipoproteins A and C, and are relatively or absolutely enriched in cholesterol, cholesteryl esters, and apolipoprotein (apo) E.[4]

In this review, the basis for the distinguishing properties of TRL remnants is described, together with the most salient evidence for their atherogenicity. In addition, the various approaches that have been proposed to quantify remnant concentrations are summarized and evaluated.

PHYSIOLOGICAL SIGNIFICANCE OF TRL REMNANTS

Remnant particles are produced from chylomicrons and VLDL during the course of TRL metabolism. Chylomicrons, which transport dietary and biliary lipids through the lymphatic system to the blood, are the vehicles of exogenous lipid transport of long-chain fatty acids and cholesterol.[1] (See Figure 25-1.) Chylomicrons are synthesized in the endoplasmic reticulum of intestinal absorptive cells (enterocytes), packaged in the Golgi apparatus and then secreted into the interstitium of intestinal villi, where they enter lacteals and are delivered via the thoracic lymph duct to the blood. Chylomicrons are secreted at all times, not only during active absorption of dietary fat.[6] For example, after an overnight fast, small chylomicrons (300–800 Å in diameter) are produced that carry lipids derived from biliary phospholipids and cholesterol together with lipids derived from sloughed intestinal epithelial cells. These small chylomicrons fundamentally resemble the much larger particles (up to 2000 Å in diameter or greater) that are produced during active dietary fat absorption.

Both small and large chylomicrons are thought to contain a single molecule of apo B-48, a truncated version of full-length apo B (B-100) secreted by the liver.[7] Apo

Figure 25–1 ♦ The Pathway of Transport of Dietary Lipids in Chylomicrons and the Formation of Chylomicron Remnants

Triglycerides (dark gray area) and cholesteryl esters (black area) are contained in the nonpolar core of the lipoprotein particles.

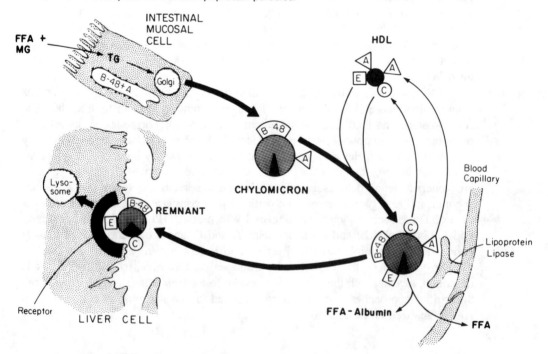

Source: *Medical Clinics of North America,* Vol. 66, 1982:319. Reproduced by permission of the publisher.

B-48, like apo B-100, is required for the assembly and secretion of TRL particles. These particles are essentially microemulsions composed of a hydrophobic core containing predominantly triglycerides together with cholesteryl esters and some unesterified (free) cholesterol, surrounded by a monomolecular layer of phospholipids and free cholesterol, together with specific apoproteins, principally apo B-48, apo A-I, and apo A-IV.[1]

After secretion, chylomicrons acquire additional apoproteins, including apo E, apo C-I, apo C-II, and apo C-III from HDL in lymph and blood plasma.[1] (See Figure 25-1.) Chylomicrons bind rapidly to lipoprotein lipase, which in turn is bound to proteoglycans on the surface of blood capillaries, mainly in muscle and adipose tissue. This binding is followed by rapid hydrolysis of most of the component triglycerides and some of the phospholipids in the particle. Apo C-II is an essential cofactor for efficient hydrolysis, which is accompanied by transfer of C apoproteins, together with essentially all of the apo A-I and apo A-IV on the chylomicron surface, to HDL. The chylomicron remnant, normally produced in only a few minutes, can be defined as a lipid-depleted chylomicron particle that retains its component cholesterol and cholesteryl esters, apo B-48 and apo E, and is depleted not only of triglycerides and phospholipids, but also of most of the C apoproteins and essentially lacks A apoproteins.[4] The remnant particle dissociates from lipoprotein lipase on the capillary surface and is delivered to the liver, where it is efficiently captured by molecules residing on the surface of liver cells, including hepatic lipase and lipoprotein receptors, predominantly the LDL receptor and the LDL receptor-related protein.

Receptor-binding is followed by endocytosis of the remnant particles via coated pits on the surface of hepatocytes, leading to catabolism of the lipid and protein components within 30–60 min.[8] The capacity of lipoprotein lipase to hydrolyze chylomicron triglycerides is normally very high, so that triglyceride clearance is not ordinarily saturated even after a substantial fat-containing meal.[9] This presumably reflects binding of many lipase molecules to a single large chylomicron particle, yielding very rapid catalysis. By contrast, removal of chylomicron remnants by the liver is relatively slow, occurring over 15 min or more, and remnant clearance is generally saturated after a fat-containing meal. Thus, those lipoprotein particles found in the blood that are derived from the intestine can be considered to be remnants in the postprandial state, and probably in the postabsorptive state as well.[9]

The secretion and catabolism of VLDL follow the same general scenario as for chylomicrons, with some notable exceptions.[1] (See Figure 25-2.) VLDL particles secreted from hepatocytes contain a single molecule of apo B-100, together with other apoproteins, including apo A-I, A-II, and A-IV, the three C apoproteins, and apo E. After secretion, additional apo E and the C aproproteins are acquired from HDL, and remnants are produced in the same general manner as occurs with chylomicrons, although at a considerably slower rate. VLDL particles therefore may circulate normally without appreciable hydrolysis for several minutes or more.

VLDL are known to be converted via the action of lipases to LDL. Previously, it was thought that human VLDL are progressively delipidated to form progressively smaller particles to ultimately yield LDL. Research in other mammals, however, showed that only a small fraction of VLDL is converted to LDL (each containing a single molecule of apo B-100). The remainder follow the pathway described for chylomicron remnants, namely uptake and endocytosis into hepatocytes. It is now recognized that,

Figure 25–2 ✧ The Pathway of Transport of Endogenous Lipids in VLDL, and the Formation of VLDL Remnants and LDL

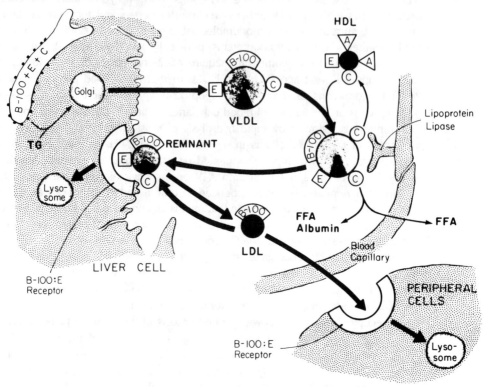

Source: *Medical Clinics of North America,* Vol. 66, 1982:321. Reproduced by permission of the publisher.

even in humans, one-half or more of VLDL particles are so metabolized and less than one-half are converted to LDL.[10] (For additional information on the fate of LDL particles, refer to Chapters 1 and 2.)

VLDL remnants isolated from functionally hepatectomized rats resemble chylomicron remnants: they are smaller than nascent VLDL (250–700 vs. 300–800 Å in diameter) and are depleted of triglycerides and phospholipids, together with all the non-B apoproteins except for apo E.[4] Particles resembling rat VLDL remnants can be separated from plasma of some normal humans by virtue of their reduced electrophoretic mobility (reflecting the altered apoprotein composition).[11] These apo E-enriched and apo C-depleted particles have "slow" rather than "fast" prebeta electrophoretic mobility and are smaller than the fast-migrating particles (~ 360 vs. 430 Å in average diameter).

In humans, partially catabolized VLDL are contained not only in TRL (defined operationally as lipoprotein particles with a hydrated density of < 1.006 Kg/L), but also in intermediate density lipoproteins (IDL) (with hydrated densities between 1.006 and 1.019 Kg/L).[1] IDL (diameter about 280 Å) represent further delipidation products of VLDL that contain relatively more cholesteryl esters and less triglycerides, one molecule of apo B-100, and usually at least one molecule of apo E. LDL particles, the final product of VLDL-delipidation, are 220–270 Å in diameter, with hydrated densities between 1.019 and 1.063 Kg/L, in which apo B-100 is the sole protein component. The core of LDL is composed predominantly of cholesteryl esters.

CLINICAL RELEVANCE OF TRL REMNANTS

In the 1970s, two lines of evidence led to the hypothesis that TRL remnants may have atherogenic potential. First, it was shown that the cholesterol-enriched TRL remnants that accumulate in familial dysbetalipoproteinemia, a monogenic disorder associated with accelerated atherosclerotic disease, resemble chylomicron and VLDL remnants, including enrichment in apo E relative to C apoproteins.[12] Point mutations of apo E impair binding of TRL particles to the LDL receptor in familial dysbetalipoproteinemia, and the clearance of chylomicrons as well as VLDL particles is greatly reduced.[13] Second, the cholesterol-enriched VLDL that accumulate in the plasma of rabbits and some other animals fed cholesterol-enriched diets were also shown to be enriched in apo E.[14] These particles have been implicated in the formation of fatty streak lesions in the arteries of such animals. Subsequently, the concentrations of IDL and small VLDL were shown to be the best predictors of the extent of spontaneous atherosclerosis developing on a standard chow diet in genetically hyperlipidemic (St. Thomas) rabbits.[15]

TRL remnants containing mainly apo B-48 accumulate at very high concentrations in apo E-knockout mice. These mice develop lipid-rich atherosclerotic lesions rapidly, even on a low-fat (chow) diet.[16] Most recently, overexpression of lipoprotein lipase in cholesterol-fed LDL receptor-knockout mice, which dramatically reduced the concentration of TRL that resemble remnants, almost abolished lipid-rich arterial lesions (an 18-fold reduction).[17] The concentration of LDL was little affected by overexpression of the enzyme in these mice.

In 1979, Zilversmit proposed that postprandial TRL remnants (principally chylomicron remnants) are important atherogenic particles.[18] His proposal was based in part on studies suggesting that the remnant particles that accumulate in cholesterol-fed rabbits are derived from chylomicrons. Subsequent work showed that these particles contain primarily apo B-100 and are in fact derived from the liver.[19] Other studies have shown that small VLDL and IDL particles enter the artery wall of humans and rabbits from the blood at an appreciable rate, albeit somewhat more slowly than LDL (owing to their larger size), whereas influx of larger VLDL is much slower.[20]

Apo E-enriched TRL containing apo B-100 but not apo B-48 have been isolated from human atherosclerotic lesions obtained from femoral arteries at endarterectomy.[21] Such particles account for about one-third of the total apo B-100-containing lipoproteins that can be readily extracted from such lesions as well as lipoproteins that are bound to the connective tissue matrix.

Apo E-enriched particles, such as the beta-VLDL that accumulate in cholesterol-fed rabbits, are readily taken up by macrophages via receptors that recognize apo E (mainly the LDL receptor) without chemical modification, such as the oxidative alterations of LDL that are prerequisite to their uptake via scavenger receptors.[22] In this connection, however, it must be pointed out that the apo B-48-rich remnants that accumulate in apo E knockout mice evidently are also taken up readily by macrophages, in a process that clearly involves apo E-independent mechanisms. Gianturco, Bradley and their colleagues have shown that both chylomicron-derived particles and large VLDL particles from hypertriglyceridemic subjects can be readily taken up by monocyte-macrophages by an apo E-independent mechanism, leading to foam cell formation.[23] This uptake appears to be mediated by a novel receptor for TRL that may recognize domains on apo B. Thus, considerable evidence suggests that some TRL particles derived from liver or intestine can accumulate in arteries and lead to formation of macrophage foam cells—a hallmark of the fatty streaks that are thought to be the precursor of the more advanced atherosclerotic lesions that lead to ischemic complications.

TRL may also lead to atherosclerotic disease through effects upon blood coagulation and fibrinolysis. Thus, TRL may activate blood coagulation factor VII and increase secretion of plasminogen activator inhibitor-1 (PAI-1) into the blood.[24] Large VLDL particles from hypertriglyceridemic subjects, presumably related to those that are actively taken up by monocyte-macrophages, are particularly potent in stimulating PAI-1 secretion.[25] Such data suggest that at least some TRL particles not only promote atherogenesis, but complicating thrombotic events as well.

During the last 15 years, clinical studies in diverse populations have provided considerable support for the atherogenicity of particles that resemble remnants. Several case-control studies have found increased concentrations of certain remnant lipoproteins, particularly IDL, to be the salient lipoprotein abnormality in patients with CHD.[26-30] In the National Heart, Lung and Blood Institute (NHLBI) Type II Coronary Intervention Study, in which coronary arterial lesions were assessed angiographically over a five-year period of treatment with cholestyramine or placebo, IDL concentrations, assessed by analytical ultracentrifugation, predicted progression of atherosclerotic lesions.[31] In this study, LDL-C concentrations, also assessed by analytical ultracentrifugation, did not predict disease progression.

In a larger intervention study of a calcium channel blocker, Nicardipine, in which lipoprotein cholesterol and triglycerides were quantified after preparative ultracentrifugation, lesion progression over a two-year period, assessed by a quantitative coronary artery angiographic method, was independently associated with the concentration of remnant lipoproteins.[32] In this study, the remnant particles were estimated by the extent of enrichment of TRL with cholesterol as compared with triglycerides, together with the concentration of IDL-cholesterol (IDL-C). Over a period averaging 4.7 years after completion of the trial, remnant-cholesterol concentrations were also independently associated with clinical cardiovascular events: sudden death, myocardial infarction, or requirement of coronary bypass surgery or angioplasty. As with the NHLBI Type II study, LDL concentrations were not predictive of angiographically assessed disease progression. In addition, LDL-C concentrations did not predict subsequent clinical events, whereas HDL-cholesterol (HDL-C) concentrations predicted (inversely) both progression and clinical events.

There are several points to be made about the Nicardipine Trial results:

First, patients were selected by the number and character of their coronary lesions at baseline, not by their lipoprotein concentrations. (In the NHLBI Type II trial, patients with high LDL-C concentrations while on dietary treatment were selected.) As expected, these patients (272 men and 63 women), whose age at entry was < 65 years, had only modestly elevated LDL-C concentrations at baseline (147 and 159 mg/dL; 3.80 and 4.11 mmol/L). By contrast, concentrations of VLDL-C (37 and 31 mg/dL; 0.96 and 0.80 mmol/L) and IDL-C (16 and 18 mg/dL; 0.41 and 0.47 mmol/L) were considerably higher than those observed in healthy young adults. Thus, these patients' lipoprotein concentrations were typical of younger CHD populations.

Second, LDL-C, as assessed in this trial, included lipoprotein (a) [Lp(a)] but not IDL-C. In most prospective and interventional studies of lipoproteins as CHD risk factors, LDL-C assessed by the Friedewald formula or by the beta-quantification method, which involves separation of TRL at a density of 1.006 Kg/L, includes IDL-C as well as Lp(a) cholesterol.

Third, the Nicardipine Trial was conducted in Montreal, Canada, and included mainly patients of French-Canadian origin, whereas the NHLBI Type II trial included men residing in the eastern United States. Both trials identified, by different methods, particles considered to be TRL remnants, mainly of hepatic origin, as independent risk factors for progression of coronary artery atherosclerosis.

Given the limited size and power of these prospective studies, their results clearly do not negate the much more extensive body of evidence that LDL-C, which includes mainly "true" LDL ($1.019 < \rho < 1.063$ Kg/L), is an important predictor of atherosclerotic disease and its complications. They do, however, suggest that TRL remnants, including IDL, may be particularly robust predictors of CHD risk.

Taken together, the substantial experimental animal and clinical evidence summarized here suggests that lipoprotein particles with properties of TRL remnants should be included in assessment of risk for atherosclerotic disease. Remnant lipoproteins have not been commonly measured in clinical and population studies because of the lack of practical, validated methods. It is, therefore, important to develop simple and reliable methods to assess remnant concentrations.

APPROACHES TO QUANTIFICATION OF TRL REMNANTS

Since the 1970s, several methods have been proposed to quantify remnant lipoproteins, but at this time, no generally recognized procedure has emerged that is both practical and has a sound theoretical basis. Nonetheless, some new methods have recently been developed that hold promise for useful clinical application. The various methods are summarized in Table 25–1 and are described and evaluated in the following sections.

Agarose Gel Electrophoresis

Upon electrophoresis of plasma proteins in supporting media, the prebeta component of lipoproteins, stained with a lipophilic dye, is often composed of two components with "fast" and "slow" mobilities.[11, 33, 34] In some cases, the slow component represents Lp(a), in which the apo (a) protein is in disulfide linkage to apo B-100 of LDL. Lp(a) is also found in the 1.006 Kg/L density infranatant fraction of ultracentrifuged plasma (termed "sinking prebeta lipoprotein"). The TRL lipoproteins with a density < 1.006 Kg/L, however, may also contain a slowly migrating component, which has been shown to have all of the expected properties of VLDL remnants:[11] smaller size and enrichment in cholesteryl esters and apo E relative to C apoproteins. The slow prebeta

Table 25–1 ❖ Proposed Methods to Quantify TRL Remnants*

Method	Property of TRL Assessed	Reference	Evaluation
Agarose gel electrophoresis of TRL	TRL "slow prebeta" band	11	Requires preliminary separation of TRL. Separation from "fast prebeta" band may be imprecise and arbitrary.
Quantification of IDL	Particle density (cholesterol assay)	32, 35	Requires ultracentrifugation at two densities.
	Selective precipitation of IDL by heparin-MgCl$_2$	36	Applied to serum, but technically complex.
	Capillary isotachophoresis	37	Performance characteristics uncertain
Cholesterol-enrichment of TRL	Cholesterol-triglyceride ratio	32	Requires preliminary ultra-centrifugation of serum and apo E phenotyping.
Polyacrylamide gel electrophoresis of plasma	Mobility between VLDL and LDL	38	May be confounded by Lp(a). Performance characteristics uncertain.
Immunochemical separation of TRL-subfraction	Reactivity of TRL with monoclonal antibody to apo B-100	41, 43	Facile, but requires cholesterol assay of high sensitivity. In principle, includes all chylomicron remnants but not all VLDL remnants.
Quantification of apo B-48	Specific immunoreactivity of C-terminus of apo B-48	48	Measures chylomicron remnants only.

*As applied to blood plasma from postabsorptive subjects; does not include measurements on postprandial plasma obtained after fat-containing challenge meals.

component thus resembles the "beta-VLDL" that accumulate in plasma of patients with familial dysbetalipoproteinemia. The differences from fast-migrating VLDL are, however, less pronounced, and slow prebeta VLDL may be found in individuals with any of the apo E phenotypes other than E 2/2, although it is more frequently found in individuals with a single ϵ_3 or ϵ_4 allele.

The prevalence of "double prebeta VLDL" as examined by agarose gel electrophoresis may be as high as 50% in adult populations,[11] but this value appears to be dependent upon the particular technique used. Furthermore, apo E may dissociate from TRL particles during ultracentrifugation, which could affect their mobility. The distinction between single and double prebeta VLDL is sometimes difficult to judge visually or by scanning techniques, so that quantification of the two components frequently may be arbitrary. For these reasons, and also because the method requires ultracentrifugation to separate TRL, this approach has not been widely applied in clinical studies, even though it has a sound theoretical basis.

Quantification of IDL-C

IDL include those TRL-remnants that are immediate precursors of LDL. Originally, IDL were defined as lipoproteins of density intermediate to that of VLDL and LDL (1.019< ρ < 1.063 Kg/L) with Svedberg flotation rates of 12–20 units. IDL-C can be quantified after separation of IDL by standard sequential ultracentrifugation,[35] or by simultaneous ultracentrifugation of serum at densities of 1.006 and 1.019 Kg/L, in which case the concentration of IDL-C is calculated as the difference between VLDL-C and VLDL+IDL-C.[32] Alternatively, IDL-C can be calculated as the difference between the cholesterol concentration in the "bottom" fractions obtained at these two densities.

IDL-C can also be quantified after separation of IDL from LDL by a two-step agarose electrophoretic technique.[36] In this method, IDL are selectively precipitated with heparin and $MgCl_2$ after the first step. This immobilizes IDL, but not LDL particles; the latter move toward the anode in a second electrophoretic step, after which the cholesterol in the precipitated IDL is extracted and quantified.

IDL can also be separated from VLDL and LDL by capillary isotachophoresis of serum prestained with a lipophilic dye or fluorescent phospholipid analog.[37] The performance characteristics of this method have not been fully described.

Based on kinetic studies of the conversion of VLDL particles to LDL, some investigators have broadened the definition of IDL to include smaller VLDL particles, so that IDL have been considered to encompass particles with S_f rates of 12–60 units,[30] which are separated from those of higher S_f rates by rate ultracentrifugation. This approach has theoretical appeal but is more demanding than the standard method of sequential ultracentrifugation; hence, it is unlikely to find use in large-scale studies. Furthermore, it is now recognized that nascent VLDL entering the blood have a wide range of sizes, which may include some particles of S_f 20–60 and even S_f 12–20 units.

Cholesterol-Enrichment of TRL

In patients with familial dysbetalipoproteinemia and in individuals with double pre-beta VLDL, TRL are enriched in cholesterol (both free cholesterol and cholesteryl esters) relative to triglycerides).[11] This property has been exploited to estimate TRL remnants, taking into account the fact that the average size of TRL particles generally increases with increasing triglyceride concentration, so that the ratio of cholesterol to triglycerides tends to fall. Phillips et al. used the average ratio of cholesterol to triglycerides at a given triglyceride concentration in subjects with an apo E 3/3 phenotype as a baseline from which they estimated remnant-cholesterol in individual samples as a positive or negative number.[32] The estimated TRL-remnant cholesterol concentration correlated with that of cholesterol in IDL (r = 0.47); therefore the two values were summed to obtain an estimate for remnant-cholesterol concentration. This method appeared to have value in that the concentration of remnant cholesterol independently predicted progression of coronary atherosclerosis and ischemic cardiovascular events;[11] however, it is evidently arbitrary in the definition of TRL-remnant cholesterol concentration and requires ultracentrifugation to separate both VLDL and IDL.

Disk Electrophoresis in Polyacrylamide Gel

With this method, lipoproteins separated according to size in a low concentration of polyacrylamide (~ 3%) are stained with a lipophilic dye.[38] Components migrating between VLDL and LDL, termed "midband lipoproteins," are often seen and have been reported to be more prevalent in patients with CHD.[28, 39] In Japanese populations, midband lipoproteins correlate with cholesterol-triglyceride ratios in TRL and with IDL cholesterol and triglyceride concentrations.[28] Increased concentrations of Lp(a) may also appear as midband lipoproteins,[39] so that a midband may reflect increased concentrations of small TRL, Lp(a), or both. Since both of these lipoproteins may be atherogenic, detection and quantification of midband lipoproteins by densitometry may be clinically useful, and the method can be applied to unfractionated plasma or serum. The lack of specificity is, however, a serious limitation of this method from a theoretical standpoint.

Immunochemical Separation of Remnant-like Particles

It is now recognized that even in plasma obtained after an overnight fast, TRL remnants include an appreciable complement of chylomicron remnants derived from the intestine as well as VLDL remnants derived from the liver.[40] A monoclonal antibody (Mab) to apo B-100 has been found to be useful in separating such TRL particles from plasma. This Mab (JI-H) recognizes an epitope in the region of apo B-51.[41] It binds to LDL and most TRL, but not to a minor fraction of TRL particles containing apo B-100 that is enriched in apo E.[42] This antibody also fails to recognize chylomicron-derived particles containing apo B-48, which, as explained earlier, are essentially chylomicron remnants.

The unbound TRL particles in plasma of fasting subjects are enriched in apo E and contain more cholesteryl esters and free cholesterol than those that bind to Mab JI-H; however, the average particle diameter of the unbound particles is larger than that of the bound TRL, which contain only apo B-100.[42] This larger diameter is in part due to the content of chylomicron-derived particles, but the apo B-100 particles that fail to bind to Mab JI-H are also somewhat larger on average than the bound VLDL particles. The electrophoretic mobility of the unbound particles is reduced, as compared with the bound VLDL. In normolipidemic individuals, the unbound particles account for about 15% of the total apo B in TRL; this value tends to be higher in subjects with endogenous hypertriglyceridemia and familial dysbetalipoproteinemia. The affinity of the unbound particles for the LDL receptor far exceeds that of VLDL that bind to Mab JI-H, and is comparable to that of total VLDL from individual subjects.[42] Thus, it appears that the TRL that are not recognized by Mab JI-H include not only chylomicron-derived particles (chylomicron remnants), but also apo E-enriched VLDL particles that have properties resembling VLDL remnants and which are somewhat larger than other VLDL remnants that presumably bind to Mab JI-H.

Based upon these properties of Mab JI-H, an immunochemical procedure has been devised to separate the remnant-like TRL from other plasma lipoproteins in plasma by use of an immunoaffinity matrix in which Mab JI-H and a Mab to apo A-I are bound to agarose beads.[43] When incubated with serum or plasma, almost all LDL and HDL particles, as well as the bulk of VLDL, are bound to the matrix. In this test, serum or plasma is mixed with the immunoaffinity matrix and, after incubation and sedimentation of the agarose beads, cholesterol and/or triglycerides are measured in the supernatant fluid.[41, 43] In clinical studies in Japan, the concentration of unbound cholesterol, designated "remnant-like particle cholesterol" (RLP-C), has been found to be highly correlated with that of plasma triglycerides.[41, 43] In groups of patients with CHD, RLP-C concentrations are substantially higher than in control subjects, even when plasma triglyceride concentrations are within normal limits.[43] RLP-C concentrations also have been found to be increased in several other clinical states, including familial dysbetalipoproteinemia[42, 44] and chronic renal failure.[45]

This test, which is now being evaluated in North America, is technically facile and suitable for use in clinical studies, although it does require highly sensitive assays for cholesterol and triglycerides, owing to the large dilution of plasma when it is mixed with the immunoaffinity matrix. The test appears to have a good theoretical basis and it provides a measure of all remnants derived from chylomicrons together with particles resembling VLDL remnants. Values for RLP-C are low in most healthy, normolipidemic subjects (< 7 mg/dL; 0.18 mmol/L). In plasma from such subjects, much of the measured cholesterol is contained in the small amount of LDL and HDL that fails to bind to the immunoaffinity matrix.[41]

Other studies in subjects with elevated RLP-C concentrations have shown that the unbound lipoproteins are readily taken up by monocyte-macrophages, causing foam cell formation.[46] RLP may include the large TRL particles, found especially in hypertriglyceridemic subjects, that are readily taken up by macrophages via the apo E-independent TRL receptor to form foam cells[23] and promote secretion of PAI-1.[25] Thus, it appears that the remnant particles contained in the unbound fraction have functional properties consistent with those of atherogenic lipoproteins.

Quantification of Apo B-48

Recent studies have shown that the molar concentration of apo B-48 in TRL is 5–8% of that of apo B-100 in plasma of postabsorptive normolipidemic subjects.[47] The concentrations of apo B-48 and apo B-100 in TRL are well correlated, owing to competition between these particles for lipoprotein lipase binding and triglyceride hydrolysis. The hepatic LDL receptor is responsible for the endocytosis of most chylomicron as well as VLDL remnants,[8] and it is reasonable to postulate that the concentration of apo B-48, representing chylomicron remnants, may be surrogate for that of VLDL remnants as well. The validity of this postulate remains untested, however, and it is known that chylomicron remnants can also be taken up by the liver by at least one other lipoprotein receptor, the LDL receptor-related protein, which is regulated independently of the LDL receptor.[8] Furthermore, the regulation of apo B-100 production by the liver is largely independent of that of apo B-48 by the intestine.

Until recently, quantification of apo B-48 has been accomplished by ultracentrifugal separation of TRL followed by denaturing polyacrylamide gel electrophoresis of apo-TRL, staining of the separated protein, and densitometry.[47] A new method, based on antibodies recognizing the conformation of the C-terminal region of apo B-48, promises to permit quantification of apo B-48 in unfractionated plasma.[48] Since apo

B-48, unlike apo B-100, is contained almost exclusively in TRL, this method may permit a practical approach to quantification of chylomicron remnants in clinical studies.

Quantification of TRL Remnants Postprandially

Recent studies have applied methods to quantify apo B-48 and apo B-100 in TRL as a measure of the intestinal and hepatic contributions to postprandial lipemia.[9, 40] It has been shown that, whereas particles containing apo B-48 account for most of the increase in TRL-triglycerides postprandially, the absolute increase in particles containing apo B-100 exceeds that of particles containing apo B-48. Furthermore, the increase in triglycerides late in the postprandial phase (6 h or more after a fat-containing meal) may be contributed mainly by particles containing apo B-100. The increase in VLDL particle concentrations evidently reflects the effective competition of postprandial chylomicrons for lipoprotein lipase binding related to the larger size of chylomicrons in relation to VLDL.[49, 50] However, the concentration of particles containing apo B-48 postprandially increases substantially, as expected given the saturation of remnant particle clearance. This enables evaluation of the effectiveness of hepatic clearance mechanisms, which may be related to atherogenic risk.[36, 51] Therefore, future research should address not only the concentration of apo B-48 and TRL remnants more generally in the postabsorptive state, but also the response of these analytes to challenge meals. ◇

REFERENCES

1. Havel RJ. Origin, metabolic fate and metabolic function of plasma lipoproteins. In: Steinberg D, JM Olefsky, eds. Contemporary issues in endocrinology and metabolism, Vol. 3. New York: Churchill Livingstone, 1986:117–41.
2. Austin MA, Hokanson JE. Epidemiology of triglycerides, small dense low-density lipoprotein, and lipoprotein(a) as risk factors for coronary heart disease. Med Clin N Am 1994;78:99–115.
3. Adult Treatment Panel II. National cholesterol education program: second report of the expert panel on detection, evaluation, and treatment of high blood cholesterol in adults. Circulation 1994;89:1333–1445.
4. Mjøs OD, Faergeman O, Hamilton RL, Havel RJ. Characterization of remnants produced during the metabolism of triglyceride-rich lipoproteins of blood plasma and intestinal lymph in the rat. J Clin Invest 1975;56:603–15.
5. Havel RJ. McCollum award lecture, 1993. Triglyceride-rich lipoproteins and atherosclerosis: new perspectives. Am J Clin Nutr 1994;59:795–9.
6. Havel RJ. Contrasts and similarities between the metabolism of intestinal and hepatic lipoproteins: the role of particle size. In: Windler E, Greten H, Zuckschwerdt W, eds. Intestinal lipid and lipoprotein metabolism. Munich: Verlag, 1989:168–173.
7. Kane JP, Havel RJ. Disorders of the biogenesis and secretion of lipoproteins containing the B-apolipoproteins. In: Scriver CR, Beaudet AL, Sly WS, Valle DS, eds. The metabolic basis of inherited disease, 7th ed. New York: McGraw-Hill, 1994:1853–85.
8. Havel RJ. Chylomicron remnants: hepatic receptors and metabolism. Curr Opin Lipidol 1995;6:312–16.
9. Havel RJ. Postprandial hyperlipidemia and remnant lipoproteins. Curr Opin Lipidol 1994; 5:102–9.
10. Havel RJ. The formation of LDL: mechanisms and regulation. J Lipid Res 1984;25: 1570–6.

11. Pagnan A, Havel RJ, Kane JP, Kotite L. Characterization of human very low density lipoproteins containing two electrophoretic populations: double pre-beta lipoprotein-emia and primary dysbetalipoproteinemia. J Lipid Res 1977;18:613-22.

12. Havel RJ, Kane JP. Primary dysbetalipoproteinemia: predominance of a specific apoprotein species in triglyceride-rich lipoproteins. Proc Natl Acad Sci USA 1973;70:2015-19.

13. Stalenhoef AFH, Malloy MJ, Kane JP, Havel RJ. Metabolism of apolipoproteins B-48 and B-100 of triglyceride-rich lipoproteins in patients with familial dysbetalipoprotein-emia. J Clin Invest 1986;78:722-8.

14. Mahley RW. Dietary fat, cholesterol and accelerated atherosclerosis. In: Paoletti R, Gotto Jr AM, eds. Atherosclerosis Reviews, Vol. 5. New York: Raven Press, 1979:1-24.

15. Nordestgaard BG, Lewis B. Intermediate density lipoprotein levels are strong predictors of the extent of aortic atherosclerosis in the St. Thomas's Hospital rabbit strain. Atherosclerosis 1991;87:39-46.

16. Breslow JL. Mouse models of atherosclerosis. Science 1966;272:685-8.

17. Shimada M, Ishibashi S, Inaba T, Yagyu H, Harada K, Osuga J, et al. Suppression of diet-induced atherosclerosis in low density lipoprotein receptor knockout mice over-expressing lipoprotein lipase. Proc Natl Sci USA 1996;93:7242-6.

18. Zilversmit DB. Atherogenesis: a postprandial phenomenon. Circulation 1979;60:473-85.

19. Havel RJ. The role of the liver in atherosclerosis. Arteriosclerosis 1985;5:569-80.

20. Nordestgaard BG, Tybjaerg-Hansen A. IDL, VLDL, chylomicrons and atherosclerosis. Eur J Epidemiol 1992;8 (Suppl.):92-8.

21. Rapp JH, Lespine A, Hamilton RL, Colyvas N, Chaumeton AH, Tweedie-Hardman J, et al. Triglyceride-rich lipoproteins isolated by selected-affinity anti-apolipoprotein B im-munosorption from human atherosclerotic plaque. Arterioscler Thromb 1994;14: 1767-74.

22. Koo C, Wernette-Hammond ME, Garcia A, Malloy MJ, Uauy R, East C, et al. Uptake of cholesterol-rich remnant lipoproteins by human monocyte-derived macrophages is mediated by low density lipoprotein receptors. J Clin Invest 1988;81:1332-40.

23. Gianturco SH, Ramprasad MP, Lin AH-Y, Song R, Bradley WA. Cellular binding site and membrane binding proteins for triglyceride-rich lipoproteins in human monocyte-macrophages and THP-1 monocytic cells. J Lipid Res 1994;35:1674-87.

24. Hypertriglyceridaemia and vascular risk. Report of a meeting of physicians and scientists, University College London Medical School. Lancet 1993;342:781-7.

25. Stiko-Rahm A, Wiman G, Hamsten A, Nilsson J. Secretion of plasminogen activator inhibitor-1 from cultured human umbilical vein endothelial cells is induced by very low density lipoprotein. Arteriosclerosis 1990;10:1067-73.

26. Avogaro P, Bittolo Bon G, Cazzolato G, Rora E. Relationship between apolipoproteins and chemical components of lipoproteins in survivors of myocardial infarction. Atherosclerosis 1980;37:69-76.

27. Tatami R, Mabuchi H, Ueda K, Ueda R, Haya T, Kametani T, et al. Intermediate-density lipoprotein and cholesterol-rich very low density lipoprotein in angiographically deter-mined coronary artery disease. Circulation 1981;64:1174-84.

28. Kameda K, Matsuzawa Y, Kuba M, Ishikawa K, Maejima I, Yamamura T, et al. Increased frequency of lipoprotein disorders similar to type III hyperlipoproteinemia in survivors of myocardial infarction in Japan. Atherosclerosis 1984;51:241-9.

29. Reardon MF, Nelstel PJ, Craig IH, Harper RW. Lipoprotein predictors of the severity of coronary artery disease in men and women. Circulation 1985;17:881-8.

30. Steiner G, Schwartz L, Shumak S, Poapst M. The association of increased levels of intermediate-density lipoproteins with smoking and with coronary heart disease. Cir-culation 1987;75:124-30.

31. Krauss RM, Lindgren FT, Williams PT, Kelsey SF, Brensike J, Vranizan K, et al. Inter-mediate-density lipoproteins and progression of coronary artery disease in hypercholes-terolaemic men. Lancet 1987;000:62-6.

32. Phillips NR, Waters D, Havel RJ. Plasma lipoproteins and progression of coronary artery disease evaluated by angiography and clinical events. Circulation 1993;88:2762-70.

33. Carlson LA, Ericsson M. Quantitative and qualitative serum lipoprotein analysis. Part 1: Studies in healthy men and women. Atherosclerosis 1975;21:417-33.

34. Hedstrand H, Vessby B. Serum lipoprotein concentration and composition in healthy 50-year-old men. Upsala J Med Sci 1976;81:161-8.

35. Havel RJ, Eder H, Bragdon J. The distribution and chemical composition of ultracentrifugally separated lipoproteins in human serum. J Clin Invest. 1955;34:1345-53.

36. Wikinski RLW, Schreier LE, Rosental SB. New method for isolating and quantifying intermediate and β-very-low-density lipoprotein cholesterol. Clin Chem. 1991;37:1913-16.

37. Schmitz G, Möllers C. Capillary isotachophoresis of lipoproteins in human body fluids. In: Rifai N, Warnick GR, eds. Laboratory measurement of lipids, lipoproteins and apolipoproteins. Washington DC: AACC Press, 1994:334-40.

38. Mead MG, Dangerfield WG. The investigation of "mid-band" lipoproteins using polyacrylamide gel electrophoresis. Clin Chim Acta 1974;51:173-82.

39. Tashiro J, Nishide T, Shinomiya M, Shirai K, Saito Y, Yoshida S, et al. The "midband" lipoprotein is a coronary risk factor in Japanese patients with familial hypercholesterolaemia. Scand J Clin Lab Invest 1993;53:335-8.

40. Bergeron N, Havel RJ. Assessment of postprandial lipemia: nutritional influences. Curr Opin Lipidol, in press.

41. Nakajima K, Okazaki M, Tanaka A, Want T, Pullinger C, Nakano T, et al. Separation and determination of remnant-like particles in human serum using monoclonal antibodies to apo B-100 and Apo A-1. J Clin Ligand Assay, in press.

42. Campos E, Nakajima K, Tanaka K, Havel RJ. Properties of an apolipoprotein E-enriched fraction of triglyceride-rich lipoproteins isolated from human blood plasma with a monoclonal antibody to apolipoprotein B-100. J Lipid Res 1992;33:369-80.

43. Nakajima K, Saito T, Tamura A, Suzuki M, Nakano T, Adachi M, et al. Cholesterol in remnant-like lipoproteins in human serum using monoclonal anti apo B-100 and anti apo A-I immunoaffinity mixed gels. Clin Chim Acta 1993;223:53-71.

44. Nakajima K, Saito T, Tamura A, Suzuki M, Nakano T, Adachi M, et al. A new approach for the detection of Type III hyperlipoproteinemia by RLP-Cholesterol Assay. Atheroscler Thromb 1994;1:30-36.

45. Sekihara T, Nakano T, Nakajima K. High postprandial plasma remnant-like particles-cholesterol in patients with coronary artery diseases on chronic maintenance hemodialysis. Japanese J Nephrol 1996;38:220-8.

46. Shige H, Nishiwaka M, Tomiyasu K, Suzuki J, Namiki M, Yamashita T, et al. Studies for atherogenicity of remnant-like particles (RLP) from cultured cells. J Jpn Atheroscler Soc 1991;19:991.

47. Bergeron N, Kotite L, Havel RJ. Simultaneous quantification of apolipoproteins B-100, B-48 and E separated by SDS-PAGE. In: Methods in enzymology, plasma lipoproteins. Part C: Quantitation. 1996; 263:82-94.

48. Lovegrove JA, Isherwood SG, Jackson KG, Williams CM, Gould BJ. Quantitation of apolipoprotein B-48 in triacylglycerol-rich lipoproteins by a specific enzyme-linked immunosorbent assay. Biochim Biophys Acta 1996;1301:221-9.

49. Schneeman BO, Kotite L, Todd KM, Havel RJ. Relationships between the responses of triglyceride-rich lipoproteins in blood plasma containing apolipoproteins B-48 and B-100 to a fat-containing meal in normolipidemic humans. Proc Natl Acad Sci, USA 1993;90:2069-73.

50. Björkegren J, Packard CJ, Hamsten A, Bedford D, Caslake M, Shepherd J, et al. Accumulation of large very low density lipoprotein in plasma during intravenous infusion of a chylomicron-like triglyceride emulsion reflects competition for a common lipolytic pathway. J Lipid Res 1996;37:76-86.

51. Karpe F, Steiner G, Uffelman K, Olivecrona T, Hamsten A. Postprandial lipoproteins and progression of coronary atherosclerosis. Atherosclerosis 1994;106:83-97.

Determination and Clinical Significance of Low-Density Lipoprotein Receptors

26

Anne K. Soutar

BACKGROUND AND INTRODUCTION

❖   The low-density lipoprotein (LDL) receptor is a cell surface receptor that mediates the specific uptake by cells of lipoproteins containing apolipoproteins B or E. After uptake of lipoproteins by the LDL receptor and their delivery to the lysosomal compartment, the apolipoprotein is degraded and the cholesteryl esters in the core of the particles are hydrolysed. The free cholesterol generated in this way is either used for new membrane synthesis, as a precursor for biosynthetic pathways, or it can be re-esterified and stored as lipid droplets. In cultured cells, LDL-receptor gene expression and key enzymes in cholesterol biosynthesis are regulated at the level of gene transcription by the intracellular free sterol content, and thus the main function of the receptor is to maintain cholesterol homeostasis in the cell. This also appears to be the case in the whole body, but in addition, the hepatic LDL receptor pathway *in vivo* plays a central role in regulating the concentration of cholesterol in human serum, as it is the predominant means by which LDL is removed from the circulation.[1] Furthermore, since the LDL receptor is able to recognize not only LDL itself, but also the immediate precursors of LDL in plasma, namely the remnants of very-low-density lipoproteins (VLDL remnants) and intermediate-density lipoproteins (IDL), hepatic LDL receptor activity influences the rates of both synthesis and catabolism of plasma LDL.

The importance of the LDL receptor in human lipoprotein metabolism has been deduced from the marked increase in serum LDL concentration that occurs in patients with familial hypercholesterolemia (FH), who have a defect in the LDL receptor gene that affects the function of the protein.[2] Numerous different mutations in the LDL receptor gene have been found in FH patients throughout the world. Patients homozygous for the disorder, or who have two defective alleles, frequently have a plasma cholesterol concentration that is more than four-fold higher than the ideal normal upper limit of 200 mg/dL (5.2 mmol/L). This results in the deposition of cholesterol in the skin and tendons as xanthomata from an early age and, more significantly, accelerates the rate of formation of atherosclerotic plaques in the arterial wall. This leads to a greatly increased risk of coronary heart disease (CHD) and, indeed, death due to coronary disease, which can occur as early as the second or third decade of life.

FH is inherited as a co-dominant disorder, and although heterozygous FH patients are less seriously affected than the very rare homozygous FH patients, they nonetheless have an approximately two-fold increase in serum LDL compared to unaffected individuals, which puts them at considerably increased risk of developing CHD in early middle age.[3] There has also been some speculation that minor genetic variation in the LDL receptor gene could influence its level of expression and thereby contribute to milder forms of hypercholesterolemia and polygenic CHD.[4]

CLINICAL RELEVANCE

Although heterozygous FH is one of the commonest inherited disorders of metabolism, affecting about 1 in 500 people in most populations, it is estimated to be the underlying cause in only a small fraction of all individuals with hypercholesterolemia. However, an FH patient is considered to be at greater risk of premature CHD than an individual who has the same LDL-cholesterol concentration due to some secondary cause, mainly because the FH patient will have been exposed to the high concentration of cholesterol from birth, while secondary hypercholesterolemia generally occurs only much later in life.[5] Thus, it is important that an accurate diagnosis of FH be made so that appropriate advice and treatment can be given to the patient, preferably before the onset of overt CHD, and counselling can be offered to the patient's family.

A clinical diagnosis of definite heterozygous FH is given to a patient with a serum LDL-cholesterol (LDL-C) concentration $\geq$ 190 mg/dL (5.0 mmol/L) if certain other criteria are fulfilled. These include the presence of tendon xanthomata in the patient or a first-degree relative, and a positive family history of high serum cholesterol or severe premature CHD. If these criteria are not met fully, but it is suspected that severe hypercholesterolemia is inherited, then a diagnosis of possible FH is given.[5] Not surprisingly, many patients fall into the second category, and determining whether or not they do have a heritable defect in LDL receptor function is not always straightforward. Other factors, genetic or environmental, appear to influence the phenotype of heterozygous FH patients, as shown by the observation that the severity of the disease in FH patients differs quite widely, even among patients who have the same defect in the LDL receptor gene.[6]

A mutation in the gene for apolipoprotein (apo) B has been identified that results in substitution of an arginine residue in the protein (Arg3500) with glutamine. This affects its ability to bind to the LDL receptor and results in a clinical phenotype very similar to that seen in patients with a defect in the LDL receptor gene.[7] This disorder is now referred to as familial defective apo B (FDB). With the currently available lipid-lowering drugs, it is probably not critical to distinguish between FDB and FH when managing an individual patient at risk of premature CHD due to inherited hypercholesterolemia,[8] but this may not always remain so.

Ideally, identification of a genetic defect in the LDL receptor gene that affects LDL receptor function provides the only unequivocal diagnosis of FH but, as discussed in Chapter 31, this is not yet feasible for every patient. This is partly because of the huge number of different mutations that cause FH—almost as many different mutations as there are FH patients in some clinics[6]—and partly because some potential mutations, such as those distant from the coding region or occurring in introns, would not be detected by current methods. For this reason, many assays have been devised to measure LDL receptor activity or LDL receptor protein content in human tissues or cells as a means of detecting defective LDL receptor function. However, as discussed below, none of these assays has proved able to discriminate unequivocally between all heterozygous FH patients and the normal population.

REVIEW OF CURRENT METHODS

Measurement of LDL Receptors in Cultured Cells

Sound, reliable methods are described in the literature and, indeed, are widely used in research for the measurement of binding, internalization, and degradation of ^{125}I-labelled LDL by cultured cells. An example is human skin fibroblasts,[9] based on the pioneering work of Brown and Goldstein and colleagues.[10, 11] LDL receptor protein content of cells can also be determined by semi-quantitative immunoblotting or ligand blotting of cell extracts fractionated by polyacrylamide gel electrophoresis,[12] or by radioimmunoassay of a membrane fraction of whole cell extracts.[13]

All these techniques are ideal for elucidating, for example, the effects of stimulatory or inhibitory factors of LDL receptor gene expression in an individual cell line, but the absolute values obtained for different cell lines vary considerably, even when no defect in receptor function is suspected. This is probably because LDL receptor expression is very sensitive to the sterol content of the cells and is barely detectable in cells that have been preincubated in medium containing serum.[10] Thus, cells must be pre-incubated in sterol-free medium, usually one containing lipoprotein deficient serum (LPDS), which is prepared by ultracentrifugation of serum to remove all lipoproteins that float at a density of > 1.2 kg/L. Pre-incubation of cells in such a medium removes the source of the large majority of exogenous sterols, but some traces of free sterol may remain. Furthermore, pre-incubation of cells with sterol-free medium stimulates the rate of cholesterol synthesis in the cell,[11] and excess newly synthesized cholesterol will also down-regulate LDL receptor expression. Inhibitors of hydroxymethylglutaryl-coenzyme A (HMG-CoA) reductase, a key enzyme in the pathway of cholesterol biosynthesis, can be included in the pre-incubation medium, but cultured cells will not survive for long if deprived entirely of a source of sterols. The rate of growth of the cells in culture can also be affected by, for example, the presence of growth factors or other mitogens in the medium,[14-16] and this will influence the demand for cholesterol for membrane synthesis. Thus, the balance between synthesis and utilization of cholesterol can vary between different cells, or even between the same cells on different days, and this critically influences the absolute level of LDL receptor gene expression.

This variability causes virtually insoluble problems for making a diagnosis of heterozygous FH based on LDL receptor activity in cultured cells from an individual patient. Cells from a homozygous patient normally can be clearly identified in this way, because the residual LDL receptor activity is almost always less than 10–20% of normal, even when the mutant protein from both alleles retains some activity. However, the clinical phenotype of homozygous FH is normally unmistakable,[2] and there is rarely a need to assay receptor function for clinical purposes. A few patients have been described in whom a diagnosis of homozygous FH is suspected, but some doubt exists because only one or neither of the parents is clearly hypercholesterolemic.[17] On such occasions it can be useful to assay receptor activity in the patient's cells to confirm or, in some instances, preclude a diagnosis of homozygous FH.

The problems arise in attempting to distinguish between heterozygous FH and hypercholesterolemia due to other causes, because although the mean values for LDL receptor activity or protein content between suspected FH and control groups are clearly different, the region of overlap between them is too great to permit unambiguous discrimination of all individuals. This overlap occurs even when the FH group comprises only patients with defined mutations in the LDL receptor gene. This is partly because of the experimental variability described above, and partly because some mutations are less deleterious than others to the function of the protein.[18] Some mutations result in the production of no protein at all from the mutant allele, or of one with undetectable residual activity, while others result in only a partial reduction in the LDL receptor activity of the protein encoded by that allele. It must also be remembered that cells from a heterozygous FH patient produce the normal amount of LDL receptor protein from the unaffected allele, and thus retain half the normal level of LDL receptor activity, apparently regardless of the defect in the mutant allele.[19] The result is that the activity in heterozygous FH cells can vary from 50% to 100% of a normal range that is itself quite wide, as is demonstrated by the data shown in Figure 26–1. Thus, it is not possible to confirm that a particular individual has a defect in one allele of his or her LDL receptor gene by assaying LDL receptors in the individual's cultured cells.

Measurement of LDL Receptors in Freshly Isolated Cells

A further disadvantage of attempting to measure LDL receptors in cultured cells as a diagnostic tool is the length of time required to establish cell lines. Cultures of skin fibroblasts can take many weeks before sufficient cells grow out of the biopsy for experiments to be feasible, and obtaining a skin biopsy is an invasive procedure. Lymphocytes from fresh human blood can be transformed with Epstein-Barr virus to produce immortalized lymphoblasts, and in this case sufficient cells can be obtained within 3–4 weeks. However, these cells grow in suspension, which makes assays of binding of LDL to the cell surface less reliable, and lymphoblasts are less well characterized in terms of their regulation of LDL receptor expression than cultured skin fibroblasts.[21]

This inevitable delay in obtaining results from cultured cells, together with the considerable labor and cost involved in their maintenance, has led to the development of methods to measure LDL receptors in freshly isolated white blood cells by flow cytometry. For most of the methods described, non-adherent mononuclear cells have been incubated either with LDL labelled with a hydrophobic fluorescent molecule that

Figure 26–1 ✧ Comparison of LDL Receptor Activity and
Immuno-detectable LDL Receptor Protein in Epstein-Barr Virus
(EBV)-Transformed Lymphocytes in Patients with a Clinical
Diagnosis of Heterozygous FH and Normolipemic Controls

LDL-receptor activity (O) was determined as the maximum rate of saturable degradation of ^{125}I-labelled LDL by cells pre- incubated for 48 h in medium containing lipoprotein-deficient serum and compactin. LDL-receptor protein (●) content
was determined by semi-quantitative immunoblotting of the cell extracts fractionated by SDS-polyacrylamide gel electrophoresis with monoclonal antibodies specific for the LDL receptor. A genetic defect in the LDL receptor gene was
identified in some of the heterozygous FH patients (htz FH - mutation known).
No genetic defect in the gene for apo B or for the LDL receptor was detected in
the remaining patients (htz FH - defect unknown). The dotted line represents the
lower limit of the normal range. Data from Sun et al.[20]

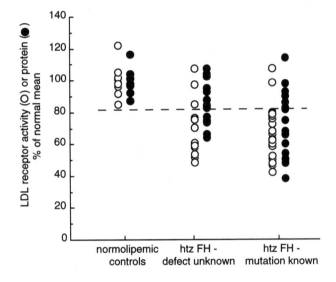

is localized in the lipid core of the particle,[22-26] or with a specific antibody to the LDL
receptor that is then detected with a second antibody conjugated to a fluorescent
label.[24, 27] The advantage of using labelled LDL is that only functional LDL receptors
are measured, while the antibody may also bind to non-functional mutant protein on
the cell surface. However, isolated LDL has a very limited shelf life, so it must be
prepared frequently from fresh plasma. The level of activity in freshly isolated cells is
too low to be detected, and pre-incubation for one to several days with a sterol-depleted
medium has been found to be necessary to induce measurable LDL receptor expression.[28] Some researchers have also found it necessary or beneficial to stimulate the
cells by pre-incubating them with cytokines or mitogens, while others believe that this
increases experimental variability because the cell population appears to be less homogeneous with respect to LDL receptor expression.[24, 25, 29]

The absolute requirement for cholesterol for cell proliferation has been exploited to assess LDL receptor activity in peripheral blood mononuclear cells (PBMCs). Freshly isolated PBMCs in which cholesterol biosynthesis is inhibited are entirely dependent on an external supply of cholesterol for growth in response to a mitogenic stimulus.[30] Low concentrations of LDL, in the range of 2–3 µg of LDL-cholesterol per mL, can supply cholesterol for cells with the normal complement of functional LDL receptors, but concentrations approximately two-fold higher are required to support the proliferation of cells with half the number of functional LDL receptors which are obtained from patients with heterozygous FH.[31]

In practice, freshly isolated cells are incubated in medium containing LPDS and mevinolin, a potent inhibitor of cholesterol biosynthesis, together with LDL in varying concentrations in the range of 0–10 µg of cholesterol per mL, with or without the mitogen phytohemagglutinin in the medium. The proliferative response in the presence of different concentrations of LDL is then determined as the difference in the rate of incorporation of 3H-thymidine after 4 days of incubation with or without the mitogen. As originally described, this method showed that there was a clear difference between control cells and cells from heterozygous FH patients.[31] However, the authors later demonstrated that the response was "normalized" in cells from heterozygous FH patients treated with lipid-lowering drug therapy,[32] suggesting that the response in cells from different patients might be affected by a variety of factors, and that the method is not likely to be totally reliable for diagnostic purposes in today's lipid clinics.

Although all the various methods have been able to show a significant difference in the mean activity between freshly isolated lymphocytes from normolipemic individuals and from patients with a clinical diagnosis of heterozygous FH, in practice all these methods suffer from the same drawback as those used for cultured cells: that the region of overlap between heterozygous FH and control subjects is too great to permit discrimination in a significant number of cases. Unfortunately, these patients often will be the very ones in whom the clinical diagnosis of FH is in some doubt. No flow cytometric studies have been performed in which cells only from individuals with known defects in the LDL receptor gene have been compared to cells from individuals with no detectable defect, so that the frequency of false negatives or positives could be assessed. Nor have any instances been published in which a diagnosis of possible heterozygous FH has been confirmed or refuted by measurement of LDL receptor activity in the patient's cells.

These problems are clearly demonstrated by a recent careful study of 384 patients with a clinical diagnosis of heterozygous FH based on serum cholesterol levels, family history, and clinical symptoms.[24] In the study, LDL-receptor-dependent binding of LDL and of anti-LDL-receptor antibody to freshly isolated PBMC was determined by flow cytometry. Based on the flow cytometric assay results, LDL receptor deficiency was thought to be present in only 72% of the patients. Therefore, it has to be concluded that, by this technique, the diagnosis apparently remained unconfirmed in one out of every three to four potential FH patients. In a smaller study, but one in which every possible care was taken to standardize the flow cytometric assay of LDL binding,[29] a similar proportion of patients with a clinical diagnosis of heterozygous FH, including the presence of tendon xanthomata in the patient, were found to have LDL receptor activity within the normal range.

Measurement of LDL Receptors in the Whole Body

To assess whether or not variation in LDL receptor activity between individuals has a significant influence on their plasma lipoprotein concentration or risk of premature CHD, it is essential to be able to measure LDL receptor activity under the physiological conditions of sterol balance that exist in the whole body. Clearly, this is not possible by any of the methods described above, not even with freshly isolated lymphocytes because it is necessary to deprive these cells of all exogenous sterols to induce measurable amounts of LDL receptor protein or activity. Thus, the activity measured in fully induced cultured cells will reflect the maximum genetic potential of the cells to express LDL receptors, although this is always influenced to some extent by the state of growth of the cells, as described above. It certainly will not reflect the physiologically regulated level of expression in different tissues in the whole body, where the flux of cholesterol varies in response to numerous physiological changes. Hence, there is considerable doubt that the low level of LDL receptor activity expressed in circulating lymphocytes accurately reflects that expressed in the liver.

With the exception of malignant cells,[33] lymphocytes have little need of cholesterol for cell membrane synthesis or for biosynthetic purposes, while there is considerable flux of cholesterol in the liver, where cholesterol is converted to bile acids that are secreted in the bile, together with free cholesterol. The liver also secretes cholesterol-containing lipoproteins, thereby further depleting hepatocytes of cholesterol. As a result, the expression of LDL receptors is much higher in the liver than in circulating white blood cells. LDL receptor activity in most tissues other than the liver appears to be very low, with the exception of those that synthesize steroid hormones, but these tissues normally make only a small contribution to LDL receptor activity in the whole body in comparison to the liver.[34]

Unfortunately, any methods that can or have been devised to measure hepatic LDL receptor expression directly, whether by immunoassay of LDL receptor protein,[12] by measurement of binding of ^{125}I-labelled LDL to hepatic membranes,[35] or by assay of the amount of LDL receptor mRNA,[36] require a liver biopsy. Thus, these methods are suitable only for research purposes, with strictly limited numbers of patients who are undergoing biopsy or surgery for other reasons, and not for routine clinical measurement. The potential exists for LDL uptake in the liver to be determined by noninvasive whole-body imaging after the administration of a trace of labelled LDL, and this has been achieved in rabbits by scintigraphy following injection of radionuclide-labelled LDL.[37] However, the much higher concentration of LDL in the human circulation would greatly reduce the sensitivity of this or any other imaging technique, as any specific binding or uptake would be superimposed on a high background.

The same limitation of lack of feasibility for routine clinical purposes applies to the indirect measurement of LDL receptor function by determining the rate of turnover of LDL in the whole body. This technique relies on following the fate in plasma of an administered trace of autologous labelled lipoprotein.[38] With radioactively labelled lipoproteins, specific LDL receptor-mediated uptake can be assessed by comparison of the rate of removal of a trace of normal LDL with that of a trace of a chemically modified form of LDL that is not recognized by the LDL receptor but is otherwise metabolized normally.[39] More recently, measurement of LDL turnover has been made less invasive by the use of stable isotopes as an endogenous label, generally administered as a single dose of a deuterated amino acid[40] rather than ^{125}I-labelled lipoproteins as tracers for apo B; however, receptor-mediated uptake cannot be distinguished from non-receptor-mediated uptake by this method.

The major drawback of the procedure, one which precludes its use for routine diagnostic purposes, is that with either type of labelling technique, blood samples must be taken daily for at least 7–10 d after administration of the dose, during which time the patient must consume a carefully controlled diet. In addition, the subsequent experimental procedure for analysis of the samples is very labor intensive, and with either an endogenous label or a radioactive trace to measure LDL turnover, a number of assumptions must be made in order to equate LDL catabolism with LDL receptor expression.

One of the least valid assumptions that must be made, at least for FH patients, is that LDL is cleared primarily by the LDL receptor pathway. Although the fractional rate of catabolism of LDL is reduced in FH, the absolute amount of LDL cleared from the circulation each day by FH patients can actually exceed that of normolipemic individuals.[41] Clearly, alternative pathways for the removal of LDL exist, especially when the concentration of LDL in the circulation is high. The specificity of determining the activity of the LDL receptor pathway in the whole body could be increased by assaying the uptake of a specific antibody to the LDL receptor protein that is bound and internalized in the same way as a lipoprotein ligand.[42] This has been successfully carried out in rabbits,[43] but the potential problems associated with administering a foreign protein has precluded the development of this method for human subjects.

SUMMARY AND CONCLUSIONS

Although all the methods described above have been used successfully for research purposes, there is little direct evidence that they have proved useful for routine clinical diagnosis of heterozygous FH in a typical clinic. Several of the groups who have set up flow cytometric methods for the measurement of LDL-receptor-dependent binding of fluorescently labelled LDL state that this method is likely to be useful as an aid to diagnosis. Thus far, this technique probably provides the best discrimination between heterozygous FH patients and normal controls based on LDL receptor activity, but no one has yet provided a clear description of cases where results from flow cytometric analysis of LDL receptor activity in cells has changed the course of clinical management.

It should also be borne in mind that obtaining reproducible results with this method requires a high level of technical expertise, as well as specialized equipment that is expensive and may not always be available in the routine laboratory. In practice, a combination of a sound clinical examination and knowledge of the family history, supported where possible with analysis of the mutation or polymorphisms in the LDL receptor gene,[44] provides the best diagnosis of heterozygous FH for routine clinical management. ✦

REFERENCES

1. Brown MS, Goldstein JL. A receptor-mediated pathway for cholesterol homeostasis. Science 1986;232:34-47.
2. Goldstein JL, Hobbs H, Brown MS. Familial hypercholesterolaemia. In: Scriver CR, Beaudet AL, Sly WS, Valle D, eds. The metabolic and molecular bases of inherited disease, Vol. II, New York: McGraw-Hill, 1995:1281-2030.
3. Slack J. Risk of ischaemic heart disease in familial hyperlipoproteinaemic states. Lancet 1969;ii:1380-1382.
4. Pedersen JC, Berg, K. Gene-gene interaction between the low density lipoprotein receptor and apolipoprotein E loci affects lipid levels. Clin Genet 1990;38:287-94.
5. Scientific Steering Committee on behalf of the Simon Broome Register Group. Risk of fatal coronary heart disease in familial hypercholesterolaemia. BMJ 1991;303:893-6.
6. Webb JC, Sun X-M, McCarthy SN, Neuwirth C, Thompson GR, Knight BL, Soutar AK. Characterisation of mutations in the low density lipoprotein (LDL)-receptor gene in patients with familial hypercholesterolaemia (FH) and frequency of these mutations in FH patients in the UK. J Lipid Res, in press.
7. Myant NB, Gallagher JJ, Knight BL, McCarthy SN, Frostegard J, Nilsson J, Hamsten A, Talmud P, Humphries SE. Clinical signs of familial hypercholesterolemia in patients with familial defective apolipoprotein B-100 and normal low density lipoprotein receptor function. Arterioscler Thromb 1991;11:691-703.
8. Maher VM, Gallagher JJ, Thompson GR, Myant, NB. Response to cholesterol-lowering drugs in familial defective apolipoprotein B-100. Atherosclerosis 1991;91:73-6.
9. Goldstein JL, Basu SK, Brown MS. Receptor-mediated endocytosis of low-density lipoprotein in cultured cells. Methods Enzymol 1983;98:241-60.
10. Goldstein JL, Brown MS. Binding and degradation of low density lipoproteins by cultured human fibroblasts. Comparison of cells from a normal subject and from a patient with homozygous familial hypercholesterolemia. J Biol Chem 1974;249:5153-62.
11. Goldstein JL, Basu SK, Brunschede GY, Brown MS. Release of low density lipoprotein from its cell surface receptor by sulfated glycosaminoglycans. Cell 1976;7:85-95.
12. Soutar AK, Harders SK, Wade DP, Knight, BL. Detection and quantitation of low density lipoprotein (LDL) receptors in human liver by ligand blotting, immunoblotting, and radioimmunoassay: LDL receptor protein content is correlated with plasma LDL cholesterol concentration. J Biol Chem 1986;261:17127-33.
13. Knight BL, Preyer S, Soutar AK. Immunoassay of bovine and human low-density-lipoprotein receptors using monoclonal antibodies. Biochem J 1986;238:405-10.
14. Moorby CD, Gherardi E, Dovey L, Godliman C, Bowyer DE. Transforming growth factor-beta 1 and interleukin-1 beta stimulate LDL receptor activity in Hep G2 cells. Atherosclerosis 1992;97:21-8.
15. Nicholson AC, Hajjar, DP. Transforming growth factor-beta up-regulates low density lipoprotein receptor-mediated cholesterol metabolism in vascular smooth muscle cells. J Biol Chem 1992;267:25982-7.
16. Chait A, Ross R, Bierman EL. Stimulation of receptor-dependent and receptor-independent pathways of low-density lipoprotein degradation in arterial smooth muscle cells by platelet-derived growth factor. Biochim Biophys Acta 1988;960:183-9.
17. Harada SM, Tajima S, Yokoyama S, Miyake Y, Kojima S, Tsushima M, Kawakami M, et al. Siblings with normal LDL receptor activity and severe hypercholesterolemia. Arterioscler Thromb 1992;12:1071-8.
18. Soutar AK, Familial hypercholesterolaemia. In: Humphries SE, Malcolm S, eds. From genotype to phenotype. Oxford, UK: Bios, 1994:83-103.
19. Goldstein JL, Sobhani MK, Faust JR, Brown MS. Heterozygous familial hypercholesterolemia: failure of normal allele to compensate for mutant allele at a regulated genetic locus. Cell 1976;9:195-203.

20. Sun X-M, Patel DD, Knight BL, Soutar AK, with the Familial Hypercholesterolaemia Regression Study Group. Comparison of the genetic defect with LDL-receptor activity in cultured cells from patients with a clinical diagnosis of heterozygous familial hypercholesterolaemia. Arterioscler Thromb Vasc Biol, in press.

21. Lombardi P, de Wit E, Frants RR, Havekes LM. Characterisation of the LDL receptor in Epstein-Barr virus transformed lymphocytes. Biochim Biophys Acta 1990;1044: 127-32.

22. Lestavel DS, Benhamamouch S, Agnani G, Luc G, Bard JM, Brousseau T, Billardon C, et al. Evidence of non-deficient low-density lipoprotein receptor patients in a pool of subjects with clinical familial hypercholesterolemia profile. Metabolism 1994;43:397-402.

23. Ranganathan S, Hattori H, Kashyap ML. A rapid flow cytometric assay for low-density lipoprotein receptors in human peripheral blood mononuclear cells. J Lab Clin Med 1995;125:479-86.

24. Schmitz G, Bruning T, Kovacs E, Barlage, S. Fluorescence flow cytometry of human leukocytes in the detection of LDL receptor defects in the differential diagnosis of hypercholesterolemia. Arterioscler Thromb 1993;13:1053-65.

25. Suzuki K, Hara M, Kitani A, Harigai M, Norioka K, Kondo K, Hirata F. et al. Augmentation of LDL receptor activities on lymphocytes by interleukin-2 and anti-CD3 antibody: a flow cytometric analysis. Biochim Biophys Acta 1990;1042:352-8.

26. Traill KN, Jurgens G, Bock G, Huber L, Schonitzer D, Widhalm K, Winter U, et al. Analysis of fluorescent low density lipoprotein uptake by lymphocytes: paradoxical increase in the elderly. Mech Ageing Dev 1987;40:261-88.

27. Benhamamouch S, Kuznierz JP, Agnani G, Marzin D, Lecerf JM, Fruchart JC, Clavey, V. Determination of the LDL receptor binding capacity of human lymphocytes by immunocytofluorimetric assay. Biochim Biophys Acta 1989;1002:45-53.

28. Bilheimer DW, Ho YK, Brown MS, Anderson RGW, Goldstein JL. Genetics of low density lipoprotein receptor: diminished receptor activity in lymphocytes from heterozygotes with familial hypercholesterolemia. J Clin Invest 1978;61:678-696.

29. Lohne K, Urdal P, Leren TP, Tonstad S, Ose, L. Standardization of a flow cytometric method for measurement of low-density lipoprotein receptor activity on blood mononuclear cells. Cytometry 1995;20:290-5.

30. Cuthbert JA, Lipsky, PE. Provision of cholesterol to lymphocytes by high density and low density lipoproteins: requirement for low density lipoprotein receptors. J Biol Chem 1987;262:7808-18.

31. Cuthbert JA, East CA, Bilheimer DW, Lipsky PE. Detection of familial hypercholesterolemia by assaying functional low-density-lipoprotein receptors on lymphocytes. N Engl J Med 1986;314:879-83.

32. Cuthbert JA, East CA, Lipsky, PE. Normalization of LDL receptor function by lymphocytes of patients with heterozygous familial hypercholesterolemia after treatment with plasma cholesterol lowering agents. Am J Med Sci 1989;298:152-60.

33. Rudling MJ, Peterson CO. A simple binding assay for the determination of low-density lipoprotein receptors in cell homogenates. Biochim Biophys Acta 1985;833:359-65.

34. Rudling MJ, Reihner E, Einarsson K, Ewerth S, Angelin B. Low density lipoprotein receptor-binding activity in human tissues: quantitative importance of hepatic receptors and evidence for regulation of their expression in vivo. Proc Natl Acad Sci USA 1990; 87:3469-73.

35. Harders-Spengel K, Wood CB, Thompson GR, Myant NB, Soutar AK. Difference in saturable binding of low density lipoprotein to liver membranes from normocholesterolaemic subjects and patients with heterozygous familial hypercholesterolaemia. Proc Natl Acad Sci USA 1982;79:6355-9.

36. Rudling M. Hepatic mRNA levels for the LDL receptor and HMG-CoA reductase show coordinate regulation in vivo. J Lipid Res 1992;33:493-501.

37. Huettinger M, Corbett JR, Schneider WJ, Willerson JT, Brown MS, Goldstein JL. Imaging of hepatic low density lipoprotein receptors by radionuclide scintiscanning in vivo. Proc Natl Acad Sci USA 1984;81:7599-603.

38. Shepherd J, Bicker S, Lorimer AR, Packard, CJ. Receptor-mediated low density lipo-protein catabolism in man. J Lipid Res 1979;20:999–1006.

39. Slater HR, Packard CJ, Shepherd, J. Measurement of receptor-independent lipoprotein catabolism using 1,2-cyclohexanedione modified low density lipoprotein. J Lipid Res 1982;23:92–96.

40. Packard CJ. The role of stable isotopes in the investigation of plasma lipoprotein metabolism. Baillieres Clin Endocrinol Metab 1995;9:755–72.

41. Packard CJ, Third JL, Shepherd J, Lorimer AR, Morgan HG, Lawrie TD. Low density lipoprotein metabolism in a family of familial hypercholesterolemic patients. Metabolism 1976;25:995–1006.

42. Huettinger M, Schneider WJ, Ho YK, Goldstein JL, Brown MS. Use of monoclonal anti-receptor antibodies to probe the expression of the low density lipoprotein receptor in tissues of normal and Watanabe heritable hyperlipidemic rabbits. J Clin Invest 1984; 74:1017–26.

43. Fitzsimmons C, Bush R, Hele D, Godliman C, Gherardi E, Bowyer DE. Measurement of the absolute number of functioning low-density lipoprotein receptors in vivo using a monoclonal antibody. Biochem J 1995;305:897–904.

44. Soutar AK. Investigation and diagnosis of disorders of lipoprotein metabolism. In: Rapley R, Walker MR. Molecular Diagnostics. Oxford, UK: Blackwell Scientific Publications, 1993:139–68.

New Approaches to the Use of Lipoprotein Electrophoresis in the Clinical Laboratory

27

Herbert K. Naito, Kory M. Ward, Gerd Schmitz,
Christoph Möllers, Alfred Böttcher, Judith Ploch,
and Gary L. Myers

INTRODUCTION

❖ Methods used to separate the major lipoprotein classes—chylomicrons, very-low-density lipoproteins (VLDL), low-density lipoproteins (LDL), and high-density lipoproteins (HDL)—include ultracentrifugation, chromatography, electrophoresis, and various immunochemical techniques. The electrophoretic methods became popular in the routine clinical laboratories when Fredrickson et al.[1] proposed a classification system for the five (later modified to six[2]) hyperlipoproteinemia phenotypes based on elevations of the four major classes of plasma lipoproteins. This classification system was a major breakthrough in categorizing elevations of cholesterol and triglycerides into distinct and recognizable lipoprotein patterns. The subsequent use of the lipoprotein classification system lead to the understanding that each of the six lipoprotein phenotypes were not appropriately categorized as discrete lipoprotein disorders, but rather that each pattern might represent a variety of biochemical abnormalities.[3] Today, we recognize the complexity of lipoprotein metabolism and the heterogeneity of the different lipoprotein families in such properties as size and function, and their association with the risk for coronary heart disease (CHD).

Evolving knowledge about the association between the lipoproteins and CHD risk, and especially publication of expert guidelines by the National Cholesterol Education Program (NCEP),[4, 5] shifted clinical decision making from observing lipoprotein patterns to measuring cholesterol content in the lipoprotein fractions: LDL-cholesterol (LDL-C) and HDL-cholesterol (HDL-C). Since electrophoretic methods were used primarily in clinical laboratories for qualitative observations of lipoprotein patterns, their use diminished with the change to quantitative measurements. Early attempts to adapt qualitative lipoprotein methods for quantitative analysis were largely unsuccessful due to poor precision.

In order to obtain the lipoprotein cholesterol values, the clinical laboratory generally measured serum triglycerides, total cholesterol, and HDL-C and used the Friedewald equation[6] to estimate LDL-C. The use of this formula for calculating LDL-C was recognized to have some major limitations:

1. Patients must be fasting overnight to avoid the presence of chylomicrons and for accurate determination of triglycerides in the fasting state.

2. Lipemic specimens—triglycerides > 200 mg/dL (2.2 mmol/L)—can cause some error, and values > 400 mg/dL (4.5 mmol/L) can cause major inaccuracies in the calculated LDL-C value.[7]

3. The equation cannot be used if the patient has Type III hyperlipoproteinemia (disbetalipoproteinemia).

4. Accuracy is dependent on accurate measurement of all three analytes—total cholesterol, triglycerides, and HDL-C—and on the influence of biological variation of the three analytes at the time of specimen collection.

These drawbacks of the widely used estimation technique for LDL-C and recommendations from National Cholesterol Education Program and other consensus groups[8, 9] motivated development of methods for direct measurement of LDL (see Chapter 8). The direct-LDL method, which has become somewhat common, uses an immunoseparation technique and generally has been reported to demonstrate improved performance compared to the estimation technique.[10-13] Recommendations for direct-LDL measurement also sparked interest in improving electrophoretic systems for direct quantitation of the lipoprotein fractions.[14]

The conventional precipitation methods for HDL-C which became common in routine practice also have disadvantages. They usually require a manual pretreatment step that is labor intensive, time consuming, and subject to greater variation than, for example, cholesterol measurements alone.[15-17] With precipitation methods for the isolation of HDL, a major source of inaccuracy is interference resulting from incomplete precipitation of lipoproteins containing apolipoprotein (apo) B, which are associated with hypertriglyceridemia. Chylomicrons, in particular, tend to cause greater interference problems than VLDL, depending on the method used. Increasing demand in routine clinical laboratories for full automation, lower cost per test, and faster methods with smaller sample and reagent volume requirements led to improvements in the technology,[18] culminating in the recent development of direct and fully automated HDL methods, the so-called homogeneous assays (see Chapter 7). These methods are based on a one-step procedure whereby the discrimination between the lipoproteins is accomplished on-line and the chemistry analyzer only measures HDL-C.[19, 20] The method is faster due to the elimination of the pretreatment steps: manual addition of a precipitation reagent to the specimen, mixing, centrifugation, and decanting of the supernatant solution. Although reagents tend to be more expensive, the total cost is less due to decreased labor costs. The disadvantages associated with the conventional precipitation methods for HDL-C have also stimulated interest in quantitative electrophoretic procedures.

The national guidelines for acceptable analytical performance for LDL-C[9] and HDL-C[17] measurements suggest that the conventional methods involving manual pretreatment for HDL-C and calculation of LDL-C will have difficulties in meeting the current proficiency standards. The newer, more automated methods that involve fewer procedural steps are more likely to meet the national guidelines for analytical performance.

Electrophoretic methods have served a useful purpose in the clinical laboratory for over 25 years. In earlier years they were used primarily for profiling patients with dyslipoproteinemias.[1, 2] In subsequent years interest in phenotyping faded and electrophoresis became limited primarily to research purposes for characterizing unusual lipoprotein profiles, assessing dysbetalipoproteinemias (Type III hyperlipoproteinemia), resolving the purity of isolated lipoprotein fractions, identifying different apolipoproteins, determining the molecular weight of polypeptides, and studying subclasses of lipoproteins.

Today, the use of electrophoretic methods for quantitation of the lipoproteins seems to be making a modest comeback in the routine clinical laboratory. Electrophoretic systems have remained in the routine laboratory for analysis of other proteins and have progressively become more sophisticated and more conducive to automation. The fact that one can simultaneously quantitate all of the major lipoprotein fractions, and to some extent even the minor ones, and visually inspect the gels for unusual patterns after electrophoresis has stimulated renewed interest in these systems.

Electrophoresis of plasma lipoproteins has been performed on a number of different support media, such as starch gel,[21] cellulose acetate,[22-25] paper,[26-30] agarose,[31-35] polyacrylamide gel (PAG),[36-40] and others.[41-45] Each of the media has its strengths, weaknesses, and advantages for different types of procedures. Several comprehensive reviews of electrophoretic techniques for lipoprotein analysis are available.[46-50]

The support media used will not only determine how well lipoproteins can be separated, but also how well they can be quantitated. While paper electrophoresis can be considered a classical medium for obtaining lipoprotein patterns, the relatively poor separation of the pre-beta bands from the beta bands is a disadvantage. Also, paper is relatively opaque and quantitation by reflectance spectrophotometry is not ideal because of the background staining of the paper. For this purpose, paper as a support medium has been largely replaced by media which have better resolving power and are more suitable for quantitation by densitometry.

Starch-gel has not been used to any great extent in the clinical laboratory. However, for the isolation of lipoproteins in large quantities, the starch-block electrophoretic technique has been useful in the research laboratory. One can prepare these gels by using partially hydrolyzed potato starch, and such gels will separate lipoproteins on the basis of both electrical charge and molecular size.[21, 51] Lipoproteins isolated by this method can be used for immunological, chemical composition, physical-chemical, and electron microscopic studies. Because this technique can isolate large amounts of lipoproteins, it has been used along with column chromatographic techniques to further purify the lipoproteins—in making antibodies to lipoproteins, for example.

PAG, like starch gel, separates lipoproteins on the basis of both the electrical charge and molecular size. The molecular sieving action of the PAG slows the large VLDL band to a position between the origin and the LDL band (the reverse of the pattern seen with agarose, paper, and cellulose acetate media, in which VLDL migrates to the pre-beta band). The molecular sieving effect in PAG also results in lipoprotein fractions being separated with a higher degree of resolution.

PAG electrophoresis has been used extensively in the research laboratory because of its greater resolving power to separate subclasses of major lipoprotein fractions. However, this apparent advantage can become an obstacle when a large number of lipoproteins separate into so many discrete bands that it is difficult to identify the individual bands. One commercial PAG system for lipoprotein separation, Lipophor

(Quantimetrix, Redondo Beach, CA), has remained in use by clinical laboratories for many years.[40]

Agarose gel has become the most widely used support medium for the electrophoretic separation of lipoproteins (see Figure 27–1). The resolving power of this gel is greater than that of paper or cellulose acetate. The relatively clear matrix of the agarose gel allows for better quantitation of the lipoprotein fractions with the use of a scanning densitometer.

Attempts have been made to quantitate the lipoprotein fractions by densitometric scanning of the electrophoretograms on different support media, including paper,[26] cellulose acetate,[22, 50] agarose gel,[32–34, 52] and PAG.[53] In earlier methods, the densitometric scanning was based on integrating the intensity of each major lipoprotein band stained with a lipid dye (fat red 7B, oil red O, Sudan black B, nitroblue tetrazolium) and quantitation was by comparison with a calibration curve. There were several problems with these early quantitative electrophoretic methods:

Figure 27–1 ✧ Lipoprotein Patterns by Conventional Agarose Gel Electrophoresis

Patients 1, 2, and 3 have hypobetalipoproteinemia. Patient 4 has Type IIa hyperbetalipoproteinemia. Patient 5 has Type IIb hyperlipoproteinemia. Patient 7 has a normal lipoprotein profile. Note that when only two lipoprotein bands (alpha and beta) are involved (Patients 1, 2, and 3), the separation is very discrete. On the other hand, when the pre-beta lipoproteins are present (Patients 4, 5, and 7), the separation of the pre-beta band from the beta band is not as discrete: the pre-beta band often trails off from the anodal edge of the band to the beta band.

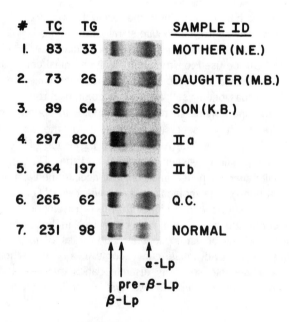

#	TC	TG		SAMPLE ID
1.	83	33		MOTHER (N.E.)
2.	73	26		DAUGHTER (M.B.)
3.	89	64		SON (K.B.)
4.	297	820		II a
5.	264	197		II b
6.	265	62		Q.C.
7.	231	98		NORMAL

α-Lp
pre-β-Lp
β-Lp

1. The heterogeneity of each lipoprotein fraction causes poor resolution, making it difficult for the analyst to precisely delineate between the lipoprotein fractions (see Figure 27–2).

2. The lipid stains have different affinities for the different classes of lipids (cholesteryl esters, free cholesterol, triglycerides, phospholipids) which vary in their proportions in each lipoprotein class. This causes different degrees of dye intensity in relation to the total amount of lipids affecting the quantitation of the lipoprotein fractions. To circumvent this problem, attempts have been made to use other means for visualizing the lipoproteins, such as polyanion precipitation after electrophoresis with scanning of the turbidity in the lipoprotein bands.[51]

3. No method has been found to calibrate the integrated peaks or dye intensity against a "gold standard" method that accurately quantitates lipoprotein concentrations. In the past, the calibration of electrophoretic methods was based on preparative or analytical ultracentrifrugal data. However, the bands separated by electrophoretic techniques are not exactly equivalent to the classes separated by ultracentrifugation.

4. A constant lipid-dye and alcohol concentration from one batch to the next, or from one electrophoretic run to the next, could not be maintained.

In addition to these problems, several factors can cause poor resolution of lipoprotein bands and make manual or automatic demarcation of one lipoprotein fraction from another very difficult: (a) the support media used, (b) the environmental conditions (relative humidity, room temperature), (c) the voltage/current and electrophoretic time used, (d) the different sizes and electronegativity of lipoproteins, which

Figure 27–2 ✦ Densitometric Tracing of a Normal Lipoprotein Pattern

The figure shows the separation of beta lipoproteins (LDL), pre-beta lipoproteins (VLDL), fast pre-beta lipoproteins [Lp(a)], and alpha-lipoproteins (HDL).

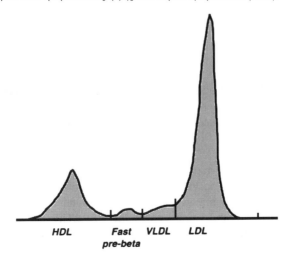

HDL   *Fast*   *VLDL*   *LDL*
       pre-beta

can all cause a change in their mobility or can cause an overlap of the lipoprotein bands on electrophoretograms. Poor resolution of incomplete separation of lipoprotein fractions can lead to inaccurate quantitation of each of the lipoprotein fractions, especially the pre-beta lipoproteins (VLDL) and beta-lipoproteins (LDL).

Adding to the problem of inaccurate lipoprotein quantitation are specimens with chylomicrons or high levels of heterogeneous VLDL, which tend to cause trailing from the application point to the $alpha_1$-globulin area, which can also create significant positive interference in the quantitation of the other lipoprotein fractions. In addition, the presence of unusual lipoproteins such as beta-migrating VLDL and lipoprotein (a) [Lp(a)] can cause biases in the quantitation of VLDL because in many systems both of these variant lipoproteins migrate in the same zone as the VLDL.

Finally, changing the electronegativity of the lipoproteins can change the normal migration patterns of the electrophoretogram. For instance, physiological stress conditions (the epinephrine effect) can cause increased lipolysis of triglycerides in adipose tissue, resulting in increased levels of free fatty acids (FFA) in the bloodstream. The FFA bind preferentially to albumin, but once albumin is saturated, the lipoproteins are the next transport vehicle for the FFA, which changes their electronegativity and thus their migration pattern. Injecting the patient with a bolus dose of heparin can have the same effect because heparin will activate the intravascular lipoprotein lipase to cause hydrolysis of the circulating triglycerides, which results in high concentrations of blood FFA and glycerol.

The recent resurgence of interest in lipoprotein electrophoresis has resulted in new approaches such as increased automation;[14] modified agarose gels for quantitation of lipoprotein cholesterol, including intermediate-density lipoprotein (IDL) and Lp(a);[54] high-resolution PAG for evaluating size distributions;[44] and capillary isotachophoresis using Biogel A 150m for quantitation of lipoproteins and subclasses.[49] Two of the newer electrophoretic systems for lipoprotein analysis—an automated agarose-gel method and a capillary isotachophoresis system—are described below in more detail.

QUANTITATION OF LIPOPROTEIN CHOLESTEROL BY AGAROSE-GEL ELECTROPHORESIS

Although many attempts have been made to use different support media for the separation and quantitation of lipoprotein fractions, we focus here on agarose as a method of choice because of the technological and automated advances that have occurred.

The most recent addition to quantitative lipoprotein cholesterol methods is the fully automated Cholesterol Profile-15 Electrophoresis System (Helena Laboratories, Beaumont, TX), which uses the Rapid Electrophoresis Analyzer II (REP II). The procedure is based on the electrophoretic separation of the major lipoprotein classes on an agarose-gel support medium that has 15 specimen application slots. After a 40-minute electrophoresis and a 2-minute air-drying period, the gel is overlaid with a cholesterol reagent for 15 minutes to visualize the lipoprotein bands. The gel is immersed in a washing solution for 5 minutes, placed in tap water for 5 minutes, and then blotted and dried at 54° C for 7 minutes in the REP. The 15 specimens with separated lipoprotein bands (Figure 27–3) are simultaneously quantitated using the REP II with a densitometer at 570 nm. The analytic system is linear up to 400 mg/dL of cholesterol per lipoprotein band and has an analytical sensitivity of 2.5 mg/dL per lipoprotein band. If the patient specimen quantitations exceed the linearity limits, the sample is

Figure 27–3 ✧ Lipoprotein Patterns on the New High-Definition Agarose Gel from Helena Laboratories

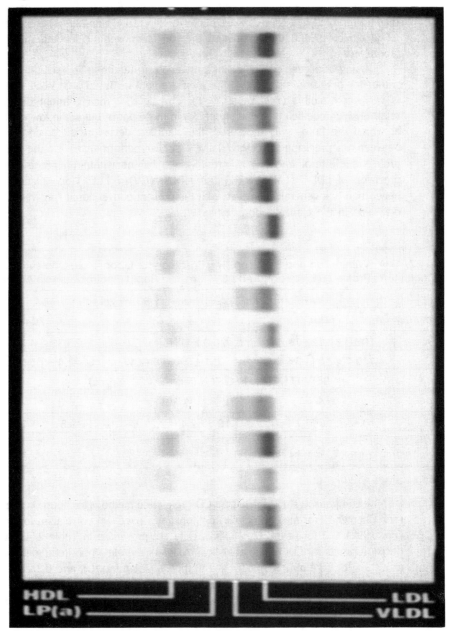

diluted with deionized water and re-electrophoresed. The reformulation of the newer agarose gel permits better separation of the VLDL from the LDL, allowing the IDL to migrate into the LDL band rather than forming a bridge between VLDL and LDL. In addition, the new gel separates the Lp(a) from the LDL, with Lp(a) migrating as a fast pre-beta lipoprotein band between VLDL and HDL (see Figure 27–2).

To circumvent the historical imprecision problems of electrophoretic methods, the manufacturer has improved the uniformity in gel manufacturing and has installed a precise Peltier temperature control device in the REP II. The simultaneous, direct quantitation of LDL-C, HDL-C, VLDL cholesterol (VLDL-C), and Lp(a) cholesterol [Lp(a)-C] is attractive, and the automated method is convenient for the modern clinical laboratory.

Using two-level quality control materials from the manufacturer, our data on within-day precision suggest that the measurement of the LDL-C, VLDL-C, and HDL-C is very reproducible (see Table 27–1). The Lp(a)-C measurement demonstrates a relatively high coefficient of variation (CV) in these pools, but at the low concentrations at which the Lp(a) was measured, the standard deviation is considered low. The between-run precision suggests relatively similar performances for the different lipoprotein cholesterol fractions as are revealed by the within-run precision data. The precision of LDL-C (CV of 3.7%) and HDL-C (CV of 11.6%) quantitation is actually better than that generally achieved with the present conventional (pre-treatment) methods used in the clinical laboratory today.

Table 27–1 ✧ Within-Run and Between-Run Precision for Lipoprotein Cholesterol Using the Cholesterol Profile 15 Electrophoresis System and Rapid Electrophoresis Analyzer II*

WITHIN-RUN PRECISION (Mean ± 1 SD, mg/dL)			
Pool	LDL-C	VLDL-C	HDL-C
A	100.0 ± 2.7 (2.7% CV)	20.0 ± 1.1 (5.4% CV)	35.3 ± 2.4 (6.8% CV)
B	149.1 ± 2.0 (1.3% CV)	8.1 ± 0.4 (5.3% CV)	41.4 ± 1.5 (3.6% CV)
BETWEEN-RUN PRECISION (Mean ± 1 SD, mg/dL)			
Pool	LDL-C	VLDL-C	HDL-C
B	103.4 ± 3.8 (3.7% CV)	19.6 ± 2.4 (12.2% CV)	33.5 ± 3.9 11.6% CV)

*n = 10 replicate determinations
To convert mg/dL to mmol/L, divide by 38.66.

A comparison study against the CDC reference methods for lipoprotein cholesterol (see Chapter 12 for method details) demonstrates excellent correlation for both HDL-C (r = 0.992) and for LDL-C (r = 0.998). Data are presented in Table 27–2. At medical decision points for LDL-C, the analytical biases of the electrophoretic method are 5.8% at 130 mg/dL (3.4 mmol/L), 6.0% at 160 mg/dL (4.1 mmol/L), and 6.2% at 190 mg/dL (4.9 mmol/L), with an average overall bias of 6.0%. Based on the above data, the total error for LDL-C is calculated to be 13.3%, which is slightly above the recommended analytical goal of 12.0%.[9]

Table 27–2 ✦ Lipoprotein Cholesterol Comparison Studies: Electrophoresis Method Against the CDC Reference Methods*

Statistics	LDL-C	VLDL-C	HDL-C
Regression Equation	$y = 1.783 + 1.071x$	$y = 0.734 + 0.389x$	$y = -2.449 + 1.1x$
Correlation Coefficient	$r = 0.99809$	$r = 0.97682$	$r = 0.99241$
$S x/y$	3.2674	0.9399	1.2396

*Intercept results in mg/dL. To convert to mmol/L, divide by 38.66.

The comparison study suggests that the HDL-C determined by the electrophoresis method has a bias of 3.1% at 35 mg/dL (0.9 mmol/L) and of 6.0% at 60 mg/dL (1.54 mmol/L)—two important medical decision points. This translates to a total error of 27.3%, which is slightly above the recommended analytical goal of 22% for total error.[17] Most of the HDL-C total error obtained by the electrophoretic method is due to the imprecision of the method, i.e., 11.6% at an HDL-C concentration of 33.5 mg/dL. Precision studies at higher HDL-C concentrations (e.g., > 50 mg/dL (1.29 mmol/L) are in progress to determine whether the precision of the assay is better at the higher concentrations.

While this electrophoretic method clearly separates and quantitates the Lp(a)-C with reasonable precision, we did not assess accuracy against a comparison method. The work of Nauck et al.[54] suggests that precision for Lp(a)-C with this method is between 6.8 and 16.4% CV. Their comparison of the Lp(a)-C values with those of a nephelometric Lp(a) assay gave a relationship by linear regression of r = 0.906, y = 4.21 mg/dL + 0.238x.

In view of these findings, it is encouraging that an agarose method has been refined to achieve many of the criteria that clinical laboratories are seeking to help improve the convenience, speed, accuracy, and economy of measuring lipoprotein cholesterol for the assessment of CHD risk. In addition to having the ability to simultaneously quantitate LDL-C and HDL-C with reasonable performance, the electrophoretic method can also resolve and quantitate Lp(a)-C. Another model soon to be released by Helena Laboratories, the REP III, will accommodate 60 specimens at a time and will include a fluorescent scanner that is claimed to be faster, more automated, and more sensitive than the current model.

ANALYTICAL CAPILLARY ISOTACHOPHORESIS OF HUMAN SERUM LIPOPROTEINS

An analytical free-flow capillary isotachophoresis (ITP) procedure has been developed for the detailed analysis of lipoproteins on commercially available capillary electrophoresis systems. The original technique was based on the specific staining of lipoproteins with the lipophilic dye Sudan Black B before performing capillary ITP.[55, 56] Since Sudan Black B shows no saturation kinetic in lipoprotein staining, we looked for another lipophilic dye which was composition independent but surface area or particle size dependent. Fluorescence-tagged phospholipid analogs have been tested and NBD-ceramide was identified as a good compromise for specific labeling and quantitation of individual lipoprotein classes.

As demonstrated in Figure 27–4, NBD-ceramide shows a saturation kinetic for lipoprotein labeling. After blood clotting, centrifugation, and one-minute incubation with NBD-ceramide, serum samples are applied by pressure between leading and terminating buffer into a fused-silica capillary (180 μm inner diameter, 20 cm length to detector) that is inserted between two electrolyte reservoirs. Under the electric field, the stained lipoproteins are separated within 6 minutes according to their net electrophoretic mobility. The addition of non-fluorescent spacer compounds allows the discrimination of 9 individual lipoprotein subclasses monitored with laser-induced fluorescence detection (ex 488 nm; em 510 nm; see Figure 27–5).

HDL are separated into three major subpopulations:

1. the fast-migrating HDL subpopulation, containing mainly apo A-I and phosphatidylcholine

2. the subpopulation with intermediate mobility, consisting of particles rich in apo A-II, apo E, and apo C

3. the slow-migrating HDL subfraction, containing mainly particles rich in apo A-I, apo A-IV, cholesteryl ester transfer protein (CETP), clusterin (apo J), phospholipid transfer protein (PLTP), and lecithin:cholesterol acyltransferase (LCAT) activity.

The apo-B–containing lipoproteins can be subdivided into three functional groups. The first group comprises chylomicron-derived particles and large, triglyceride-rich,

Figure 27–4 ✧ Saturation Kinetics for Sudan Black B and NBD-Ceramide as Lipoprotein-Specific Dyes

Serum samples were incubated with increasing amounts of specific dye and subsequently analyzed by analytical capillary isotachophoresis.

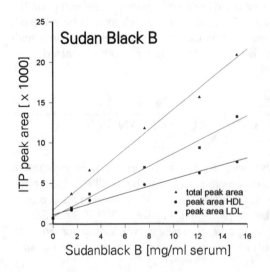
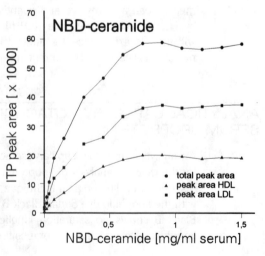

very-low density lipoproteins (VLDL). The second group consists of small VLDL and IDL particles. The third and fourth groups represent the low-density lipoproteins (see Figure 27–5).

Lipoprotein data obtained by capillary isotachophoretic analysis were compared with routinely used techniques for HDL-C and LDL-C quantitation, including quantitative lipoprotein electrophoresis, lipoprotein cholesterol analysis with precipitation procedures, and turbidimetric determination of the apolipoprotein content. The correlation of HDL-C and LDL-C determined by capillary ITP and precipitation procedures is shown in Figure 27–6 for a group of 52 samples obtained from patients of our university hospital. The correlation coefficients for HDL-C and LDL-C are 0.9 and 0.91, respectively, demonstrating the excellent correlation between lipoprotein quantitation by capillary ITP and routinely used techniques.

Beyond quantitation of HDL-C and LDL-C particles as a whole, the analytical capillary isotachophoretic technique allows further insights into plasma lipoprotein metabolism by estimation of major lipolytic enzyme activities with the help of an appropriate precursor/product concept. The ratio between precursor- and product-lipoprotein peaks influenced by a defined lipolytic enzyme allows the estimation of lipoprotein conversion

Figure 27–5 ✧ Representative Isotachopherogram of Human Serum Obtained from a Healthy Volunteer

Serum was incubated with NBD-ceramide and subsequently separated by analytical capillary isotachophoresis. The first peak (I) represents the internal marker compound carboxyfluorescein.

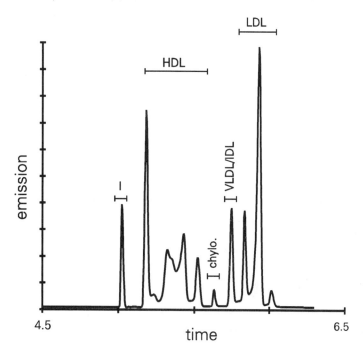

Figure 27–6 ✧ Correlation Analysis of HDL and LDL Cholesterol Levels
Determined by Capillary Isotachophoresis and Precipitation Procedures

HDL-C has been determined by phosphotungstic acid precipitation and LDL-C in
accordance with the Lipid Research Clinics protocol. Total cholesterol levels of
the sample group ($n = 52$) were 67–391 mg/dL (1.73–10.11 mmol/L) with a
mean of 210 mg/dL (5.43 mmol/L).

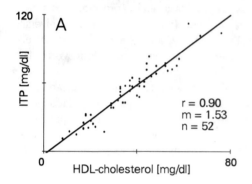

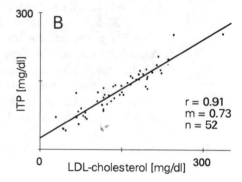

rates. In human plasma, pre-beta HDL particles are converted by LCAT to alpha-migrating lipoprotein particles. Since the fast-migrating HDL subpopulation consists of alpha-migrating lipoproteins, the ratio between slow- and fast-migrating HDL in an ITP lipoprotein pattern permits a rough estimate of the LCAT activity in human plasma. To analyze the distribution of pre-beta-migrating apo A-I in HDL subpopulations obtained by capillary ITP, we used a micropreparative-free solution isotachophoresis technique, under the same conditions as those used for capillary isotachophoresis, to separate HDL into fast-, intermediate-, and slow-migrating subfractions. We subsequently reanalyzed the individual fractions using the two-dimensional gel electrophoresis procedure described by Castro and Fielding.[57]

As shown in Figure 27–7, the fast-migrating HDL subfraction consists mainly of α-Lp(AI). Pre-β2-Lp(AI) first appears in the intermediate-migrating HDL and increases in the slow-migrating subpopulation. Pre-β1-Lp(AI) is only detectable in the slow-migrating HDL fraction. Therefore, capillary ITP is the only quantitative technique to analyze pre-beta HDL particles resembling slow-migrating HDL. Furthermore, capillary ITP allows further insights into the lipoprotein metabolism in hereditary lipoprotein disorders such as HDL deficiency with xanthomas and Tangier disease.[58]

Chylomicrons and large triglyceride-rich VLDL particles are the precursors for lipoprotein lipase. Lipoprotein lipase converts this subpopulation into particles with intermediate density. In capillary ITP, peak 5 resembles mainly unhydrolyzed triglyceride-rich lipoproteins, including chylomicrons and large VLDL, whereas IDL particles primarily migrate in peak 6. Thus, the ratio of peak 5 and peak 6 provides a rough estimate of the lipoprotein lipase activity in human plasma.

In vivo IDL particles are further metabolized by the hepatic triglyceride lipase (HTGL) into LDL particles. Therefore, the relative distribution of VLDL/IDL and LDL

Figure 27–7 ✧ Distribution of Pre-β-Migrating Apo A-I and Particle Size in Apo A-I Containing Subfractions Obtained by Micropreparative Free Solution Isotachophoresis of Human Plasma

FAST-MIGRATING HDL

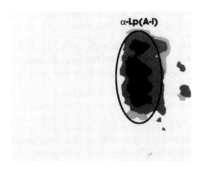

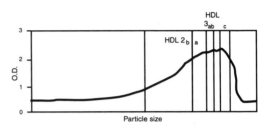

INTERMEDIATE-MIGRATING HDL

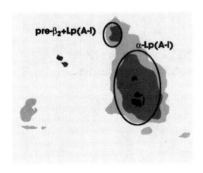

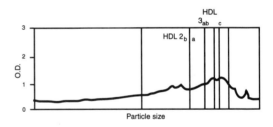

SLOW-MIGRATING HDL

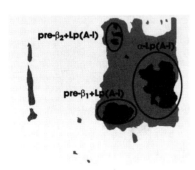

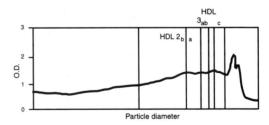

particles in capillary ITP permits the analysis of hepatic triglyceride lipase activity in mixed hyperlipidemias.

Intraplasmatic lipoprotein metabolism can be studied under postprandial conditions after an oral fat load and repetitive capillary isotachophoresis. To ascertain whether patients with borderline hyperlipidemia can still effectively metabolize oral fat, we monitored changes occurring in the lipoprotein pattern under postprandial conditions in normal subjects and in patients with Type IV hyperlipidemia and familial hypobeta-lipoproteinemia.[59] Analyses were made from fasting and postprandial sera 2, 3, 4, 5, and 6 h after fat ingestion. Significant differences among the analyzed patients were observed in the metabolism of apo-B–containing lipoproteins, allowing the detection of metabolic disturbances in the conversion of these lipoproteins. Besides postprandial studies of plasma triglyceride metabolism, Type III hyperlipoproteinemia can be easily detected by the presence of increased chylomicron-derived particles in capillary ITP.

The analytical capillary isotachophoresis of lipoproteins also permits quantification of chylomicrons and IDL particles in human serum. To study the value of our analytical ITP technique in separation and quantitation of atherogenic IDL particles, we analyzed a group of male patients with angiographically documented coronary artery disease (CAD) ($n = 17$) versus a control group ($n = 22$). The CAD patients had either mildly elevated or normal levels of total and LDL cholesterol or triglycerides (see Figure 27–8). However, compared to the control group, in the CAD group LDL-C was significantly increased and HDL-C was significantly decreased. These data are consistent

Figure 27–8 ✧ Comparison of Lipid Data Obtained from Male Patients with Coronary Sclerosis and from Healthy Volunteers

Black boxes represent patients with coronary sclerosis. White boxes represent healthy volunteers. Significance levels, when calculated, are indicated.

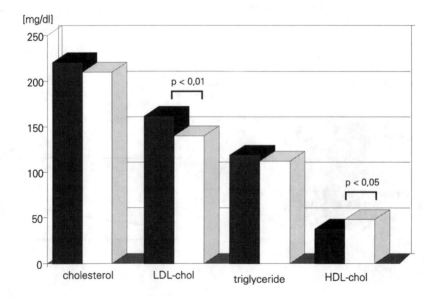

with the data obtained by capillary ITP, in which the LDL peak areas were increased and the HDL peak areas were significantly reduced in the CAD group (see Figure 27–9). Furthermore, in capillary ITP the IDL subpopulation in CAD patients is significantly increased, and the ratio of IDL versus LDL is also increased compared to the control group. These data give evidence for an ineffective conversion of IDL to LDL by hepatic lipase in CAD patients. Thus, capillary ITP allows the estimation of highly atherogenic IDL particles in parallel to HDL-C and LDL-C determination, which improves the analysis of atherosclerotic risk factors.

Analytical capillary ITP can be performed directly from whole serum, plasma, and other biological fluids. The technique allows simultaneous quantitation of HDL-C and LDL-C within 7 minutes, with an excellent correlation to routinely used techniques. Furthermore, the data summarized in this chapter clearly indicate that ITP analysis of human serum lipoproteins significantly improves the diagnosis of disorders in lipoprotein metabolism. In addition to the estimation of major lipolytic enzyme activities in human serum, the current procedure permits the quantitation of large, triglyceride-rich VLDL, cholesteryl-ester–enriched VLDL remnants, and IDL particles, thus improving the diagnosis of familial combined hyperlipidemia, one of the most common lipoprotein disorders associated with increased risk for CAD. Furthermore, capillary ITP is the only analytical technique to quantify pre-beta HDL in human plasma. Therefore, analytical capillary isotachophoresis can be a helpful method for a fast, reliable, and automated analysis of lipoprotein subclass patterns in the clinical laboratory.

Figure 27–9 ✧ Comparison of Lipoprotein ITP Peak Areas Obtained from Male Patients with Coronary Sclerosis and from Healthy Volunteers

Black boxes represent patients with coronary sclerosis. White boxes represent healthy volunteers. Significance levels, when calculated, are indicated.

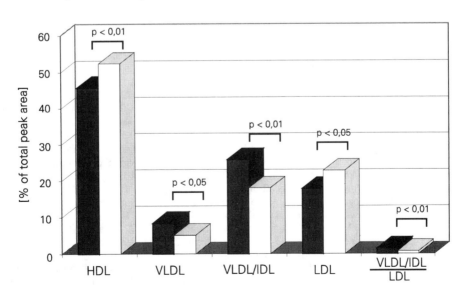

SUMMARY

Two new electrophoretic methods for quantitating lipoproteins have been described in this chapter. The modified agarose electrophoresis method takes about an hour and can directly and simultaneously quantitate VLDL-C, LDL-C, and HDL-C concentrations in plasma or serum. The method also can be used to separate and quantitate Lp(a)-C. The analytical performance of this method is reasonably good. The major problem is in delimiting or separating the beta and pre-beta bands, which requires some judgment by the operator.

The analytical capillary ITP method can also be used to directly quantitate HDL-C and LDL-C. The precision of this 7-minute procedure agrees well with that of methods currently in routine use. The technology has the advantage of also facilitating estimation of the major serum lipolytic enzyme activities, based on relative levels of large, triglyceride-rich VLDL, cholesteryl-ester–enriched VLDL remnants, IDL, and pre-beta HDL.

REFERENCES

1. Fredrickson DS, Levy RI, Lees RS. Fat transport in lipoproteins: an integrated approach to mechanisms and disorders. N Engl J Med 1967;276:34-44, 94–103, 148–56, 215–225, 273–81.
2. Beaumont JL, Carlson LA, Cooper GR, Fetpas Z, Fredrickson DS, Strasser T. Classification of hyperlipidemias and hyperlipoproteinemias. Bull WHO 1970,43:891–915.
3. Schaefer EJ, Levy RI. Pathogenesis and Management of Lipoprotein Disorders. N Engl J Med 1985;312(20):1300–10.
4. Report of the National Cholesterol Education Program Expert Panel on Detection, Evaluation, and Treatment of High Blood Cholesterol in Adults. Arch Intern Med 1988;148: 36–60.
5. Summary of the second report of the National Cholesterol Education program (NCEP) Expert Panel on Detection, Evaluation, and Treatment of High Blood Cholesterol in Adults (Adult Treatment Panel). JAMA 1993;269:3015–23.
6. Friedewald WT, Levy RI, Frederickson DS. Estimation of the concentration of low-density lipoprotein cholesterol in plasma, without use of the preparative ultracentrifuge. Clin Chem 1972;18:499–502.
7. McNamara Jr., Cohn JS, Wilson PWF, Schaefer EJ. Calculated values for low-density lipoprotein cholesterol in the assessment of lipid abnormalities and coronary disease risk. Clin Chem 1990;36:36–42.
8. Position statement of the CSCC and CAP Task force on the measurement of lipids for the assessment of risk of CHD. Clin Biochem 1989;22:231–7.
9. Bachorik PS, Ross JW. National Cholesterol Education Program recommendations for measurement of low-density lipoprotein cholesterol: executive summary. Clin Chem 1995;41:1414–20.
10. Jialal I, Hirany SV, Devaraj S. Sherwood TA. Comparison of an immunoprecipitation method for direct measurement of LDL cholesterol with B-quantitation (ultracentrifugation). Am J Clin Pathol 1995;104:76–81.
11. McNamara JR, Cole TG, Controls JH, Ferguson CA, Ordovas JM, Schaefer EJ. Immunoseparation method for measuring low-density lipoprotein cholesterol directly from serum evaluated. Clin Chem 1995;41:232–40.
12. Harris N, Neufeld EJ, Newburger JW, Ticho B, Baker A, Ginsburg GS, et al. Analytical performance and clinical utility of a direct LDL-cholesterol assay in a hyperlipidemic pediatric population. Clin Chem 1996;42:1182–8.
13. Schectman G, Patsches M, Sasse EA. Variability in cholesterol measurements: comparison of calculated and direct LDL cholesterol determinations. Clin Chem 1996;42: 732–7.

14. Warnick GR, Leary, ET, Goetsch J, Electrophoretic quantitation of LDL-cholesterol using the Helena REP. Clin Chem 1993;39;6:1122

15. Warnick GR, Marian CC, Albers JJ. Comparison of current methods for high density lipoprotein cholesterol quantitation. Clin Chem 1979;25:596–604.

16. Demacker PN, Vos-Janseen HE, Hijmans AG, Van't Laar A, Jansen AP. Measurement of high-density lipoprotein cholesterol in serum: comparison of six isolation methods combined with enzymatic cholesterol analysis. Clin Chem 1980;26:1780–86.

17. Warnick GR, Wood PD, National Cholesterol Education Program recommendations for measurement of high-density lipoprotein cholesterol: executive summary. Clin Chem 1995;41:1427–33.

18. Naito HK, Kwak YS. The evaluation of a new high-density lipoprotein cholesterol (HDL-C) technology: selective separation of lipoproteins by magnetic precipitation. Clin Chem 1995;41:S135.

19. Sugiuchi H, Yoshinori U, Hiroaki O, et al. Direct measurement of high-density lipoprotein cholesterol in serum with polyethylene glycol-modified enzymes and sulfated α-cyclodextrin. Clin Chem 1995;41;5:717–23.

20. Park JK, Naito HK. Performance characteristics of the new-generation, direct, automated high-density lipoprotein cholesterol (HDL-C) method. Clin Chem, in press.

21. Lewis LA. Starch-gel electrophoresis of lipoproteins. In: Lewis LA, Opplt JJ, eds. Handbook of electrophoresis (Vol. I): Lipoproteins: basic principles and concepts. Boca Raton, FL: CRC Press, 1980;221–7.

22. Chin HP, Blankenhorn DH. Separation and quantitation of serum lipoproteins by means of electrophoresis on cellulose acetate. Clin Chim Acta 1968;20:305–14.

23. Charman RC, Landowne RA. Separation of human plasma lipoprotein by electrophoresis on cellulose acetate. Anal Biochem 197;19:177–9.

24. Iammarino RM, Humphrey M, Antolik P. Agar gel lipoprotein electrophoresis: a correlated study with ultracentrifugation. Clin Chem 1969;15:1218–29.

25. Winkelman J, Ibbott FA, Sobel C, Wybenga DR. Studies on the phenotyping of hyperlipoproteinemias: evaluation of cellulose acetate technique and comparison with paper electrophoresis. Clin Chim Acta 1969;26:33–39.

26. Hatch FT, Mazrimas JA, Moore JL, Lindgren FT, Jensen LC, Wills RD, et. al. Semiquantitative paper electrophoresis of serum lipoproteins. Clin Biochem 1970;3:115–23.

27. Lewis LA. Paper as a support media for lipoprotein electrophoresis. In: Lewis LA, Opplt JJ, eds. Handbook of electrophoresis (Vol. I): Lipoproteins: basic principles and concepts. Boca Raton, FL: CRC Press, 1980;129–49.

28. Jencks WP, Hyatt MR, Jetton MR, Maltingly TW, Durrum EL. A study of serum lipoproteins in normal and atherosclerotic patients by paper electrophoretic techniques. J Clin Invest 1956:35:980–90.

29. Dangerfield WG, Smith EB. Investigation of serum lipids and lipoproteins by paper electrophoresis. J Clin Pathol 1955:8:132–9.

30. Lees RS, Hatch FT. Sharper preparation of lipoprotein species by paper electrophoresis in albumin-containing buffer. J Lab Clin Med 1963;61:518–28.

31. Noble RP. Electrophoretic separation of plasma lipoproteins in agarose gel. J Lipid Res 19:68;9:693–700.

32. Hulley SB, Cook SG, Wilson WS, Nichaman MZ, Hatch FT, Lindgren FT. Quantitation of serum lipoproteins by electrophoresis on agarose gel: standardization in lipoprotein concentration units (mg-100 mL) by comparison with analytical ultracentrifugation. J Lipid Res 1971;12:420–33.

33. Hatch FT, Lindgren FT, Adamson GL, Jensen LC, Wong AW, Levy RI. Quantitative agarose gel electrophoresis of plasma lipoproteins: a single technique and two methods for standardization. J Lab Clin Med 1973;81:946–60.

34. Opplt JJ. Agarose-gel electrophoresis of lipoproteins. In: Handbook of electrophoresis (Vol. I): Lipoproteins: basic principles and concepts. Boca Raton, FL: CRC Press, 1980; 151–82.

35. Gros M, Jurman-Gros T. Electrophoretical separation of pre-stained serum lipoproteins on cellulose acetate, agarose gel and polyacrylamide. Clin Chim Acta 1973;45:165–7.

36. Davis BJ. Disc electrophoresis. II. Method and application to human serum proteins. Ann NY Acad Sci 1964;121:404-27.

37. Narayan KA, Narayan S, Kummerow FA. Disc electrophoresis of human serum lipoproteins. Nature 1965;205:246-8.

38. Naito HK, Wada M. The use of polyacrylamide-gel electrophoresis for the detection of dyslipoproteinemia. In: Lewis LA, Opplt JJ, eds. Handbook of electrophoresis (Vol. I): Lipoproteins: basic principles and concepts. Boca Raton, FL: CRC Press, 1980;183-219.

39. Pratt JJ, Dangerfield WG. Polyacrylamide gels of increasing concentration gradient for the electrophoresis of lipoproteins. Clin Chim Acta 1969;23:189-201.

40. Muniz N. Measurement of plasma lipoproteins by electrophoresis on polyacrylamide gel. Clin Chem 1977;23:1826-33.

41. Reissell PK, Hagopian CM, Hatch FT. Thin-layer electrophoresis of serum lipoproteins. J Lipid Res 1966;7:551-7.

42. Oriente P. Lipoprotein electrophoresis on cellogel: a practical method for screening hyperlipoproteinemias. Adv Exp Med Biol 1973;38:247-58.

43. Wieland H, Seidel D. Changes in the plasma lipoprotein system due to liver disease. In: Lewis AL, Opplt JJ, eds. Handbook of electrophoresis (Vol. II): Lipoproteins in disease. Boca Raton, FL: CRC Press, 1980;79-101.

44. Nichols AV, Blanche PJ, Gong EL. Gradient gel electrophoresis of human plasma high density lipoproteins. In: Lewis LA, ed. Handbook of electrophoresis (Vol. III): Lipoprotein methodology and human studies. Boca Raton, FL: CRC Press, 1983;29-47.

45. Mahley RW, Weisgraber KH. Subfractionation of high density lipoproteins in two metabolically distinct subclasses by heparin affinity chromatography and Geon-Pevikon electrophoresis. In: Report of the High Density Lipoprotein Methodology Workshop (NIH Pub. No. 79-1661). Bethesda, MD: National Institutes of Health, 1977;356-67.

46. Bachorik PS. Electrophoresis in the determination of plasma lipoprotein patterns. In: Lewis AL, Opplt JJ, eds. Handbook of electrophoresis (Vol. II): Lipoproteins in disease. Boca Raton, FL: CRC Press, 1980;7-27.

47. Lindgren FT, Jensen LC, Hatch FT. The isolation and quantitative analysis of serum lipoproteins. In: Nelson G, ed. Blood lipids and lipoproteins: quantitation composition, and metabolism. New York: Wiley Interscience, 1972;181-274.

48. Lindgren FT, Adamson GL, Krauss RM. Automated quantitative lipoprotein microelectrophoresis. In: Lewis LA, Opplt JJ, eds. Handbook of electrophoresis (Vol. I): Lipoproteins: basic principles and concepts. Boca Raton, FL: CRC Press, 1980;229-49.

49. Demacker PNM, Otvos JD, Schmitz G, Mollers C, Lombardi P, Cost B, et al. Alternative approaches to lipoprotein analysis. In: Rifai N, Warnick GR, eds. Laboratory measurement of lipids, lipoproteins and apolipoproteins. Washington, DC: AACC Press, 1994; 323-47.

50. Winkelman J, Wynbenga Dr, Ibbott F. Quantitation of lipoprotein components in the phenotyping of hyperlipoproteinemias. Clin Chim Acta 1970;27:181-3.

51. Naito HK. Coronary artery disease and disorders of lipid metabolism. In: Kaplan LA, Pesce AJ, eds. Clinical chemistry: theory, analysis, correlation. St. Louis: Mosby, 1996; 642-81.

52. Wieland H, Seidel D. Quantitative lipoprotein electrophoresis. In: Lewis LA, ed. Handbook of electrophoresis (Vol. III): Lipoprotein methodology and human studies. Boca Raton, FL: CRC Press, 1983;83-102.

53. Moran RF, Casteilli WP, Moran MV. Quantitation of beta lipoprotein (LDL) cholesterol by densitometric evaluation of disc electrophoretograms. Clin Chem 1972;118:217-21.

54. Nauck M, Winkler K, Marz W, Wieland H. Quantitative determination of high- and very-low-density lipoproteins and lipoprotein(a) by agarose gel electrophoresis and enzymatic cholesterol staining. Clin Chem 1995;41:1761-7.

55. Nowicka G, Bruning T, Bottcher A, Kahl G, Schmitz G. Macrophage interaction of HDL subclasses separated by flow isotachophoresis. J Lipid Res 1990;31:1947.

56. Nowicka G, Bruning T, Grothaus B, Kahl G, Schmitz G. Characterization of apolipoprotein B-containing lipoproteins separated by preparative free flow isotachophoresis. J Lipid Res 1990;31:1173-86.

57. Castro Gr, Fielding CJ. Early incorporation of cell-derived cholesterol into pre-beta-migrating high-density lipoprotein. Biochemistry 1988;27:25-9.

58. Lackner KJ, Dieplinger H, Nowicka G, Schmitz G. High density lipoprotein deficiency with xanthomas. J Clin Invest 1993;92:2262-73.

59. Nowicka G, Gheeraert P, Schmitz G. Monitoring of postprandial changes in the serum lipoprotein pattern by analytical capillary isotachophoresis. In: Windler E, Greten H, eds. Intestinal lipid and lipoprotein metabolism. Munchen: W. Zuckschwerdt Verlag, 1989.

Measurement of Lipoprotein Subclass Profiles by Nuclear Magnetic Resonance Spectroscopy

28

James D. Otvos

CLINICAL SIGNIFICANCE OF LIPOPROTEIN SUBCLASSES

❖ It is well accepted in clinical practice that total plasma cholesterol (TC) is not the best indicator of a patient's risk of coronary heart disease (CHD). The reason is that cholesterol is a constituent of all of the major lipoproteins found in fasting plasma: very low-density lipoprotein (VLDL), low-density lipoprotein (LDL), and high-density lipoprotein (HDL). As a result, patients with widely differing concentrations of VLDL, LDL, and HDL can have exactly the same TC concentration. This situation would have no impact on the accuracy of CHD risk assessment were it not for the fact that VLDL, LDL, and HDL have differing associations with CHD. As is well known,[1, 2] VLDL and LDL have positive associations with CHD (elevated concentrations confer increased risk), whereas HDL levels have a negative association (higher concentrations confer protection). Thus, even though it is analytically more difficult and costly to determine the distribution of a patient's cholesterol among the three lipoprotein classes, and thereby obtain an indication of how much VLDL, LDL, and HDL is present, there is general acceptance of the medical necessity of acquiring this information before firm conclusions are drawn about the degree of risk and how best to manage that risk therapeutically. This is not to say that TC has no role to play as a CHD risk factor, since many people have very high or very low TC levels and their risk is adequately predicted on this basis. There are simply many more people with intermediate TC levels, and for these people CHD risk cannot be accurately evaluated without the higher-order lipoprotein information.

The foregoing discussion is directly relevant to the question of what clinical value might accrue from measuring lipoprotein subclass levels. As depicted in Figure 28-1, VLDL, LDL, and HDL each comprise a heterogeneous group of particles that differ in size and, in many cases, in their observed associations with CHD.[3] (There are also differences in density and chemical composition among subclasses, but we focus here on size since that is the property exploited by the nuclear magnetic resonance (NMR) analysis method described in this chapter.)

With recent advances in knowledge about the complexity of lipoprotein subclass metabolism and the mechanisms of atherogenesis,[4] it is not difficult to understand why people with the same concentrations of LDL-C and HDL-C, but with different subclass distributions, might differ significantly in CHD risk. There is, for example, abundant evidence that LDL particle size is an important determinant of CHD risk[5-10] (see Chapter 14). Several cross-sectional and prospective studies have shown that individuals with predominantly small, dense LDL particles (subclass pattern B) are at increased risk for CHD even when levels of LDL-C are not elevated. Other studies indicate that intermediate-density lipoprotein (IDL), which is operationally part of the LDL fraction as measured by standard methods, may be particularly atherogenic as well.[11] Differing associations of HDL subclasses with CHD have also been noted (see Chapter 13). Of the five subclasses separable by gradient gel electrophoresis, the three largest (HDL$_{2b}$, HDL$_{2a}$, and HDL$_{3a}$) show the expected inverse correlation with disease incidence and severity, whereas the two smallest subclasses (HDL$_{3b}$ and HDL$_{3c}$) show a positive association.[12, 13]

Thus, for the same reason that TC is often an unreliable indicator of CHD risk, HDL-C levels might not accurately predict the degree of CHD protection because of variability among individuals in the relative amounts of the atherogenic and anti-atherogenic subclasses. No efficient high-resolution method is available to measure VLDL subclasses, and consequently little is known about their relations to CHD risk. There is some indication, however, that increased numbers of large VLDL particles in fasting plasma correlate with impaired rates of chylomicron clearance, which independently predict CHD risk.[14, 15]

Figure 28–1 ✧ Lipoprotein Subclasses and CHD Risk

Shown are the lipoprotein subclasses quantified by NMR and the differential associations they and the standard cholesterol risk factors have with CHD. Plus signs indicate positive association with CHD and minus signs indicate negative association with CHD. The larger plus signs represent stronger associations with CHD.

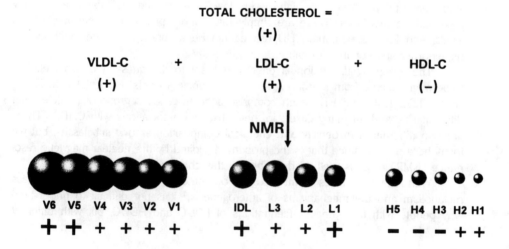

LIMITATIONS OF EXISTING METHODS OF SUBCLASS MEASUREMENT

All methods of measuring lipoproteins require the performance of two sequential operations: *separation* of the lipoprotein to be measured from the others, and *quantification*. The only reason these procedures consist of two steps rather than one is that quantification is commonly based on the concentration of one or more of the chemical constituents of the particles (usually cholesterol, but sometimes other lipid or apolipoprotein moieties), and none of these is found uniquely in any particular class or subclass of lipoprotein. If a particular (sub)class contained a distinct, assayable chemical component or had some other unique characteristic that could serve as a marker for its concentration, the fractionation step would not be needed and quantification could proceed directly using whole plasma.

Several important benefits would be gained by avoiding the physical separation step(s), particularly when quantifying lipoprotein subclasses. First and foremost would be significant cost savings in time and labor. Even the routine methods of HDL and LDL separation using selective chemical or immunoprecipitation are considerably more time-consuming and less automatable than TC or triglyceride (TG) measurements that do not require any fractionation.[16] Because the subclasses of a lipoprotein are so closely similar to one another in size, density, and composition, their separation is an order of magnitude more difficult than separation of the major lipoprotein classes.[3] The techniques used most frequently for subclass fractionation (described in Chapters 13, 14, 24, 27, 29, and 30) include various types of ultracentrifugation, electrophoresis, chemical precipitation, and chromatography. They often take several hours to several days to complete and usually achieve only partial resolution of the subclasses. Understandably, accuracy and precision are limited by the many potential sources of analytical error introduced during the separation process.

SUBCLASS QUANTIFICATION BY NMR SPECTROSCOPY: A NEW PARADIGM

Advantages of Spectroscopic Lipoprotein Subclass Analysis

Several years ago, we proposed that it might be possible to simultaneously quantify a large number of lipoprotein subclasses without employing physical fractionation of the plasma.[17, 18] The procedure would exploit what appeared to be natural, but generally unappreciated, proton NMR spectroscopic differences exhibited by lipoprotein particles of different sizes. Development work on this new process is now largely complete. Using a dedicated intermediate-field (360 MHz) NMR analyzer, routine quantification of 15 different subclasses of VLDL, LDL, and HDL is achieved in about one minute. As might be expected of a method that uses no reagents and requires minimal sample manipulation, accuracy and precision are as good or better than those achieved by the best alternative procedures. With the measurement efficiency of the NMR process, for the first time it will be possible to conduct research studies of large populations to examine subclass associations with CHD and other diseases and assess the impact of various treatment regimens on subclass levels and clinical outcomes. In high-volume testing environments, it will also be possible to cost-effectively produce NMR LipoProfiles for the routine clinical assessment and management of CHD risk.

Description of the NMR Method: The "Tolling of the Bells"

The basic concepts underlying NMR lipoprotein subclass analysis are quite simple and require no background in NMR spectroscopy to understand. Quantification is achieved in a three-step process consisting of *measurement* of the plasma NMR spectrum followed by computer *deconvolution* of the spectral data and *calculation* of the subclass concentrations. The measurement step, which is performed automatically on untreated plasma or serum specimens (~0.5 mL), takes less than one minute. The deconvolution and calculation steps, which are performed on the digitized data using specialized analysis software running off-line on a personal computer, require just a few seconds.

A typical plasma NMR spectrum is shown in Figure 28–2, highlighting the spectral region at ~0.8 ppm that contains the information used to extract the subclass concentrations. This region contains signals from the methyl groups of the four types of lipid

Figure 28–2 ✧ Typical Proton NMR Spectrum of Plasma Acquired at 360 MHz and 46° C

Shown are the composite methyl lipid signal (shaded) and a schematic representation of lipoprotein lipid structure, depicted as a neutral lipid core of cholesterol ester (CE) and triglyceride (TG) surrounded by a shell consisting of phospholipid (PL) and free (unesterified) cholesterol (FC).

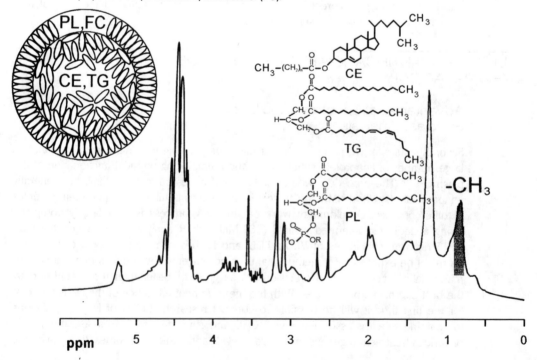

present in the particles: phospholipids, cholesterol, cholesterol ester, and TG. The methyl signals from the different lipids in each particle are inherently indistinguishable from one another, so they combine to produce a composite "bulk lipid" signal. The size of this signal serves as a measure of the lipoprotein concentration of the sample, in exactly the same way that the band intensities on a lipid-stained gel measure the amounts of electrophoretically separated lipoproteins. What makes it possible to exploit the methyl lipid signal for lipoprotein subclass quantification (without separating the subclasses first) is a fairly obscure magnetic property of lipoproteins that causes the methyl signal of larger particles to differ in frequency and shape from the corresponding signals of smaller particles.[19]

The simplest way to conceptualize the origin of these spectral differences is to draw an analogy between the bulk lipid of different lipoprotein subclasses and the metal in church bells of varying size. We accept without question that, despite being composed of the same metal, bells of different size produce distinguishable sound signals. It is for related reasons associated with the *shape* of lipoprotein particles that different subclasses broadcast distinguishable lipid NMR signals. Extending the analogy, if we take care to strike a group of bells with equal-force blows, we expect the amplitude (loudness) of the resultant sound signal to be linearly dependent on the number of bells. Thus, measuring the amplitude of sound produced by ringing an unknown number of bells can serve to quantify the bells, so long as advance knowledge exists about the quantitative relationship between bell number and sound amplitude. If we were interested instead in knowing the total weight (mass) of the bells, all that would be needed is the conversion factor relating sound amplitude to bell mass.

This analogy makes clear that the quantitative subclass information is derived by performing a simple NMR *measurement* (recording the signals produced by the "tolling of the bells"), and then performing *calculations* that convert the subclass signal amplitudes to whatever units of concentration we choose: particle number (nmol/L), total lipid mass (mg/dL), cholesterol mass (mg/dL), molar cholesterol (mmol/L), TG mass (mg/dL), and so on. Of course, a considerable amount of information needs to be accumulated in advance about the relations between signal amplitude and subclass concentration to make the calculations possible, but the calculations themselves are trivial and take only seconds.

The reason why the NMR process entails a third step, *deconvolution*, is that there is no way to selectively ring only one size bell at a time. Instead, all of the subclasses in a plasma sample are stimulated simultaneously (and equivalently) by the radiofrequency excitation pulse, and they then broadcast their characteristic signals at the same time. It is this composite signal that is recorded in the measurement step. Because the various subclass signals add together linearly to produce the recorded plasma signal, it is not difficult to compute the subclass signal amplitudes, using linear least-squares regression, by working backwards from the plasma signal. This would not be possible, however, without substantial prior knowledge of the characteristics (frequency and shape) of the signals emitted by each subclass in the sample. Again, although a substantial effort was needed to accumulate a complete library of subclass spectral information, the actual computer deconvolution step takes very little time.

There is no need to recount here the experimental details of the NMR methodology since most of these have been published elsewhere.[17, 18, 20] A fully automated

NMR system that requires no NMR experience of the operator will soon be available for analysis of lipoprotein subclasses. All of the advance work to acquire the knowledge used to interpret the plasma NMR data has already been done. That information, which is incorporated into the analysis software, consists mainly of a library of reference spectra of lipoprotein subclasses of narrow particle size range isolated by a combination of ultracentrifugation and agarose gel filtration from the plasma of normolipidemic and dyslipidemic subjects. These reference spectra were acquired under very reproducible, well-defined conditions identical to those used for collection of subsequent plasma spectra; hence, signal amplitudes can be used reliably to infer subclass concentrations.

The bell-like properties of lipoprotein particles are due to differences in magnetic susceptibility induced by the orientational order of the phospholipids in the shell surrounding the neutral lipid core.[19] The equations describing this effect predict that every lipoprotein particle of different diameter should have a different lipid NMR signature. (The diameter referred to is that of the phospholipid shell.) In practice, however, particles of closely similar diameter have NMR properties that are not sufficiently distinct to have a noticeable impact on the observed spectrum. We have determined empirically that the resolving power of the NMR method is sufficient to allow reliable quantification of six VLDL, four LDL, and five HDL subclasses (see Figure 28–1). It should be understood, however, that these subclasses represent groupings of particles of similar but not identical size, and that there is no implication of metabolic distinctness. The approximate diameter ranges (in nm) of the reference subclasses, determined by electron microscopy and polyacrylamide gradient gel electrophoresis, are as follows:

V6: 150 ± 70, V5: 70 ± 10, V4: 50 ± 10, V3: 38 ± 3,
V2: 33 ± 2, V1: 29 ± 2

IDL: 25 ± 2

L3 (large LDL): 22 ± 0.7, L2 (intermediate LDL): 20.5 ± 0.7,
L1 (small LDL): 19 ± 0.7

H5/HDL$_{2b}$: 11.5 ± 1.5, H4/HDL$_{2a}$: 9.4 ± 0.6, H3/HDL$_{3a}$: 8.5 ± 0.3,
H2/HDL$_{3b}$: 8.0 ± 0.2, H1/HDL$_{3c}$: 7.5 ± 0.2.

Not represented in this list are chylomicrons, which are larger than the V6 subclass, the largest lipoprotein particles found in fasting plasma. Inclusion of chylomicron reference spectra in the fitting model permits nonfasting specimens to be analyzed.

Since the only basis of NMR distinction between lipoproteins is the diameter of the lipid shell, it is not possible to distinguish between chylomicron remnants and VLDL particles of similar size. Likewise, the presence of the extra attached apolipoprotein (a) protein on lipoprotein (a) [LP(a)] particles does not affect the diameter of the lipid shell; therefore, Lp(a) and LDL cannot be distinguished by NMR. Although one might expect the methyl groups of the apolipoproteins to appear in the same spectral region as those of the lipids, they are significantly broader and therefore do not appreciably contribute to the bulk lipid signal that is the basis of the subclass quantification. Using the bell analogy again, the apolipoproteins on the particle surface can be likened to different designs painted on the bells to give them a unique visual appearance. Since these designs have no effect on the sounds the bells produce, they exert no adverse influence on the quantification. If the apolipoproteins did contribute measurably to the methyl NMR signal, or if the extensive chemical heterogeneity of the lipids created significant spectral variability, accurate NMR subclass analysis would be impossible.

Quantification Issues

Figure 28–3 shows the results of a typical plasma methyl signal analysis. The close similarities of the subclass reference spectra shown at the bottom are apparent, and reinforce the need to conduct the measurements under very reproducible conditions. The analysis software automatically converts the signal amplitudes of the 15 subclasses, derived by linear least-squares deconvolution of the plasma signal, to concentration units using empirically measured conversion factors. In this way, calculated subclass cholesterol and TG concentrations (mg/dL) are obtained. The program then sums the respective subclass concentrations to give values for TC, TG, VLDL-TG, LDL-C, and HDL-C. In addition, the average particle diameters (in nm) of VLDL, LDL, and HDL are determined by weighting the relative percentage of each subclass by its diameter. Finally, the program performs another set of calculations that converts the subclass signal amplitudes to particle concentrations (in units of nmol/L for VLDL and LDL

Figure 28–3 ✧ Representative Lineshape Fit of a Plasma Methyl Lipid Signal

Beneath the experimental (solid line) and calculated (dashed line), plasma spectra are the calculated amplitudes of the 15 VLDL, LDL, and HDL subclasses that contribute to the plasma signal, plus the background signal from plasma proteins of density > 1.21 g/L.

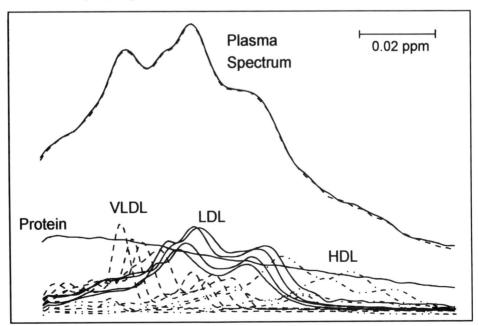

Figure 28–4 ◇ Relations of LDL-C and HDL-C for 49 Plasma Specimens Calculated by the NMR Method and Measured by Beta-Quantification

Each graph shows the line of identity and measured correlation coefficient. (To convert cholesterol values in mg/dL to mmol/L, multiply by 0.0259.)

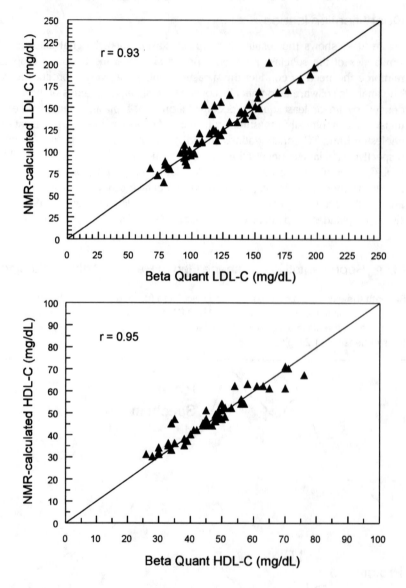

subclasses and μmol/L for HDL subclasses). These calculations involve dividing the NMR-derived lipid mass concentration by the amount of lipid/particle using standard assumptions about lipoprotein structure.[21] By summing LDL subclass particle concentrations, a value is obtained for total LDL particle concentration. Evidence suggests that NMR provides a more reliable estimate of true LDL particle concentration than does LDL–apolipoprotein B concentration (unpublished observation).

Several validation studies have recently been completed using fresh and frozen plasma and serum specimens comparing NMR-derived variables to lipoprotein lipid concentrations measured by the beta-quantification procedure, and to LDL and HDL subclass distributions measured by gradient gel electrophoresis. The results (to be published elsewhere) support the accuracy and high degree of precision of the method.

Figure 28–4 shows an example of the good agreement found between LDL-C and HDL-C levels calculated by NMR and measured chemically. Correlation coefficients for LDL-C are typically in the 0.91–0.95 range, while those for HDL-C are between 0.93–0.97. In both measurements, analytical error is responsible for some of the observed scatter in the data, but most is due to lipid compositional variability. Recall that the NMR estimates of LDL-C and HDL-C are based on the assumption of a constant relationship between a particle's bulk lipid signal amplitude and its cholesterol concentration. This means that any variability in a subclass's lipid composition will lead directly to discrepant results. It is not uncommon for some individuals, especially those with high TG levels, to have LDL and HDL that contain less cholesterol and more TG than normal as a result of cholesterol ester transfer protein (CETP)-catalyzed neutral lipid exchange.[22] For such people with cholesterol-depleted particles, cholesterol measurements give a falsely low impression of the amount of LDL and HDL actually present. This is not the case for the NMR-calculated values, which are derived from measurement of a bulk lipid signal whose amplitude is unaffected by the mutual exchange of core cholesterol ester for TG. (Both of these lipids contribute three methyl groups to the measured signal, as shown in Figure 28–1.)

NMR LipoProfiles

The NMR LipoProfile is one way of displaying the large amounts of information produced by a single NMR lipoprotein measurement. Two examples are shown in Figure 28–5. Each profile displays the NMR-calculated concentrations of the variables included in a standard lipid panel: total plasma cholesterol, total plasma triglyceride, LDL-C, and HDL-C (box upper right). Bar graphs indicate the concentrations (in mg/dL) of the individual subclasses, with VLDL concentrations expressed in terms of TG and LDL and HDL in terms of cholesterol. Also included are the weighted-average particle sizes (nm diameter) of VLDL, LDL, and HDL as well as the LDL particle concentration (nmol/L).

Some impression of the potential clinical value of the NMR subclass data can be gained by comparing the two profiles in Figure 28–5. Both subjects are middle-aged males who have virtually identical LDL-C and HDL-C levels. According to current NCEP guidelines,[23] the LDL-C levels indicate relatively low risk, while the HDL-C levels, which are below the 35 mg/dL (0.9 mmol/L) cutpoint, signify increased risk. Despite the close similarities of the standard lipid risk factors, the subclass distributions are markedly

Figure 28–5 ✧ NMR LipoProfiles of Two Subjects

Note that the subjects have very different lipoprotein subclass distributions, despite having comparable LDL-C and HDL-C levels. (To convert cholesterol values in mg/dL to mmol/L, multiply by 0.0259. To convert triglycerides in mg/dL to mmol/L, multiply by 0.0113.)

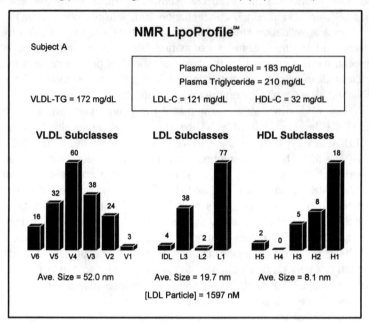

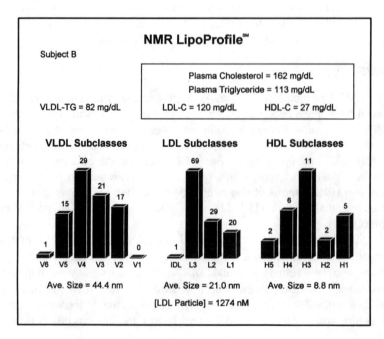

different for the two subjects, signifying important differences in lipoprotein metabolic state and CHD risk.

Based on what we know from recent clinical studies, Subject A would be assigned a significantly higher risk owing to the prevalence of small, dense LDL (pattern B)[5-10] and the fact that most of the HDL is in the smallest subclasses (H1 and H2), which appear to confer little (or none) of the protection offered by the larger subclasses.[12, 13] Subject A also has more TG and more large VLDL subclasses (V6 and V5), which are correlated with delayed chylomicron clearance and increased CHD risk.[14, 15] Importantly (we believe), Subject A has 25% more LDL particles than Subject B, despite having the same LDL-C concentration—a consequence of having smaller LDL particles. The overall impression gained from the NMR LipoProfile of Subject A is one of high enough risk to suggest the advisability of LDL-lowering therapy, something that would certainly not have been considered necessary based on the traditional lipid risk factors. Subject B, on the other hand, could be assured that his risk was fairly minimal despite his low HDL-C level.

We have observed many similar examples where an individual's lipid metabolic status and associated risk of CHD were almost certainly not assessed correctly by standard cholesterol measurements. On the other hand, there are many low-risk individuals—for example, those with very low LDL-C or very high HDL-C levels—who would not benefit significantly from the higher-order information in an NMR LipoProfile. ✧

Acknowledgments. *This work was supported by NIH Grant HL-43230. The author wishes to thank Elias Jeyarajah, Dr. Dennis Bennett, Qun Zhou, and Irina Shalaurova for research assistance and Drs. Lawrence Rudel and Ernst Schaefer for helpful discussions and assistance with calibration and validation of the NMR analytical method.*

REFERENCES

1. Castelli WP, Garrison RJ, Wilson PWF, Abbott RD, Kalousdian S, Kannel WB. Incidence of coronary heart disease and lipoprotein cholesterol levels: The Framingham Study. JAMA 1986;256:2835-8.
2. Austin MA. Plasma triglyceride and coronary heart disease. Arterioscler Thromb 1991; 11:2-14.
3. Musliner TA, Krauss RM. Lipoprotein subspecies and risk of coronary disease. Clin Chem 1988;34(Suppl):B78-83.
4. Steinberg D, Witztum JL. Lipoproteins and atherogenesis: current concepts. JAMA 1990;264:3047-52.
5. Austin MA, Breslow JL, Hennekens CH, Buring JE, Willett WC, Krauss RM. Low-density lipoprotein subclass patterns and risk of myocardial infarction. JAMA 1988;260:1917-21.
6. Griffin BA, Freeman DJ, Tait GW, Thomson J, Caslake MJ, Packard CJ, Shepherd J. Role of plasma triglyceride in the regulation of plasma low density lipoprotein (LDL) subfractions: relative contribution of small, dense LDL to coronary heart disease risk. Atherosclerosis 1994;106:241-53.
7. Campos H, Genest JJ, Blijlevens E, McNamara JR, Jenner JL, Ordovos JM, Wilson PWF, Schaefer EJ. Low density particle size and coronary artery disease. Arterioscler Thromb 1992;12:187-95.
8. Gardner CD, Fortman SP, Krauss RM. Association of small low-density lipoprotein particles with the incidence of coronary artery disease in men and women. JAMA 1996; 276:875-81.

9. Stampfer MJ, Krauss RM, Ma J, Blanche PJ, Holl LG, Sacks FM, Hennekens CH. A prospective study of triglyceride level, low-density lipoprotein particle diameter, and risk of myocardial infarction. JAMA 1996;276:882-88.

10. Lamarche B, Tchernof A, Moorjani S, Cantin B, Dagenais GR, Lupien PJ, Després J-P. Small, dense, low-density lipoprotein particles as a predictor of the risk of ischemic heart disease in men: prospective results from the Québec Cardiovascular Study. Circulation 1997;95:69-75.

11. Krauss RM. Relationship of intermediate and low-density lipoprotein subspecies to risk of coronary artery disease. Am Heart J 1987;113:578-82.

12. Wilson HM, Patel JC, Russe D, Skinner ER. Alterations in the concentration of an apolipoprotein E-containing subfraction of plasma high density lipoprotein in coronary heart disease. Clin Chim Acta 1993;220:175-87.

13. Johansson J, Carlson LA, Landou C, Hamsten A. High density lipoproteins and coronary atherosclerosis: a strong inverse relation with the largest particles is confined to normotriglyceridemic patients. Arterioscler Thromb 1991;11:174-82.

14. Karpe F, Bell M, Bjorkegren J, Hamsten A. Quantification of postprandial triglyceride-rich lipoproteins in healthy men by retinyl ester labeling and simultaneous measurement of apolipoproteins B-48 and B-100. Arterioscler Thromb Vasc Biol 1995;15:199-207.

15. Patsch JR, Miesenböck G, Hopferwieser T, Mühlberger V, Knapp E, Dunn JK, Gotto AM Jr, Patsch W. Relation of triglyceride metabolism and coronary artery disease: studies in the postprandial state. Arterioscler Thromb 1992;12:1336-45.

16. Working Group on Lipoprotein Measurement. NCEP recommendations on lipoprotein measurement. (NIH Publication No. 95-3044). Bethesda, MD: National Institutes of Health, 1995.

17. Otvos JD, Jeyarajah EJ, Bennett DW. Quantification of plasma lipoproteins by proton nuclear magnetic resonance spectroscopy. Clin Chem 1991;37:377-86.

18. Otvos JD, Jeyarajah EJ, Bennett DW, et al. Development of a proton nuclear magnetic resonance spectroscopic method for determining plasma lipoprotein concentrations and subspecies distributions from a single, rapid measurement. Clin Chem 1992;38: 1632-8.

19. Lounila J, Ala-Korpela M, Jokisaari J. Effects of orientational order and particle size on the NMR line positions of lipoproteins. Phys Rev 1994;72:4049-52.

20. Otvos J, Jeyarajah E, Bennett D. A spectroscopic approach to lipoprotein subclass analysis. J Clin Lig Assay 1996;19:184-9.

21. Tall AR, Small DM, Atkinson D. Studies of low density lipoproteins isolated from *Macaca Fascicularis* fed an atherogenic diet. J Clin Invest 1978;62:1354-63.

22. Tall AR. Plasma cholesteryl ester transfer protein. J Lipid Res 1993;34:1255-74.

23. The Expert Panel. Summary of the Second Report of the National Cholesterol Education Program (NCEP) Expert Panel on Detection, Evaluation, and Treatment of High Blood Cholesterol in Adults (Adult Treatment Panel II). JAMA 1993;269:3015-23.

The Use of Ultracentrifugation for the Separation of Lipoproteins

29

Muriel J. Caslake and Christopher J. Packard

INTRODUCTION

❖   Lipoproteins are complexes of phospholipid, triglyceride, cholesteryl ester, and free cholesterol with apolipoproteins that mediate the transport of lipid through the bloodstream. The lipid content of particles, especially that of the hydrophobic components, triglyceride, and cholesteryl ester, gives these complexes the unique property of having a density substantially less than that of most of the other constituents in plasma. Therefore, they can be prepared virtually pure by ultracentrifugation. Triglyceride-rich lipoproteins (chylomicrons and VLDL) have a density less than that of plasma and will float under increased gravity. The other cholesterol-rich lipoproteins have densities in the range 1.006–1.21 kg/L, quite distinct from the density of proteins at about 1.7 kg/L and that of the only other major lipid-transporting protein, albumin, which carries fatty acids. Increasing the non-protein solvent density of plasma permits the isolation, in a stepwise fashion, of the major classes of lipoproteins (Table 29-1).

The most widely used nomenclature defines five main classes of lipoproteins based on their hydrated density.[1] Other ways of describing lipoproteins include electrophoretic mobility, apolipoprotein composition, and the rate of flotation through a salt solution expressed in Svedberg units (S_f).[2] These lipoproteins have been proved to be structurally heterogeneous, with differing metabolic properties and atherogenicity.

Chylomicrons are particles of density less than 0.94 kg/L and have a flotation rate greater than S_f 400. They are the large triglyceride-rich lipoproteins of enteric origin that carry exogenous triglycerides into the plasma. Circulation of chylomicrons distributes dietary triglyceride to adipose tissue and to muscle.

Very-low-density lipoproteins (VLDL) have a density between 0.94 and 1.006 kg/L with a flotation rate S_f 20–400 in a NaCl solution of density 1.063 kg/L at 26° C. VLDL is synthesized in the liver and is the endogenous triglyceride transporter in plasma.

Intermediate-density lipoproteins (IDL) have a density greater than 1.006 kg/L but less than 1.109 kg/L with a flotation rate S_f 12–20 at solvent density 1.063 kg/L. IDL is generated from VLDL by lipolysis.

Low-density-lipoproteins (LDL) consist of particles with a density between 1.019 kg/L and 1.063 kg/L and have a flotation rate S_f 0–12 at solvent density 1.063 kg/L. LDL is the product of lipolysis of IDL and is the major cholesterol carrier in plasma.

Table 29-1 ◆ Lipoprotein Classes				
Class	*Density (kg/L)*	*Flotation Constant (S_f)**	*Diameter (nm)*	*Molecular Weight*
Chylomicrons	<0.94	>400	75–1,200	$50–1,000 \times 10^6$
VLDL	0.94–1.006	20–400	30–80	$10–80 \times 10^6$
IDL	1.006–1.019	12–20	25–35	$5–10 \times 10^6$
LDL	1.019–1.063	0–12	18–25	$2–3 \times 10^6$
HDL	1.063–1.21	$F_{1.20}$ 0–9	5–12	$65–386 \times 10^3$
Lp(a)	1.05–1.08			
*S_f = Svedberg units				

Its normal function is to deliver cholesterol to the peripheral tissues, principally for the maintenance of cell membranes, and to the liver to support bile acid synthesis.

High-density lipoproteins (HDL) have a hydrated density of 1.063–1.21 kg/L and float in a solvent density 1.20 kg/L with a rate between 0 and 9 Svedbergs ($F_{1.20}$ 0–9). These are the smallest lipoprotein particles and are involved in reverse cholesterol transport, i.e., the centripetal movement of cholesterol from the peripheral tissues back to the liver.

Lipoprotein (a) [Lp(a)], is a complex of LDL bound to apolipoprotein (a) and varies in mass between 300–800 kDa. Its normal function is not known, but the homology with plasminogen has led to the speculation that Lp(a) might serve as the link between atherosclerosis and thrombosis. It cannot be isolated by ultracentrifugation techniques alone because of the overlapping densities with LDL and HDL.

A number of centrifugal techniques are available, each of which has its own advantages and disadvantages. Prior to embarking upon separation by ultracentrifugation, it is important to recognize the need for accurate determination of density of solutions employed in these procedures.

DETERMINATION OF SOLUTION DENSITY

The most important requirement for reliable separations is the control and monitoring of density of solutions used. There are two main methods: densitometry and refractometry.

Densitometry

The density meter is based on the principle that the frequency of oscillation of a hollow glass tuning fork depends on the mass of any solution with which it is filled. This is the method of choice in our laboratory, and our instruments (Paar Scientific Ltd., London, UK) can rapidly and accurately measure the density of solutions to three to six decimal places in volumes less than 1 mL.

Refractometry

Refractometry is a simple way of estimating the density of a solution of a single salt from its known correlation with the refractive index of the solution. Relevant tables are available in the Handbook of Chemistry and Physics (CRC Press Inc., West Palm Beach, USA). However, it is not an optimal technique when the solution contains a mixture of salts. With an Abbe type refractometer, one drop of solution is sufficient for measurement. A monochromatic source of light is required, preferably from a sodium lamp. The refractive index of solutions have been tabulated and such tables are available elsewhere.[3]

CHOICE OF CENTRIFUGAL TECHNIQUE

Particles sediment or float at a rate which is proportional to the applied centrifugal force. The viscosity of the sample solution and the physical properties of the particle also affect the sedimentation rate of individual particles. From Stokes' Law, at a fixed centrifugal force and liquid viscosity, the sedimentation rate of the particle is proportional to its size (molecular weight) and the difference between its density and the density of the solution.

$$V = \frac{d^2 (P_p - P_l)}{18\mu} \times g$$

where V = Sedimentation rate, d = diameter, P_p = particle density, P_l = liquid density, μ = viscosity of liquid medium, and g = gravitational force

Density gradient centrifugation of lipoproteins is usually performed using salts such as NaCl, NaBr, and KBr, which are known not to disrupt lipoprotein structure. Two main techniques have been applied to lipoprotein separation: rate zonal ultracentrifugation and isopycnic ultracentrifugation.

Rate Zonal Ultracentrifugation

In the rate zonal technique, a sample solution containing particles to be separated is layered under a preformed gradient. The density of the sample is adjusted to prevent mixing prior to centrifugation. Under centrifugal force the particles float through the gradient in separate zones, each consisting of particles of a given flotation rate. To achieve a rate zonal separation, the density of the particles must be greater or less than the density at all positions along the gradient. The run is terminated before any of the separated particle zones reaches the top of the tube or, in the special case of cumulative flotation, when the particles reach the top of the tube at the end of a specific run time.

Isopycnic Technique

In the isopycnic technique, the density gradient column includes the whole range of densities of the sample particles. Each particle floats/sediments to the position in the centrifuge tube at which the gradient solution density is equal to its own density and remains there. The isopycnic technique therefore separates particles into zones solely on the basis of their density differences.

In many density gradient experiments, elements of both the rate zonal and isopycnic principles may contribute to the final separation. For example, the gradient may be of such a density range that one component sediments to the bottom of the tube while another component sediments to its isopycnic position.

RECOVERY OF SEPARATED LIPOPROTEINS

After centrifugation, if particles can be detected visually, a Pasteur pipette can be used to carefully remove the individual fractions (zones). It is best to use an elongated glass pipette and to illuminate the centrifuge tube with a light. Touch the tip of the meniscus at the side of the tube, carefully remove the lipoprotein fraction in a stream of bubbles, and transfer it into a volumetric flask. Take care not to disturb the gradient and to place the pipette under the surface of the liquid to prevent the lighter layer from floating down as the underlying solution is removed. This technique requires skill and practice but gives excellent recovery of the separated fractions.

An alternative technique is to use the tube slicer, a device which holds the tube firmly between two rubber rings. A lance-shaped slicing knife is used to minimize flattening of the tube during cutting. With care, several cuts can be made at different levels of the tube. The sample is then removed by piercing the tube with a needle and syringe. Tube slicers are commercially available [Beckman Instruments (UK) Ltd., High Wycombe, UK].

The entire contents of the tube may be fractionated using a fraction recovery system (e.g., Maxidens, Nycomed Pharma AS, Oslo, Norway) which permits heavy liquid to be introduced at the bottom of the tube so that the contents are displaced upwards. A spectrometer and fraction collector may be used if required. This process is illustrated in Figure 29–1.

Figure 29–1 ✧ Recovery of Separated Lipoproteins Using a Fraction Recovery System

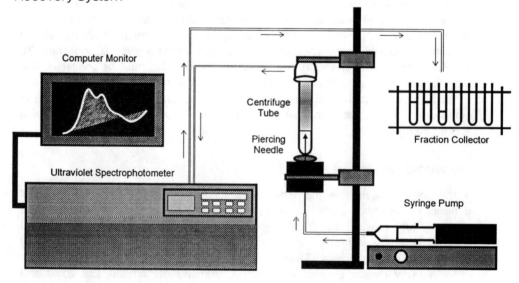

ISOLATION OF LIPOPROTEINS BY SEQUENTIAL FLOTATION ULTRACENTRIFUGATION IN A FIXED-ANGLE ROTOR

This method is valuable for the preparation of lipoproteins for compositional analysis and experimental purposes. It is dependent on operator skill and requires calculation of recovery if quantitative estimates of fraction concentrations are required.

Principle: The solvent density of plasma (or lipoprotein) is adjusted to the upper limit of the fraction to be isolated, and the sample is then subjected to ultracentrifugation. The lipoproteins of density less than that to which the solution was adjusted float to the top, while the heavier ones sediment to the bottom. The supernatant lipoproteins are removed as described above. The residue in the tube is mixed, its solvent density is adjusted to the upper limit of the next required lipoprotein fraction, and centrifugation is repeated. By readjusting the solvent density of the infranatant to successively higher values, a sequence of lipoprotein fractions can be isolated.

Disadvantage: Fractions overlap because particles close to the density of the solvent migrate very slowly to the upper part of the tube. This may be solved by repeated washing and ultracentrifugation at the upper density. This tends to remove adsorbed plasma proteins, but involves prolonged manipulation that may lead to degradation of the lipoprotein, loss of its apolipoproteins, and poor recovery.

Preparative Isolation of VLDL, IDL, LDL, HDL

This method is suitable for the isolation of large quantities of lipoproteins. It is convenient to start with 200–250 mL plasma. Isolation may be carried out using either a Ti 60 or Ti 50.2 rotor [Beckman Instruments(UK) Ltd., High Wycombe, UK] which hold thick-walled 25 mL polycarbonate bottles (Beckman Catalog No. 355654). The procedure is as follows:

1. Place 20 mL plasma in a polycarbonate bottle and carefully overlayer with 5 mL 0.15M NaCl.

2. If the sample is not from a fasting subject and if it is necessary to isolate chylomicrons, centrifuge at 20,000 rpm at 4° C for 30 minutes. Carefully remove the top 5 mL and replace with 0.15M NaCl.

3. Centrifuge at 40,000 rpm at 10–15° C for 20 h or at 4° C for 24 h.

4. Remove the upper layer of VLDL in 2–2.5 mL and carefully remove the next clear non-lipoprotein layer in a volume of 2.0–2.5 mL.

5. Resuspend the pellet in the infranatant and measure its volume.

6. Raise the density by the addition of solid KBr according to the formula

$$x = \frac{Vo\,(d - do)}{1 - d\,\overline{v}}$$

where x = amount of KBr (g), Vo = initial volume (mL), do = initial density (1.006 for plasma), d = final density required, and v = apparent specific volume of KBr.

Table 29-2 indicates the weights of KBr to add per mL of infranatant to achieve the desired density. This has the advantage in that the volume to be ultracentrifuged is only minimally increased.

Table 29-2 ✧ Density Adjustment Using Potassium Bromide (KBr)		
Density (kg/L)	g KBr/mL	Lipoprotein
1.006-1.019	0.0190	IDL
1.019-1.063	0.0658	LDL
1.006-1.063	0.0834	IDL + LDL
1.063-1.125	0.0955	HDL_2
1.125-1.215	0.1449	HDL_3
1.063-1.21	0.236	HDL
1.006-1.225	0.357	Total lipoproteins

7. Place 20 mL of this solution in the centrifuge tubes and overlayer with 0.15M NaCl, 0.01% EDTA solution at the same density.

8. Centrifuge at 40,000 rpm, 10–15° C for 20 h or at 4° C for 24 h.

9. Remove upper layer as before and adjust to the appropriate density. If HDL or total lipoproteins are being isolated, increase the centrifugation time to 48 h.

This technique can be used to isolate a single lipoprotein fraction, or several fractions when the steps are combined to reduce time. A common use is to isolate total lipoproteins or to prepare lipid-deficient plasma.

Quantitative Estimation of VLDL, IDL, LDL, and HDL in Plasma

When measurement of plasma lipoproteins for clinical purposes is required, a method giving better recovery and requiring smaller samples is more suitable. Disposable 6.5 mL ultraclear tubes (Beckman Catalog No. 344088) are suitable. The Beckman Ti 50.3 or Ti 40.3 rotors hold 18 such tubes and the Ti 50.4 rotor holds 44 tubes [all from Beckman Instruments (UK) Ltd., High Wycombe, UK]. The procedure is as follows:

1. Place 4 mL plasma in 6.5 mL tube and overlayer with 2 mL $d = 1.006$ kg/dL solution.

2. If it is necessary to isolate chylomicrons, centrifuge at 10,000 rpm at 4° C for 30 minutes.

3. Carefully remove top 2 mL and overlayer with 2 mL $d = 1.006$ kg/dL solution.

4. Centrifuge at 40,000 rpm at 15° C for 18 h or 4° C for 24 h.

5. Remove VLDL from the top 2 mL by tube slicing or using a Pasteur pipette.

6. Adjust the infranatant to d = 1.109 kg/L by adding 0.32 mL of solution at d = 1.182 kg/L.

7. Mix and transfer to a new centrifuge tube.

8. Overlayer with 1.68 mL d = 1.019 kg/L density solution.

9. Centrifuge at 40,000 rpm at 15° C for 18 h or at 4° C for 24 h.

10. Remove IDL (d = 1.006–1.109 kg/L) in top 2 mL by tube slicing or using a Pasteur pipette.

11. Adjust the infranatant to d = 1.063 kg/L by the addition of 1.47 mL of solution at d = 1.182 kg/L.

12. Mix and transfer to a new centrifuge tube.

13. Overlayer with 0.53 mL solution at d = 1.063 kg/L.

14. Centrifuge at 40,000 rpm at 15° C for 18 h or at 4° C for 24 h.

15. Remove LDL (d = 1.019–1.063 kg/L) in 2 mL by tube slicing or using a Pasteur pipette.

16. Adjust the infranatant to d = 1.21 kg/L by the addition of 2 mL of solution at d = 1.478 kg/L.

17. Remove HDL (d = 1.063–1.21 kg/L) in 2 mL by tube slicing or using a Pasteur pipette.

In our laboratory this technique is routinely employed in lipoprotein quantification (beta-quantification) according to the Lipid Research Clinic Program Manual of Laboratory Operations[4] when VLDL is isolated as in steps 1, 4, and 5. The apolipoprotein-B–containing lipoproteins in the infranatant are precipitated by the addition of an equal volume of sodium heparin (5×10^5 units)/Mn Cl_2 (0.092 M),[5] followed by centrifugation at 10,000 rpm at 4° C for 30 minutes. This leaves HDL in solution. Cholesterol measurements are carried out on total plasma and on VLDL and HDL fractions. LDL cholesterol concentration is obtained by subtracting the HDL-cholesterol level from the total cholesterol concentration in the d > 1.006 kg/L fraction. Please note that IDL and Lp(a) are also included in the LDL fraction.

It is also possible to use this technique to separate subfractions of HDL. In some laboratories it is used to further fractionate LDL into LDL-I (d = 1.026–1.032 kg/L) and LDL-III (d = 1.040–1.054).[6]

DENSITY GRADIENT ULTRACENTRIFUGATION

The separation of lipoprotein classes by density gradient ultracentrifugation in swinging bucket rotors has gained increasing popularity in recent years. It has the major advantage over sequential ultracentrifugation in that the centrifugation time is much reduced. In our experience the separation is superior to that of fixed-angle centrifugation described above.

Principle: Density gradient ultracentrifugation depends on floating the lipoprotein particles through a gradient formed by layering solutions of decreasing density (NaCl,

NaBr, or KBr) above a sample of plasma adjusted to a high density. Centrifugation in a swinging bucket rotor causes the lipoprotein to float through the gradient. Methods employing either discontinuous or continuous gradients can be used. A discontinuous gradient is prepared by layering solutions of successively lower densities one above the other. This allows the lipoproteins of different densities to be isolated as they float to the top of the tube in a cumulative fashion. In the continuous format the lipoproteins float to a particular part of the gradient dependent on their hydrated density and are then isolated by displacement of the tube contents.

Disadvantages: This technique is time consuming and requires a high level of technical skill. Care needs to be taken when overlayering the gradient, as it is easily disturbed. When the gradient is constructed, the tubes need to allow smooth flow of liquid down the interior surface. We routinely coat the inner surface with polyvinyl alcohol as described by Holmquist,[7] which allows salt solutions to gravity-feed smoothly down the sides.

The procedure for surface modification of swing-out Ultraclear centrifuge tubes is as follows:

1. In a round-bottom flask dissolve 10 g polyvinyl alcohol in 250 mL distilled water while stirring and heating to achieve gentle reflux.

2. Slowly add 250 mL propan-2-ol while continuously stirring and heating until the solution is clear.

3. Cool the solution to room temperature.

4. Fill the ultracentrifuge tubes with the polyvinyl alcohol solution and leave for 15 minutes.

5. Remove the solution, being careful to remove all the solution from the bottom of the tubes.

6. Dry overnight.

7. Fill the tubes with distilled water and let them stand overnight.

8. Pour off all the water and flush each tube briefly with distilled water.

9. Tap tubes to remove excess water.

10. Leave to dry in air at room temperature.

CUMULATIVE FLOTATION ULTRACENTRIFUGATION

Specific details of the separation of various subfractions of chylomicrons, VLDL, IDL, and LDL described here are based on the original method of Lindgren et al.[2]

Isolation of Chylomicrons ($S_f > 3200$, $S_f > 1100$, $S_f > 400$)

Sample Preparation

Three mL of plasma are adjusted to $d = 1.065$ kg/L by the addition of 0.254 g of NaCl.

Formation of Gradient

The density solutions and samples are carefully overlayered in tubes for a Beckman SW 25.3 rotor as in Table 29-3.

Table 29–3 ◆ Density Gradient for Isolation of Chylomicron Subfractions		
Solution Number	*Density kg/L*	*Volume (mL)*
—	1.182	0.5 Bottom
—	plasma at 1.065	3.0
1	1.0464	1.0
2	1.0336	1.0
3	1.0271	3.0
4	1.0197	3.0
5	1.0117	3.0
6	1.0064	3.0 Top

Run Conditions

The samples are centrifuged at 23° C for a total centrifugal force (calculated as centrifugal force multiplied by time [$g \times min$]), of 0.739×10^6 g minutes to recover a 0.5 mL fraction of $S_f > 3200$, a further 1.32×10^6 g minutes to recover a 0.5 mL fraction of $S_f > 1100$, and a further 3.384×10^6 g minutes to recover a 0.5 mL fraction of $S_f > 400$. The following formula is useful if you wish to use a rotor with a different path length (or radius):

$$RCF = 1.12 \times r \times (rpm/1,000)^2$$

where RCF is the relative centrifugal force or g, r is the radius of the rotor in mm, and rpm is revolutions per minute.

Isolation of VLDL₁ (S_f 60–400), VLDL₂ (S_f 20–60), IDL (S_f 12–20), LDL (S_f 0–12)

Density Solutions

Stock solutions at $d = 1.006$ kg/dL and $d = 1.182$ kg/dL in 0.195 M NaCl, 0.01% EDTA were prepared as described and mixed to prepare six solutions as in Table 29-4. The density of the solutions should be checked.

Table 29–4 ✧ Density Gradient Solutions (d = 1.0588–1.0988 kg/L)			
Solution Number	*Density kg/L*	*mL d = 1.006 kg/L*	*mL d = 1.182 kg/L*
1	1.0988	50	55.78
2	1.0860	50	41.66
3	1.0790	75	53.16
4	1.0722	75	46.50
5	1.0641	75	36.93
6	1.0588	100	42.92

Solution at d = 1.006 kg/L: Dissolve 22.8 g NaCl, 0.2 g Na_2 EDTA, and 2 mL 1N NaOH and make up to a volume of 2 L with distilled water.

Solution at d = 1.182 kg/L: Dissolve 249.8 g NaBr in 1 L of solution at *d* = 1.006 kg/L.

Sample Preparation

Plasma density is adjusted to 1.118 kg/L by the addition of 0.341 g of NaCl to 2 mL plasma. The sample is mixed well without frothing and allowed to stand at room temperature for at least 30 minutes before being placed in the centrifuge tube (Beckman Catalog No. 344060).

Formation of Gradient

The density solutions and sample are carefully overlayered in a coated SW40 Beckman centrifuge tube as described in Table 29–5. This may be done by hand, but for speed and reproducibility it is recommended that a multichannel peristaltic pump be used at a speed of 1 mL/minute.

Table 29–5 ✧ Density Gradient Solutions for Preparation of Lipoproteins S_f 0–400		
Solution Number	*Density (kg/L)*	*Volume (mL)*
—	1.182	0.5 Bottom
—	plasma at 1.118	2
1	1.0988	1
2	1.0860	1
3	1.0790	2
4	1.0722	2
5	1.0641	2
6	1.0588	2 Top

Run Conditions

Centrifuge in a L8 Beckman ultracentrifuge run at 23° C at normal acceleration and zero deceleration according to the speeds and times given in Table 29–6. Alternative run times may be calculated using g minutes. Samples are removed using specially elongated Pasteur pipettes placed on the surface of the meniscus and at the side of the tube as previously described.

Table 29–6 ❖ Ultracentrifugation Conditions for Preparation of Lipoproteins S_f 0–400

Lipoprotein (S_f)*	Speed (rpm)	Time (h/min)	$\omega^2 t\,(\times 10^{11})$	Sample Volume (mL)
VLDL$_1$ (60–400)	39,000	1.38	1.03	1.0**
VLDL$_2$ (20–60)	18,500	15.41	2.12	0.5
IDL (12–20)	39,000	2.35	1.63	0.5
LDL (0–12)	30,000	21.10	7.52	1.0

*S_f = Svedberg units
**After removal of 1 mL VLDL$_1$, carefully overlayer with 1 mL d = 1.0588 kg/L density solution.

Isolation of VLDL$_1$ (S_f 60–400), VLDL$_2$ (S_f 20–60), IDL$_1$ (S_f 16–20), IDL$_2$ (S_f 12–16), LDL$_1$ (S_f 8–12), LDL$_2$ (S_f 1.5–8)

In our laboratory we use this density gradient to fractionate IDL and LDL into fractions at S_f 16–20, 12–16, 8–12, and 1.5–8 using a Beckman SW40 rotor and the run conditions described in Table 29–7.

Table 29–7 ❖ Ultracentrifugation Conditions for VLDL$_1$, VLDL$_2$, IDL$_1$, IDL$_2$, LDL$_1$, and LDL$_2$

Lipoprotein (S_f)*	Speed (rpm)	Time (h/min)	Sample Volume (mL)
VLDL$_1$ (60–400)	39,000	1.43	1.0**
VLDL$_2$ (20–60)	18,500	15.46	0.5***
IDL$_1$ (16–20)	39,000	1.15	0.5
IDL$_2$ (12–16)	39,000	1.22	0.5
LDL$_1$ (8–12)	39,000	2.09	0.5
LDL$_2$ (1.5–8)	40,000	17.00	0.5

*S_f = Svedberg units
**Replace with 1 mL d = 1.0588 kg/dL density solution
***Replace with 0.5 mL d = 1.0588 kg/dL density solution

LDL SUBFRACTIONATION BY DENSITY GRADIENT ULTRACENTRIFUGATION

A variety of ultracentrifugation methods have been developed to identify and characterize subfractions in the LDL density spectrum. These procedures employ sequential separation at various densities, rate zonal ultracentrifugation, and density gradient ultracentrifugation. They differ in the ways the gradient is constructed. Care should be taken when reading the literature as there is no universal classification system and the terms "large," "small," "buoyant," and "dense" refer to different species depending on the method of isolation. In addition to the LDL subfraction gradient used in our laboratory,[8] two methods of density gradient ultracentrifugation were described by Krauss and Burke[9] and Guerin et al.[10] which generally agree in size and classification based on gradient gel electrophoresis. These are listed in Table 29-8.

Table 29-8 ❖ Separation LDL Subfractions

Krauss and Burke[9]				Guerin et al.[10]			Griffin et al.[8]		
Class	Density (kg/L)	Peak Size (nm)	S f*	Class	Size	Density (kg/L)	Class	Density (kg/L)	Peak Size (nm)
I	1.022–1.032	26.5–28.5	7.5–11	1	light	1.019–1.023	I	1.024–1.034	26.0
				2		1.023–1.029			
IIa	1.032–1.038	26.0–26.5	5.5–8	3	intermediate	1.029–1.039	II	1.034–1.044	25.5
IIb		25.5–26.0	5–6						
IIIa	1.038–1.050	24.7–25.5	3–5	4	dense	1.039–1.050	III	1.044–1.063	24.7
IIIb		24.2–24.7	0–4						
IVa	1.050–1.063	23.2–24.2		5		1.050–1.063			
IVb		22.0–23.2							

*S$_f$ = Svedberg units

LDL Subfractionation Method of Griffin et al.[8]

We have developed a density gradient procedure that permits the separation of three LDL subfractions directly from plasma within 24 h. This has the advantage in that it fractionates fresh plasma, as LDL has been found to be unstable during prolonged centrifugation and during freezing.

Sample Preparation

The density of plasma is adjusted to 1.09 kg/L.

Density Solutions

Stock solutions at d = 1006 kg/dL and d = 1.182 kg/dL in 0.195 M NaCl, 0.01% EDTA were prepared as described and mixed to prepare six solutions as shown in Table 29-9. The density of these solutions should be checked as described above.

Table 29-9 ❖ Density Solutions for Subfractionation of LDL			
Solution Number	*Density (kg/L)*	*mL d = 1.006*	*mL d = 1.182*
6	1.019	100	8.5
5	1.024	100	13.6
4	1.034	100	18.6
3	1.045	100	27.8
2	1.056	100	42.9
1	1.060	100	49.3
Source: Griffin et al.[8]			

    Solution at d = 1.006 kg/L: Dissolve 22.8 g NaCl, 0.2 g Na$_2$ EDTA and 2 mL N NaOH and make up to a volume of 2 L with distilled water.
    Solution at d = 1.182 kg/L: Dissolve 249.8 g NaBr in 1 L of solution at d = 1.006 kg/L.

Formation of Gradient

The density solutions and sample are carefully overlayered in a coated SW 40 centrifuge tube (Beckman Catalog No. 344060) as described in Table 29-10. This may be done by hand, but for reproducibility and speed the use of a multichannel peristaltic pump at a speed of 1 mL/minute is recommended.

Table 29-10 ❖ Density Gradient for LDL Subfractionation			
Solution Number	*Density (kg/L)*	*Volume (mL)*	
—	1.182	0.5	Bottom
—	plasma at 1.09	3.0	
1	1.060	1.0	
2	1.056	1.0	
3	1.045	1.0	
4	1.034	2.0	
5	1.024	2.0	
6	1.019	1.0	Top
Source: Griffin et al.[8]			

Run Conditions

Centrifuge in an Beckman L8 ultracentrifuge run at 23° C with slow acceleration and no deceleration at 40,000 rpm for 24 h. The gradient containing separated LDL subfractions is displaced upwards as described. This procedure allows to resolve three subfractions, namely LDL-I (d = 1.025–1.034 kg/L), LDL-II (d = 1.034–1.044), and LDL-III (d = 1.044–1.060). Typical LDL subfraction profiles are illustrated in Figure 29–2.

Figure 29–2 ◇ The Separation of LDL Subfractions Using Density Gradient Centrifugation

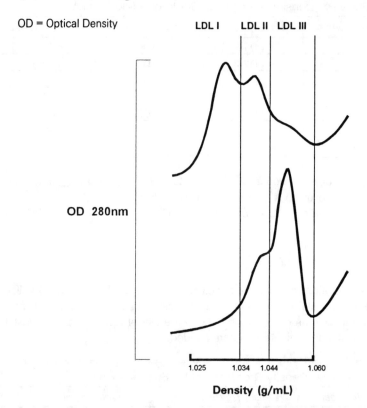

LDL Subfractionation Method of Krauss and Burke[9]

This is an equilibrium density procedure which was one of the first methods described. Application has revealed the existence of up to four discrete isopycnic LDL bands.

Sample Preparation

LDL (d = 1.009–1.063 kg/L) is isolated from plasma by sequential ultracentrifugation. The density is adjusted to 1.04 kg/L by overnight dialysis against NaBr solution of density 1.04 kg/L.

Formation of Gradient

Table 29–11 describes the gradient formed by carefully layering NaBr density solutions in a Beckman SW45 centrifuge tube.

Table 29–11 ❖ Gradient Solutions for LDL Separation	
Density (kg/L)	*Volume (mL)*
1.054	2.5
LDL at *d* = 1.040	2.0
1.0275	2.5
Source: Krauss and Burke[9]	

Run Conditions

The tubes are centrifuged in a Beckman SW45 rotor at 39,000 rpm at 22–24° C for 40 h. The contents of the tube are withdrawn starting with the top 0.5 mL, then six 1 mL fractions and finally the bottom 0.5 mL fraction.

LDL Subfractionation Method of Guerin et al.[10]

The method described here is a recent modification of the original procedure[11] in which 15 subfractions of LDL were isolated from LDL at *d* = 1.006–1.063 kg/L. This technique separates VLDL, five LDL subfractions, and four HDL subfractions directly from plasma.

Sample Preparation

The density of 3 mL of plasma is adjusted to 1.21 kg/L by addition of solid KBr.

Formation of Gradient

Density solutions are NaCl/KBr, pH 7.4, and contain 0.01% sodium azide, 0.01% EDTA, and 0.005% gentamycin. A discontinuous density gradient is constructed as in Table 29–12 in a Beckman SW 41 centrifuge tube.

Table 29–12 ❖ Gradient Solutions for LDL Subfractionation	
Density (kg/L)	*Volume (mL)*
1.24	2.0
plasma at *d* = 1.21	3.0
1.063	2.0
1.019	2.5
1.006	2.5
Source: Guerin et al.[10]	

Run Conditions

Centrifugation is at 40,000 rpm at 15° C for 44 h in a Beckman SW Ti 41 rotor. After centrifugation, gradients are collected from the top of the tube in 12 fractions, shown in Table 29–13.:

Table 29–13 ✧ Lipoprotein Fractions		
Fraction	*Lipoprotein*	*Density (Kg/L)*
1	VLDL	< 1.017
2	IDL	1.018–1.019
3	LDL-1	1.019–1.023
4	LDL-2	1.023–1.029
5	LDL-3	1.029–1.039
6	LDL-4	1.039–1.050
7	LDL-5	1.050–1.063
8	HDL$_{2b}$	1.063–1.091
9	HDL$_{2a}$	1.091–1.110
10	HDL$_{3a}$	1.110–1.133
11	HDL$_{3b}$	1.133–1.156
12	HDL$_{3c}$	1.156–1.179

IDL SUBFRACTIONATION

The following method for separating IDL into different fractions was published by Musliner, Giotas, and Krauss in 1986.[12] Lipoprotein fractions obtained by nonequilibrium density gradient ultracentrifugation were further fractionated by equilibrium density gradient ultracentrifugation to isolate two fractions of IDL at d = 1.008–1.022 kg/L and d = 1.013–1.028 kg/L.

Nonequilibrium Density Centrifugation

Sample Preparation

Lipoproteins d < 1.063 kg/L are adjusted to d = 1.21 kg/L by the addition of solid NaBr.

Formation of Gradient

Density solutions are overlayered in a Beckman SW41 tube as described in Table 29–14.

Table 29–14 ❖ Non-equilibrium Density Gradient Ultracentrifugation		
Solution Number	*Density (kg/L)*	*Volume (mL)*
—	Sample at 1.21	4.5 Bottom
1	1.020	3.0
2	1.010	3.0
3	1.000	1.5 Top
Source: Musliner, Giotas, and Krauss[12]		

Run Conditions

The tubes are centrifuged at 40,000 rpm at 17° C for 6 h and decelerated without brake. The tube contents are withdrawn by pipetting four successive 1 mL fractions followed by six 0.5 mL fractions.

Equilibrium Density Ultracentrifugation

Sample Preparation

The density of fractions 5, 6, 7, and 8 from the nonequilibrium technique described above is adjusted to $d = 1.020$ kg/L by dialysis against four changes of NaBr solution over a 24 h period.

Formation of Gradient

The solutions are carefully layered in a Beckman SW41 centrifuge tube according to the scheme presented in Table 29–15.

Table 29–15 ❖ Equilibrium Density Gradient Ultracentrifugation		
Solution Number	*Density (kg/L)*	*Volume (mL)*
1	1.040	1.0 Bottom
2	1.030	3.5
3	Sample at 1.020	3.5
4	1.010	3.0
5	1.000	1.0 Top
Source: Musliner, Giotas, and Krauss[12]		

Run Conditions

The tubes are centrifuged in a Beckman SW 41 rotor at 40,000 rpm at 17° C for 60 h and allowed to coast to stop without braking. The tube contents are withdrawn in 1 mL fractions. IDL1 is isolated at $d = 1.008–1.022$ kg/dL and IDL2 at $d = 1.013–1.028$ kg/dL.

RATE ZONAL ULTRACENTRIFUGATION

Advantages: Conventional sequential or density gradient ultracentrifugation is limited by small capacity of centrifuge tubes. This can be overcome by the use of zonal rotors Ti 14 and Ti 15 from Beckman Instruments, which have the capacity of 665 mL and 1665 mL respectively. There is an added advantage in that, due to the much shorter path lengths, isolation can be completed in a relatively short time.

Disadvantages: This technique requires capital investment in rotors, apparatus to load and unload the rotor, equipment to monitor and record the lipoprotein fractions as the rotor is being unloaded, and time-consuming care and maintenance of equipment necessitated by the effects of heavy salt solutions. Also, only one sample can be fractionated in each run. The zonal rotor has been utilized to isolate fractions of VLDL and HDL and for large-scale preparations of LDL.

VLDL Isolation by Rate Zonal Centrifugation[13]

In this procedure, seven fractions of VLDL are isolated on the basis of differing flotation rates. With decreasing flotation rates, free cholesterol, cholesteryl ester, phospholipid, and apolipoprotein B content increase and triglyceride content decreases.

Sample Preparation

Eight to 15 mL plasma are adjusted to $d = 1.15$ kg/L.

Formation of Gradient

Stock solution of NaBr are prepared in 0.35 mM EDTA, pH 7.6. A linear gradient of $d = 1.0$–1.15 kg/L is formed in a Ti 14 zonal rotor from Beckman Instruments, while centrifuging at 3,500 rpm. The plasma at $d = 1.15$ kg/L is carefully loaded on the outside of the gradient, followed by a cushion of 25 mL of $d = 1.15$ kg/L solution.

Run Conditions

Centrifugation is at 42,000 rpm at 14° C for 45 minutes. The rotor is unloaded at 3,500 rpm by pumping solution $d = 1.15$ kg/L through the peripheral line of the loading head. The eluate is monitored at OD = 280 nm and 10 mL fractions are collected to yield seven fractions of VLDL ranging from S_f 20–400 as indicated in Table 29–16.

Table 29–16 ✧ VLDL Fractions Isolated by Rate Zonal Centrifugation	
Subfraction	S_f*
$VLDL_1$	424.2–181.9
$VLDL_2$	189.6–121.4
$VLDL_3$	128.7–77.7
$VLDL_4$	86.3–59.1
$VLDL_5$	69.5–41.7
$VLDL_6$	47.7–32.9
$VLDL_7$	36.6–21.4
*S_f = Svedberg units	

LDL Isolation by Rate Zonal Centrifugation

In our laboratory, isolation of LDL by rate zonal ultracentrifugation is the method of choice for preparing LDL during metabolic studies, as LDL can be rapidly isolated from plasma, radioactively labelled, and reinjected into the subject within hours of venepuncture.

Sample Preparation

The density of 50 mL plasma is adjusted to 1.3 kg/L by the addition of 15 g NaBr.

Formation of Gradient

Density solutions at 1.0 and 1.3 kg/L are prepared in 0.1 M Tris-0.01% Na_2 EDTA (w/v), pH 7.6, by the addition of NaBr.

A linear gradient of d = 1.0–1.3 kg/L is formed in a Beckman Ti 14 rotor while centrifuging at 3,500 rpm. Fifty mL plasma at d = 1.3 kg/L are carefully loaded onto the outside of the gradient, followed by a cushion of 25 mL d = 1.3 kg/L density solution.

Run Conditions

Centrifugation is at 45,000 rpm at 10° C for 140 minutes. The rotor is unloaded at 3,500 rpm by pumping solution at density 1.3 kg/L through the peripheral line of the loading head. The eluate is monitored at OD = 280 nm and the appropriate fractions of LDL are pooled. Figure 29-3 shows a typical LDL profile obtained from zonal ultracentrifugation.

Figure 29-3 ✧ Separation of LDL Using Rate Zonal Centrifugation

OD = Optical Density

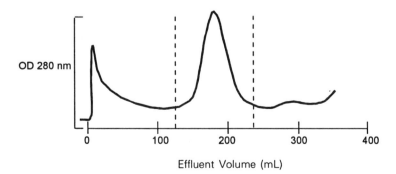

Effluent Volume (mL)

HDL Isolation by Rate Zonal Centrifugation[14]

In this procedure, VLDL and LDL are first removed by centrifugation through a discontinuous gradient of density 1.00–1.40 kg/L. This allows separation of HDL_2 and HDL_3 subfractions uncontaminated by other plasma proteins.

Sample Preparation

The density of 50 mL plasma is adjusted to 1.4 kg/L by the addition of 26.6 g NaBr.

Formation of Gradient

Density solutions at 1.0 and 1.4 kg/L are prepared in 0.1 M Tris-0.01% (w/v) Na_2 EDTA, pH 7.6, by the addition of NaBr. A stepwise gradient of d = 1.0–1.4 kg/L is formed in a Beckman Ti 14 rotor while centrifuging at 3,500 rpm. Fifty mL plasma at density 1.4 kg/L are carefully loaded onto the outside of the gradient, followed by a cushion of 25 mL d = 1.3 kg/L density solution.

Run Conditions

Centrifugation is at 45,000 rpm at 10° C for 18 h. The rotor is unloaded at 3,500 rpm by pumping solution at density 1.4 kg/L through the peripheral line of the loading head. The eluate is monitored at OD = 280 nm and the appropriate fractions of HDL pooled. HDL_2 is the first fraction eluted, followed by HDL_3. Figure 29–4 illustrates a typical HDL profile obtained in our laboratory.

Figure 29–4 ✧ Separation of HDL Using Rate Zonal Centrifugation

OD = Optical Density

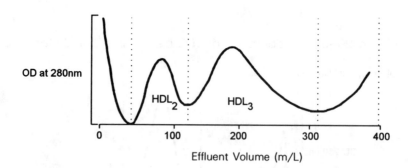

CONCLUSIONS

The advantage of ultracentrifugation is that it separates useful entities, The disadvantage is that the isolated fractions are still heterogeneous—for instance, with respect to the content of apolipoproteins B, C, and E. Moreover, there is an exchange of apolipoproteins among the lipoprotein particles as well as shedding of apolipoprotein E during centrifugation. Plasma contains enzymes, such as cholesteryl ester transfer protein (CETP), lecithin:cholesterol acyltransferase (LCAT), lipoprotein lipase (LPL), and hepatic lipase (HTGL), which modify the composition and structure of lipoproteins. These phenomena continue during centrifugation, but their effects can be minimized by carrying out procedures at 4° C, or by the addition of inhibitors such as 1.5 mM Ellman's reagent [5,5-dithiobis(2-nitro-benzoic acid)], 2 mM diisopropyl fluorophosphonate, or thiomersal. Lipoproteins are also susceptible to oxidative modification, and it is common practice to collect blood in K_2 EDTA at a final concentration of 1 kg/L, and to add 1 mM Na_2 EDTA to all solutions to sequester the heavy metal catalysts. ✧

REFERENCES

1. Havel RJ, Eder HA, Bragdon JH. The distribution and chemical composition of ultracentrifugally separated lipoproteins in human serum. J Clin Invest 1955;34:1345-53.
2. Lindgren FT, Jensen LC, Hatch FT. The isolation and quantitation analysis of serum lipoproteins. In: Nelson GJ, ed. Blood lipids and lipoproteins: quantitation, composition and metabolism. New York: Wiley Interscience, 1972:181-274.
3. Mills GL, Lane PA, Weech PK. The isolation and purification of plasma lipoproteins. In: Burdon RH, Knippenberg PH, eds. Laboratory techniques in biochemistry and molecular biology: a guidebook to lipoprotein technique. Amsterdam: Elsevier, 1984:18-116.
4. Lipid Research Clinics Program. Manual of Laboratory Operations. Vol. 1: Lipid and lipoprotein analysis. National Institutes of Health Publication No. 1975:(NIH)75-628. Bethesda, MD: U.S. Department of Health, Education and Welfare.
5. Warnick GR, Albers JJ. A comprehensive evaluation of the heparin/manganese precipitation procedure for estimating HDL cholesterol. J Lipid Res 1978;9:65-76.
6. Tribble DL, van den Berg JJM, Motchnik PA, Ames BN, Lewis DM, Chait A, Krauss RM. Oxidative susceptibility of low density subfractions is related to their ubiquinol-10 and α-tocopherol content. Proc Natl Acad Sci USA 1994;91:1183-7.
7. Holmquist R. Surface modification of ultraclear centrifuge tubes. J Lipid Res 1982;23:1249-50.
8. Griffin BA, Caslake MJ, Yip B, Tait GW, Packard CJ, Shepherd J. Rapid isolation of low density lipoprotein (LDL) subfractions from plasma by density gradient ultracentrifugation. Atherosclerosis 1990;83:59-67.
9. Krauss RM, Burke DJ. Identification of multiple subclasses of plasma low density lipoproteins in normal humans. J Lipid Res 1982;23:97-104.
10. Guerin M, Bruckert E, Dolphin PJ, Turpin G, Chapman MJ. Fenofibrate reduces plasma cholesteryl ester transfer from HDL to VLDL and normalizes the atherogenic, dense LDL profile in combined hyperlipidemia. Arterioscler Thromb Vasc Biol 1996;16:763-72.
11. Chapman MJ, Goldstein S, Lagrange D, Laplaud PM. A density gradient ultracentrifugal procedure for the isolation of the major lipoprotein classes from human serum. J Lipid Res 1981;22:339-58.
12. Musliner TA, Giotas C, Krauss RM. Presence of multiple subpopulations of lipoproteins of intermediate density in normal subjects. Arteriosclerosis 1986;6:79-87.
13. Patsch W, Patsch JR, Kostner GM, Sailer S, Braunsteiner H. Isolation of subfractions of human very low density lipoproteins by zonal ultracentrifugation. J Biol Chem 1978:4911-15.
14. Patsch W, Schonfeld G, Gotto AM, Patsch JR. Characterisation of human high density lipoproteins by zonal ultracentrifugation. J Biol Chem 1980;255:3178-85.

Analysis of Plasma Lipoproteins by Gel Permeation Chromatography

30

Mitsuyo Okazaki, Keiko Sasamoto, Toshio Muramatsu
and Seijin Hosaki

INTRODUCTION

❖   It is widely known that an increase in low density lipoprotein-cholesterol (LDL-C) or a decrease in high-density lipoprotein-cholesterol (HDL-C) represent a major risk factor for the development of atherosclerotic arterial diseases.[1] Consequently, reliable methods for determining total serum cholesterol and cholesterol in lipoprotein fractions including chylomicrons (CM), very-low-density lipoprotein (VLDL), intermediate-density lipoproteins (IDL), LDL, and HDL are of interest for appropriate preventive strategies for atherosclerosis-dependent heart disease. In the most commonly used routine method, LDL-C concentration is estimated from the measurements of total cholesterol (TC), triglycerides (TG), and HDL-C by the Friedewald equation.[2] However, new and optimized quantitative methods for cholesterol determination in major lipoprotein classes are desirable for routine laboratory assays.

Until now, the major serum lipoprotein classes have been separated on the basis of differences in density by ultracentrifugation or on the basis of electrical charge by electrophoretic techniques.[3] Separation on the basis of particle size by gel permeation chromatography has also been attempted.[4, 5] Heterogeneities in size within each lipoprotein class have been examined using conventional agarose gels with fractionated lipoprotein samples obtained by ultracentrifugation. Because of the low flow rate and large sample volumes required for analysis, this technique is limited to use in research laboratories.

In 1980, Hara et al.[6] successfully applied the high-performance liquid chromatography (HPLC) technique to lipoprotein analysis. In those studies, the TSKgel columns (TSKgel SW and PW type, TOSOH, Japan) were used and post-column detection of lipid components such as cholesterol,[6–8] phospholipids,[9] and TG[10] were performed by enzymatic reactions. The post-column detection method could make it possible to obtain lipoprotein profiles from a very small amount of whole serum (< 20 μL) within 60 minutes. Okazaki et al.[11–13] and several other investigators[14–20] have confirmed the reliability of this technique by comparison with other established techniques. Many valuable clinical studies have also been reported based on subsequent work.[21-28] However, these have remained as alternative methods because of the difficulties in eliminating the non-specific adsorption of lipoproteins to TSK gel materials.

In 1990, Kieft et al.[29] reported a rapid on-line determination method for lipoprotein cholesterol by HPLC using a single, relatively inexpensive column (Superose 6HR 10/30). Lipoprotein analysis using Superose 6 columns on a Pharmacia fast protein liquid chromatography (FPLC) system have been reported by several investigators.[30-39] The FPLC system may be used as an analytical approach in combination with post-column detection of cholesterol as well as a preparative method by collecting a number of consecutive eluant fractions for analysis of lipid components and apolipoproteins. In this technique, three separate fractions related to VLDL, LDL, and HDL can be obtained within a relatively short time.

In 1993, improved gel permeation columns (TSKgel Lipopropak and Lipopro-pakXL, TOSOH) and specifically prepared eluents (TSKeluent LP-1 and LP-2, TOSOH) became available for quantitative separation of lipoproteins.[40] Using the new columns and eluents, a simple, rapid, and accurate quantification technique for cholesterol in major serum lipoprotein classes—CM, VLDL, LDL, and HDL—has been reported.[41-43] Additionally, the automated TOSOH Lipoprotein Analytical System is now commercially available for routine assay of cholesterol concentration in major lipoprotein classes in a time period of 16 min per sample (80–90 samples can be processed in a working day).

In this chapter, we describe the usefulness and reliability of the gel permeation chromatography method for the separation and quantitation of the major serum lipo-protein classes, and the application and prospective development of the chromato-graphic method for lipoprotein analysis in clinical laboratories as well as in research laboratories.

ANALYTICAL METHODS FOR MAJOR LIPOPROTEIN CLASSES

Gel permeation columns obtainable from various suppliers can be used for separation of serum lipoproteins in various chromatographic systems (see Table 30–1). Agarose gel beads consisting of 4% and 6% Bio-Gel A15m and A5m can be used to separate the major lipoprotein classes, namely, VLDL, LDL, and HDL. Lipoproteins can be separated by loading a sample of whole plasma on an agarose column. Alternatively, samples prepared by a single ultracentrifugation of plasma to isolate all the lipoproteins with density < 1.21 Kg/L can be applied and elution monitored at A_{280}, which allows collection of the eluant fractions corresponding to major lipoprotein classes in a single step. For quantitation purposes, the amount of cholesterol in each of the pooled fractions can be determined and the cholesterol concentration calculated. The recovery of lipoproteins from these agarose gel columns was reported to be 89.5 ± 8.8% by Rudel and Pitts.[44] The conventional method of agarose chromatography required 5–8 mL of plasma and an elution time of over 16 h.[4, 5]

A fast protein liquid chromatography (FPLC) system has been used for the separation of plasma lipoproteins on a Superose 6 column.[30-39] Elution profiles mon-itored by A_{280} for the lipoproteins isolated by ultracentrifugation from 3–4 mL of plasma as the fraction of lower density than 1.21 Kg/L showed three major peaks corresponding to VLDL, LDL, and HDL. Elution profiles monitored by cholesterol assay in each of the collected fractions also showed three separated peaks corresponding to VLDL, LDL, and HDL.

Table 30–1 ✦ Gel Permeation Columns for Lipoprotein Separation		
Column	*Source*	*Lipoprotein Classes*
Bio-Gel A50m	Bio-Rad Laboratories	CM, VLDL subclasses
Bio-Gel A15m	Bio-Rad Laboratories	CM + VLDL, LDL, HDL
Bio-Gel A5m	Bio-Rad Laboratories	HDL subclasses
Superose GHR 10/30	Pharmacia Biotech	CM+VLDL, LDL, HDL
TSKgel G5000PW	TOSOH Corporation	CM, VLDL, LDL, HDL
TSKgel G4000PW	TOSOH Corporation	CM+VLDL, LDL, HDL
TSKgel G3000PW	TOSOH Corporation	HDL subclasses
TSKgel G4000SW	TOSOH Corporation	CM+VLDL, LDL, HDL
TSKgel G3000SW	TOSOH Corporation	HDL subclasses
TSKgel Lipopropak	TOSOH Corporation	CM, VLDL, LDL, HDL
TSKgel LipopropakXL	TOSOH Corporation	CM, VLDL, LDL, HDL
Fractogel 65-F	Bodman Chemicals	CM, VLDL subclasses
GF-450	DuPont	CM, VLDL subclasses

Compared to conventional agarose gel chromatography, the FPLC method greatly reduces the separation time and improves the analysis of lipoproteins, März et al.[30] reported a new method for quantitation of cholesterol in VLDL, LDL, and HDL fractions by loading 20 µL of plasma on a 300 mm prepacked Superose 6 column in the FPLC system. Lipoproteins were detected on-line at 500 nm after post-column reaction by cholesterol reagent. The elution patterns showed three separate peaks corresponding to VLDL, LDL, and HDL, and their cholesterol values were calculated on the basis of relative peak area and total cholesterol. Analytical time per sample was 80 minutes. The FPLC interassay precision assessed by 13 consecutive analyses of a normolipidemic sample was reported to be 5.8%, 2.0%, and 1.9% for VLDL-C, LDL-C, and HDL-C, respectively.[30] Moreover, the correlation coefficients of the FPLC method with a combined ultracentrifugation and precipitation method were reported to be 0.979, 0.978, and 0.933 for VLDL-C, LDL-C, and HDL-C, respectively.[30] Despite a high correlation between the two methods, overestimation of LDL-C and underestimation of VLDL-C by the FPLC method were reported because 15–20% of the VLDL fraction with density < 1.006 Kg/L coeluted with LDL. The authors asserted that the FPLC method might be a useful complement to conventional methods in selected patients' samples, because the number of analyses was only 10–20 samples per working day.[30] The recovery of lipoproteins from this Superose 6 column was reported to be over 90%.[29, 34]

In the HPLC technique used by Hara et al. in the early 1980s,[12] a post-column detection method involving enzymatic reaction was adopted to obtain lipoprotein profiles directly from whole serum. Subsequently this technique has been used successfully in the Pharmacia FPLC system as described above.[30] Okazaki et al.[8] proposed a procedure for quantitation of cholesterol in the major lipoprotein classes (CM + VLDL,

LDL, HDL$_2$, and HDL$_3$) from cholesterol monitoring patterns obtained by loading 10 µL of whole serum on TSKgel G4000SW + G3000SW columns. The amount of cholesterol in each lipoprotein class was calculated from the relative peak area and the TC level in serum. Each area was divided by drawing a line perpendicular to the baseline at the elution volume corresponding to the following particle diameters: 30 nm, 16 nm, 10 nm, and 8 nm. A high correlation (r = 0.83–0.99) between the G4000SW + G3000SW column system and the ultracentrifugation method of Havel et al.[45] has been reported by Okazaki et al.[8] Comparison studies of the HPLC method using TSKgel columns with density gradient ultracentrifugation by Williams et al.,[19] with agarose gel chromatography by Carroll and Rudel,[14] and with rate zonal ultracentrifugation by Oida et al.[20] have supported the reliability of lipoprotein separation by the HPLC method. Although the recovery of lipoproteins from TSK gel materials was reported to be over 90%,[14, 17–19] considerable adsorption of lipoproteins to the gel materials has been found.[30, 37]

IDENTIFICATION AND QUANTIFICATION OF LIPOPROTEIN CLASSES

In order to separate all major lipoprotein classes–CM, VLDL, LDL, and HDL–simultaneously and quantitatively, a gel permeation column with separation characteristics ranging from 5 nm to 100 nm in diameter and without non-specific adsorption of lipoproteins is required. Recently, new columns (TSKgel Lipopropak and LipopropakXL, TOSOH) and eluents (TSKeluent LP-1 and LP-2) suitable for this purpose have become commercially available. Using the new HPLC columns and eluents, over 99.8% recovery was reported by Kitamura et al.[40] Although the TSKeluent LP-1 is limited only to cholesterol quantification, the LP-2 eluent can be used for cholesterol, TG, and phospholipids. The use of column and eluents with post-column enzymatic reaction to obtain serial cholesterol patterns allows cholesterol concentration in all major lipoprotein classes to be quantified conveniently.

The major lipoprotein classes—CM, VLDL, LDL, and HDL—were defined by Hara and Okazaki[12] on the basis of the following particle diameter range: CM, over 80 nm; VLDL, 30–80 nm; LDL, 16–30 nm; HDL, 8–16 nm. The identification of each lipoprotein class was based on particle diameter estimated by the elution time for each column system. This conversion was carried out using a column calibration curve, a plot of logarithm of the particle diameter of standard samples, latex beads (Magsphere Inc.) and high-molecular-weight standards (Pharmacia) against their elution times. The peak with the elution time corresponding to the size range between 8 and 16 nm was assigned to HDL. The peak at the void volume with particle diameter over 80 nm was assigned to CM. Likewise, the peak having the elution time corresponding to size from 23 to 28.5 nm was assigned to LDL, and the peak observed between the void volume and the LDL peak was assigned to VLDL.

The peak areas of major lipoprotein classes was obtained as follows: In most samples, the HDL peaks were clearly separated from other lipoproteins; the HDL area was obtained by drawing a vertical line from the minimum point between the LDL and HDL peaks down to the baseline (x axis). The area corresponding to the column void volume was defined as CM regardless of the presence of a peak. The areas corresponding to VLDL and LDL peaks were separated mathematically because of a continuous size distribution from VLDL to LDL, suggesting the presence of numerous subclasses in these lipoproteins. A Gaussian curve-fitting approach using computer-assisted data processing[41] was applied to separate peaks corresponding to VLDL and LDL.

The concentration of cholesterol in each lipoprotein fraction was calculated from its peak area using a certified reference serum as a calibrator. The identification of the lipoprotein classes was also confirmed based on the peak elution times for LDL and HDL of a calibrator having similar particle sizes as those of LDL and HDL in fresh, normolipidemic human serum.

The average particle diameter and heterogeneity of size distribution within identified classes were also obtained from peak time and peak width. Further analytical procedures for lipoprotein subclass separation using these peak elution profiles are described below.

THE TOSOH LIPOPROTEIN ANALYTICAL SYSTEM FOR ROUTINE LIPOPROTEIN SEPARATION

The automated TOSOH Lipoprotein Analytical System, which was modeled on the concept described above, is now commercially available. This system is composed of a routine HPLC system (CCP & 8020, TOSOH) with two connected columns (TSKgel LipopropakXL, 7.8 mm in diameter, 300 mm in length, TOSOH) and the TSKeluent LP-1 was used at a flow rate of 0.7 mL/min. A 5 µL aliquot of whole serum was applied to the columns with an interval between samples of 16 minutes. The cholesterol in the effluent from the columns was detected at an absorbance wave length of 550 nm after an on-line enzymatic reaction using a cholesterol determination kit (Determiner L TC, Kyowa Medex, Tokyo) in a reaction tube (Reaction Coil K, 0.4 mm i.d., 7.5 m in length, TOSOH) at 45° C. In an on-line reaction, the effluent was mixed with reagent 1 (ascorbic acid oxidase, cholesterol oxidase, peroxidase, *N*-ethyl-*N*-(3-methyl phenyl)-*N'*-succinyl-ethylenediamine) at a flow rate of 0.263 mL/min and reagent 2(cholesterol oxidase, peroxidase and 4-aminoantipyrine) at a flow rate of 0.087 mL/min. With other cholesterol reagent kits, the optimum reaction conditions, dimension of the reaction coil, reaction temperature, and flow rate of the cholesterol reagent might need to be modified.

Analyses were carried out consecutively and automatically by placing a calibrator and test samples in the autosampler and entering the sample numbers and concentration of total cholesterol of the calibrator into the computer. The elution time (in minutes) and concentration of cholesterol (mg/dL and mmol/L) for major lipoprotein classes (peak 1, CM; peak 2, VLDL; peak 3, LDL; peak 4, HDL) were reported together with the HPLC patterns. Representative HPLC patterns and analytical data are shown in Figure 30–1. As calibrator for this system, a commercial control prepared from human pooled sera such as certified reference serum WCHL 952M (Health Care Technology Foundation, Standard Reference Center, Kawasaki, Japan), Determiner HDL-C reference serum; Lot 121AFF (Kyowa Medex) or chemistry control serum; EXA Liquid Abnormal Lot/0296A (Sanko Junyaku) could be used. Prolonged sample storage after thawing can affect the measurement of TC, LDL, and HDL sizes in frozen control sera; therefore, reference sera should be used within 1 day after thawing.

Figure 30–1 ◆ HPLC Patterns Obtained Using the TOSOH Lipoprotein Analytical System

Samples: whole serum (5 µL): (a) normolipidemic healthy man, TG = 59 mg/dL (0.67 mmol/L); (b) familial hypercholesterolemia (Type IIa), TG = 35 mg/dL (0.40 mmol/L); (c) diabetes mellitus (Type IIb), TG = 244 mg/dL (2.76 mmol/L); (d) patient (c) before drug treatment (Type IV), TG = 400 mg/dL (4.52 mmol/L); (e) lipoprotein lipase deficiency (Type I or Type V), TG = 347 mg/dL (9.32 mmol/L); (f) apo E$_{2/2}$ phenotype (Type III), TG = 216 mg/dL (2.44 mmol/L). Phenotyping of the dyslipidemias was carried out using the HPLC method as described in the text. Analytical data are reported together with the HPLC pattern. ET = Elution Time.

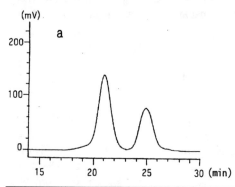

No.	Class	Elution Time min.	Elution Time nm	Cholesterol mg/dL	Cholesterol mmol/L
1	CM	–		0.0	0.00
2	VLDL	–		9.7	0.25
3	LDL	21.10	25.8	99.5	2.57
4	HDL	24.95	11.1	63.3	1.64
			TOTAL	172.5	4.46

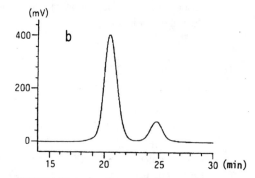

No.	Class	Elution Time min.	Elution Time nm	Cholesterol mg/dL	Cholesterol mmol/L
1	CM	–		0.1	0.00
2	VLDL	–		11.4	0.29
3	LDL	20.93	26.8	297.2	7.69
4	HDL	25.11	10.7	60.4	1.56
			TOTAL	369.0	9.54

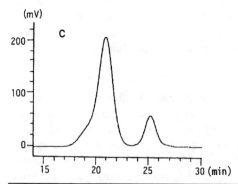

No.	Class	Elution Time min.	Elution Time nm	Cholesterol mg/dL	Cholesterol mmol/L
1	CM	–		0.0	0.00
2	VLDL	–		50.6	1.31
3	LDL	21.06	26.0	171.5	4.43
4	HDL	25.26	10.4	44.6	1.15
			TOTAL	266.7	6.90

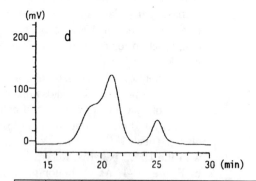

No.	Class	Elution Time min.	Elution Time nm	Cholesterol mg/dL	Cholesterol mmol/L
1	CM	–		0.1	0.00
2	VLDL	–		92.9	2.40
3	LDL	21.10	25.8	88.9	2.30
4	HDL	25.28	10.3	32.5	0.84
			TOTAL	214.4	5.54

Figure 30–1 ✧ Continued

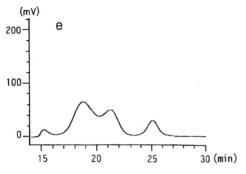

No.	Class	Elution Time min.	Elution Time nm	Cholesterol mg/dL	Cholesterol mmol/L
1	CM	15.40	89.8	6.4	0.17
2	VLDL	18.99	40.9	96.5	2.50
3	LDL	21.46	23.8	44.3	1.15
4	HDL	25.32	10.3	23.1	0.60
			TOTAL	147.2	3.81

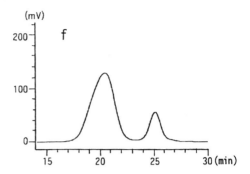

No.	Class	Elution Time min.	Elution Time nm	Cholesterol mg/dL	Cholesterol mmol/L
1	CM	—		0.1	0.00
2	VLDL	20.58	28.8	124.7	3.22
3	LDL	—		47.3	1.22
4	HDL	25.17	10.5	39.5	1.02
			TOTAL	211.7	5.47

The reliability of the TOSOH Lipoprotein Analytical System was investigated by analyzing a large number of clinical samples. The within-run precision of cholesterol determination in each lipoprotein class and particle diameters of the identified lipoprotein classes are summarized in Table 30–2. Sensitivity of the detection of lipoprotein peaks has been markedly improved compared to the earlier HPLC method.[12] The peaks of LDL and HDL in a normolipidemic subject can be clearly detected using a very small amount of whole serum, as little as 0.02 µL. When 5 µL of whole serum was applied, a linear relationship between loaded amount of sample and peak areas of LDL and HDL was observed at serum cholesterol concentrations ranging from 7.7 to 464 mg/dL (0.2 to 12 mmol/L), and the detection limit for each peak was 0.2 mg/dL (0.005 mmol/L). Consecutive analyses of more than 2,000 samples per column system have been performed.[43]

Comparison of the New HPLC Method with Other Available Techniques

The TC concentration obtained as the sum of each lipoprotein class in this system was identical to that determined by conventional enzymatic analysis on a chemistry analyzer.[40, 42] The cholesterol values in major lipoprotein classes measured by this system were found to be identical to those measured by sequential ultracentrifugation,[45] except for subjects with high concentrations of lipoprotein(a) [Lp(a)].[43]

Results for 191 subjects with normal and high Lp(a) were compared separately (see Figure 30–2). For both groups, the values for LDL-C by HPLC were consistent

Table 30–2 ❖ Within-run Precision of TOSOH Lipoprotein Analytical System (n = 5)

Sample[c]		Cholesterol Concentration (mmol/L)[a]					Particle Diameter (nm)[b]			
		CM	VLDL	LDL	HDL	Total	CM	VLDL	LDL	HDL
No. 1	Mean	0.0140	0.530	2.230	1.615	4.395	93.03		25.66	10.73
	SD	0.0005	0.0049	0.0045	0.0047	0.0097	0.31	ND	0.02	0.02
	CV%	3.70	0.92	0.20	0.29	0.22	0.34		0.10	0.15
No. 2	Mean	0.0011	0.057	2.934	1.514	4.505			25.88	11.32
	SD	0.0003	0.0007	0.018	0.0052	0.014	ND	ND	0.05	0.03
	CV%	27.54	1.19	0.61	0.34	0.32			0.18	0.26
No. 3	Mean	0.0026	3.635	2.277	1.048	6.963		40.81	24.21	10.25
	SD	0.0007	0.026	0.010	0.007	0.032	ND	0.06	0.02	0.01
	CV%	26.52	0.71	0.44	0.70	0.046		0.15	0.07	0.10

[a] To convert cholesterol concentration from mmol/L to mg/dL, multiply by 38.67.
[b] The data were obtained from additional analysis using column calibration curve
[c] No. 1: Determiner HDL-C reference serum (Lot 121AFF, Kyowa Medex, Tokyo)
No. 2: Normolipidemic subject (TG = 77 mg/dL [0.87 mmol/L])
No. 3: Hyperlipidemic subject (TG = 798 mg/dL [9.01 mmol/L])
ND = Peak not detected.

with the sum of IDL-C and LDL-C measured by the sequential ultracentifugation method. In the normal Lp(a) group, (CM + VLDL)-C and HDL-C by HPLC were consistent with VLDL-C and (HDL$_2$ + HDL$_3$ + VLDL)-C determined by the sequential ultracentrifugation method. In contrast, in the high Lp(a) group, despite a good correlation, a qualitative discrepancy was observed between the two methods, namely, Lp(a) was measured as VLDL-C by the HPLC method and as HDL$_2$-C by the sequential ultracentrifugation method.

HDL-C values obtained by the HPLC method were compared to those obtained by precipitation methods based on different principles: phosphotungstate-MgCl$_2$, poly-ethylene glycol, and isoelectric point methods.[42, 46, 47] The values obtained by isoelectric point and phosphotungstate-MgCl$_2$ methods were markedly lower than those obtained by the HPLC method, while the polyethylene glycol method showed values very close to those of the HPLC method. The values of HDL-C (y) obtained by a direct or homogeneous measurement method[48] (Determiner HDL-C, Kyowa Medex) showed good correlation with those (x) obtained by the HPLC method (y = 1.016x-0.008

mmol/L, $r = 0.998$, $n = 74$).[49, 50] The corresponding values (y') obtained by the phosphotungstate-MgCl$_2$ precipitation method were $y' = 0.842x+0.117$ mmol/L, r = 0.987, $n = 74$.[50]

Quantitative HPLC analysis of supernates obtained by precipitation methods revealed that the reason for the lower values of HDL-C by the phosphotungstate-MgCl$_2$ method compared to those obtained by the HPLC method was that this particular

Figure 30–2 ◆ Correlation of Lipoprotein Cholesterol Concentrations by HPLC Method with those by Chemical Autoanalyzer (Hitachi 7070) and Sequential Ultracentrifugation

Open circle: normal Lp(a) subjects ($n = 174$) with TG = 28–820 mg/dL (0.32–9.27 mmol/L).

Closed circle: high Lp(a) subjects ($n = 17$) with TG = 36–416 mg/dL (0.41–4.70 mmol/L)

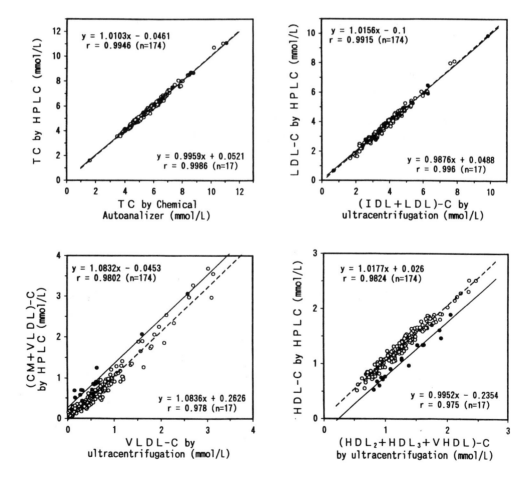

commercial reagent precipitated part of HDL. This discrepancy could be improved by using a modified reagent with lower $MgCl_2$ concentration.[50]

Analyses of Subclasses within Major Lipoprotein Classes

The degree of heterogeneity within each lipoprotein class has been examined by gel permeation chromatography. Sata et al.[4] examined the characterization of subfractions of TG-rich lipoproteins using 2% agarose chromatography. Williams and Kushwaha[51] demonstrated that CM and VLDL subclasses could be conveniently separated by HPLC using a CF-450 column (DuPont, USA) or a Fractgel 65-F column (Bodman Chemicals, USA). The size heterogeneity of the VLDL fraction isolated by ultracentrifugation were examined by Oida et al.[20] on HPLC using a TSKgel G5000PW column.

HDL Subfractions

Studies on HDL subclasses have been reported using a Superose 6 column in the FPLC system[31] as well as a TSKgel G3000SW column in an HPLC system.[18, 52-54.] Okazaki et al.[52] reported that HDL for normal males and females consisted of 5 subclasses having the following particle diameters: 12.2 ± 0.28 nm, 11.0 ± 0.21 nm, 9.75 ± 0.18 nm, 8.67 ± 0.13 nm and 7.63 ± 0.16 nm. More detailed characterization of HDL has been carried out in the new HPLC system[43] using four TSKgel LipopropakXL columns connected in series, which has succeeded in separating HDL into seven subclasses: HDL_{p1}, HDL_{p2}, HDL_{p3}, HDL_{p4}, HDL_{p5}, HDL_{p6}, and HDL_{p7} in order of particle size, by analysis using the Gaussian summation method. The HDL_{p1} and HDL_{p2} subclasses were prominent in subjects with high HDL-C, such as in cholesterol ester transfer protein (CETP) deficiency, but were negligible in normal subjects. The particle diameters of five subclasses, excluding HDL_{p1} and HDL_{p2}, were found to be identical to those of the previously reported five subclasses in the earlier HPLC system.[52] The correlations of cholesterol concentration in each subclass with the serum levels of apo A-I or apo A-II showed a significant difference among subclasses. Similar results were obtained for the correlation of HDL_2-C and HDL_3-C with apo A-I or apo A-II (authors' unpublished observation). Hence, the analysis of HDL subclasses by the HPLC method is clinically interesting.

Non-denaturing gradient gel electrophoresis and density gradient ultracentrifugation have been used to determine LDL and HDL subclasses.[55, 56] In contrast to these methods, the lipoprotein profile obtained by the TOSOH Lipoprotein Analytical System can provide information about subclasses of LDL and HDL simultaneously. As for the subjects with a ratio of VLDL-C to LDL-C less than 0.5, where the amounts of VLDL may have no influence on peak time or peak width of LDL, the relationship between the parameters of LDL subclasses (the ratio of IDL-C to LDL-C) and the particle diameter or peak width of LDL correlate as shown in Figure 30-3. The results indicate that an increase in LDL leads to an increase in the average size of LDL as well as a broadening of LDL peaks. As for HDL subclasses, a high correlation was observed between the ratio of HDL_2-C to HDL_3-C and mean particle diameter of HDL, as shown in Figure 30-3. This correlation may allow estimation of HDL_2-C and HDL_3-C from the HDL particle diameter.

Figure 30–3 ✧ Analysis of HDL and LDL Subclasses by HPLC and Sequential Ultracentrifugation Methods

Top: Relationship of HDL₂/HDL₃ ratio to HDL particle diameter.
Bottom: Relationship of IDL/LDL ratio to LDL particle diameter and peak width.

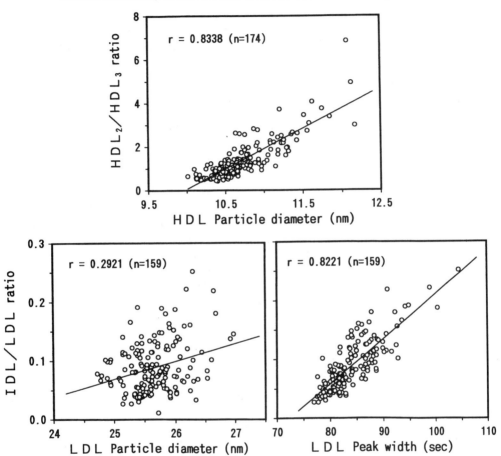

DIAGNOSTIC APPLICATIONS

Qualitative and quantitative information simultaneously obtained by the HPLC method could be successfully used in the diagnosis of lipoprotein abnormalities. Serum lipoprotein profiles of healthy human subjects and patients with various lipoprotein disorders had been examined by the earlier HPLC systems using TSKgel columns (reviewed by Okazaki et al.[13]). Abnormal lipoproteins were detected in lecithin:cholesterol acyltransferase (LCAT) deficiency by Kodama et al.[21] and in Tangier disease by Takizawa et al.[22] A marked enlargement of HDL size was reported in subjects with CETP deficiency[23] and a change in HDL size induced by drug therapy was examined.[24, 25]

Decreased serum HDL_3 cholesterol levels in liver cirrhosis were reported by Okazaki et al.[26] The differentiation of asymptomatic primary biliary cirrhosis from symptomatic cirrhosis was achieved by the HDL size in the elution profile.[27] Matsuzawa et al.[28] reported that no peak corresponding to LDL was detected for the subjects with apo $E_{2/2}$. This finding was clearly demonstrated by the TOSOH Lipoprotein Analytical System as shown in pattern *f* of Figure 30-1, and the particle size of VLDL in a patient with apo $E_{2/2}$ was smaller than that in a patient with lipoprotein lipase (LPL) deficiency. This information can assist diagnosis of dislipoproteinemia of Type III hyperlipidemia with apo $E_{2/2}$.

APPLICATION OF QUANTITATIVE AND QUALITATIVE DATA

Qualitative and quantitative information about lipoprotein profiling could be used for phenotyping of hyperlipoproteinemias as proposed by the World Health Organization (WHO) according to the following definition.[57] In all subjects, except for rare cases such as LCAT deficiency, Tangier disease, severe hyperbilirubinemia, and primary biliary cirrhosis, peaks corresponding to HDL were clearly observed.[43, 57]

Excluding HDL peaks, subjects could be classified into three groups: LDL only peak, VLDL and LDL peaks, and VLDL only peak. Subjects in group 1 could be sub-grouped to Types IIa, IIb, and IV hyperlipoproteinemia based on levels of VLDL-C and LDL-C, 20 mg/dL (0.52 mmol/L) and 150 mg/dL (3.88 mmol/L), respectively. Subjects in groups 2 and 3 were identified to be Type V and III, respectively. The results of phenotyping by HPLC method according to this definition are presented in Figure 30-1, in which a patient with LPL deficiency is successfully identified to be Type I or Type V and those with apo E deficiency (pattern not shown) or with apo $E_{2/2}$ were Type III. Although the current criteria for the phenotyping of hyperlipoproteinemia proposed by WHO are essentially based on the qualitative information from electrophoretic analysis,[58] the information obtained by the TOSOH Lipoprotein Analytical System can be valid for phenotyping of hyperlipoproteinemias.

In addition to the above phenotyping, atherogenic lipoprotein profiles which have been reported using other techniques were clearly demonstrated by the HPLC method. Decreased LDL and HDL sizes, increased or decreased LDL-C levels, increased VLDL-C, and decreased HDL-C levels were observed in subjects with dyslipidemia as compared to normolipidemic subjects.

FURTHER APPLICATION OF HPLC IN LIPOPROTEIN STUDIES

Because of the high sensitivity of lipoprotein detection, the new HPLC method could be successfully applied to analyze lipoproteins of low concentration, such as unbound lipoproteins in supernates of mixtures of serum and immunoaffinity gel of antibodies to apolipoproteins[56-61] and secreted lipoproteins in supernates of culture media of $HepG_2$ cells or hepatocytes of the WHHL rabbit.[62] Typical examples are shown in Figure 30-4, which ilustrates remnant-like particles (RLP)[63, 64] and supernates of culture medium, with cholesterol concentration ranging from 0.30 to 0.32 mg/dL (0.0078 to 0.0083 mmol/L). These patterns clearly reveal that the major components of RLP fraction in Type III hyperlipidemia with apo $E_{2/2}$ are lipoproteins of intermediate size

Figure 30–4 ✦ HPLC Patterns Obtained from Samples with Very Low Cholesterol Concentration

Non-concentrated sample of 250 μL for (a) unbound fraction to immunoaffinity gels (mono-clonal antibodies anti-human apo B-100 and apo A-I, RLP immunoseparation reagent, JIMRO, Japan) of serum from a subject with Type III dyslipidemia with apo $E_{2/2}$; (b) and (c) supernates of conditioned medium for rat hepatocytes and HepG$_2$ cells were applied to four connected columns (TSKgel LipopropakXL, TOSOH), and eluted at a flow rate of 0.60 mL/min using TSK eluent LP-2. Cholesterol in the effluent from the column was monitored under the same conditions as TOSOH Lipoprotein Analytical System. The detection range of cholesterol (absorbance at 550 nm) is 6 mV (0.006 OD) in full scale. The arrows show the average elution positions of VLDL, LDL, and HDL for human subjects.

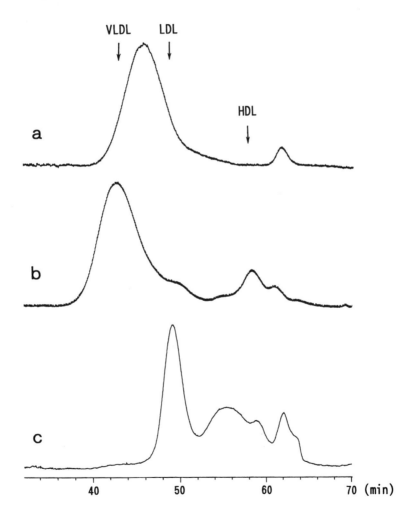

between VLDL and LDL, and that HepG$_2$ cells secrete both LDL and larger size HDL, while rat hepatocytes secrete mainly VLDL. The HPLC technique provides a quantitative lipoprotein cholesterol profile by particle size using samples with cholesterol concentration as low as 1/1000 of normal plasma.

Lipoprotein profiles of various species other than humans were reported by many investigators using the Superose 6 column.[29, 33-35, 65] and the earlier HPLC system.[17, 19, 51, 66-70] Lipoprotein profiles of experimental animals were examined using the new HPLC system. Lipoprotein profiles of apo-E-deficient and LDL-receptor-deficient transgenic mice[71] and a hypertriglyceridemic strain of WHHL rabbits[72] have been successfully carried out.

In conclusion, application of HPLC in combination with appropriate analytical reagents can greatly facilitate studies on serum lipoprotein classes. The use of HPLC can provide quantitative, qualitative, and diagnostic information on diseases with underlying lipoprotein abnormalities. Unlike conventional methods, the HPLC method can be used for the analysis of samples available in tiny amounts or samples containing very low levels of lipoproteins of particular interest.   ✧

Acknowledgments: *The authors wish to thank Dr. A. R. Saniabadi for editing the text and Drs. K. Nakajima, Y. Matsuzawa, S. Yamashita, H. Kamido, and H. Tomoike for useful discussion.*

REFERENCES

1. Miller JE, Miller NE. Plasma-high density lipoprotein concentration and development of ischaemic heart-disease. Lancet 1975;1:1-16.
2. Friedewald WT, Levy RI. Fredrickson DS, Estimation of the concentration of low-density lipoprotein cholesterol in plasma, without use of the preparative ultracentrifuge. Clin Chem 1972;18:499-502.
3. Hatch FT, Lees RS. Practical methods for plasma lipoprotein analysis. Adv Lipid Res 1968;6:1-68.
4. Sata T, Havel RJ, Jonas AL. Characterization of subfractions of triglyceride-rich lipoproteins separated by gel chromatography from blood plasma of normolipidemic and hyperlipidemic humans. J Lipid Res 1972;13:757-68.
5. Rudel LL, Marzetta CC, Johnson FL. Separation and analysis of lipoproteins by gel filtration, Methods Enzymol 1986;129:45-57.
6. Hara I, Okazaki M, Ohno Y. Rapid analysis of cholesterol of high density lipoprotein and low density lipoprotein in human serum by high performance liquid chromatography, J Biochem 1980;87:1863-5.
7. Okazaki M, Ohno Y, Hara I. Rapid method for the quantitation of cholesterol in human serum lipoproteins by high performance liquid chromatography, J Biochem 1981; 89:879-87.
8. Okazaki M, Itakura H, Shiraishi K, Hara I. Serum lipoprotein measurement—liquid chromatography and sequential floatation (ultra-centrifugation) compared, Clin Chem 1983; 29:768-73.
9. Okazaki M, Hagiwara N, Hara I. High performance liquid chromatography of human serum lipoproteins: selective detection of choline-containing phospholipids by enzymatic reaction. J Chromatogr 1982;231:13-23.
10. Hara I, Shiraishi K, Okazaki M, High performance liquid chromatography of human serum lipoproteins: selective detection of triglycerides by enzymatic reaction. J Chromatogr 1982;239:549-57.

11. Okazaki M, Hara I. Lipoprotein separations by high performance gel permeation chromatography. In: Hancock WS, ed. CRC handbook of HPLC for the separation of amino acids, peptides, and proteins. Boca Raton FL: CRC Press, 1984:393–403.
12. Hara I, Okazaki M. High-performance liquid chromatography of serum lipoproteins. Methods Enzymol 1986;129:57–78.
13. Okazaki M, Muramatsu T, Makino K, Hara I. High performance liquid chromatography of serum lipoproteins. In Mukherjee KD, Weber N, eds. CRC handbook of chromatography: analysis of lipids. Boca Raton, FL: CRC Press, 1993:101–14.
14. Carroll RM, Rudel LL. Lipoprotein separation and low density lipoprotein molecular weight determination using high performance gel-filtration chromatography. J Lipid Res 1983;24:200–7.
15. Williams MC, Kelley JL, Kushwaha RS. Detection of an abnormal lipoprotein in a large colony of pedigreed baboons using high-performance gel exclusion chromatography. J Chromatogr 1984;308:101–9.
16. Busbee DL, Payne DM, Jasheway DW, Carlisle S, Lacko AG. Separation and detection of lipoproteins in human serum by use of size-exclusion liquid chromatography: a preliminary report. Clin Chem 1981;27:2052–8.
17. Williams MC, Stenoien CG, Kushwaha RS. Rapid method or measuring plasma low-density lipoprotein turnover using high-performance gel exclusion chromatography. J Chromatogr 1986;375:233–43.
18. Holmquist L, Carlson LA. Subfractionation and characterization of native and incubation enlarged human plasma high density lipoprotein particles by high performance gel filtration. Lipids 1985;20:378–88.
19. Williams MC, Kushwaha RS, McGill HC. Quantitation of baboon lipoproteins by high performance gel exclusion chromatography. Lipids 1987;22:366–74.
20. Oida K, Nakai T, Miyabo S, Krul ES, Schonfeld G. Detection of size heterogeneity of very low density lipoproteins by high performance liquid chromatography. J Jpn Atheroscler Soc 1987;15:889–95.
21. Kodama T, Akanuma Y, Okazaki M, Aburatani H, Itakura H, Takahashi K et al. Abnormalities in plasma lipoprotein in familial partial lecithin:cholesterol acyltransferase deficiency. Biochim Biophys Acta 1983;752:407–15.
22. Takizawa A, Komoda T, Hokari S, Sakagishi Y, Tanaka A, Hara I. Evaluation of the particle size distribution of plasma lipoprotein in a patient with Tangier disease by high performance liquid chromatography. Clin Chim Acta 1990;193:85–8.
23. Yamashita S, Matsuzawa Y, Okazaki M, Kako H, Yasugi T, Akioka H, et al. Small polydisperse low density lipoproteins in familial hyperalphalipoproteinemia with complete deficiency of cholesterol ester transfer activity. Atherosclerosis 1988;70:7–12.
24. Yamamoto A, Matsuzawa Y, Yokoyama S, Funahashi T, Yamamura T, Kishino B. Effects of probucol on xanthomata regression in familial hypercholesterolemia. Am J Cardiol 1986;57:29H–35H.
25. Matsuzawa Y, Yamashita S, Funahashi T, Yamamoto A, Tarui S. Selective reduction of cholesterol in HDL$_2$ fraction by probucol in familial hypercholesterolemia and hyper-HDL$_2$ cholesterolemia with abnormal cholesterol ester transfer. Am J Cardiol 1988; 62:66B–72B.
26. Okazaki M, Hara I, Tanaka A, Kodama T, Yokoyama S. Decreased serum HDL$_3$ cholesterol levels in cirrhosis of the liver. N Engl J Med 1981;304:1608.
27. Teramoto T, Kato H, Hashimoto Y, Kinoshita M, Toda G, Oka H. Abnormal high density lipoprotein of primary biliary cirrhosis analyzed by high performance liquid chromatography. Clin Chim Acta 1985;149:135–48.
28. Matuszawa Y, Sho N, Kameda K, Kubo M, Hirobe K, Tarui S, et al. Characterization of lipoprotein abnormalities in type III hyperlipoproteinemia associated with apo E$_3$ deficiency (E$_{2/2}$ phenotype). J Jpn Atheroscler Soc 1984;11:1243–8.
29. Kieft KA, Bocan TMA, Krause BR. Rapid on-line determination of cholesterol distribution among plasma lipoproteins after high-performance gel filtration chromatography. J Lipid Res 1991;32:859–66.

30. März W, Siekmeier R, Scharnagl H, Seiffert UB, Gross W. Fast lipoprotein chromatography: new method of analysis for plasma lipoproteins. Clin Chem 1993;39:2276-81.

31. Clifton PM, MacKinnon AM, Barter PJ. Separation and characterization of high-density lipoprotein subpopulations by gel permeation chromatography. J Chromatogr 1987; 414:25-34.

32. Van Gent T, van Tol A. Automated gel permeation chromatography of plasma lipoproteins by preparative fast protein liquid chromatography. J Chromatogr 1990;525: 433-41.

33. Maagdenberg AMJM, Hofker MH, Krimpenfort PJA, Bruijn IG, Vlijmen B, Boom H, et al. Transgenic mice carrying the apolipoprotein E3-Leiden gene exhibit hyperlipoproteinemia. J Biol Chem 1993;268:10540-5.

34. Ha YC, Barter PJ. Rapid separation of plasma lipoproteins by gel permeation chromatography on agarose gel Superose 6B. J Chromatogr 1985;341:154-9.

35. Jiao S, Cole TG, Kitchens RT, Pfleger B, Schonfeld G. Genetic heterogeneity of lipoproteins in inbred strain of mice: analysis by gel-permeation chromatography, Metabolism, 1990;39:155-60.

36. Lagorist L, Gambert P, Meuneier S, Morgado P, Desgres J, d'Athis P, et al. Correlation between apolipoprotein A-IV and triglyceride concentrations in human sera, J Lipid Res 1989;30:701-10.

37. Cost B, Harvekes LM. Analysis of plasma lipoproteins by fast protein liquid chromatography, In: Rifai N, Warnick GR, eds. Laboratory measurement of lipids, lipoproteins and apolipoproteins. Washington DC: American Association for Clinical Chemistry Press, 1994:333-4.

38. Nyyssönen K, Salonen JT. Comparison of gel permeation chromatography, density gradient ultracentrifugation and precipitation methods for quantitation of very-low-, low- and high-density lipoprotein cholesterol, J Chromatogr 1991;570:382-9.

39. Gerdes LU, Gerdes C, Klausen IC, Faergeman O. Generation of analytical plasma lipoprotein profiles using two prepacked Superose 6B columns. Clin Chim Acta 1992;205: 1-9.

40. Kitamura T, Ito S, Kato Y, Sasamoto K, Okazaki M. Analysis of serum lipoproteins by high performance gel filtration chromatography. J Jpn Anal Chem 1996;41:103-6.

41. Kitamura T, Ito S, Moriyama H, Kato Y, Sasamoto K, Okazaki M. Quantitative analysis of serum lipoproteins (CM, VLDL, LDL and HDL) by high-performance gel filtration chromatography. Chromatography 1996;17:33-7.

42. Sasamoto K, Okazaki M, Muramatsu T, Yanagisawa T, Ando Y, Kamei, et al. Quantitation of total cholesterol and HDL-cholesterol by the HPLC method: comparison with the automated enzymatic method and the precipitation method. Jpn J Clin Chem 1996; 25:28-34.

43. Okazaki M, Clinical application of HPLC for Lipoprotein analysis. RINSHOKAGAKU 1996;40: 1281-92.

44. Rudel LL, Pitts LL. Male-female variability in the dietary cholesterol-induced hyperlipoproteinemia of cynomolgus monkey (Macaca fascicularis). J Lipid Res 1978;19: 992-1003.

45. Havel RJ, Eder HA, Bragden JH. The distribution and chemical composition of ultracentrifugally separated lipoproteins in human plasma. J Clin Invest 1955;34:1345-53.

46. Okazaki M, Sasamoto K, Muramatsu T, Jitsukata K, Horiuchi K, Kubono K. Quantitation of HDL-cholesterol by the improved HPLC method: comparison with ultracentrifugation, precipitation and direct methods. Jpn J Clin Chem 1995;24:245-52.

47. Sasamoto K, Okazaki M, Muramatsu T, Kawamura K, Kimura N, Kurihara-A Y, et al. HPLC analysis of HDL-cholesterol by precipitation method: comparison between different precipitation reagents. Jpn J Clin Chem 1996;25:234-42.

48. Sugiuchi H, Uji Y, Okabe H, Irie T, Uekama K, Kayahara N, et al. Direct measurement of high-density lipoprotein cholesterol in serum with polyethylene glycol-modified enzymes and sulfated α-cyclodextrin. Clin Chem 1995;41:717-23.

49. Okazaki M, Sasamoto K, Mashige H. Evaluation of direct methods for HDL-cholesterol

measurements by HPLC method. J Anal Bio-Sc 1996;19:389–97.

50.　Okazaki M, Sasamoto K, Muramatsu T, Hosaki S. Evaluation of the precipitation and direct methods for HDL-cholesterol assay by HPLC. Clin Chem, in press.

51.　Williams MC, Kushwaha RS. Fractionation of baboon chylomicrons and very-low-density lipoproteins by high-performance liquid chromatography. J Chromatogr 1988;433: 257–63.

52.　Okazaki M, Hagiwara N, Hara I. Heterogeneity of human serum high density lipoproteins on high performance liquid chromatography. J Biochem 1982;92:517–24.

53.　Kurasawa T, Yokoyama S, Miyake Y, Yamamura T, Yamamoto A. Rate of cholesterol ester transfer between high and low density lipoproteins in human serum and a case with decreased transfer rate in association with hyperalphalipoproteinemia. J Biochem 1985;98:1499–508.

54.　Ide H, Tsuji M, Shimada M, Kondo T, Fujiya S, Akanuma Y, et al. An evaluation of serum high density lipoproteins-phospholipids. Tohoku J Exp Med 1988;155:261–70.

55.　Austin MA, Hokanson JE, Brunzell JD. Measurement and clinical significance of low-density lipoprotein subclasses. In: Rifai N, Warnick GR, eds. Laboratory measurement of lipids, lipoproteins and apolipoproteins. Washington DC: American Association for Clinical Chemistry Press, 1994:223–34.

56.　Warnick GR. Measurement and clinical significance of high-density lipoprotein sub-classes. In: Rifai N, Warnick GR, eds. Laboratory measurement of lipids, lipoproteins and apolipoproteins. Washington DC: American Association for Clinical Chemistry Press, 1994:207–22.

57.　Okazaki M. Analysis of dislipoproteinemia by HPLC method. J Anal Bio-Sc 1997;20: 1100–10.

58.　Fredrickson DS, Lees RS. A system for phenotyping hyper-lipoproteinemia. Circulation 1965;31:321–7.

59.　Okazaki M, Sasamoto K, Muramatsu T, Hosaki S. Binding capacities of immunoassay reagents for remnant-like particles to LDL and HDL by the improved HPLC method. Jpn J Clin Chem 1994;23:236–42.

60.　Okazaki M, Sasamoto K, Muramatsu T, Hosaki S, Fukuda Y, Nakano T, Nakajima K. Analysis of lipoprotein components in remnant-like particle (RLP) fraction by an improved HPLC method. Clin Chem 1996;42:S295.

61.　Okazaki M, Sasamoto K, Muramatsu T, Nozaki S, Yamashita S, Takemura K, et al. The lipoprotein analysis of RLP (remnant like particle) by an improved HPLC method. I: Abnormally high RLP-cholesterol levels. J Jpn Atheroscler Soc 1995;22:939–46.

62.　Tanaka M, Otani H, Yokode M, Kita T. Regulation of apolipoprotein B secretion in hepatocytes from Watanabe heritable hyperlipidemic rabbit, an animal model for familial hypercholesterolemia Atherosclerosis 1995;114:73–82.

63.　Nakajima K, Saito T, Tamura A, Suzuki M, Nakano T, Adachi M, et al. Cholesterol in remnant-like lipoproteins in human serum using monoclonal anti-apo B-100 and anti-apo A-I immunoaffinity mixed gel. Clin Chim Acta 1993;223:53–71.

64.　Nakajima K, Saito T, Tamura A, Suzuki M, Nakano T, Adachi M, et al. A new approach for the detection of type III hyperlipoproteinemia by RLP-cholesterol assay. J Jpn Atheroscler Soc 1994;1:30–6.

65.　Shimano H, Yamada N, Katsuki M, Shimada M, Gotoda T, Harada K, et al. Overexpression of apolipoprotein E in transgenic mice: marked reduction in plasma lipoproteins except high density lipoprotein and resistance against diet-induced hypercholesterolemia. Proc Natl Acad Sci USA 1992:89:1750–54.

66.　Okazaki M, Ohno Y, Hara I. High-performance aqueous gel permeation chromatography of human serum lipoproteins. J Chromatogr 1980;221:257–64.

67.　Tanaka K, Inoue S, Ohkawa S, Asami M, Takamura Y, Murase T, et al. Abnormalities of rat serum lipoproteins after partial hepatectomy. J Jpn Atheroscler 1985;13:499–506.

68.　Hirai K, Ohno Y, Nakano T, Izutani K. Effects of dietary fats and phytosterol on serum fatty acid composition and lipoprotein cholesterol in rats. J Nutr Sci Vitaminol 1984; 30:101–12.

69. Iijima N, Kayama M, Okazaki M, Hara I. Time course change of lipid distribution in carp plasma lipoprotein after force-feeding with soybean oil. Bull Jpn Soc Sci Fisheries 1985;51:467–71.

70. Iijima N, Aihara M, Kayama M, Okazaki M, Hara I. Composition of carp plasma lipoproteins under starved and fed conditions. Bull Jpn Soc Sci Fisheries 1989;55:2001–7.

71. Ishibashi S, Zhong C, Osuga J, Harada K, Inaba T, Yague H, et al. Combined elevation of LDL and remnant lipoproteins accelerates atherosclerosis in mice lacking both LDL receptor and apo E. Manuscript submitted for publication.

72. Tomoike H, Ito I, Zhang C, Ohwada K, Okazaki M. Hereditary hypertriglyceridemia in WHHL rabbits relates to augmented elevation in VLDL cholesterol. Manuscript submitted for publication.

Consideration of the Clinical Utility of Tests of Three Well-Known Genes: APOE, APOB, and LDLR

31

Ian N. M. Day and Steve E. Humphries

BACKGROUND

❖ Over 100 years separated the observation that xanthomata and coronary heart disease could be heritable[1] and the isolation of the gene involved.[2] Genetic variation, some characterized, most as yet uncharacterized, underpins many of the more severe dyslipidemias, and in addition underpins polygenic variation important to setting plasma lipid levels in the general population. Characterization of structure and variation in apolipoprotein genes and other genes involved in lipid metabolism has proven valuable in better understanding of lipoprotein metabolism and has led to the development of new therapeutic approaches such as powerful cholesterol-lowering drugs. There remains much research to be undertaken in this field. However, except for centers with specialist research interests, gene tests are little used in lipidology.

This chapter examines potential applications where such tests could satisfy the criteria of altering management in some way. Additionally, such tests depend on the satisfaction of a range of performance criteria—accuracy, reproducibility, robustness, sensitivity, specificity, cost, influence, etc.—sufficient to merit their use.[3] Examples are considered with reference to these criteria.

Influence of Assays on Management

Laboratory assays are traditionally categorized to have four potential influences on management:

1. *Diagnosis,* e.g., amylase levels in establishing that pancreatitis is the cause of a patient's abdominal pain.

2. *Prognosis,* e.g., low paracetamol level post-overdose indicates that conservative management will lead to spontaneous recovery.

3. *Monitoring,* e.g., serial measure of tumor markers to assess tumor change or response to chemotherapy.

4. *Screening,* e.g., neonatal bloodspot to identify neonates with phenylketonuria, who need special diet to prevent mental retardation.

A fifth category, counselling, is particularly relevant where genetic status is concerned and should be added.

At present, the most obvious potential for the clinical use of genetic tests would be in categories 1, 2, 4, and 5. Category 3, monitoring, does not apply because we are concerned with germ line rather than somatic cell variation.

Criteria for Evaluating New Laboratory Tests

In a system of unlimited resources, any analysis which could add to a clinical evaluation in any way would be justifiable. However, because limited resources are available for health care, some system of priority and equity has to evolve. Clearly, an analysis which would alter management of an important clinical condition would take priority. Frequently, most of the cost is for drugs and in clinical staff time, so the impact of a test on these aspects rather than its cost will be the more important criterion. Such considerations lead to the recognition of a range of parameters important in evaluating potential new laboratory tests.

Accuracy and precision are important criteria for quantitative tests. For gene tests, classification is usually qualitative rather than quantitative. However, in contrast to the typical biochemical assay used for monitoring, gene tests are not usually repeated. They may be the determinant of lifelong decisions, concerns, behavior, and lifestyle, of reproductive decisions, and of substantial counselling time which may involve a whole family. However, gene tests can be problematic in many ways:

1. The laboratory techniques used can be susceptible to inaccuracy. Suitable reference materials and quality controls must be used.

2. Unexpected genetic variation can confound a test, e.g., a second site of variation never previously observed can give a misleading outcome dependent on the design of the test.

3. *De novo* mutation scanning will lead to the identification of possible gene defects never previously observed. Testing for known gene defects generally presupposes that the natural history is known, but where complex spectra of mutations occur (true for most genes), previously unknown mutations have to be identified. Sometimes interpretation is clearcut, as in the case of a premature stop codon in a haploinsufficiency disorder, such as in the low-density lipoprotein receptor (LDLR) gene in familial hypercholesterolemia (FH); but the effect of an amino acid variation may be more difficult to predict because the natural history of that variation is unknown—it might be silent, mild, or severe—and functional tests (cellular, etc.) are usually not readily available.

Such considerations bear on the use of a gene test for diagnosis, differential diagnosis, prognosis, and counselling. Screening adds a further layer of complexity. In contrast with diagnosis and prognosis, where the patient or proband has presented to the clinical system, screening seeks to take at-risk groups, often large numbers of individuals, and to identify a few who are at higher risk. The implication of "making patients of individuals" and of the mechanisms and politics of dealing with wide catchments of the population are substantial. There is substantial potential for a screening program to fail. The criteria of Wilson and Jungner[4] should be observed:

1.　The test should be capable of identification of presymptomatic risk.

2.　The test should be implementable and affordable.

3.　Treatment and management should be possible.

4.　Management should be affordable.

Two important parameters for evaluating test performance are sensitivity and specificity. An insensitive test—one which failed to find most or all at-risk individuals—would not be effective; it would be inefficient, would provide false reassurance, and would lead to "unexpected" disease. A non-specific test would also be problematic; false positives would cause unnecessary alarm and, where there are many, an overload of follow-up tests.

Simple, cheap high-throughput tests must be implemented. Clinical laboratories have to evaluate tests in relation to equipment needed, staffing skills, turnover and turnaround time, and in relation to alternative tests that answer the same question.

In this chapter, three genes, each much vaunted in the literature for its diagnostic applicability, are explained and considered in the context of the utility measures discussed above. Rather than representing a comprehensive catalog of possibilities, these tests have been chosen to illustrate the relationship between molecular genetics and the reference lipid laboratory. The basic techniques are straightforward and are not generally difficult to establish. However, any deviation from a described protocol or test can be difficult to troubleshoot for laboratorians new to analytical molecular genetics. In particular, polymerase chain reaction (PCR)[5, 6] is biochemically reproducible (with the caveat that the manufacturer's DNA polymerase remains unaltered), but the thermal cycling conditions are much less reproducible due to differences in the performance (ramp times, overshoots, thermal accuracy, and precision and spatial homogeneity across the PCR block) among models of thermal cycler. In consequence, PCR tends to be defined as "people's choice reaction" on a good day, but as "pretty confusing result" on a bad day. Since most post-PCR analytical procedures hinge on the yield, quality, and purity of the initial PCR, "perfect PCR" should be an important objective. PCR-based analysis of the APOE, APOB, and LDLR genes is considered below.

THE APOE GENE

Type III Hyperlipidemia, Vascular Disease, and Apolipoprotein E Defects

Type III hyperlipidemia is characterized by lipoprotein particles with properties intermediate between very-low-density lipoprotein (VLDL) and low-density lipoprotein (LDL). On electrophoresis, these particles appear as a broad beta band between the LDL (beta) and VLDL (pre-beta) bands. On ultracentrifugation, these particles float with the VLDL fraction ("beta-migrating VLDL"). More precise definition hinges on the measurement of cholesterol and triglyceride content of the VLDL fraction.

The intermediate nature of this lipoprotein fraction reflects its pathological origin as "remnant" particles representing partially delipidated VLDL and chylomicrons. These particles are unusually rich in apolipoprotein (apo) E, but although apo E is the usual ligand for specific receptor-mediated clearance, the apo E of patients with Type III hyperlipidemia is unable to mediate lipoprotein clearance. The genetic basis of Type III hyperlipidemia remained obscure until apo E phenotyping by isoelectric focusing was initiated[7] and it was shown that there were several patterns marking different alleles, termed initially II, III and IV.[8] The pattern representing homozygosity for allele IV was present in Type III patients, who characteristically display palmar xanthomata and an increased incidence of early coronary and peripheral arterial disease.

The identification of the amino-acid sequence of apo E[9] and demonstration that alleles E2, E3, and E4 contained at positions 112 and 158—respectively, cysteine/cysteine, cysteine/arginine and arginine/arginine—were consistent with the results of isoelectric focusing. It was further shown that most Type III patients have the E_2/E_2 phenotype. The absence of arginine at these positions appears to cause poor receptor binding and delayed clearance from the circulation, and in support of this model, chemical conversion of the cysteines to a positively charged derivative confers upon apo E_2 good receptor binding.[10] However, the E_2/E_2 phenotype occurs in an estimated 1% of the population, whereas only a small percentage (fewer than 5%) of E_2/E_2 individuals display Type III hyperlipidemia. The dyslipidemia is generally only apparent in adults, unmasked by obesity, diabetes, and aging, all of which increase VLDL secretion, and also by hypothyroidism or other disease. In hypothyroidism the conversion of inter-mediate density lipoprotein (IDL) to LDL by hepatic lipase is poor. It seems likely that any secondary compromise, genetic or environmental, to IDL clearance which is critically rate-limited by apo E_2/E_2 phenotype could precipitate Type III hyperlipidemia.

In addition to the common variants of apo E described above, a number of rare variants have also been described. In contrast with E_2/E_2, some are dominant in their effect on plasma lipid phenotype and are associated with Type III hyperlipidemia.[11] Characterization of such variants is generally only within the scope of the research laboratory and is not considered further here.

APOE Genotype and Alzheimer's Disease

This disease, first recognized in 1907 by Alois Alzheimer, is now known to be a common disease which is the predominant cause of dementia over the age of 65 years. Progression from mild short-term memory problems to massive loss of memory, language, and orientation leads to incapacitation of the individual. As survival to old age increases, society is faced with the future care of vast numbers of patients with dementia whose quality of life is poor.

Evidence gathered from multiplex families with late-onset dementia suggests that familial clustering was unlikely due to chance alone and, in 1991, Pericak-Vance et al.[12] used affected pedigree member analysis to show that a region of chromosome 19 was common to affected pedigree members more frequently than random chance would predict. This linkage was confirmed, but the much earlier report by Schellenberg et al.[13] of an association of a restriction fragment length polymorphism (RFLP) allele of the APOCII gene with Alzheimer's dementia did not replicate in these data. The APOCII gene is adjacent to the APOE gene on chromosome 19; the failed replication of the APOCII gene association, and the fact that apo C-II and apo E were regarded as lipoprotein components relevant to atherosclerosis, diverted attention from these genes as candidates for the Alzheimer locus. However, apo E was shown by Strittmatter et al.[14] to bind Alzheimer amyloid beta peptide, and furthermore, apo E antisera stained senile plaques and neurofibrillary tangles, prompting investigation of APOE genotype in Alzheimer's disease.

There are three common isoproteins of apo E, designated 2, 3, and 4, with allele frequencies of 6%, 78% and 16% respectively. The differences are at amino acids 112 and 158, the isoforms containing respectively, cysteine and cysteine (2), cysteine and arginine (3), or arginine and arginine (4). Many laboratories have now confirmed the association of APOE genotype with susceptibility, with APOE4 marking increased risk, in family and sporadic late-onset disease in many studies in various racial groups.[15]

The effect of APOE4 is dose-dependent:[16] The E_4/E_4 genotype has the most severe effect, advancing age of onset by about 8 years per allele, from 84 years if no E_4 allele is present to an age of 68 years for the E_4/E_4 genotype. APOE2 seems to mark reduced risk relative to E3. However, the observed associations do not prove that these genotypes are the functional feature on chromosome 19; they could simply be acting as linkage disequilibrium markers for other genetic diversity in a nearby gene, which causes the true pathological effect. However, the circumstantial evidence, the expression of apo E in the nervous system, the strong enhancement of expression in response to nerve injury, the difference in expressed isoproteins (which, at least in the cardiovascular system, confers differences in interactions, with lipoprotein receptors, for example), and differential effects of isoform-specific beta–very-low-density lipoprotein on neurite extension *in vitro*, leave APOE genotype with very strong candidacy as representing the etiological site within this genomic region of chromosome 19. The APOE gene has thus come to the forefront for its role in a new area: the "lipidology of the nervous system."

APOB Gene and Familial Defective apo B

In 1989, Innerarity et al.[17] described a disorder called familial defective apo B-100 (FDB), involving an amino acid change of arginine to glutamine at position 3500 in the APOB gene. This single amino acid change reduces binding of the LDL containing apo B-Gln, resulting in the accumulation of such LDL, thus causing hyperlipidemia and atherosclerosis. In an FDB heterozygote as much as 70% circulating LDL will be LDL-Gln. The mechanism of the effect has been elucidated by studying the differential binding of monoclonal antibodies, and using carbon-13 nuclear magnetic resonance,[18] which showed that the six lysine residues within the region of amino acid 3500 have altered pK in the presence of Gln_{3500}. Lysine residues are known to be involved in the binding of apo B100 to the LDL receptor, and because of its large effect on the conformation of the surrounding area of the protein, the substitution of $Arg_{3500} \rightarrow Gln$ alters the microenvironment of the receptor binding domain.

Individuals with FDB have been identified in the United States, Canada, Austria, the United Kingdom, Denmark, Germany, Italy, and France, but not in Finland.[19]

Haplotype analysis using APOB gene polymorphisms has shown that in all cases reported to date, the mutation is identical by descent, and thus all FDB carriers have a common ancestor. The mutation was originally identified in a patient who was moderately hypercholesterolemic.[20]

Among patients with a clinical diagnosis of FH, approximately 3% were heterozygous for the APOB-3500 mutation. Therefore, this mutation can be associated with severe hypercholesterolemia, tendon xanthomas, and a family history of premature CHD; it is thus clinically indistinguishable from FH caused by receptor defects. However, as discussed later in the section on clinical relevance, it is not always expressive as hypercholesterolemia, nor as coronary disease.

Low-Density Lipoprotein Receptor Gene and Familial Hypercholesterolemia

The clinical significance of the LDL receptor is described in Chapter 26.

CLINICAL RELEVANCE

APOE Gene

Diagnosis means the identification of the underlying cause of a patient's clinical condition. It is thus evident that the APOE 2/2 genotype will frequently, but not always, be found in Type III dyslipidemia. In the presence of a characteristic phenotype (clinical features, plasma cholesterol, and triglyceride levels), genotype identification can add strong support to the diagnosis. However, a more precise phenotypic diagnosis is possible using lipoprotein electrophoresis, isoelectric focusing, apo E immunoblotting, ultracentrifugation, or some combination of these. In a subset of individuals such as rarer APOE gene variants, and where there are confounding features in the phenotype (for example, different glycation patterns of apo E in diabetes mellitus[21]), the genotype and phenotype methods will yield apparently discrepant results. The resolution of such discrepancies can be highly complex, more the domain of the research laboratory than of a service laboratory. Nevertheless, in most patients, the gene test for E_2/E_2 genotype would concord with phenotyping.

What practical value is the gene test? A biochemical or genetic diagnosis of Type III dyslipidemia is useful. The clinical categorization defines likely natural history (prognosis); suggests additional investigations for possible trigger conditions such as hypothyroidism, diabetes, and obesity, which may represent the primary problem; gives access to knowledge of optimal therapeutic approaches and possibility of new trials; defines potential risk to siblings; and gives the doctor and patient a clearcut disease entity to address.

The importance of allele E_4 in the onset of late onset Alzheimer's disease presents new challenges. While not relevant to conventional lipidology, it is an extremely important aspect of the "lipidology of the nervous system" and instructive to future lipidology in general. In many populations, over 20% percent of individuals have an E_4 allele, and therefore an APOE genotype analysis makes a prediction for them of risk for late-onset Alzheimer's (an odds ratio approximately 4 for one E_4 allele, and estimated near 20 for the E_4/E_4 genotype[15])—a risk ratio considerably greater than that of high-density lipoprotein (HDL) level as a predictor of coronary risk.

In contrast with coronary risk, there is no opportunity at present of averting the onset of Alzheimer's disease, and traditional clinical wisdom is that a test must offer some opportunity for management to be justifiable. However, some individuals consider that "forewarned is forearmed" and will cope with their risk and modify their lives accordingly.[22] Additionally, it is also possible that a therapeutic approach will be found. After counselling, only a small number of patients at risk for the devastating consequences of Huntington's chorea elect to have genetic testing, but nevertheless for some it brings immense relief and for others effective life planning.

A comparable view has been endorsed for APOE testing,[22] and although of limited predictive value (i.e., of those who do possess an E_4 allele), we cannot predict who will develop Alzheimer's disease or when. Public demand could prevail if public knowledge were greater. Needless to say, an E_4 genotype should not be reported to a patient tested for E_2/E_2 genotype in the context of dyslipidemia, but here we have a prognostic test which might be applicable in conjunction with prior counselling. In a patient with Alzheimer's disease, of treatable or untreatable cause, it could add to the picture of diagnostic evaluation. In the seemingly remote future of a preventive therapy, it could become a screening test in later life, as part of a "retirement screening program," for example. These ideas are pure conjecture, but hopefully even the most conservative reader will appreciate that E_4 genotyping could become a massive demand on future laboratory services, compared to the highly selective instances in which E_2 genotyping is currently requested.

APOB Gene

As explained above, FDB attributable to mutation R3500Q is a contributor (1–5%), among people of Western European descent, to the pool of patients and families presenting with the clinical characteristics of familial hypercholesterolemia. Genotype analysis is simple, by one of several methods, and therefore offers a diagnostic test for patients with Type IIa hyperlipidemia. Is this useful? Firstly, it does not presently alter management per se. This is based on cholesterol levels and other risk factors such as age, gender, smoking, hypertension, and diabetes, and would be the same whether the LDLR or APOB gene were involved. In general, the R3500Q mutation is considerably less expressive in clinical terms than LDLR gene mutations.[19]

By contrast with LDLR gene mutations, where the majority of gene carriers develop coronary disease, fewer FDB-positive individuals develop coronary disease, family tracing leads to quite a few individuals who are genotype positive but have cholesterol levels within the reference range, hyperlipidemia may be less evident in childhood and have a much higher coefficient of variation in adulthood,[23] and cholesterol-years, a potentially important prognostic factor, may thus be lower. Additionally, FDB homozygotes do not develop coronary disease in childhood, and not necessarily later in life—a further pointer to the lesser clinical expressivity of FDB.[24] If gene tests are to be used, the counselling necessary thus will be quite complex. On these grounds, FDB is less important than the classical LDLR gene mutations. While it represents one simple test, easily achieved, it should be considered as a small component of the overall system for FH molecular diagnostics (see discussion below).

LDLR Gene

Genetic Diagnosis

As with many other single-gene diseases, a wide range of mutations occurs. In general, the number of different mutations accounting for the majority of FH is inversely proportional to the complexity of the target population. These mutations often differ among different populations. Founder populations, specific ethnic subsets, and smaller populations (less than 5–10 million) may have a handful of specific mutations accounting for the majority of FH. In larger, outbred and historically older (10,000 rather than 1,000 years) populations, the complexity may be one or two orders of magnitude greater.

The ease of setting up direct assays is proportional to the number of mutations, as is the cost. There must come a point at which *de novo* mutation scanning (e.g., by denaturing gradient gel electrophoresis or single-strand conformation polymorphism technique) presents an equally efficient first-line test, and in the United Kingdom we have focused our efforts on this strategy. Ultimately, oligonucleotide binding assays for thousands of different mutations (over 300 are known worldwide at present, with continued linear increment of reports) converges with *de novo* sequencing-by-hybridization using chip technology, as has been developed for the breast cancer BRCA1 gene and mitochondrial genome.[25]

Lipidologists can often recognize the proband for an FH family and make a clearcut diagnosis on the basis of clinical and biochemical features and family history. A gene test in such individuals is confirmatory, may have a "galvanic" effect in dietary and therapeutic compliance and stopping smoking, but despite improved life expectancy can compromise life insurance, mortgage, and employment opportunities. However, with suitable counselling, family tracing in conjunction with definitive gene tests seems sensible. Regional diagnostics laboratories in the United Kingdom undertake such complex gene tests for a variety of disorders, and it is accepted and explained to probands that a definitive mutation identification can take weeks and may prove impossible. This philosophy differs from the lipid clinic used to monitoring tests (which cost cents or dollars in contrast with hundreds of dollars for gene scanning), with guaranteed results and more rapid turnaround. Additionally, the cost of attempting to establish a direct gene test for family tracing seems high, but as a once-in-a-lifetime test, the cost is small compared to the costs of long-term drug therapy.

Deduction of genotype from cholesterol values may give a genetic misdiagnosis to 10% of family members with polygenic hypercholesterolemia,[26] and physicians may not have age- and gender-specific reference ranges available or be skilled at using them. In large, complex populations there seems little option except to use this technology in central, specialized regional laboratories that maintain collections of reference mutations, stocks of many oligonucleotides, and specialized knowledge base and expertise. This approach will be most cost effective as well.

Differential Diagnosis

A frequent question asked with hypercholesterolemic patients is, "Does this patient have FH, the single gene disorder?" If family history is not available, or if the hypercholesterolemia is less profound, a secondary gene-based laboratory test following the finding of a "significantly" elevated LDL-cholesterol level would be valuable. Only in low-complexity populations is current technology capable of this.

Screening

Population screening such as a two-tiered approach is theoretically possible, but would not currently satisfy the criteria for a targeted screening program. If the objective were to identify phenotype risk, why not stop at total or LDL/HDL cholesterol values? A more holistic approach to coronary risk,[27] the main cause for concern, should seek to identify individuals whose global risk is beyond a cutpoint defined from epidemiological surveys such as the Framingham study. Many FH gene carriers would fall well below such a cutpoint for coronary risk and would be at no greater risk of rising above the cutpoint than a new smoker or a new hypertensive. Additionally, in complex populations the technology currently available could not support genetic diagnosis either in sensitivity, throughput, or cost.

Screening of high-risk groups is generally applied already at the level of plasma cholesterol tests, and in this group the semantic distinction between screening, diagnosis, and genetic diagnosis (proband for family, test for family members) can become blurred.

Prenatal Diagnosis

Prenatal diagnosis for homozygous FH affecting 1 child per million and 1 couple per quarter million would be appropriate where both parents are heterozygotes. If direct mutation testing is to be applied, both parents would have to be ascertained and characterized in advance. Linkage using RFLPs or microsatellite polymorphisms[28] would also be possible, and would complement cellular assays which have been established previously, particularly for non-null mutations where the cellular assay may be uninformative.[2]

SELECTED METHODOLOGIES AND COMMENTS

APOE Genotyping

The gene test demands the analysis of two separate single-base variations in codons 112 and 158. These can be analyzed within the span of one PCR fragment, and a wide range of methods has been published. The wide range of published methods may in part reflect the fact that two sites have to be genotyped, and also that the region is quite rich in G+C bases and hence needs some care to achieve good PCR amplification of high yield and free of PCR misproducts. Many laboratories use the method of Hixson and Vernier,[29] which relies on the fact that both sites alter a HhaI restriction site. Six different genotype band patterns are then recognizable (see Figure 31-1). We have previously addressed every aspect of this protocol[30] to achieve robust high throughput, from sample acquisition and processing to electrophoretic typing. Sample preparation for PCR is, in our view, underaddressed.

The typical clinical chemistry analysis starts from plasma or serum separated from blood after a brief centrifugation. DNA templates suitable for PCR usually come from a multi-step purification which may take several hours. Blood is commonly the source, but most of the content of blood is red cells, which are devoid of DNA but contribute massive excess of undesired membrane and protein and including heme, an inhibitor of PCR. Buccal wash or scrapes, in our experience, lead to simpler (2-5 minute) sample preparation and high-quality DNA template in a yield sufficient to support thousands of PCRs if needed. Additionally, sample acquisition needs no vene-section skill, presents lower infection hazard, and is comfortable, stable to transport, repeatable, and feasible by post. These considerations are important if genotyping is to compete with, or complement, phenotyping.

The typical district hospital laboratory could expect to receive only single or small batches of samples for analysis in any week. Thus, APOE genotyping would benefit from running in parallel with other PCR-based analyses. At present, few are in use in clinical chemistry, but this situation may change. The utility of the final common pathway of analysis enabled by PCR can be compared with the utility of adapting enzyme assays to common indicators such as NAD. Core equipment for PCR and post-PCR analysis can then be established, with cost savings and ability to offer a diverse repertoire of tests. This contrasts with unique individual phenotyping assays.

PCR technology is very different from the phenotyping methods and therefore needs separate staff training and separate equipment, with a likely startup cost of $15,000-$30,000. Thus, the decision to use APOE genotyping in a laboratory not using PCR technology is likely to be a generic one involving the potential utility of PCR throughout the entire repertoire of services offered. Clearly a central laboratory covering applications in genetic disease, infectious disease, hematology, and clinical chemistry could not operate without the technology, but a small clinical chemistry laboratory could not readily justify the need. In the right environment, APOE genotyping for E_2/E_2 can probably be made cheaper and faster than several of the phenotyping methods, and thus either competitive with or complementary to them. For rarer variants, the considerations are akin to the LDLR gene discussed below.

Protocol

GENERAL

In our experience, many apparently minor variables which do not affect many other PCR reactions affect the success of APOE gene PCR, and re-optimization may be necessary if the reaction is to be carried out in a different type of PCR machine or different sources of reagents or template DNA prepared by a different method are to be used, even within the same laboratory. The equipment and reagents listed below were used for the current work:

Figure 31-1 ✦ Band Patterns of the Six Common APOE Genotypes after HhaI Restriction Digest of PCR Product, in a MADGE Format Array

Top view: schematic. Bottom view: close-up of real image.

The full format contains wells in an 8 × 12 array. Band sizes for the homozygous genotypes are as follows:

E_2/E_2: 91, 83, 63 b.p. E_3/E_3: 91, 63, 48, 35 b.p. E_4/E_4: 73, 63, 48, 35 b.p.

Heterozygotes show the bands of both relevant homozygous genotypes.

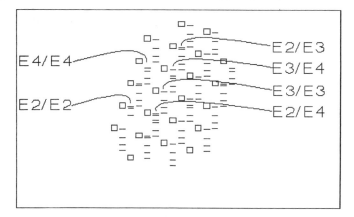

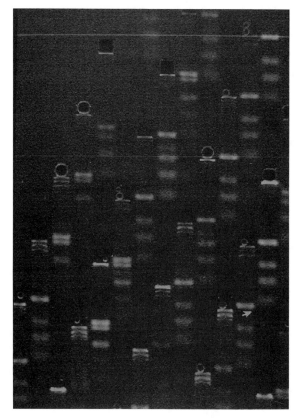

Equipment:

✧   deep 96-well plates (Beckman, High Wycombe, Bucks, UK)

✧   96-well Omniplates (Hybaid, Teddington, Middlesex, UK) with and loose-fitting lids (Falcon, Becton Dickinson, Oxford, UK)

✧   0.5–10 µL 8-channel multipipette (Finnipipette, Life Sciences, Basingstoke, Hants, UK)

✧   100 µL repeater pipette (Biohit, Alpha Laboratories, Eastleigh, Hants, UK)

✧   centrifuge (Sorvall T60000B, du Pont, Newtown, CT, USA)

✧   Omnigene PCR machine (Hybald, Teddington, Middlesex, UK)

✧   polystyrene block (10 cm × 7.5 cm)

✧   incubator (Sanyo-Gallenkamp, Leics, UK)

✧   horizontal gel electrophoresis tank (11.5 cm × 21 cm)

✧   7.5% MADGE gels (genetiX, Wimborne, Dorset, UK)

✧   UV transilluminator, charge-coupled-device camera, Imagestore 5000 frame grabber for digital images and video copy processor (UV Products, Cambridge, UK).

Reagents:

✧   10× "polmix" (500 mmol/L KCl, 100 mmol/L Tris (pH 8.3), 0.01% gelatin, 2 mmol/L of each dNTP)

✧   15 mmol/L $MgCl_2$

✧   dimethylsulphoxide (BDH, Lutterworth, Leics, UK)

✧   PCR primers (Genosys, Cambridge, UK)

✧   "FH49" 5'-GAACAACTGACCCCGGTGGCGG (100 pmol/µL)

✧   "FH50" 5'-GGATGGCGCTGAGGCCGCGCTC (100 pmol/µL)

✧   Taq polymerase (5 U/µL) (GibcoBRL cat. No. 18038-026)

✧   paraffin oil

✧   HhaI, 20,000 U/mL (New England Biolabs, Hitchen, Herts, UK)

✧   10× NE buffer 4 (New England Biolabs)

✧   bovine serum albumin, 10 mg/mL (New England Biolabs)

✧   10× Tris-borate (TBE) pH 8.3

✧   formamide loading buffer: 98% ionized formamide, 10 mm EDTA (pH 8.0), 0.025% xylene cyanole Ff, 0.025% bromophenol blue

✧   1 kilobase molecular weight marker ladder (GibcoBRL, Renfrewshire, Scotland)

✧   ethidium bromide, 10 mg/mL in water

DNA TEMPLATES AND PRE-PCR SETUP

Genomic DNA:

Genomic DNA was isolated from potassium-EDTA anticoagulated whole blood (either fresh or frozen at –20° C until used), using serial steps of cellular lysis with a sucrose buffer, nuclear lysis including sodium dodecyl sulphate and overnight protein digestion by proteinase K, salt precipitation of residual debris, and ethanol precipitation of DNA, as previously described.[31]

Template DNA stock was redissolved to approximately 0.16 mg/mL in Tris-EDTA and aliquots were placed in deep-well 96-well Beckman plates. Dilutions in water to 0.0256 mg/mL were set up in a replica array, from which 2.5 μL aliquots containing 40 ng DNA were drawn to set up either 10 or 20 μL PCRs. DNA samples for this work were anonymous samples for research studies approved by local ethical committees.

Mouthwash DNA:

10 mL mouthwashes were in 0.9% (w/v) saline. Patients were supplied a 20 mL universal tube containing 10 mL saline and asked to draw the liquid into their mouth, swill it around for approximately 30 sec, and spit it back into the tube. Sample transit of 1–3 days at room temperature and/or storage at –20° C until used gave acceptable PCR template DNA.

Mouthwashes were vortexed before removal of 1 mL into an Eppendorf tube. This was centrifuged at approximately 10,000 ×g for 2 min and the supernatant removed. The pellet was then resuspended in 400 μL of 10 mmol/L NaCl-EDTA, vortexed, and centrifuged for a further 2 min. The supernatant was again removed and the resultant pellet fully resuspended in 100 μL of 20 mmol/L NaOH and heated to 95°C for 15–20 minutes. Before removal of a 2.5 μL aliquot for use either neat or diluted with water as template for PCR, the preparation was pulse centrifuged to pellet cell debris. A 1 in 10 dilution was made of each DNA sample and pipetted into a deep-well Beckman plate, leaving a few of the 96 wells empty (for positive/negative controls). This array was used to transfer 2.5 μL of each DNA into its corresponding coordinate of a 96-well omniplate, to the very base of the well. The empty wells on the plate were used to pipette 2.5 μL of DNA from reference genotypes or of water for negative controls. The DNAs (approximately 40 ng DNA in each well) were then allowed to dry, and the dried DNA array stored at room temperature (up to months) until required for PCR.

PCR CONDITIONS

A total volume of 1000 μL PCR mix, sufficient for one 96-well omniplate (96 × 10 μL reactions), contained:

- ❖ 100 μL 10× Polmix
- ❖ 100 μL 15 mmol/L MgCl$_2$
- ❖ 50 μL DMSO
- ❖ 40 μL Oligonucleotide pair (FH49/50 at 20 pmol/μL each)

❖   704 µL Sterile distilled water

❖   6 µL Taq polymerase (stock at 5 U/µL)

A volume of 10 µL of this PCR mix was pipetted into each of the 96 wells, and overlaid with an equal volume of paraffin oil. The plate was covered with a lid and centrifuged for 1 min at 1600 ×g ready for thermal cycling. The following cycling conditions were used:

❖   95° C for 10 min

❖   95° C for 1 min

❖   72° C for 3 min (5 cycles)

❖   95° C for 1 min

❖   55° C for 1 min

❖   72° C for 1 min (30 cycles)

RESTRICTION DIGESTS

The amplified DNA was then digested using 4 U of HhaI using the procedure illustrated below. For one 96-well plate, 260 µL digest mix was prepared as follows:

❖   sterile distilled water 91 Ll

❖   10× NE buffer 4 130 µL

❖   13 µL 100× BSA (10 mg/mL)

❖   26 µL HhaI (20 U/µL)

The digest mix was subsequently aliquotted into a column of 8 wells on a clean 96-well plate, and this then used to pipette 2.0 µL into each well of a clean plate using 8-channel multipipette. To each well, 8.0 µL of PCR product was transferred across from its identical coordinate on the PCR plate.

The plate was centrifuged at 1600 ×g for 1 min and digested in an incubator at 37° C for at least 1 h.

MICROPLATE ARRAY DIAGONAL GEL ELECTROPHORESIS (MADGE) IMAGING AND ANALYSIS

After digestion, 5.0 µL of each sample was added to 2.0 µL formamide dye mix (formamide, 0.5 mol/L EDTA, 0.025% w/v of both bromophenol blue and xylene cyanole), and 5.0 µL of this mix was loaded into the well of a 7.5% MADGE gel (pre-stained in a solution of 10 µL of 10 mg/mL ethidium bromide in 100 mL 1 × TBE for 10 mins) in an electrophoresis tank containing 1 × TBE. MADGE gels were prepared as described previously.[32]

Briefly, the gels are supported on glass, contain ninety-six 2 mm cubic wells for sample loading in an 8 × 12 array, with the long axis of the array at an angle of 71.6 degrees relative to the electrodes and with the edges of the wells parallel and per-pendicular to the line of electrophoresis. A 1 kb ladder was also loaded into one well of the gel. Electrophoresis was at 10 V/cm at room temperature for 45 min, after which time the gel was observed using an ultraviolet transilluminator and a digital image of the gel acquired using a ccd camera and frame grabber (see Figure 31-1).

Gene Tests for FDB (R3500Q)

This laboratory has used many methods for R3500Q genotyping. Tests often are performed on singletons or small batches. The method of forced restriction site analysis of Mamotte and van Bockxmeer[33] has proven the simplest, most comprehensive and most robust, requiring only PCR oligonucleotides and a restriction enzyme. The method allows both a sensitive assay in which normal PCR product should cut to completion (i.e., residual undigested PCR product may represent FDB, a different mutation at the site, or failed restriction digest) and a specific assay forcing the surrounding base sequence such that only the R3500Q allele results in a restriction site. For high throughput, the method is also compatible with microplate PCR and microplate array diagonal gel electrophoresis (MADGE) devised in this laboratory.

Protocol

GENERAL

Template DNA, PCR equipment, and general procedures including PCR volumes and oligonucleotide concentrations were as above.

SPECIFIC

Conditions were identical with those of Mamotte and van Bockxmeer.[33]
The upstream PCR primer was 5′-TCTCGGGAATATTCAGGAACTATTG.
The "ARG" primer is 5′-GCCCTGCAGCTTCACTGAGGAC.
The "GLN" primer is 5′-GCCCTGCAGCTTCACTGAGTAC.

Sensitive Assay:

In the sensitive assay for screening for FDB mutations in a set of samples, the upstream and ARG PCR primers are used. The ARG primer contains a base mismatching the native wild-type sequence (four bases away from the site of the mutation) and forces the occurrence of a Sau96I restriction site: any base change within this site, including the R3500Q base change, will eliminate the restriction site.

Specific Assay:

In the specific assay for confirming FDB R3500Q mutations, the upstream and GLN PCR primers are used. The GLN primer contains two bases mismatching the native wild-type sequence (at positions three and four bases away from the mutation site) and forces the occurrence of a ScaI restriction site, but only if the R3500Q base change is also present. Any base change within this site, including the R3500Q base change, will eliminate the restriction site.

Enzyme concentrations identical with those used above were found to be satisfactory, rather than the high concentration of ScaI used by the original authors.

Comments on Restriction Enzyme Based Genotyping

Specific mutations can be tested for in many ways: direct sequencing, single strand conformation polymorphism technique, denaturing gradient gel electrophoresis, chemical cleavage, oligo binding, allele-specific PCR, oligonucleotide ligation assay, restriction site assay, PCR-induced restriction site assay, minisequencing, fluorescence decoupling during PCR (e.g., TaqMan system, etc.). See Landegren[34] for a review of most of these techniques. However, specific mutations can only be proven in three ways: by direct sequencing, which is very laborious; by oligonucleotide binding using an oligonucleotide specific to that mutation; or by restriction enzyme assay, where an enzyme site can be found that only cuts the mutant or where a specific site can be induced by using a mismatched PCR primer.

Oligonucleotide binding assays offer a generic system applicable to any sequence region, but considerable care is necessary in achieving informative conditions of hybridization wash stringency, i.e., carefully controlled salt concentration and temperature conditions must be established to distinguish perfect match from mismatch binding. Unless non-radioisotopic labelling is used, oligo binding is time consuming for singleton assays since the oligo must first be labelled. If non-radioisotopic labelling is used, then a suitable detection system must be available such as a colorimeter, fluorimeter, or DELFIA instrument.

For restriction enzyme analysis, it typically will be necessary to incubate the digest at 37° C (incubator, water bath, dry block, or simply program the PCR block to hold the temperature), then to perform a simple agarose or polyacrylamide gel electrophoresis followed by ethidium bromide staining, and imaging (photographic or digital imaging) during excitation on an ultraviolet transilluminator.

In our laboratory the availability of equipment makes restriction enzyme analysis the most favorable and is compatible both with singleton and large batch analysis (the latter using the MADGE system). However, the availability of different equipment in different laboratories—for example, of high capital cost systems such as DELFIA in service clinical chemistry laboratories—may lead to a different choice of method. The methods we use are simple, robust, and cheap to set up and therefore recommended for a laboratory with no adaptable systems. For APOE genotype analysis, the electrophoresis-based method is recommended irrespective of any other possible methods which could be set up.

LDLR Gene Tests in FH

In all but the lowest complexity populations (e.g., founder populations, populations in isolated regions, and ethnic groups numbering less than a few million), it is unlikely that direct mutation assays will account for more than the minority of FH mutations. A few such examples are listed in Table 31–1.

Table 31–1 ✧ Common Nucleotide Variations Causing Hyperlipidemias

Gene	Sequence Change	Comments
LDLR	10 kb deletion, promoter, exon 1	63% of French-Canadian FH patients
	deletion exons 16, 17, part of 18	FH-Helsinki accounts for 56% of FH in east Finland
	deletion 7nt in exon 6	FH-North Karelia accounts for 34% of FH in east Finland
	Asp206Glu (exon 4)	69% of Afrikaner FH
	Asp154Asn (exon 4)	10% of Afrikaner FH
	Val408Met (exon 9)	15% of Afrikaner FH
	Stop 660 (TGC to TGA) (exon 14)	Christian Lebanese
	deletion codon Gly197 (exon 4)	35% of Ashkenazi Jews from Lithuania
APOB	codon change Arg3500Gln	FDB is a phenocopy of FH. Estimated 1/700 in several countries in Europe. Probable origin central Europe.
APOE	E_2 allele differs from E_3 and E_4, having Cys not Arg at positions 112 and 158	Approximately 1% of individuals are E_2/E_2, and 1% of these develop Type III hyperlipidemia

The authors have recently discussed[35] the progress of Schuster and colleagues[36] in developing direct mutation multiplex tests for a range of German FH mutations. We have also set up a Web site (accessible by any standard Web browser, such as Netscape, at http://www.ucl.ac.uk/fh/) which provides a sequence workbook containing all exons, protein sequence, functional elements, known polymorphisms, and locations of most mutations described in the literature. Many mutations remain unpublished, but this Web site has an electronic publication area to facilitate effective international communication in this field. Sites of PCR primers which have been used in our laboratory, as well as other sundry data, are also available. In addition, a searchable mutation database is provided. An excerpt from this Web site is shown in Figure 31–2.

Our view is that *de novo* mutation scanning and direct sequencing would be necessary in most geographical locations, but that this restricts the application to highly specialized laboratories that use these techniques for many genes. We recommend the use of two techniques: single strand conformation polymorphism (SSCP) and denaturing gradient gel electrophoresis (DGGE).[34] The former offers greater ease of setup; the latter is more complex to set up, but is now tending to be more favored by diagnostics laboratories due to its greater reproducibility and apparently higher sensitivity to more of the possible base variations within a PCR product. However, SSCP is considerably more reproducible if thermostatted electrophoresis apparatus is used, a feature which has long been addressed for DGGE (the typical run temperature is 60° C) but is only now being addressed by manufacturers of SSCP (the typical run temperature needed is 20° C).

Figure 31–2 ✧ An Excerpt of Information Available from a Web Site for LDLR Gene Mutations: Familial Hypercholesterolemia

A segment of exon 3 is shown, with a segment from the mutations table. For example, one might have used oligo FH4 as a PCR then as a sequencing primer to read through the sequence shown. One might find heterozygosity at a G base which can immediately be seen to be at nucleotide 301 (codon E80). Three mutations are known (arbitrary code numbers 13, 175 and 201) at this position, and they can then be looked up in more detail. The reverse process is also possible. It can be seen that E80 is in a binding domain motif, DXXSDE, increasing the likelihood that an amino acid change would have a functional effect.

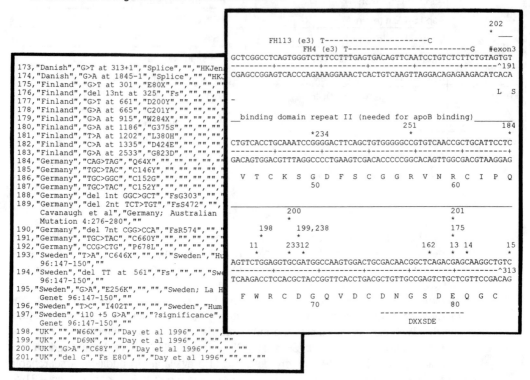

```
173,"Danish","G>T at 313+1","Splice","","HKJen
174,"Danish","G>A at 1845-1","Splice","","HKJ
175,"Finland","G>T at 301","E80X","","","",""
176,"Finland","del 13nt at 325","Fs","","","
177,"Finland","G>T at 661","D200Y","","","",
178,"Finland","G>A at 665","C201Y","","","",
179,"Finland","G>A at 915","W284X","","","",
180,"Finland","G>A at 1186","G375S","","","",
181,"Finland","T>A at 1202","L380H","","","",
182,"Finland","C>A at 1335","D424E","","","",
183,"Finland","G>A at 2533","G823D","","","",
184,"Germany","CAG>TAG","Q64X","","","","","
185,"Germany","TGC>TAC","C146Y","","","","",
186,"Germany","TGC>GGC","C152G","","","","",
187,"Germany","TGC>TAC","C152Y","","","","",
188,"Germany","del 1nt GGC>GCT","FsG303","","
189,"Germany","del 2nt TCT>TGT","FsS472","",
   Cavanaugh et al","Germany; Australian
   Mutation 4:276-280",""
190,"Germany","del 7nt CGG>CCA","FsR574","",
191,"Germany","TGC>TAC","C660Y","","","","",
192,"Germany","CCG>CTG","P678L","","","","",
193,"Sweden","T>A","C646X","","","Sweden","Hu
   96:147-150",""
194,"Sweden","del TT at 561","Fs","","","Swe
   96:147-150",""
195,"Sweden","G>A","E256K","","","Sweden; La H
   Genet 96:147-150",""
196,"Sweden","T>C","I402T","","","Sweden","Hum
   Genet 96:147-150",""
197,"Sweden","i10 +5 G>A","","?significance",
   Genet 96:147-150",""
198,"UK","","W66X","","Day et al 1996","","",
199,"UK","","D69N","","Day et al 1996","","",
200,"UK","G>A","C68Y","","Day et al 1996","","",
201,"UK","del G","Fs E80","","Day et al 1996","","",""
```

The methodologies in this field are rapidly evolving at present, and it is impossible to give a detailed discussion of the advantages and disadvantages of each. Instead, we recommend that a series of books, papers, and reviews[34, 37–42] be used in conjunction with the Web site, which will save several weeks' time in getting orientated on the sequence to set up laboratory work.

CONCLUSIONS

There is no overwhelming case to apply gene tests in the typical lipidology service. Their influence on management is relative rather than absolute. However, a well-resourced and forward-thinking clinical laboratory should gain valuable and wide-ranging experience by exploring some of the applications described in this chapter. This will result in an improved quality of the "genetic" component of the service. With rapidly developing technology and a widening array of treatment options, these approaches seem likely to disseminate more widely. The approach with E4 alleles and Alzheimer's disease risk is justifiably cautious, but this test is a "wild card" which could lead to a massive upswing in Apo E genotyping if public knowledge and culture, or therapy, were to evolve. ✧

REFERENCES

1. Fogge CH. General xanthelasma or vitilogoidea. Trans Path Soc Lond 1872;24:242.
2. Goldstein JL, Brown MS. Familial hypercholesterolemia. In: Scriver CR, Beaudet AL, Sly WS, Valle D, eds. The metabolic basis of inherited disease, 6th ed. New York: McGraw Hill, 1989;1215-50.
3. Gowenlock AH, ed. Varley's practical clinical biochemistry, 6th ed. Oxford UK: Heinemann Medical Books, 1988.
4. Wilson JMG, Jungner G. Principles and practice of screening for disease. Public Health Papers 34. Geneva: World Health Organization, 1968
5. Erlich HA. PCR technology principles and applications for DNA amplification. New York: Stockton Press, 1989.
6. Mullis KB, Ferre F, Gibbs RA, eds. PCR: The polymerase chain reaction. Boston: Birkhauser, 1994.
7. Utermann G, Pruin N, Steinmetz A. Polymorphism of apolipoprotein E III: effect of a single polymorphic gene locus on plasma lipid levels in man. Clin Genet 1979;15:63-72.
8. Zannis VI, Just PW, Breslow JL. Human apolipoprotein E isoprotein subclasses are genetically determined. Am J Hum Genet 1981;33:11-24.
9. Rall SCJ, Weisgraber KH, Innerarity TL, Mahley RW. Structural basis for receptor binding heterogeneity of apolipoprotein E from type III hyperlipoproteinemic subjects. Proc Natl Acad Sci USA 1982;79:4696-700.
10. Weisgraber KH, Innerarity TL, Mahley RW. Abnormal lipoprotein receptor-binding activity of the human E apoprotein due to cysteine-arginine interchange at a single site. J Biol Chem 1982;257:2518-21.
11. Rall SC, Mahley RW. The role of apolipoprotein E genetic variants in lipoprotein disorders. J Int Med 1992;231:653-9
12. Pericak-Vance MA, Bebout JL, Gaskell PC, Yamaoko LH, Hung WY, Alberts MJ, et al. Linkage studies in familial Alzheimer's disease: evidence for chromosome 19 linkage. Am J Hum Genet 1991;48:1034-50.
13. Schellenberg GD, Deeb S, Boehnke LM, Bryant EM, Martin GM, Lampe LM, et al. Association of apolipoprotein CII allele with familial dementia of the Alzheimer type. J Neurogenetics 1987;4:97-108.
14. Strittmatter WJ, Weisgraber KH, Huang DY, Dong LM, Salvesen GS, Pericak-Vance M, et al. Binding of human apolipoprotein E to synthetic amyloid beta-peptide: isoform-specific effects and implications for late-onset Alzheimer's disease. Proc Natl Acad Sci USA 1993;90:8098-102.
15. M-S Tsai, Tangalos EG, Petersen RC, Smith GE, Schaid DJ, Kokmen E, et al. Apolipoprotein E: risk factor for Alzheimer Disease. Am J Hum Genet 1994;54:643-9
16. Corder EH, Saunders AM, Strittmatter WJ, Schmechel DE, Gaskell PC, Small GW, et al. Gene dose of apolipoprotein-E type-4 allele and the risk of Alzheimer's disease in late onset families. Science 1993;261:921-3.
17. Innerarity TL, Weisgraber KH, Arnold KS, Mahley RW, Krauss RM, Vega GL, Grundy SM. Familial defective apolipoprotein B-100: low density lipoproteins with abnormal receptor binding. Proc Natl Acad Sci USA 1987;84:6919-23.

18. Katz SL, Ibadah JA, Letizia JY, Thomas MT, Philips MC. A ^{13}C NMR characterisation of lysine residues in apolipoprotein B and their role in binding to the low density lipoprotein receptor. J Biol Chem 1988;263:13831-8.

19. Myant NB. Familial defective apolipoprotein B-100: a review, including some comparisons with familial hypercholesterolemia. Atherosclerosis 1993;104:1-18.

20. Vega GL, Grundy SM. In vivo evidence for reduced binding of low density lipoproteins to receptors as a cause of primary moderate hypercholesterolemia. J Clin Invest 1986; 78:1410-14.

21. Stavljenic-Rukavina A, Sertic J, Salzer B, Dumic M, Radica A, Fumik K, Krajina A. Apolipoprotein E phenotypes and genotypes as determined by polymerase chain reaction using allele-specific oligonucleotide probes and the amplification refractory mutation system in children with insulin-dependent diabetes mellitus. Clin Chem Acta 1993;216:191-8.

22. Alzheimer's Disease Society. Memorandum. In: House of Commons Science and Technology Committee, Third Report. Human genetics: the science and its consequences, Volume II. London: HMSO, 1995:23.

23. Miserez AR, Keller U. Differences in the phenotypic characteristics of subjects with familial defective B-100 and familial hypercholesterolemia. Arterioscler Thromb Vasc Biol 1995;15:1719-29.

24. Gallagher JJ, Myant NB. The affinity of low density lipoproteins and of very-low-density lipoprotein remnants for the low density lipoprotein receptor in homozygous familial defective apolipoprotein B-100. Atherosclerosis 1995;115:263-72.

25. Chee M, Yang R, Hubbell E, Berno A, Huang XC, Stern D, et al. Accessing genetic information with high-density DNA arrays. Science 1996;274:610-14.

26. Williams RR, Hunt SC, Schumacher MC, Hegele RA, Leppert MF, Ludwig EH, et al. Diagnosing heterozygous familial hypercholesterolemia using new practical criteria validated by molecular genetics. Am J Cardiol 1993;72:171-6.

27. Haq IU, Ramsay LE, Pickin DM, Yeo WW, Jackson PR, Payne JN. Lipid-lowering for prevention of coronary heart disease: what policy now? Clin Sci 1996;91:399-413.

28. Day INM, Haddad L, O'Dell SD, Day LB, Whittall R, Humphries S. Identification of a common low density lipoprotein receptor mutation (R329X) in the South of England: complete linkage disequilibrium with an allele of microsatellite D19S394. J Med Genet 1997;34:111-16.

29. Hixson JE, Vernier DT. Restriction isotyping of human apolipoprotein E by gene amplification and cleavage with HhaI. J Lipid Res 1990;31:545-8.

30. Bolla M, Haddad L, Winder AF, Humphries SE, Day INM. High-throughput method for determination of apolipoprotein E genotypes with use of restriction digestion analysis by microplate array diagonal gel electrophoresis (MADGE). Clin Chem 1995;41:1599-1604.

31. Miller SA, Dykes DD, Polesky HF. A simple salting out procedure for extracting DNA from human nucleated cells. Nucleic Acids Res 1988;16:1215.

32. Day INM, Humphries SE. Electrophoresis for genotyping: microtitre array diagonal gel electrophoresis (MADGE) on horizontal polyacrylamide (H-PAGE) gels, Hydrolink or agarose. Anal Biochem 1994;222:389-95

33. Mamotte CDS, van Bockxmeer FM. A robust strategy for screening and confirmation of familial defective apolipoprotein B-100. Clin Chem 1993;39:118-21

34. Landegren U, ed. Laboratory protocols for mutation detection. Oxford: Oxford University Press, 1996.

35. Day INM, Humphries SE. Genetic tests for familial hypercholesterolemia. Nature Biotechnology 1996;14:1227-8.

36. Baron H, Fung S, Aydin A, Bahring S, Luft FC, Schuster H. Oligonucleotide ligation assay (OLA) for the diagnosis of familial hypercholesterolemia. Nature Biotechnology 1996;14:1279-82.

37. Orita M, Suzuki Y, Sekiya T, Hayashi K. Rapid and sensitive detection of point mutations and DNA polymorphisms using the polymerase chain reaction. Genomics 1989;5:874-9.

38. Myers RM, Maniatis T, Lerman LS. Detection and localisation of single base changes by denaturing gradient gel electrophoresis. Meth Enzymol 1987;155:501-27.

39. Vidal-Puig A, Moller DE. Comparative sensitivity of alternative single-strand conformation polymorphism (SSCP) methods. Biotechniques 1994;17:490-6.

40. Sheffield VC, Beck JS, Kwitek AE, Sandstrom DW, Stone EM. The sensitivity of single-strand conformation polymorphism analysis for the detection of single base substitutions. Genomics 1993;16:325-32.

41. Hobbs HH, Brown MS, Goldstein JL. Molecular genetics of the LDL receptor gene in familial hypercholesterolemia. Human Mutation 1992;1:445-66.

42. Day INM, Whittall R, O'Dell SD, Haddad L, Bolla M, Gudnason V, Humphries S. Spectrum of LDL receptor gene mutations in heterozygous familial hypercholesterolemia. Human Mutation, in press.

Appendix:
Lipid and Lipoprotein Values

Lipid and lipoprotein values for white and black males and females by age. Data presented as mean and 5–95 percentile values in mg/dL (Tables I.A–IV.A) and in mmol/L (Tables I.B–IV.B).

Source: Hainline A, Karon J, Lippel K, eds. *Manual of Laboratory Operations,* Lipid Research Clinics Program, and *Lipid and Lipoprotein Analysis,* 2nd ed., Bethesda, MD: U. S. Department of Health and Human Services, 1982.

Table I.A   Plasma Total and Lipoprotein Cholesterol and Triglyceride Mean and Percentile Values (mg/dL) for White Males, by Age.

Age in Years	N	Cholesterol (mg/dL) X (5–95 % tile)	Triglycerides (mg/dL) X (5–95 % tile)	Cholesterol in					
				HDL (mg/dL) N	X (5–95 % tile)	LDL (mg/dL) N	X (5–95 % tile)	VLDL (mg/dL) N	X (5–95 % tile)
0	(10)	143	63						
1	(36)	150	73						
2	(49)	158	55						
3	66	151 (110–193)	53 (28–84)						
4	77	159 (115–221)	52 (29–89)						
5	72	156 (113–203)	56 (26–88)						
6	278	158 (120–201)	54 (31–96)	66	56.0 (38–72)	61	95.0 (69–129)	61	6.9 (0–16)
7	275	159 (122–195)	55 (29–107)						
8	332	162 (121–206)	56 (29–101)	68	55.6 (39–73)	65	90.5 (65–123)	64	9.6 (0–21)
9	294	161 (123–203)	58 (30–111)				-		
10	455	159 (127–196)	58 (29–105)	94	57.3 (38–76)	87	96.8 (64–131)	90	10.4 (2–23)
11	409	162 (124–211)	57 (29–106)						
12	572	160 (121–203)	68 (34–125)	144	55.9 (39–75)	139	95.4 (64–129)	138	9.0 (1–19)
13	411	153 (115–195)	71 (35–143)						
14	426	152 (114–195)	73 (35–134)	129	49.2 (34–69)	129	95.5 (57–130)	127	10.7 (0–25)
15	508	149 (111–194)	74 (34–134)						
16	639	149 (113–192)	77 (35–146)	160	45.6 (30–62)	160	93.2 (64–129)	160	13.5 (2–27)
17	417	150 (110–204)	79 (39–160)						
18	238	152 (113–199)	81 (39–155)	67	43.7 (32–60)	66	99.3 (62–142)	66	13.8 (2–25)
19	173	154 (114–196)	85 (44–172)						
20–24	882	166.5 (124–218)	100.3 (44–201)	118	45.4 (30–63)	118	103.3 (66–147)	118	13.7 (1–28)
25–29	2042	182.2 (133–244)	115.8 (46–249)	253	44.7 (31–63)	253	116.7 (70–165)	253	17.4 (3–36)
30–34	2444	192.2 (138–254)	128.3 (50–266)	403	45.5 (28–63)	403	126.4 (78–185)	403	21.3 (5–48)
35–39	2320	201.3 (146–270)	144.9 (54–321)	371	43.4 (29–62)	371	133.2 (81–189)	372	24.1 (3–56)
40–44	2428	206.5 (151–268)	151.4 (55–320)	383	44.3 (27–67)	385	135.6 (87–186)	384	25.5 (5–56)
45–49	2296	212.2 (158–276)	151.7 (58–327)	325	45.4 (30–64)	325	143.9 (98–202)	326	24.4 (5–51)
50–54	2138	212.7 (158–277)	151.8 (58–320)	340	44.1 (28–63)	340	142.3 (89–197)	340	26.8 (8–62)
55–59	1621	213.9 (156–276)	141.4 (58–286)	261	47.6 (28–71)	261	145.8 (88–203)	261	21.6 (3–49)
60–64	905	213.0 (159–276)	142.3 (58–291)	131	51.5 (30–74)	131	146.3 (83–210)	131	18.9 (3–44)
65–69	750	212.6 (158–274)	136.7 (57–267)	105	51.1 (30–78)	105	150.4 (98–210)	105	19.7 (0–45)
70+	850	206.8 (151–270)	129.8 (58–258)	119	50.5 (31–75)	119	142.9 (88–186)	119	17.0 (0–38)

Table I.B Plasma Total and Lipoprotein Cholesterol and Triglyceride Mean and Percentile Values (mmol/L) for White Males, by Age

Age in Years	N	Cholesterol (mmol/L) X (5–95 % tile)	Triglycerides (mmol/L) X (5–95 % tile)	Cholesterol in					
				HDL (mmol/L) N	X (5–95 % tile)	LDL (mmol/L) N	X (5–95 % tile)	VLDL (mmol/L) N	X (5–95 % tile)
0	(10)	3.70	0.71						
1	(36)	3.89	0.83						
2	(49)	4.09	0.62						
3	66	3.91 (2.85–5.00)	0.60 (0.32–0.95)						
4	77	4.12 (2.98–5.72)	0.59 (0.32–1.01)						
5	72	4.04 (2.93–5.26)	0.63 (0.29–0.99)						
6	278	4.09 (3.11–5.21)	0.61 (0.35–1.08)	66	1.45 (0.98–1.87)	61	2.46 (1.79–3.34)	61	0.18 (0–0.41)
7	275	4.12 (3.16–5.05)	0.62 (0.33–1.21)						
8	332	4.20 (3.13–5.34)	0.63 (0.33–1.14)	68	1.44 (1.01–1.89)	65	2.34 (1.68–3.19)	64	0.25 (0–0.54)
9	294	4.17 (3.19–5.26)	0.65 (0.34–1.25)						
10	455	4.12 (3.29–5.08)	0.65 (0.33–1.19)	94	1.48 (0.98–1.97)	87	2.51 (1.66–3.39)	90	0.27 (0.05–0.60)
11	409	4.20 (3.21–5.46)	0.64 (0.33–1.20)						
12	572	4.14 (3.13–5.26)	0.77 (0.38–1.41)	144	1.45 (1.01–1.94)	139	2.47 (1.66–3.34)	138	0.23 (0.03–0.49)
13	411	3.96 (2.98–5.05)	0.81 (0.40–1.62)						
14	426	3.94 (2.95–5.05)	0.83 (0.40–1.51)	129	1.27 (0.88–1.79)	129	2.47 (1.48–3.37)	127	0.28 (0–0.65)
15	508	3.86 (2.88–5.02)	0.84 (0.38–1.51)						
16	639	3.86 (2.93–4.97)	0.87 (0.40–1.65)	160	1.18 (0.78–1.61)	160	2.41 (1.66–3.34)	160	0.35 (0.05–0.70)
17	417	3.89 (2.85–5.28)	0.89 (0.44–1.81)						
18	238	3.94 (2.93–5.15)	0.92 (0.44–1.75)	67	1.13 (0.83–1.55)	66	2.57 (1.66–3.34)	66	0.36 (0.05–0.65)
19	173	3.99 (2.95–5.08)	0.96 (0.50–1.94)						
20–24	882	4.31 (3.21–5.65)	1.13 (0.50–2.27)	118	1.18 (0.78–1.63)	118	2.68 (1.71–3.81)	118	0.36 (0.03–0.73)
25–29	2042	4.72 (3.44–6.32)	1.31 (0.52–2.81)	253	1.16 (0.80–1.63)	253	3.02 (1.81–4.27)	253	0.45 (0.08–0.93)
30–34	2444	4.98 (3.57–6.58)	1.45 (0.57–3.01)	403	1.18 (0.73–1.63)	403	3.27 (2.02–4.79)	403	0.55 (0.13–1.24)
35–39	2320	5.21 (3.78–6.99)	1.64 (0.61–3.62)	371	1.12 (0.75–1.61)	371	3.45 (2.09–4.90)	372	0.62 (0.08–1.45)
40–44	2428	5.35 (3.91–6.94)	1.71 (0.62–3.62)	383	1.15 (0.70–1.74)	385	3.51 (2.25–4.82)	384	0.66 (0.13–1.45)
45–49	2296	5.50 (4.09–7.15)	1.71 (0.66–3.70)	325	1.18 (0.78–1.66)	325	3.73 (2.54–5.23)	326	0.63 (0.13–1.32)
50–54	2138	5.51 (4.09–7.17)	1.72 (0.66–3.62)	340	1.14 (0.73–1.63)	340	3.69 (2.31–5.10)	340	0.69 (0.21–1.61)
55–59	1621	5.54 (4.04–7.15)	1.60 (0.66–3.23)	261	1.23 (0.73–1.84)	261	3.78 (2.28–5.26)	261	0.56 (0.08–1.27)
60–64	905	5.52 (4.12–7.15)	1.61 (0.66–3.29)	131	1.33 (0.78–1.92)	131	3.79 (2.15–5.44)	131	0.49 (0.08–1.14)
65–69	750	5.51 (4.09–7.10)	1.54 (0.64–3.02)	105	1.32 (0.78–2.02)	105	3.90 (2.54–5.44)	105	0.51 (0–1.17)
70+	850	5.36 (3.91–6.99)	1.47 (0.66–2.92)	119	1.31 (0.80–1.94)	119	3.70 (2.28–4.82)	119	0.44 (0–0.98)

Table II.A Plasma Total and Lipoprotein Cholesterol and Triglyceride Mean and Percentile Values (mg/dL) for White Females Not Taking Hormones, by Age

Age in Years	N	Cholesterol (mg/dL) X (5–95 % tile)	Triglycerides (mg/dL) X (5–95 % tile)	Cholesterol in					
				HDL (mg/dL)		LDL (mg/dL)		VLDL (mg/dL)	
				N	X (5–95 % tile)	N	X (5–95 % tile)	N	X (5–95 % tile)
0	(6)	148	82						
1	(31)	156	70						
2	(33)	152	65						
3	57	160 (118–201)	63 (32–110)						
4	59	155 (108–196)	59 (34–94)						
5	86	162 (126–195)	56 (28–93)						
6	253	165 (129–205)	57 (32–95)	58	50.1 (28–68)	53	100.5 (66–124)	50	9.8 (1–23)
7	220	160 (124–202)	61 (32–112)						
8	297	166 (129–209)	61 (34–104)	60	55.7 (37–75)	55	100.0 (67–142)	54	10.6 (1–25)
9	261	163 (120–205)	63 (32–110)						
10	417	163 (127–205)	66 (35–116)	100	51.5 (34–72)	99	98.1 (70–140)	99	11.8 (2–23)
11	338	161 (126–200)	73 (36–126)						
12	536	161 (124–203)	79 (38–132)	102	53.0 (37–69)	101	97.7 (68–133)	101	10.6 (1–23)
13	344	155 (122–192)	79 (43–136)						
14	441	157 (120–198)	79 (38–138)	122	51.0 (34–70)	120	93.5 (60–129)	120	10.6 (2–23)
15	553	155 (119–199)	74 (39–127)						
16	675	155 (121–197)	71 (37–120)	165	52.8 (35–77)	165	95.2 (57–138)	164	12.3 (3–26)
17	351	158 (119–202)	70 (40–113)						
18	193	157 (116–199)	75 (39–126)	53	53.2 (37–74)	53	101.8 (58–143)	53	11.1 (0–24)
19	137	162 (123–212)	79 (40–135)						
20–24	778	164.1 (122–216)	72.4 (36–131)	96	52.2	96	98.1	96	11.9
25–29	1329	170.7 (128–222)	74.7 (37–145)	181	56.0 (37–81)	181	106.0 (70–151)	181	12.0 (2–24)
30–34	1569	175.4 (130–231)	78.5 (39–151)	233	55.4 (38–75)	232	108.9 (67–150)	233	10.8 (0–25)
35–39	1606	184.4 (140–242)	86.3 (40–176)	241	54.7 (34–82)	242	118.8 (76–172)	240	14.4 (1–35)
40–44	1583	193.8 (147–252)	98.4 (45–191)	244	57.1 (33–87)	244	125.1 (77–174)	244	13.9 (3–29)
45–49	1515	202.5 (152–265)	104.5 (46–214)	249	57.7 (33–86)	247	129.7 (80–187)	247	16.8 (2–38)
50–54	1257	212.7 (162–285)	114.8 (52–233)	177	60.1 (37–89)	177	146.1 (90–215)	177	16.4 (0–37)
55–59	1112	230.5 (173–300)	125.0 (55–262)	172	59.1 (36–86)	172	151.8 (95–213)	172	21.2 (2–51)
60–64	723	230.8 (172–297)	127.0 (56–239)	111	62.0 (36–91)	111	156.3 (100–234)	111	17.6 (0–40)
65–69	593	232.8 (171–303)	131.3 (60–243)	101	60.5 (34–89)	101	161.6 (97–223)	101	17.6 (0–40)
70+	748	228.1 (169–289)	132.4 (60–237)	127	60.1 (33–91)	127	148.9 (96–207)	127	16.2 (0–52)

Table III.A   Plasma Total and Lipoprotein Cholesterol and Triglyceride Mean and Percentile Values (mg/dL) for White Females Taking Hormones, by Age

				Cholesterol in					
Age in Years	N	Cholesterol (mg/dL) X (5–95 %tile)	Triglycerides (mg/dL) X (5–95 %tile)	HDL (mg/dL) N	X (5–95 %tile)	LDL (mg/dL) N	X (5–95 %tile)	VLDL (mg/dL) N	X (5–95 %tile)
15–19	167	169.0 (121–231)	106.3 (49–200)	19	-----	19	-----	20	-----
20–24	788	179.2 (131–236)	105.3 (55–176)	101	54.7 (34–79)	101	108.3 (62–163)	101	15.2 (1–30)
25–29	855	183.6 (141–236)	110.4 (57–191)	132	56.1 (35–83)	132	115.9 (72–169)	132	15.3 (2–36)
30–34	579	188.5 (139–246)	115.8 (58–206)	97	58.0	95	117.4	95	15.6
35–39	406	194.4 (146–249)	126.0 (56–241)	50	57.0	50	118.9	50	20.4
40–44	466	199.4 (152–258)	128.9 (58–238)	63	61.1	63	124.8	63	17.2
45–49	627	209.4 (155–276)	129.6 (53–260)	71	65.6	71	127.3	72	19.0
50–54	729	218.1 (164–283)	130.0 (62–238)	70	67.6	70	119.7	70	18.7
55–59	577	218.1 (164–283)	126.5 (62–238)	60	70.8	60	132.5	60	19.2
60–64	341	224.4 (172–285)	126.0 (57–240)	32	70.4	32	136.6	32	13.5
65–69	224	222.5 (173–279)	129.5 (60–234)	25	76.1	25	126.4	25	15.6
70+	132	215.9 (160–274)	121.1 (60–216)	10	-----	10	-----	10	-----

Table III.B Plasma Total and Lipoprotein Cholesterol and Triglyceride Mean and Percentile Values (mmol/L) for White Females Taking Hormones, by Age

Age in Years	N	Cholesterol (mmol/L) X (5–95 % tile)	Triglycerides (mmol/L) X (5–95 % tile)	Cholesterol in					
				HDL (mmol/L)		LDL (mmol/L)		VLDL (mmol/L)	
				N (5–95 % tile)	X	N (5–95 % tile)	X	N (5–95 % tile)	X
15–19	167	4.38 (3.13–5.98)	1.20 (0.55–2.26)	19	-----	19	-----	20	-----
20–24	788	4.64 (3.39–6.11)	1.19 (0.62–1.99)	101	1.42 (0.88–2.05)	101	2.81 (1.61–4.22)	101	0.39 (0.03–0.78)
25–29	855	4.76 (3.65–6.11)	1.24 (0.64–2.19)	132	1.45 (0.91–2.15)	132	3.00 (1.86–4.38)	132	0.39 (0.05–0.93)
30–34	579	4.87 (3.60–6.37)	1.31 (0.65–2.33)	97	1.50	95	3.04	95	0.40
35–39	406	5.04 (3.78–6.45)	1.43 (0.63–2.72)	50	1.48	50	3.08	50	0.53
40–44	466	5.16 (3.94–6.68)	1.46 (0.65–2.72)	63	1.58	63	3.23	63	0.45
45–49	627	5.42 (4.01–7.15)	1.47 (0.60–2.94)	71	1.70	71	3.30	72	0.49
50–54	729	5.65 (4.32–7.23)	1.47 (0.64–2.80)	70	1.75	70	3.10	70	0.48
55–59	577	5.65 (4.25–7.33)	1.44 (0.70–2.69)	60	1.83	60	3.43	60	0.50
60–64	341	5.81 (4.46–7.38)	1.43 (0.64–2.71)	32	1.82	32	3.54	32	0.35
65–69	224	5.76 (4.48–7.23)	1.47 (0.68–2.64)	25	1.97	25	3.27	25	0.40
70+	132	5.59 (4.14–7.10)	1.37 (0.68–2.44)	10	-----	10	-----	10	-----

Table II.B Plasma Total and Lipoprotein Cholesterol and Triglyceride Mean and Percentile Values (mmol/L) for White Females Not Taking Hormones, by Age

Age in Years	N	Cholesterol (mmol/L) X (5–95 % tile)	Triglycerides (mmol/L) X (5–95 % tile)	HDL N (5–95 % tile)	HDL X	LDL N (5–95 % tile)	LDL X	VLDL N (5–95 % tile)	VLDL X
0	(6)	3.83	0.93						
1	(31)	4.04	0.79						
2	(33)	3.94	0.74						
3	57	4.14 (3.06–5.21)	0.71 (0.36–1.24)						
4	59	4.02 (2.80–5.08)	0.67 (0.38–1.06)						
5	86	4.20 (3.26–5.05)	0.63 (0.32–1.05)						
6	253	4.27 (3.34–5.31)	0.64 (0.36–1.07)	58	1.30 (0.73–1.76)	53	2.60 (1.71–3.21)	50	0.25 (0.03–0.60)
7	220	4.14 (3.21–5.23)	0.69 (0.36–1.27)						
8	297	4.30 (3.34–5.41)	0.69 (0.38–1.18)	60	1.44 (0.96–1.94)	55	2.59 (1.74–3.68)	54	0.28 (0.03–0.65)
9	261	4.22 (3.11–5.31)	0.71 (0.36–1.24)						
10	417	4.22 (3.29–5.31)	0.75 (0.40–1.31)	100	1.33 (0.88–1.86)	99	2.54 (1.81–3.63)	99	0.31 (0.05–0.60)
11	338	4.17 (3.29–5.31)	0.83 (0.41–1.42)						
12	536	4.17 (3.21–5.26)	0.89 (0.43–1.49)	102	1.37 (0.96–1.79)	101	2.53 (1.76–3.44)	101	0.28 (0.03–0.60)
13	344	4.02 (3.16–4.97)	0.89 (0.49–1.54)						
14	441	4.07 (3.11–5.13)	0.89 (0.43–1.56)	122	1.32 (0.88–1.86)	120	2.42 (1.55–3.34)	120	0.28 (0.05–0.60)
15	553	4.02 (3.08–5.15)	0.84 (0.44–1.44)						
16	675	4.02 (3.13–5.10)	0.80 (0.42–1.36)	165	1.37 (0.91–1.99)	165	2.47 (1.48–3.57)	164	0.32 (0.08–0.67)
17	351	4.09 (3.08–5.23)	0.79 (0.45–1.28)						
18	193	4.07 (3.00–5.15)	0.85 (0.44–1.42)	53	1.38 (0.96–1.92)	53	2.64 (1.50–3.70)	53	0.29 (0–0.62)
19	137	4.20 (3.19–5.49)	0.89 (0.45–1.53)						
20–24	778	4.25 (3.16–5.59)	0.82 (0.41–1.48)	96	1.35	96	2.54	96	0.31
25–29	1329	4.42 (3.32–5.75)	0.85 (0.42–1.64)	181	1.45 (0.96–2.10)	181	2.75 (1.81–3.91)	181	0.31 (0.05–0.62)
30–34	1569	4.54 (3.37–5.98)	0.89 (1.44–1.71)	233	1.43 (0.98–1.94)	232	2.82 (1.74–3.89)	233	0.28 (0–0.65)
35–39	1606	4.78 (3.63–6.27)	0.98 (0.45–1.99)	241	1.42 (0.88–2.12)	242	3.08 (1.97–4.46)	240	0.37 (0.03–0.91)
40–44	1583	5.02 (3.81–6.53)	1.11 (0.51–2.16)	244	1.48 (0.86–2.25)	244	3.24 (1.99–4.51)	244	0.36 (0.08–0.75)
45–49	1515	5.25 (3.94–6.86)	1.18 (0.52–2.42)	249	1.49 (0.86–2.23)	247	3.36 (2.07–4.84)	247	0.44 (0.05–0.98)
50–54	1257	5.64 (4.20–7.38)	1.30 (0.59–2.63)	177	1.56 (0.96–2.31)	177	3.78 (2.33–5.57)	177	0.42 (0–0.96)
55–59	1112	5.97 (4.48–7.77)	1.41 (0.62–2.96)	172	1.53 (0.93–2.23)	172	3.93 (2.46–5.52)	172	0.55 (0.05–1.32)
60–64	723	5.98 (4.46–7.69)	1.44 (0.63–2.70)	111	1.61 (0.93–2.36)	111	4.05 (2.59–6.06)	111	0.46 (0.03–1.17)
65–69	593	6.03 (4.43–7.85)	1.48 (0.68–2.75)	101	1.57 (0.88–2.31)	101	4.19 (2.51–5.78)	101	0.46 (0–1.04)
70+	748	5.91 (4.38–7.49)	1.50 (0.68–2.68)	127	1.56 (0.86–2.36)	127	3.86 (2.49–5.36)	127	0.42 (0–1.35)

Table IV.A Plasma Total Cholesterol and Triglyceride Mean and Percentile Values (mg/dL) for Black Males and Females, by Age

Age in Years	MALES N	Cholesterol (mg/dL) X (5–95 % tile)	Triglycerides (mg/dL) X (5–95 % tile)	FEMALES N	Cholesterol (mg/dL) X (5–95 % tile)	Triglycerides (mg/dL) X (5–95 % tile)
0	(0)			(2)	124	86
1	(2)	139	49	(6)	154	52
2	(4)	154	52	(5)	160	43
3	(8)	149	46	(7)	167	51
4	(3)	164	64	(4)	147	68
5	(8)	166	46	(8)	183	51
6	97	164 (128–213)	53 (33–94)	102	172 (138–216)	57 (29–108)
7	52	167 (116–208)	49 (33–75)	60	170 (126–216)	52 (27–82)
8	103	167 (129–218)	54 (28–96)	100	172 (124–226)	54 (31–90)
9	74	168 (135–200)	53 (33–81)	68	176 (133–235)	60 (33–100)
10	118	167 (126–206)	53 (29–95)	131	169 (128–211)	60 (39–97)
11	68	167 (133–191)	52 (30–81)	65	168 (131–213)	61 (33–92)
12	120	171 (127–216)	63 (32–100)	128	161 (121–203)	68 (37–109)
13	88	159 (124–195)	58 (33–90)	70	167 (120–219)	70 (37–112)
14	91	157 (115–195)	58 (32–98)	80	161 (120–205)	66 (38–110)
15	138	154 (110–200)	59 (28–97)	150	166 (129–211)	64 (34–121)
16	200	157 (120–199)	57 (31–102)	192	162 (120–206)	59 (32–95)
17	126	156 (118–208)	65 (32–122)	83	166 (124–208)	62 (36–107)
18	(38)	163	65	(23)	167	66
19	(12)	160	60	(6)	166	55
20–29	97	178.5	81.3	129	178.1 (125–234)	71.3 (36–127)
30–39	178	191.6 (138–253)	106.9 (42–224)	291	186.4 (132–243)	76.4 (38–140)
40–49	167	206.9 (148–267)	126.1 (52–294)	188	201.8 (145–267)	95.1 (43–175)
50–59	70	206.5	142.2	80	215.5	102.1
60+	46	220.7	108.5	48	233.6	115.4

Table IV.B Plasma Total Cholesterol and Triglyceride Mean and Percentile Values (mmol/L) for Black Males and Females, by Age

| | | MALES | | | FEMALES | |
| | | Cholesterol (mmol/L) | Triglycerides (mmol/L) | | Cholesterol (mmol/L) | Triglycerides (mmol/L) |
Age in Years	N	X (5–95 % tile)	X (5–95 % tile)	N	X (5–95 % tile)	X (5–95 % tile)
0	(0)			(2)	3.21	0.97
1	(2)	3.60	0.55	(6)	3.99	0.59
2	(4)	3.99	0.59	(5)	4.14	0.49
3	(8)	3.86	0.52	(7)	4.33	0.58
4	(3)	4.25	0.72	(4)	3.81	0.77
5	(8)	4.30	0.51	(8)	4.74	0.58
6	97	4.25 (3.32–5.52)	0.60 (0.37–1.06)	102	4.46 (3.57–5.59)	0.64 (0.33–1.22)
7	52	4.33 (3.00–5.39)	0.56 (0.37–0.85)	60	4.40 (3.26–5.59)	0.59 (0.31–0.93)
8	103	4.33 (3.34–5.65)	0.61 (0.32–1.08)	100	4.46 (3.21–5.85)	0.61 (0.35–1.02)
9	74	4.35 (3.50–5.18)	0.60 (0.37–0.92)	68	4.56 (3.44–6.09)	0.68 (0.37–1.13)
10	118	4.32 (3.44–4.95)	0.60 (0.33–1.07)	131	4.38 (3.32–5.47)	0.68 (0.41–1.09)
11	68	4.32 (3.44–4.95)	0.59 (0.34–0.92)	65	4.35 (3.39–5.52)	0.69 (0.37–1.04)
12	120	4.43 (3.29–5.59)	0.71 (0.36 1.13)	128	4.17 (3.13–5.26)	0 77 (0.42–1.23)
13	88	4.12 (3.21–5.05)	0.65 (0.37–1.02)	70	4.33 (3.11–5.67)	0.79 (0.42–1.27)
14	91	4.07 (2.98–5.05)	0.65 (0.36–1.10)	80	4.17 (3.11–5.67)	0.75 (0.43–1.24)
15	138	3.99 (2.85–5.18)	0.66 (0.32–1.09)	150	4.30 (3.34–5.47)	0.72 (0.38–1.37)
16	200	4.07 (3.11–5.15)	0.64 (0.35–1.15)	192	4.20 (3.11–5.34)	0.67 (0.36–1.07)
17	126	4.04 (3.06–5.39)	0.74 (0.36–1.38)	83	4.30 (3.21–5.39)	0.70 (0.41–1.21)
18	(38)	4.22	0.74	(23)	4.33	0.75
19	(12)	4.14	0.68	(6)	4.20	0.75
20–29	97	4.62	0.92	129	4.61 (3.24–6.06)	0.81 (0.41–1.44)
30–39	178	4.96 (3.57–6.55)	1.21 (0.48–2.53)	291	4.83 (3.42–6.29)	0.86 (0.43–1.58)
40–49	167	5.36 (3.83–6.92)	1.42 (0.59–3.32)	188	6.23 (3.76–6.92)	1.08 (0.49–1.98)
50–59	70	5.35	1.61	80	5.58	1.15
60+	46	5.72	1.23	48	6.05	1.30

Index

A

Abbott Spectrum (laboratory analyzer), 171*t*-172*t*

Abbott VISION (desk-top analyzer), 165, 169-170, 170*t*, 172*t*

Abell-Kendall reference method, 62, 101, 112

abetalipoproteinemia
  basis of, 182
  described, 186

Accutest, 243*t*

acetyl-CoA (acetyl coenzyme A), 5

Action on Secondary Prevention through Intervention to Reduce Events (ASPIRE), 55, 63

adipose tissue
  cholesterol storage in, 443
  triglyceride storage in, 3-4

adolescents and children, 80, 99, 146*t*. *See also* newborns

agarose gel electrophoresis
  lipoprotein patterns, 480*f*, 483*f*
  overview, 480
  quantitation of lipoprotein cholesterol by, 482-485

alcohol
  high-density lipoproteins and, 253, 448
  lipid, lipoprotein and apolipoprotein concentrations and, 82-83, 323-324
  triglyceride concentration and, 116

ALP (atherogenic lipoprotein phenotype), 12

alpha lipoprotein. *See* lipoprotein (a)

Alzheimer, Alois, 552

Alzheimer's disease, apolipoprotein E and, 11, 348-350, 552-555

American Academy of Family Physicians, 243*t*

American Academy of Pediatrics, 243*t*

American Association for Clinical Chemistry (AACC), 240

American Association of Bioanalysts, 243*t*

American Heart Association (AHA)
  classification of atherosclerotic lesions, 52
  dietary pamphlets, 36

American Proficiency Institute, 243*t*

American Society for Testing and Materials, 200

American Society of Internal Medicine, 243*t*

Amplification Refractory Mutation Systems (ARMS) genotyping procedure, 341

anorexia nervosa, 85

anticoagulants, testing and screening issues, 87-88

Antihypertension and Lipid-lowering Treatment to Prevent Heart Attack Trial (ALLHAT), 54

anti-oxidants
  atherosclerosis and, 359
  loss when low-density lipoproteins are oxidized, 360*t*, 366-367
  self-prescribed, 107

apolipoprotein(s). *See also specific type*
  as cofactor for enzymes, 1
  effect of ultracentrifugation on, 528-529
  function of, 1, 2*t*
  genes, 549
  in high-density lipoprotein, 12, 252
  intra-individual variation, 79
  minor, 16
  table of, 2*t*
  testing, screening and measurement
    analytical aspects of, 188-190
    with chromatography (*See* chromatography)
    clinical applications of, 321, 321*t*, 322-324
    immunological assays